Who Will Get Your Money?

Books by John Barnes

WHO WILL GET YOUR MONEY?
WHAT INVESTING IS ALL ABOUT

Who Will Get Your Money?

JOHN BARNES

WILLIAM MORROW & COMPANY, INC.

NEW YORK 1972

To my wife, Mildred

Printed in the United States of America.
Library of Congress Catalog Card Number 74-183359

5   75   74   73   72

Contents

1

Probate

EVERY DAY in this vast country of ours a great deal of property and future family security are sacrificed when property owners die. Certainly after a lifetime of saving and self-denial this was not their intention. What then causes this to happen? These unhappy results take place because those who have built a living estate know nothing, or very little, of the complex problems that are created when they transfer their property to their heirs. The property owner mistakenly feels that his heirs will simply take over where he has left off, and that somehow his assets will be left to them intact. Nothing could be further from the truth!

When serious inroads are made into the living estate, and the heirs are bewildered by what is happening to them, and they do not have access to what they rightfully feel is theirs for a period of many months or several years, whose fault is it? Usually it is no one's fault, and certainly it was not the fault of the property owner. He had been careful and had made the right decisions during his lifetime, but he had never been through probate and he had never paid his own inheritance taxes. Therefore he was not aware of the problems created by death and of the advance decisions that should have been made if he were to reduce to a minimum the delay, the frustration, the taxes, and the costs involved. And too often, because of this, the Internal Revenue Service is too big an heir at the conference table when the will is read; too often years elapse before the estate can be enjoyed by its rightful owners, its legal heirs; too often a lifetime of bitterness is the legacy, or it is riches to rags in a few short years. The way to avoid all of this is for the property owner to learn about the problems beforehand and make the decisions that will pass his death estate on to his heirs with the least trouble and expense.

It must be understood by everyone who saves money that two estates are built during a lifetime—a living estate and a death estate.

During the long process of building a living estate, the property owner becomes intimately acquainted with the problems, the decisions, and the difficulties of becoming financially independent. Most people do not inherit money; they must build an estate themselves. So the first thing they learn is the absolute essential of thrift. A part of all you earn must be yours to keep, and the best way to do this is to save regularly each month by paying yourself first. One hundred dollars saved per month is $1,200 per year, and over a long period of ten years becomes $12,000 of your money saved in a decade. After thrift has been established, it then becomes a matter of where to invest and how to invest. Income taxes, too, become a problem. And all through life it is a question of how well you learn to achieve a balance between saving something to achieve financial independence and spending something so that you can smell the roses as you go.

So in building a living estate, difficult decisions are made, and the problems are gradually solved. Financial independence is achieved, and the goal of retiring respectably is won.

But what about the death estate? Usually nothing is

done. There are those who contend that nothing should be done, except to make a will and arrange for the division of their assets among their heirs. And there are some who, because of superstition and fear of death, will not even make a will. There are many others who agree that something should be done, but they do not know what to do, because it is very difficult to obtain accurate information in the field of estate planning. Bits of information can be gleaned from here, and bits more from there, but the whole picture is not clear; and even from the meager information gathered there seems to be confusion and contradiction among those who are supposed to know, such as lawyers, trust officers, and accountants. It is true that there is more misinformation and lack of information on the subject of estate planning than in any other area of money management. So, to be able to plan intelligently and to conserve as much as possible of your hard-earned assets for your heirs, let's take a look at the problem, and the step-by-step solution of it. The first thing to understand is probate.

Probate is the legal and bureaucratic process that takes place after a man dies, enabling him to pass on his property to his legal heirs.

Mr. Adams, a widower, died in New York leaving a will, naming his four adult children—three sons and a daughter —as his heirs. He himself was successful in business and should have known what he was doing. He named his sister as his executrix. At his funeral a lawyer friend who drew the will rode alone in the limousine with the children's aunt. Back in the father's apartment after the services, the lawyer produced some legal documents and, without an explanation or a reading of the will, suggested that the four children sign the papers he presented. Fortunately, the daughter's husband was knowledgeable in estate matters, and it had been agreed upon among the four children that he would be the spokesman for all of them. He refused to let them sign and stated that they would see the lawyer later that day.

After lunch, in the lawyer's plush suite on Wall Street, the papers were again placed in front of each child for signature, where everyone, including the lawyer and his partner, the aunt, and the daughter's husband, were seated about a long table overlooking a beautiful view of Lower Manhattan.

As the youngest son admitted later, if it had not been for his brother-in-law, he would simply have signed the papers presented and hoped that some day he would inherit something. He was completely at a loss, impressed by the plush offices and the air of assurance on the part of the attorneys.

The brother-in-law was not. He asked to see a copy of the will, which was only a page and a half long, stating that the four children would divide the estate, share-and-share alike, and that Mr. Adams' sister was the executrix. Two and one-half hours later, after the lawyer's fee was established in advance and everyone was satisfied that the first conference had gone well, the papers which were first presented in the deceased's apartment were signed. But even then, with a knowledgeable relative to represent the heirs, it was four years later that the estate was finally distributed to its new owners!

What happened? Nothing, except the exasperating delay of probate. It was certainly not what Mr. Adams thought would happen. He thought his children would simply sell his investments, take over his bank account, divide the proceeds among themselves, and be grateful to their father for having the foresight to save an estate and the good judgment to leave it to them instead of to his sister, of whom he was very fond and of whom he had seen a great deal more in recent years than he had his own children. Four years! Mr. Adams would have been shocked.

The delay during probate occurs because your assets come under the jurisdiction of the probate court. Your will has to be found and read, to determine who is your executor and who you named as your heirs. But, as we have said, they do not immediately inherit. How does anyone know who are your legal heirs? "But I named them in my will!" you protest. But the law states that no one but a judge can say who are your heirs, that you didn't leave someone out, and that all of your just debts have been paid and your creditors satisfied. And above all that your taxes have been paid. And here we are not talking about income taxes, although you may still owe some of those, but about death taxes—the federal estate tax and the inheritance tax that most states impose.

These first mortgage demands against your estate must be paid first before the heirs can inherit anything. And you can be very sure that everyone is going to get his legal share before the heirs get what is left. The eventual new owners receive no income or capital, and have nothing to do with the estate, until probate is over.

Who then manages the assets? Up to the time of death the estate builder was managing his own affairs. He was in legal possession of his property, received the gross income, paid the bills and the taxes, and tended to the myriad details necessary to the proper administration of his living estate. Now who does? The executor named in his will takes over, and if no will has been left, the court names an administrator. It is the executor's job to choose the probate attorney, take an inventory of all of the assets, pay all just claims, establish a separate trustee account to receive all the income and pay all the expenses, hire an accountant to keep track of all this, arrange for the estate to be appraised, file and pay the federal estate tax and the state inheritance tax, make a final accounting of his stewardship to the heirs, get a final decree of distribution from the court, a release from the heirs of their distributive share, and change the ownership from the deceased to the new owners.

So what do most people do? As Mr. Adams did in New York, they name their Aunt Mamie, who has been a housewife all of her life, to be executrix! How can she possibly be expected to know what to do? And why was Aunt Mamie named? Simply because the property owner thought it would be nice if she collected the executor's fee instead of someone outside of the family. An estate that has taken a lifetime to build has now been placed in the hands of a financial incompetent in order to save a fee!

The first mistake made by the property owner in preparation for probate is reluctance on his part to discuss his estate plans with his heirs. He is naturally secretive about his income and the assets that he has accumulated. He feels that this is nobody's concern but his own; he certainly doesn't want his neighbors to know about them, and many people are particularly careful about keeping knowledge of their financial affairs from other members of the immediate family. Far too often this reluctance to divulge information exists between parents and children. Parents feel that what they have saved is theirs to enjoy until they die, and for that matter exhaust to the point of zero if that is their desire; while children too often generously take the attitude that their father and mother should spend everything they have and enjoy it, that they don't want any part of it. Yet it is a strange thing that the extremely wealthy do not take this attitude and freely discuss among all the family members, young and old, the eventual disposition of a sizable estate to the next generation. If this is done among the very wealthy, it is even more important that the matter be freely discussed in a

small estate, because any kind of a loss will be more severely damaging to future family security.

One father's total instruction in money matters to his
two sons was contained in the following advice: "I have
saved a little. Let's keep it." But it wasn't conserved. The
widow died broke in a few short years, and the two sons
had to set about building an estate all over again.

Widow Jones was more fortunate in that she was too
careful to dissipate what her husband had left her. But
unfortunately she had read somewhere about the disastrous effects of successive taxation from one generation to
the next, so she decided to bypass her children in her will
and leave everything in trust to her grandchildren, to be
compounded until each grandchild became twenty-one,
at which time his or her share of the estate would be distributed. She did not have a big enough estate to have
a real death tax problem, and her children failed to make
her realize their financial position. She thought that, because they lived well, her sons-in-law were well-to-do;
they were not. There was a complete breakdown of family
communication in regard to the relative value of the assets
of the two generations. As a consequence, equally disastrous results took place. The daughters were very bitter
over their mother's will, which disinherited them, and it
became a lifetime of frustration when the two sons-in-law
fared rather badly later on in life, and the ungrateful
grandchildren, when they came of age, frittered away
their inheritance in a few short years. Again everyone in
the family suffered through lack of frank discussion of
family finances prior to the death of the older generation.

How much you want to discuss with your heirs about
your assets is your business, but to keep them totally in
the dark is not wise.

As we have seen, the first step in the probate process
takes place when the will is read. From this legal docu-

ment those who are left behind can determine to whom
you left your estate and whom you named as your executor, to take over after you are gone. The attorney quite
often keeps the original of the will when he draws it and
gives you a copy. When you die, your lawyer attends your
funeral and then contacts the executor and the heirs. The
will is read, agreement is reached among everyone present
that the will is a valid one and that the executor named
should be appointed. This is why a probate attorney has
to be appointed by the executor. No one but an attorney
can go into court and ask that the will be admitted to
probate in order to determine that it is legal and that
eventually the property will be transferred to its rightful
new owners. The executor is in charge of the estate, but
he must employ an attorney to act for him in court.

Usually the attorney who drew the will is chosen as the
executor's legal representative. As a matter of fact it is
almost automatic in most cases because the attorney has
retained the original copy of the will (which is the only
copy that is valid), and he has called the meeting of the
heirs and the executor in his law office. The average executor, a family member, feels that there is no alternative
but to appoint the lawyer who drew the will. On the contrary, the executor is in complete charge of the estate and
may choose any attorney whom he sees fit.

Miss Jones was the sole heir and executrix of her
mother's estate. She met with the lawyer who drew the
will and took an immediate dislike to him. Because of this
she very wisely did not commit herself to anything at the
first meeting and went in search of information. Fortunately her investment representative understood estate
planning and assured her that she was perfectly within
her legal rights to demand that the original copy of her
mother's will be turned over to her. This was done, and

she then chose another attorney to handle the legal aspects of the probate process for her.

It is important for an executor to know this, because the attorney and executor have to work very closely together over the course of many months, and sometimes years, and any friction because of a conflict of personalities, while not disastrous, can be very unpleasant for all concerned. This is why the attorney rode with the aunt at Mr. Adams' funeral. He had the original copy of the will, and as a matter of fact was the only one up to that point who had even seen a copy of the will. Therefore, he knew the aunt was the executrix, told her so, and asked to attend the services with her; and then in advance he prepared papers for the heirs to sign, asking their written consent for the appointment of the aunt as executrix and for her appointment of him as the probate attorney. It was not legally necessary for the heirs to give their written consent, but certainly it is not prudent for the executor and the attorney to ride roughshod over those who are eventually going to inherit the property. In the last analysis, their best interests must be considered.

So the executor's first big step is to choose the proper attorney. Once chosen, however, it is important for him to realize that he, and not the attorney, is still in charge. An experienced executor, such as a bank, actually assumes full control and merely uses the lawyer to represent him in court. But poor Aunt Mamie knows nothing; therefore, for all intents and purposes, the attorney who drew the will takes charge and does all the work, and merely has Aunt Mamie come down to his office from time to time during probate to sign legal documents he has prepared.

Uncle George died leaving a handwritten will that bequeathed $500,000 to his two nieces and a nephew, all of them in their fifties with children of their own. The older niece was named executrix. Halfway through probate the heirs suddenly realized that the judge was being asked to declare that the handwritten will was not a will but a trust, that only income should be received by the two nieces and the nephew, and that not a cent of the capital should be inherited by them but should eventually be distributed to their children! Mystified and upset, they sought expert advice. The executrix was advised to dismiss the attorney, right in the middle of the probate process, and petition the court that a new lawyer be appointed. This was allowed, and the new attorney withdrew the petition asking the court to declare the will to be a trust. As a consequence the two nieces and the nephew inherited the capital, which they knew to be their uncle's wish in the first place.

The angry executrix demanded to know who had petitioned the judge to rule that the will was not a will but a trust. She was flabbergasted when the second attorney presented her with a Xerox copy of the petition, showing that she, as executrix, was the person who had signed it. The first attorney had given it to her to sign, and she had done so automatically, as she had all the other documents, because she knew nothing about her duties and responsibilities as executrix.

Why the original probate attorney felt that the uncle's handwritten will should be declared a trust and not a will is a matter of conjecture, but the main thing for an executor to know is that, during probate, *he* is in charge, not the attorney, and that he may petition the court for dismissal of the attorney at any time he does not like what is taking place.

After the will is read and the executor chooses the lawyer, the first thing that the probate attorney does is to petition the court for admission of the will to probate and for letters testamentary. "Letters testamentary" is a fancy

expression that simply means that the judge issues a written court order appointing the executor. Armed with this
document, the executor now for the first time has the
authority to take over physical possession of the deceased's
assets. The first thing he does is inventory all the documents and the assets found in the safe deposit box, if
there is one, or make a list of all the papers found in the
strong box or desk at home. This is usually the first indication of the size and character of the estate. We say
"usually." When Mr. Adams died in New York, the daughter's husband found one document in his apartment the
day of the services. It was a whole life insurance policy
for $5,000, with the youngest son named as the sole bene-
ficiary. This son, trying to support five children on a low
salary, was desperately in need of funds. Without waiting
to see the attorney after lunch, the brother-in-law and the
son went down to the insurance company's offices and
presented the policy for payment of the death benefit,
asking how soon the $5,000 would be received. The
brother-in-law knew that, regardless of what Mr. Adams'
will might say, this sum belonged to the named beneficiary. The insurance company readily agreed to the request,
a claim for settlement form was signed by the son, and
the badly needed money was paid to him in just five days,
although the balance of the estate was not distributed, as
we have said, for four years. At that first conference in the
Wall Street offices of the attorney, the aunt executrix was
aghast. What right had the brother-in-law to propose such
a thing? The lawyer told her that the youngest son had
been completely within his rights, that the insurance policy had nothing to do with the will, and since he had duly
reported the facts about the policy, everything was in
order. The aunt subsided, grumbling to herself.

Even armed with letters testamentary, it is not easy for
an executor to inventory an estate. A safe deposit box

helps. Certainly he can expect that most of the assets in the estate will be found here. An estate will consist of a part or all of the following: cash in the form of bank deposits and savings and loan accounts, government bonds, life insurance policies, securities, and titles to real estate. Notes of money lent to individuals and mortgages on property are also found. Still, in some cases, the executor and the heirs can be left in doubt that everything has been located. This is particularly true if the testator acquired a reputation during his lifetime of being worth a great deal more than the total assets that can be found by the executor. It can be a very nagging thought to the heirs for years to come. The executor, of course, should always take an inventory of the safe deposit contents in front of witnesses, such as the probate attorney and the manager of the safe deposit department. He doesn't want the unpleasant prospect of being accused by the heirs of walking off with some of the more liquid assets!

Which brings us to the point of what is the best way for the property owner, in advance, to take care of this rather perplexing problem of what assets did actually comprise his estate? It is simply one of the estate builder himself taking a confidential inventory of the assets and placing it with a copy of his will. When it is frequently updated, this list of assets is a wonderful relief to the executor when he finds it. A copy of a Confidential Inventory of Assets is reproduced on the following pages.

Page one is exceptionally important, for not only are the essential statistics given for the property owner and his wife, such as address, birth dates, and telephone numbers, but also the same information is provided for his children and grandchildren. The date of his will is also put down and where it can be found. Also, if he has trusted advisers such as an attorney, a life underwriter, an accountant, and an investment representative, information is given on them also. If the testator is still working at the time of the inventory, his business address and telephone number should also be listed.

Page two is the list of the assets and the liabilities, with the net total value of the estate as of the date of the inventory stated at the bottom of the page. Securities are listed as total value only, for as the note indicates, a detailed list of these is given on page four. Life insurance is also included; the value should be the amount that would be paid at death; double indemnity for accidental death, if provided by the policy or policies, is ignored. Liabilities listed here would include primarily mortgages on property, particularly on a home on which payments are still being made. Retired people normally do not have any liabilities except the unpaid monthly bills that all of us leave behind. These, of course, are small and are ignored.

Page three lists current income, which is important as a check list against assets, but it is actually of more value to the property owner on his living estate than to the heirs and the executor on his death estate.

Page four gives a list of the securities in detail that were simply listed as a gross amount on page two.

Page five is only for those who own a business, and this sheet should be filled out by their accountant.

Page six is for any comments that the testator might want to leave behind him for the benefit of the executor and his heirs.

A CONFIDENTIAL INVENTORY OF ASSETS

name _____ age ____ birthday _____

wife's name _____ age ____ birthday _____

address _____ telephone _____

city _____ state _____ zip code _____

Social Security number _____
total value of the estate _____

1. names of children (include name of spouse if child
   is married) birth dates—residence

   _____

   _____

   _____

   _____

2. names of grandchildren—birth dates—residence
   (if not living with parents)

   _____

   _____

   _____

3. last will and testament—date—where kept

   _____

4. your advisers: name—address—telephone
   lawyer _____
   life underwriter _____
   accountant _____
   investment representative _____

5. business address and telephone

   _____

Signature _____ date _____

Assets

	present value	ownership
1. checking accounts	$ 1st nat	
2. bank savings	Bank Dickson	
3. savings & loan associations	none	
4. credit unions	0	
5. securities (see page four)		
6. mortgages and trust deeds	0	
7. notes receivable	0	
8. home	405 Center	
9. other real estate	Scothus mill	
10. life insurance death benefit	1,000.00	
11. business equity (see page five)	1/4	
total assets	$ 300,000.00	

Liabilities

	amount
1. mortgages or trust deeds	$ 0
(a) home	0
(b) other	0
2. notes payable	0
3. other liabilities	0
total liabilities	$ 0

total assets	$
total liabilities	$
net value of the estate	$

Current Income

salary or business income	$ 5.5
bank accounts	2
savings & loan	0
credit unions	0
securities	in looke
mortgages and trust deeds	
real estate income	0
notes	0
annuities	K
company pensions	0
other pensions	5.5
Social Security	5.5
other	

total monthly income $ 22,000.00

Securities

common stocks

no. shares	company	cost basis	current value	ownership
————	————	————	————	————
————	————	————	————	————
————	————	————	————	————
————	————	————	————	————
————	————	————	————	————
————	————	————	————	————

total value $

preferred stocks

no. shares	company	cost basis	current value	ownership
————	————	————	————	————
————	————	————	————	————

total value $

industrial and municipal bonds

face amount	description	interest	current value	ownership
————	————	————	————	————
————	————	————	————	————

total value $_____

government bonds

face amount	description	interest	current value	ownership
————	————	————	————	————
————	————	————	————	————

total value $_____

total value in securities $_____

BUSINESS DATA

firm name _____

address _____   *type of business*

nature of business _____   sole proprietorship ___

business position _____   partnership _____

percentage of ownership _____   close corporation _____

are there any family relationships in the business? yes ___ no ___

business associates

name	position	birth date	percentage of ownership

do you intend that your business interest be
   sold if you die?   yes ___ no ___
is the sale prearranged by a written agreement?   yes ___ no ___
is the agreement funded by life insurance?   yes ___ no ___

employee benefits provided by the business

pension plan   yes ___ no ___   profit sharing
group life   plan   yes ___ no ___
   insurance   yes ___ no ___   group disability yes ___ no ___

number of employees _____

unusually valuable employees in the business

name	position

date business started _____   *original investment* _____

net earnings before taxes

19 _____	19 _____	19 _____	19 _____	19 _____
$ _____	$ _____	$ _____	$ _____	$ _____

Comments by the Property Owner

_____
_____
_____
_____
_____
_____
_____
_____
_____
_____
_____
_____
_____
_____
_____
_____
_____

_____   _____

date   signature

After the petition is made to the court for a hearing on the will it is necessary for all possible heirs and creditors to be notified that the testator has died. This is accomplished by publishing a notice of the date, time, and place of the first probate hearing in the local newspaper. The number of times these notices have to appear and for how long will vary according to state law.

The next step is a petition for the appointment of an inheritance tax appraiser, who in most states is a county official. Even though a federal estate tax is due, and therefore the Internal Revenue Service is involved, the federal government usually goes along with the local appraiser's valuation of the estate. This appraisal can be very time-consuming, for several reasons. Bureaucrats are busy and, as everyone knows, often tied up with red tape. If the only assets are a home and cash, the problem is quickly solved, for the appraiser simply has to appraise the house and is usually quite lenient as to its value; other real estate, however, can be a problem. In one estate the major asset was a ranch which had been in the family for many years and which had tremendously increased in value since its purchase because the testator had lived into his nineties, had outlived his son and daughter-in-law, and his only heir was a granddaughter. The inheritance tax appraiser valued the property at just under one million dollars! The heiress was fit to be tied because of the state inheritance taxes and the federal estate tax involved. She even sued in court, but it did her no good, and eventually the ranch had to be sold to pay the death taxes involved.

If a business is a part of the estate, the appraisal can be a very sticky one, for quite often the value placed upon it is way and beyond what the heirs feel is fair. The best way to solve this problem in advance is to have the owners enter into a buy-and-sell agreement drawn by a competent attorney, by which they bind themselves individually to sell their interest in the business, in the event of their demise, to their surviving partners. Certainly no one is going to agree to sell for less than the true value of the property. This would simply be another method of disinheriting the heirs. Hence, such an agreement usually results in a fair price, and a bona-fide buy-and-sell agreement—or a stock retirement plan if the business is a close corporation—is usually accepted by the appraiser. If the business is large enough, a better way to solve the problem is to go public and sell part of the shares in the open market, thus establishing a price for each share. The new issue would be sold in the over-the-counter market and thereafter be quoted in the "pink sheets" published by the National Daily Quotation Service.

Once the estate has been appraised, the executor has to complete and file a State Inheritance Tax Return showing the amount of tax that is owed. If the appraisal by the county official has been disputed, a long fight can take place, and sometimes cannot be resolved except by taking it to the judge of the probate court for his decision.

If the estate is in excess of $60,000, a Federal Estate Tax Return has to be filed, which means a further delay. The executor has two valuation dates from which to choose; he may elect the date of death, or six months later, but he cannot choose any date in between. Many executors insist upon waiting out the six months before they decide which date should be used, for if real estate and/or securities are involved and there is a declining market during the year, the estate will be appraised for less six months later and, therefore, the death taxes will be less.

Now six months have slipped by with little or nothing having been accomplished, while the heirs still sit on the sidelines in frustration. Mrs. Smith died, as a widow with no near relatives, and in her will left her entire $120,000 estate to "my very dear friend," Mary Rogers. Mrs. Smith was not young, and neither was Mary Rogers, who was poorly as well and as a consequence had planned on a trip abroad with the proceeds of her inheritance to improve her health. A year and a half after Mrs. Smith's death, she still had received nothing and could not understand what took the lawyer so long—and for that matter, why she had not even heard from him in months. Finally she asked a business friend to intercede for her, to see if he could expedite matters. The executor and the lawyer in this case were not keeping her, as the sole heir, informed and were taking their own time in settling the estate.

In the event of hardship, two devices can be used by the executor to get money over to the heirs while the estate is still tied up in probate. The first method is usually employed when a widow does not have enough income to support herself. A petition is made to the court by the executor, asking for a monthly family allowance to be paid to her. Depending upon the size of the estate and the normal living standards of the surviving spouse, the judge will set an amount and allow the executor to pay her an income by the month. The second method is called a partial distribution. Once again enough time has elapsed to determine that the will is not going to be contested and that all just claims against the estate have been paid. Now a petition is made to the court to allow the executor to pay a lump sum to the heirs out of the assets available. This can be either in cash or in liquid assets such as securities.

You would think that the executor and the attorney would be interested in expediting the estate through probate so they can be paid, since they each earn a good fee. But their motivation is somewhat blunted by the fact that they can collect part of their fees *during* probate, by the partial-distribution method. The executor has the attorney petition the court for partial payment of the fees, so that if probate drags on too long, they can be paid in one installment, or more, even though the heirs still receive nothing.

Finally, however, all death taxes and claims against the estate have been paid and a receipt for the inheritance taxes has been presented to the court. Now the executor has to prepare a final accounting of his stewardship to the heirs. In simple estates the heirs are asked to sign a waiver of accounting, but in large estates this accounting can be so complicated as to involve a small volume which, when submitted to the prospective new owners for their approval, can be the most baffling part of the entire probate procedure. It would take an experienced accountant in some of these cases to know whether or not to sign the release to the executor. Is the accounting accurate, or did someone walk off with a part of the assets of the estate or of its net income during the long period of administration? As usual, most heirs don't know and simply sign the release presented to them and assume that the executor was an honest man, which, fortunately, is true most of the time.

Once the judge is satisfied that everything is in order, he signs a final decree of distribution. The heirs are once again presented with a document to sign, this time a receipt for having received their distributive share. This is normally the end of the probate process. However, if securities are a part of the assets, another problem presents itself. Nothing can be done about changing the ownership of the stock certificates from the deceased's name to the names of the various heirs until a final decree of distribution has been ordered by the court. Now the securities have to be sent to various bank transfer agents all over the country. The transfer agent has different documentary requirements that have to be met, depending upon the state where the corporation is domiciled. If fifteen securities or more are involved, the delay will be several months. One widow had been in probate for two years when the final decree of distribution was ordered. In her case only one company's stock was involved, but the ownership was substantial, for it consisted of a thousand shares. After waiting two months with nothing happening, she finally had her stockbroker call the trust department of the bank, which was acting as executor, to find out what, if anything, had been done. It took several telephone calls by her broker and finally a visit to the trust department personally by him before he found out that the trust department individual responsible for handling the probate of the estate had sent the stock certificate to the stock transfer department on the other side of the banking floor, where nothing had been done for two months. The stock was still in the bank's vaults and had not been sent to the transfer agent at all!

There are probate costs involved in this complicated and long-drawn-out process, of course. For an estate of $100,000 or more, about 2 percent of the total value is charged by the executor, and the same amount by the attorney. On an estate of $200,000, for example, this would be a total of 4 percent or $8,000. The executor and the heirs should, however, always fix the attorney's fees in advance before they consent to engage his services. When queried by Aunt Mamie, the lawyer will usually shrug off the question and say that his fees are set by law and not to worry about it. He is perfectly correct in his reply; there is a table of probate fees, and most lawyers will not charge more than this amount. But it does not mean that he can't charge more, just as a doctor or any other professional man can charge whatever the traffic will bear once the work has been done; therefore, the executor should not be satisfied with a vague reply but should set the legal fee in advance.

The brother-in-law in Mr. Adams' case in New York telephoned the trust department of his firm's correspondent bank on Wall Street and asked the vice-president in charge about the procedure in New York State and if they would set the fee in advance if they were the executor. The answer was a positive yes, and that they would consent to the proposed fee provided it was no higher than somewhere between 2 and 3 percent of the total value of the estate.

A table showing probate costs on the first $100,000 appears below.

	Percent	Amount	Cumulative cost
First $1,000	7%	$ 70	$ 70
$1,001 to $10,000	4%	$ 360	$ 430
$10,000 to $50,000	3%	$1,200	$1,630
$50,000 to $100,000	2%	$1,000	$2,630

Most people do not realize that probate is a matter of public record. Anybody can walk off the street into the county clerk's office and demand to see the probate file of a deceased. He has to give no reason; he has the right because the probate record falls into the area of the public domain. Therefore, when you die, any stranger, friend, or relative can find out exactly of what you died possessed, down to the last penny and in what bank. Your will can be read by anyone, and in the probate file is a record of the proceedings step by step, including the names and addresses of your heirs. Most people are appalled to learn of this and will take every possible step to avoid having this happen to them. In many cases privacy is of the utmost importance.

A doctor in a small town of fifty thousand people had founded a famous clinic and died wealthy, leaving his estate in a charitable trust to his two daughters, from which they were to receive all of the income during their lifetime. Since the daughters were young when he died, never married, and inherited their famous father's sense of frugality, they did not spend even the income from the trust, but proceeded to build up an estate of their own. The trust capital also grew over a course of forty years. They became so secretive in later life that, when their banker visited their home and talked a little bit too loud about their estate while a TV repairman was in the next room, they almost had a fit. By this time their income was $9,000 per month from the trust fund, and their personal fortune had grown to three quarters of a million. The subsequent publicity of probate was agony to the surviving daughter when one of them finally died.

Assets in many states are frozen at death on the order of the state inheritance tax department. Now when the widow runs out of cash after a few days and goes down to the bank to withdraw some money, she is told that she cannot do so. Panic almost immediately ensues, for to be suddenly without funds is frightening. One state allows cash deposits in banks and savings and loan institutions to be frozen for a period of six months, claiming it takes that long to determine that all the assets have been found by the inheritance tax appraiser, and even going to the extent of maintaining that it is possible that the testator might have stashed away a sizable sum of cash in an out-of-state bank and told nobody but his heirs.

In states where such a law exists the first thing that a widow should do is go to the bank, if her name is on the accounts, and withdraw all the money, remove the contents from the safe deposit box, and open up new accounts in her name only at another bank down the street. Now

when the tax people call up the bank, they are told that
Mr. Jones does not have an account there, which is true.
The inheritance tax people have found out where he
banks, of course, simply by calling up the income tax department and getting the information from his tax return.
It is difficult for the widow to remember to do this the
very morning after her husband dies—she is too distraught
—but upset or not, it should be done. The widow who has
a joint account with the testator is not trying to escape
paying inheritance taxes. These taxes will be paid in full
when due, but in the meantime she can have access to
her own cash. No argument is given the widow by the
bank as long as the account hasn't been frozen, for after
all they do not work for the tax department.

Even a small estate, as little as $10,000, can benefit
from knowing the principles of estate planning, as we
shall see later on. The great majority of people are not
upset by the costs of probate so much as they are upset
by the long delay. There is a feeling of utter frustration
by the heirs, and there is nothing they can do about it.
It is really nobody's fault that probate takes so long,
though admittedly many executors and probate attorneys
are exasperatingly slow. The reasons are as follows:

1. Court calendars are crowded.

2. Bureaucrats are busy and tied down by red tape.

3. Appraisal of the estate and review of death tax returns take time.

4. The attorney has many clients to consider.

5. In larger estates the executor has to wait for the auditor to prepare the final accounting.

6. In many states the executor is personally liable for
any premature distribution to the heirs.

7. If securities are involved, change of ownership cannot take place until the judge orders a final decree of
distribution.

Proper advance planning by the property owner, however, can reduce materially the delay of probate, the frustration of the heirs, and in many instances eliminate entirely bitterness and lifetime enmity among children or other heirs. Trusts, too, can be created to reduce taxes and protect incompetent beneficiaries; in many cases the judicious use of gifts is invaluable. And if it is advisable and desired, it is possible to eliminate the probate process entirely.

But first, before an explanation of any of this can be undertaken, a thorough understanding of taxes is essential, because so much of estate planning revolves around this all-important problem.

2

Taxes

IT IS AN AMAZING fact that most wills and trusts are drawn
without any consideration being given to the impact of
death taxes upon the estate. As a consequence liquidity is
frequently overlooked, wills and trusts are many times
declared invalid, and estate taxes are paid to the Internal
Revenue Service that could have been considerably reduced by proper planning in advance. Even the State Inheritance Tax Department of many states will take too
large a share, because state inheritance taxes have escalated along with all other forms of taxes in recent years,
particularly since the advent of World War II. Much of
what the property owner strove so mightily to build by
acquiring a living estate is now destroyed by taxes imposed against the death estate.

Many lawyers are knowledgeable about death taxes, so
why don't these professional men, who after all are responsible for the drafting of most wills and trusts, inform
testators of the error of their ways when they ignore the
death tax problem? The answer is actually a simple one,
and it is to be found in the unfortunate image that the
legal fraternity, by its own admission, has created in the
minds of the general public. The lawyer is pictured as a
grasping individual who is interested in only one thing,

his legal fee; and many people urge their fellow men to stay away from a lawyer's office at all costs. So when the property owner asks a lawyer to draw a will, the lawyer does only that; he does not inquire, as the attorney knows he should, into the size of the estate and what assets exactly does the testator own for which he wants to make a testamentary disposition. Only by knowing the total value of the estate can the attorney know if there is a death tax problem; yet he is reluctant to bring up the matter, for fear his client will feel that he is simply looking for a larger fee.

Mr. Green, a widower, had no children, so he decided to leave a part of his $300,000 estate to a neighbor across the street. This neighbor had befriended him on countless occasions during the years since his wife had died, even to the extent of taking him once a week to the market in his car when Mr. Green arrived at the point where he could no longer drive. Unfortunately, Mr. Green did not disclose his total assets to the attorney who drew up his will, but simply dictated to whom he was going to leave them. When he eventually died, the neighbor inherited nothing, because the lawyer, assuming that he was worth a great deal more than $300,000, had not explained to him how much inheritance taxes would take out of his estate. A trust was set up within his will for $50,000 to build a new wing for the high school he had attended in his youth, another $5,000 went to each of five different friends, and $150,000 was left to a sister. His will provided that these specific bequests were to be paid first; all inheritance, estate, or death taxes that came due by reason of his death were to be paid by the executor out of the residue of the estate, and then the neighbor friend would inherit what was left. Mr. Green, knowing nothing of death taxes, completely ignored this phrase about taxes in his will when the lawyer presented it to him for his approval and signature. Federal estate taxes alone on his $300,000 estate came to $59,100, state inheritance taxes took another $16,500, and administration costs exceeded $12,000. What Mr. Green thought was going to be a substantial inheritance for a neighbor for ten years of friendly solicitude actually amounted to nothing. Only the fact that his estate had risen in value slightly from the time he drew his will to the date of his death allowed the lawyer and the executor to collect their fees from what was left after the specific bequests and the death taxes had been paid.

When drawing a will or a trust there are five taxes that must be considered.

(a) The federal estate tax;

(b) The state inheritance tax (if one is imposed in the state in which you reside);

(c) Gift taxes;

(d) Income taxes;

(e) Capital gains taxes.

On sizable estates the federal estate tax is the biggest problem. This is not an inheritance tax as such, but is a tax imposed by the Internal Revenue Service on the right to transfer your property to your heirs. Most people, when they learn about this for the first time, consider it outrageous. After paying federal and state income taxes all their lives and saving with great difficulty because of this, and with the problem further compounded by the constantly rising cost of living due to the effects of inflation, they now have to pay additional taxes on the right to transfer their living estate to their heirs. In order to understand this tax, it is better for the property owner to view it as a federal inheritance tax and not as an estate tax, although the latter term is legally and technically correct. The only true inheritance tax is imposed by the various states.

There is an important distinction in the way the federal

estate tax is levied as compared to the way a state inheritance tax is imposed. Uncle Sam says to you in effect, as
though you were not dead and could answer him: "Mr.
Johnson, how much were you worth when you died?" If
your answer is $200,000, the Internal Revenue Service
will want $31,500 in federal estate taxes. The tax is as-
sessed against you, the testator, and for the total amount
of which you died possessed; it is not levied against your
heirs. The typical state inheritance tax turns it the other
way around. The tax is not imposed against the deceased
property owner, but is assessed instead against the various
heirs. As we shall see, how much of an exemption is
granted and how much the tax rate will be depends upon
how much the individual heir inherited and what was his
relationship to the deceased. Both taxes, however, are normally paid by the executor out of the assets before the
estate is distributed.

The Federal Estate Tax table on the facing page is adjusted to include the state death tax credit.

Every estate has a $60,000 exemption; in other words
no tax is paid on this amount if that is all the testator left
behind him. This is of considerable relief to the small
property owner when he learns about it.

He has read so much comment in the newspapers about
the amount of money collected by the federal government
in estate taxes that he can hardly believe that no tax is
owed on an estate appraised at $60,000 or less. Most of the
publicity in regard to death taxes arises from the probate
of large estates. As the table shows, an estate of $10,100,-
000 pays an estate tax of $5,036,200! This is enough to
frighten anyone, particularly if the assumption is made
that the same rate of 50 percent is imposed against all
estates regardless of size. As we shall see later, the relief
to the total estate of a husband and wife is even greater

FEDERAL ESTATE TAX

Applicable to estates of persons
dying after August 16, 1954

(Adjusted to include the State Death Tax Credit)

Estate before deducting exemption*	Total tax on amount in Column 1	Rate in next higher bracket
$ 60,000.00	$ 0.00	.03
65,000.00	150.00	.07
70,000.00	500.00	.11
80,000.00	1,600.00	.14
90,000.00	3,000.00	.18
100,000.00	4,800.00	.212
110,000.00	6,920.00	.242
120,000.00	9,340.00	.272
150,000.00	17,500.00	.264
160,000.00	20,140.00	.284
200,000.00	31,500.00	.276
300,000.00	59,100.00	.268
310,000.00	61,780.00	.288
500,000.00	116,500.00	.28
560,000.00	133,300.00	.31
700,000.00	176,700.00	.302
810,000.00	209,920.00	.322
900,000.00	238,900.00	.314
1,060,000.00	289,140.00	.334
1,100,000.00	302,500.00	.326
1,310,000.00	370,960.00	.356
1,560,000.00	459,960.00	.386
1,600,000.00	475,400.00	.378
2,060,000.00	649,280.00	.418
2,100,000.00	666,000.00	.41
2,560,000.00	854,600.00	.45
2,600,000.00	872,600.00	.442
3,060,000.00	1,075,920.00	.472
3,100,000.00	1,094,800.00	.464
3,560,000.00	1,308,240.00	.494
3,600,000.00	1,328,000.00	.486
4,060,000.00	1,551,560.00	.526
4,100,000.00	1,572,600.00	.518
5,060,000.00	2,069,880.00	.558
5,100,000.00	2,092,200.00	.55
6,060,000.00	2,620,200.00	.58
6,100,000.00	2,643,400.00	.572
7,060,000.00	3,192,520.00	.602
7,100,000.00	3,216,600.00	.594
8,060,000.00	3,786,840.00	.624
8,100,000.00	3,811,800.00	.616
9,100,000.00	4,427,800.00	.608
10,060,000.00	5,011,480.00	.618
10,100,000.00	5,036,200.00	.61

* After all deductions, including marital deduction, but before
$60,000 exemption.

than the first $60,000 if the executor can claim the marital deduction.

By further examination of the estate tax table you can see that an estate valued at $65,000 would have to pay a tax of $150—the first $60,000 would be exempt and the next $5,000 would be taxed at 3 percent. The tax rate in the next higher bracket is shown in the last column of the table. You will also note that no matter how high up you go in the schedule, the exemption on the first $60,000 is always taken into account. For example on $70,000 the tax is $500, computed as follows:

$60,000 tax zero

$65,000 first $60,000 still zero, next $5,000 above the figure taxed at 3 percent, or $150

$70,000 first $60,000 still taxed at zero, first $5,000 at 3 percent, or $150; next $5,000 at 7 percent, or $350—total tax $500

Like income taxes, the estate tax seriously escalates as the value of the estate increases. A $100,000 estate is subject to a tax of $4,800, a $200,000 estate to a tax of $31,500, and, as in Mr. Green's case where he unintentionally disinherited his neighbor friend, $300,000 is taxed at $59,100. And at $500,000 the tax is $116,500!

The estate tax return, which is Form 706 of the Internal Revenue Service, is forty pages long, and regardless of the size of the estate all forty pages must be submitted when the return is filed. In addition a certified copy of the will must accompany the return. A document is certified by taking it to the county clerk's office, paying a small fee, and having it stamped and signed, which is a procedure similar to having a paper notarized by a notary public. The estate tax is due nine months after the death of the testator. Severe penalties are provided by law for willful failure to make and file the estate tax return on time, and for willful attempt to evade or defeat payment of the tax.

The first major consideration for the executor in preparation of this return is what assets have to be included, for if part of them can be omitted, obviously the estate tax will be materially reduced. All of the following assets must be included: real estate, stocks and bonds, mortgages, notes and cash, insurance, jointly owned property, other miscellaneous property, transfers during decedent's life, powers of appointment, and annuities.

Many people are under the mistaken impression that life insurance proceeds on the life of the testators do not have to be included in the estate for death tax purposes. On the contrary, the full amount of the proceeds of life insurance carried on the life of the decedent is included in the assets of the estate even though payable to named beneficiaries. The only exception, but it is an important one, is when the testator did not retain any of the incidents of ownership. If the insured made an absolute assignment of the policy to a new owner, the proceeds of the policy are not included in his estate.

Mr. Woods at the age of sixty-five held a policy on his life for $20,000, on which he was the owner and his wife the sole beneficiary. Upon the advice of his life underwriter, he transferred the ownership to his wife. When he died five years later, the $20,000 was inherited by his spouse estate tax free, resulting in a tax saving of approximately $6,000. None of the incidents of ownership in the policy, however, could have been retained by Mr. Woods. Incidents of ownership include the right to its economic benefits, the cash value, the power to change the beneficiary, to surrender or cancel the policy, to assign it, to revoke an assignment, or to pledge it for a loan. Insurance companies have forms which transfer the ownership to another person, thereby renouncing all of these incidents of ownership. It makes no difference if the insured still pays the premium; the proceeds of the policy do not have to be included on the estate tax return.

The full value of jointly owned property must be included, unless it can be shown that a part of the property originally belonged to the other tenant, or unless it can be shown that part was paid for by the other tenant. If a widow places her home in joint ownership with her only son, and he contributed nothing to the ownership, the entire value of the home would have to be included as an asset on her estate tax return. The burden of proof that the other tenant contributed to the ownership rests with the executor.

Miscellaneous property would include any of the following: debts due the decedent, interests in a business, insurance on the life of another person, rights, royalties, pensions, shares in trust funds, automobiles, household goods, and personal effects, including wearing apparel.

If the testator transferred ownership of any property during his lifetime to another person but retained the possession or enjoyment of, or the right to the income from, the transferred property, this asset would have to be included in his estate. For example, Mr. David transferred the title to a duplex he owned to his son, but he could not afford to give up the income, so the son paid the net rents to his father. The full value of the duplex had to be included in the father's estate tax return, because he had continued to receive the income from the transferred property.

Powers of appointment are a part of a will and/or trust agreement. If a testator leaves his separate property to his wife, giving her in his will the complete power to leave it to whom she pleases, he has given her a general power of appointment over the property. This important subject will be discussed more thoroughly under wills and trusts.

Where life insurance annuities are involved, and a cash

refund in one lump sum or in installments is provided by the policy, this amount must be included on the return; also all annuities purchased by an employer, under an approved plan for an employees' trust or a retirement annuity contract must be included.

By adding up these assets, the executor can now compute the value of the testator's gross estate. From this gross estate he is allowed to make certain deductions which will reduce the size of the estate for estate tax purposes. These deductions will normally include funeral expenses, executor's commissions, attorney's fees, debts of the decedent, credit for state death taxes, and (if the property owner was married) the marital deduction. They can also include, if they exist, mortgages and liens, charitable gifts, credit for tax on prior transfers, and credit for foreign death taxes.

On an estate owned by two spouses the most important of these allowable deductions is the marital deduction. This is authorized between husband and wife where property is left by the decedent to his surviving spouse. To qualify for the marital deduction, however, the inherited property must meet five conditions: (a) the survivor is entitled for life to all of the income from the entire property; (b) such income is payable annually or at more frequent intervals; (c) she has the power, exercisable in favor of herself or of her estate, to appoint the entire interest, which means she has the legal right to leave her one half of the entire estate to whom she pleases; (d) such power is exercisable by her alone; and (e) no part of her entire interest is subject to a power in anyone else to leave the property to any person other than the surviving spouse.

For the sake of clarity, the instructions make use of the masculine gender in reference to the deceased spouse and the feminine gender in reference to the survivor, but the deductions are also authorized in the reverse situation, which means that no matter which spouse dies first, the marital deduction is available. The effect of the marital deduction, provided all of the above five conditions are met, is to have only one half of the estate owned by husband and wife subject to the estate tax. In community property states this has always been so, but in noncommunity property states prior to the passage of the marital deduction rule, the entire estate was taxed when the husband died and not just his one half. The rule also applies to separate property owned prior to marriage, or assets acquired by one spouse because of an inheritance or a gift. If one half of separate property is left to a surviving spouse in a manner that qualifies it for the marital deduction, one half of this property will also not be taxed. (Community property and the marital deduction will be thoroughly treated in the chapter on ownership.)

The importance of being able to exercise the marital deduction cannot be overemphasized in estates between spouses. Mr. Price had a sizable estate of $600,000. He was a bachelor; therefore, it was all his separate property. Late in life, when in his sixties, he married a woman ten years his junior, and it proved to be a wonderful marriage. He decided to change his will, and upon the advice of his attorney he left one half of his estate outright to his wife, giving her the right to leave this one half to whomever she pleased. The other one half he left to his nieces and nephews. The result was that his adjusted gross estate was appraised at $285,000 and his estate tax was $54,960. If he had not changed his will, the entire amount would have gone to his nieces and nephews. The estate would then have been valued at $570,000, and the tax would have been $136,400. The estate tax saving by this method was $81,440! Since his wife had no relatives, she privately assured her husband that when she died the one half she inherited from him would still go to his nieces and nephews. By his old will he would have disinherited his new wife; by his new will not only did he leave her one half of his estate, but he saved a large amount in federal estate taxes for his eventual heirs. It made no difference if the Internal Revenue Service later discovered that his wife would eventually leave her half to the same nieces and nephews as under Mr. Price's first will. The fact that in his new will he gave her the right to leave it to whomever she pleased was the major factor to be considered; the other four conditions of the marital deduction rule had to be met, of course, but they were minor ones compared to this one major consideration.

In those cases where a husband leaves his half of their joint estate to his surviving spouse, the entire estate, both his half and her half, will now be taxed when she in turn dies. This can be a serious escalation of the estate tax and in effect results in the husband's half being taxed twice.

Mr. Williams died leaving his one half of their joint estate to his wife. After the marital deduction, his half amounted to $100,000, and the tax assessed was therefore $4,800. After probate was over Mrs. Williams owned the entire $200,000 which she and her husband had previously owned together. Because of this, when she subsequently died, the estate tax escalated from $4,800 to $31,500. The children were duly shocked; however, in this case Mr. Williams had been fully aware of what he was doing. He felt that his wife needed the entire estate for her protection, reasoning that $200,000 invested at 5 percent produced an income of only $10,000 per year, and therefore she needed the entire income. He was more interested in protecting his wife than in reducing the federal estate tax upon her subsequent death for the benefit of their children.

There is one table under the code, however, that would

have reduced this second tax if Mrs. Williams had not survived her husband by a full ten years, which she did in
this case and more. This table can be found on page 34
of the Federal Estate Tax Return. If Mrs. Williams had
died in less than two years after her husband's death, 100
percent of Mr. Williams' estate would not have been taxed
again. The effect of this rule would have been to have
Mrs. Williams' estate appraised for the same amount as
the estate of Mr. Williams, namely, $100,000 taxed at
$4,800, and not $200,000 taxed at $31,500, which would
have meant a tax saving to the children of $26,700.

The amount of credit against the first estate is progres-
sively reduced to zero according to the following schedule.

Period of time exceeding	Not exceeding	Percent allowable
	2 years	100
2 years	4 years	80
4 years	6 years	60
6 years	8 years	40
8 years	10 years	20
10 years		none

It should be made clear that this credit against the first
estate is available even though the estate is not transferred
to a surviving spouse. The instructions for Schedule R,
which is the schedule used to give credit for tax on prior
transfers, refers to all estates and to whomever the trans-
ferer originally left his property. These instructions are
not included under Schedule M, where they would be
found if the credit were to be given only on estates involving transfers between husband and wife.

However, despite the credit given in the table, successive taxation should be avoided if at all possible. In other
words no one should rely, in his estate planning, on being
able to use the table, because no one knows exactly when

he is going to die. People in their eighties live on into their nineties; therefore wills and trusts should *not* be drawn upon the assumption that the property owner will die in a short enough time to take advantage of the credit available within the first ten years.

Mr. Rowe, married and forty years of age, had three aunts who were in their eighties. They were secretive as to their affairs, except to confide in their nephew that everything was taken care of and that the necessary papers would be found in their respective safe deposit boxes. Mr. Rowe's father had recently died, and his son had been the executor of his estate. He knew about the problems of probate, therefore, and of the taxes involved. Knowing that he and his brother and sister would probably inherit from them, for his aunts had never married, he mildly suggested that each aunt leave her estate directly to her eventual heirs in order to save on death taxes, and not to one another. He didn't succeed in his suggestion.

Two of the aunts died, leaving $50,000 each to the surviving sister, who also had $50,000. The last aunt lived on into her nineties, surviving her two sisters by more than ten years. If each aunt had left her estate directly to her two nephews and niece, there would have been no federal estate tax. With the surviving sister now possessed of $150,000 when she died, and with no credit available against the estate of her two sisters, the federal estate tax was $17,500, which as far as the nephew was concerned was a complete waste of money. The aunts were old and never traveled anywhere, not even to visit Mr. Rowe's home, though he had lived there for ten years and was only a scant twenty miles away. In other words the wants of each of these three aunts were minor and simple; it could not be argued that the last surviving sister needed to inherit from her two sisters, and even if she did, a trust could have been created that would have solved the estate tax problem. So once again the IRS became a sizable heir at the conference table when the will was read, because assets were needlessly allowed to pile up in the estate of the sole survivor.

State inheritance taxes can no longer be ignored, because they have seriously escalated in recent years. As we have stated, in most states this tax is a true inheritance tax and is imposed against the individual heirs according to the amount that each has inherited and his relationship to the deceased. A typical state inheritance tax table is reproduced on the facing page.

The average heir is usually an adult child. As such he receives a $5,000 exemption, then the balance of the first $25,000 is taxed at 3 percent, or for $600. The next $25,000 is taxed at 4 percent, for $1,000; and the next $50,000 is taxed at 6 percent, for $3,000. An estate of $100,000 left to an adult child would be subjected, therefore, to a total state inheritance tax of $4,600. This is approximately equal to the federal estate tax which, as we have seen, is $4,800. Therefore, this tax must also be taken into consideration in estate planning.

As the table shows, the exemption is for a lesser amount, and the tax rate increases the further removed the heir is in relationship to the testator. In the above case of Mr. Rowe and his brother and sister, they were the descendants of the three maiden aunts' deceased brother. As a consequence their respective exemptions amounted to only $2,000, and the tax rate on the first $100,000 went up from 3, 4, and 6 percent to 6, 10, and 12 percent. They each inherited $50,000 from their last surviving aunt. Each heir was assessed 6 percent on $23,000, and 10 percent on the next $25,000 which amounted to $3,880 times three, or a total state inheritance tax of $11,640. When this amount was added to the federal estate tax of $17,500 the

CALIFORNIA INHERITANCE TAX

Inheritance tax is imposed on the clear market value of the property transferred, computed as of the date of the owner's death, and based upon the relationship of the person receiving the property to the deceased owner.

(Effective July 29, 1967)

Class	Relationship to Owner		Exemption	First $25,000 Less Exemption	$25,000 to $50,000	$50,000 to $100,000	$100,000 to $200,000	$200,000 to $300,000	$300,000 to $400,000	Over $400,000
A	Husband or Wife	Community Property	All Exempt*	3%	4%	6%	8%	10%	12%	14%
		Separate Property of Decedent	One half of separate property plus $5,000							
	Minor Child including Adopted		$12,000	3%	4%	6%	8%	10%	12%	14%
	Adult Child, Grandchild or Great Grandchild, including Adopted, or Ancestor		$ 5,000	3%	4%	6%	8%	10%	12%	14%
B	Brother or Sister or their Descendants Son-in-law, Daughter-in-law		$ 2,000	6%	10%	12%	14%	16%	18%	20%
C	Uncle, Aunt or their Descendants		$ 300	10%	14%	16%	18%	20%	22%	24%
	Strangers		$ 300	10%	14%	16%	18%	20%	22%	24%

*If the spouse is given a lifetime interest in and a power of appointment over decedent's community interest, its value in excess of the value of the life estate is subject to tax. Decedent's one-half of community property resulting from separate property conversions is treated as separate property.

total in death taxes imposed against an estate of $150,000 was over $29,000. It was no wonder that Mr. Rowe, having become knowledgeable because he had acted as executor of his father's estate, had made an attempt to get his maiden aunts to reduce this eventual tax, and it was unfortunate that his efforts in this regard came to naught.

In the first chapter on probate we referred to Mrs. Smith in which she left over $100,000 to "my dear friend," Mary Rogers, who was classified under the tax laws as a stranger.

The $300 exemption allowed a stranger can virtually be ignored, it is so small. Mary Rogers was taxed on the first $100,000 at 10, 14, and 16 percent which resulted in a state inheritance tax of $14,000! This was almost three times the amount of the federal estate tax!

State inheritance tax laws vary from state to state. For example, some states impose an estate tax similar to the IRS; therefore, instructions issued in regard to them must be consulted in every case. However, we can use as an example the law in the State of California.

In this state there is an inheritance tax, and the return must be filed and paid within nine months. There is no penalty for filing late, but there is an interest charge of 7 percent if the tax is not paid within the stipulated time. The law provides that an inheritance tax declaration must be filed whenever a person who was residing in California at the date of death had an interest in any type of property in the state and in all cases where there is a court proceeding to probate an estate or to terminate a joint tenancy. In order to ensure that all of the assets are reported, the law also provides that every safe deposit box must be examined by the county treasurer of the county in which it is located. If the box has not been examined by the county treasurer, arrangements have to be made promptly for him to do so. If the box was entered after death, prior to examination by the county treasurer, a "declaration of re-entry" must accompany the inheritance tax declaration. In addition the following documents are generally required:

   (a) Will and codicils
   (b) Trust documents
   (c) Blood tracing
   (d) Deeds, or deed information
   (e) County real estate tax bills

When a credit is claimed for taxes paid on the first estate, the State of California does not grant a ten-year period, as the Internal Revenue Service does, but gives credit for five years only. Also there is no percentage reduction as in the federal law. However, a full 100 percent credit is given if the second death should occur within the five-year period. Two other deductions also do not conform to the Internal Revenue Code. The first $50,000 of life insurance proceeds are exempt from the inheritance tax, regardless of whether or not the insured retained any of the incidents of ownership, and all intangible personal property is exempt. In addition the State of California does not allow an alternate valuation date; the clear market value of the estate at date of death must be used.

When two different states claim to be the decedent's domicile, there is a law entitled the "Uniform Act of Interstate Compromise of Death Taxes." This article's general purpose is to make uniform the laws of those states which enact it. The State of California has passed this law. As a consequence, when the state controller claims that a decedent was domiciled in California at the time of his death, and the taxing authorities of another state make a like claim on behalf of their state, the state controller may make a written agreement of compromise with the other taxing authorities and with the executor of the estate involved. This agreement stipulates that a certain sum shall be accepted in full satisfaction of any and all inheritance taxes imposed by the State of California. The agreement shall also fix the amount to be accepted by the other state in full satisfaction of the tax owed. By California state law the executor is specifically authorized to make such an agreement.

The third tax to be considered in effective estate planning is the gift tax, both federal and state. The testator should understand right at the outset that gift taxes are not imposed simply because a gift is made during his life-time from his living estate. These taxes are levied only if certain exclusions and exemptions are exceeded. Gifts are made by a property owner from his living estate for several reasons. The main reason is to reduce the taxes that will be imposed some day against his estate. In other words, the property owner has a living estate of sufficient size that death taxes pose a problem. Obviously, if the testator can give a part of his estate to his heirs before he dies, not having to pay taxes on these gifts, his total death estate will be less, and therefore his estate tax will be less. However, he must give away according to the rules.

Each calendar year a property owner may make gifts of $3,000 apiece or less to as many donees as he likes, without paying a gift tax or having the property that was transferred subject to death taxes, federal or state. The gifts will be completely tax free. This annual exclusion is not only allowed by the Internal Revenue Service, but is also allowed by most of the states. And what is also important, no gift tax return has to be filed; the gift can be completely ignored as far as the federal and state taxing authorities are concerned. Likewise this annual exclusion is not limited to a blood relative; the recipient of the gift can be a complete stranger.

Mr. Harrold was a very wealthy widower. Every Christmas he gave away $1,000 each to eighty-four different relatives and friends, which reduced his living estate by $84,000. He did not have to report these gifts. And since his top estate bracket was 41 percent, the estate tax against his death estate was reduced by $34,440! It pleased Mr. Harrold to be in a position to give $1,000 to eighty-four different people each Christmas, and see the happiness it gave them during his lifetime, secure in the knowledge that Uncle Sam was paying a good share of the cost in the form of lower estate taxes imposed against his death estate.

Any type of property can be given—real estate, securities, cash—simply by transferring title of the property to the donee. The gift is ignored by the recipient, for it is not income to him; it is simply a transfer of capital from one owner to another. However, if the $3,000 gift is put to work earning 4 percent, then the $120.00 annual interest has to be reported on the donee's income tax return for the year in which it was earned.

In addition to the annual exclusion, the Internal Revenue Code allows a $30,000 lifetime exemption for each individual donor. This $30,000 does not have to be donated all at once; it may be given in any increments the property owner may choose, such as $10,000 upon three different occasions, or $5,000 six different times. However, this $30,000 is all that is available during a testator's lifetime and, once used, can never be used again. It is not like the $3,000 annual exclusion which may be used year after year as long as the property owner lives.

If any part of the $30,000 lifetime exemption is used, however, a federal gift tax return must be filed by the donor on or before the fifteenth day of the second month following the close of the quarter in which the gifts are made. Why? Because the IRS wants to know when you invade any part of your lifetime exemption so that it is a matter of record. This is the only way they have of knowing when you have used up your $30,000, so that it is no longer available to you as a means of reducing your estate tax. The gift tax return must show the date of the gift, how much it was, to whom you gave it, and the exact description of the property given. The gift must be very carefully identified so that some day, when your executor prepares and files your estate tax return, he can make the deduction for the gift and reduce the size of your estate and the amount of your tax accordingly. A husband and wife each have the $3,000 annual exclusion and the $30,-000 lifetime exemption.

Mr. and Mrs. Daly were wealthy and had three married sons but as yet no grandchildren. They sought estate planning advice, and when the gift tax rules were explained to them, they decided to take advantage of them to the fullest extent possible under the law. They had six adult heirs —three sons and their wives. By joining in the gifts, Mr. and Mrs. Daly were each able to give $3,000 to their three sons and $3,000 to their three daughters-in-law under the annual exclusion. This made a total of $6,000 to each of six heirs, or a total gift of $36,000 completely estate tax, state inheritance tax, and gift tax free, without having to file a gift tax return with any taxing authority. They also each used their $30,000 lifetime exemption for a total of $60,000, giving this amount to their three sons. However, on these gifts they had to file a gift tax return form even though the federal gift tax was zero. This immediately removed $96,000 from their living estate and transferred it to their heirs, resulting in an eventual estate tax saving of approximately $35,000.

There are two additional facts, however, that must be known about the lifetime exemption. Most states do not allow it; therefore, a state gift tax return has to be filed when it is used and a state gift tax paid on the amount of the gift. Secondly, there is a three-year contemplation of death rule. If the property owner should die within three years of the date of the gift, the donation is presumed to have been made in contemplation of death, and therefore the amount of the gift would have to be included in the estate tax return and a tax paid upon it, even though title, of course, rests with the donee. This is to prevent the testator from using any or all of his $30,000 lifetime exemption by making a gift, when he knows he is about to die, for the sole and obvious purpose of reducing the impact of estate taxes against his death estate. Knowledge of this contemplation of death rule is what prompted Mr. and Mrs. Daly to make immediate use of their combined $60,000 lifetime exemption, for they knew they had to live three years in order for it to stand as a tax-free gift. This three-year rule is why a gift tax return is not filed until the following quarter; there is no hurry to file the return if the gift is not going to be allowed because of an early death.

Actually the IRS has found considerable difficulty in making this three-year contemplation of death rule hold when the estate tax return is filed by a knowledgeable executor. If it can be established that a bona-fide gift was made by the testator without his having knowledge of imminent death, and that there was a good reason besides the reduction of estate taxes for making the gift, then quite often the gift will be allowed to stand. Even so, all gifts made under the lifetime exemption should be made with the understanding that the three-year contemplation of death rule exists and may very well hold. Burden of proof to the contrary rests with the executor and not with the Internal Revenue Service.

In making gifts the annual exclusion should always be used first. The reasons are fairly obvious. First, because the annual exclusion for any one calendar year, if not used, is gone forever, while the lifetime exemption means exactly that—it is good for a lifetime. Second, the annual exclusion does not require the filing of a gift tax return. And third, the exclusion is not subject to the three-year contemplation of death rule.

No prior transfers of ownership from the living estate

to the death estate will be allowed to stand tax free if the gifts involve a *future* interest in property. The donee must have possession of and full enjoyment of the property, and in addition receive all of the income. We cited the example of Mr. David, who transferred his duplex to his son but still received the net rents. The son *did* have possession of and full enjoyment of the property, but he did *not* receive the income. Therefore it constituted a future interest in property, and the duplex had to be included in the assets of the father's estate. By not granting the income to the son during his lifetime, the father gave him only a future interest in the property—namely, the right to receive the rent only after his, the father's, death.

FEDERAL GIFT TAX
(Rates in effect January 1, 1966)

Net gifts after deducting exemptions	Total Tax on amount in Column 1.	Percent on Excess
$...............	$..................	.0225
5,000.00	112.50	.0525
10,000.00	375.00	.0825
20,000.00	1,200.00	.105
30,000.00	2,250.00	.135
40,000.00	3,600.00	.165
50,000.00	5,250.00	.1875
60,000.00	7,125.00	.21
100,000.00	15,525.00	.225
250,000.00	49,275.00	.24
500,000.00	109,275.00	.2625
750,000.00	174,900.00	.2775
1,000,000.00	244,275.00	.2925
1,250,000.00	317,400.00	.315
1,500,000.00	396,150.00	.3375
2,000,000.00	564,900.00	.3675
2,500,000.00	748,650.00	.3975
3,000,000.00	947,400.00	.42
3,500,000.00	1,157,400.00	.4425
4,000,000.00	1,378,650.00	.4725
5,000,000.00	1,851,150.00	.5025

Specific exemption $30,000.00 plus exclusion of first $3,000.00 of gifts made to any one donee during calendar year, other than gifts of future interest in property. Other allowable reductions including the marital deduction and one-half of gifts comprised of community property may be available.

In view of all the preceding, why then is there a gift tax table? Because there is such a table, and gift taxes are paid. See the federal gift tax table on the facing page. The IRS gives a reduction if you, in effect, prepay your estate tax by giving a part of your estate away before you die and pay a gift tax.

A federal gift tax is owed whenever a donor makes a gift that exceeds his annual exclusion and his $30,000 life-time exemption. Gifts in excess of this are made by wealthy people. In our previous gift tax example, if Mr. and Mrs. Daly decided to give an additional $50,000 to their heirs besides the $96,000 that they actually gave them, they could have done so, but the additional amount would have been subject to a federal gift tax. They would have ex-ceeded their combined annual exclusion and their lifetime exemption. As you can see from the federal gift tax table, the $50,000 would have been subject to a gift tax of $5,250.

Most wealthy people have long since used up their life-time exemption and quickly in any one year will use up their current calendar-year exclusion, so any gifts they make in excess of this are subject to gift taxes. They make these additional gifts for several reasons.

1. The gift tax starts at the bottom of the gift tax table and at lower percentage rates, while the amount of the gift if left in the estate will come off the top of the estate tax table. A $50,000 gift will be subject to a tax of $5,250, which is at the rate of 10½ percent. If the gift is made from an estate valued in excess of $560,000, the top estate tax rate would be 28 percent. The saving to the heirs is the difference of 17½ percent, or an estate tax saving of $8,750.

A word of warning to the wealthy—the gift tax is cumu-lative! Each $50,000 gift does not stand by itself. If a pre-vious tax was paid on $50,000, the next $50,000 will be taxed in the $50,000-to-$100,000 bracket. It looks like this:

$ 50,000 previous gift   tax paid $ 5,250
$ 50,000 present gift
─────────
$100,000 total   total tax $15,525
                                   less previous tax   5,250
                                                     ─────────
                                        tax owed $10,275,

which is at a tax rate of approximately 20 percent.

2. The gift will be free of probate delay and costs. Title to the property will have been transferred to the heirs, and therefore it will not be tied up in probate court. The executor will simply have to list the asset as a prior transfer on the return, successfully claiming it as a deduction.

3. The income from the asset transferred will now be reported on the income tax return of the donee, who in most cases will pay at a lower income tax rate than the wealthy donor.

4. Any increase in value of the property, from the date of the gift to the death of the donor, will not be taxed. The donee now owns it, and he will not pay any taxes on the increased value unless he should sell the property.

Gifts in excess of state gift tax rules are also assessed. The gift tax table for the State of California is reproduced herewith. This state gives no reduction in its gift tax rates and exemptions. The inheritance tax table and the gift tax table are identical. A state gift tax is owed on any gift that exceeds the annual exclusion of $3,000. Most states do not allow the $30,000 lifetime exemption that is granted by the IRS; therefore, when this exemption is used, a state gift tax return has to be filed and a state gift tax paid.

When Mr. and Mrs. Daly decided to use their combined $60,000 lifetime exemption, they did not pay a federal gift tax even though they had to file a federal gift tax return; but they did have to pay a gift tax to the State of California where they were domiciled. They gave this $60,000

CALIFORNIA GIFT TAX

(Effective July 29, 1967)

The tax on gifts made during lifetime is determined by the California Gift Tax table shown below except that the amount given to any one donee in any calendar year up to $3,000.00 is excluded provided no future interests in property are involved.

Class	Relationship	Exempt	0 to $25,000	$25,000 to $50,000	$50,000 to $100,000	$100,000 to $200,000	$200,000 to $300,000	$300,000 to $400,000	Over $400,000
A	Spouse* Lineal Issue, Lineal Ancestor, Adopted or Acknowledged Child	$5,000 Minor Child $12,000 Others $5,000	3%	4%	6%	8%	10%	12%	14%
B	Brother, Sister or Descendant of either, Son-in-Law or Daughter-in-Law	$2,000	6%	10%	12%	14%	16%	18%	20%
C	Uncle, Aunt or Descendant of either	$300	10%	14%	16%	18%	20%	22%	24%
	Stranger	$300	10%	14%	16%	18%	20%	22%	24%

*If separate property is transferred so as to become community property, the California Gift Tax Law should be consulted.

in the form of $20,000 to each of three adult sons. Examination of the gift tax table will show that an adult child has a $5,000 exemption and then pays 3 percent on the first $25,000. Each child was assessed 3 percent on $15,000, or $450, for a total state gift tax of $1,350. The sons did not pay it, of course; it was paid by the donors.

Gifts should be made with great caution. No estate planning move should be made solely with the object of saving death taxes. Everything should be taken into consideration, and the first person to be considered is the property owner himself, who has accumulated his living estate. He must remain financially independent. He has worked hard for his property; he must have enough capital and enough income, after the gifts, so that he will not be hurt financially in any way.

The fourth tax to be considered for effective estate planning is the income tax. Since this tax is imposed against the living estate, why should it be considered here? Mainly because the capital gains tax, which is an income tax, must be understood if proper decisions are to be made by the property owner. And the capital gains tax itself cannot be understood without the testator understanding the tax-rate schedules of the income tax return.

Consult the 1971 Tax Rate Schedule herewith. We will first use the left column only, which is Schedule Y— Married Taxpayers Filing Joint Returns. Everyone, including the millionaire, pays only 14 percent on the first $1,000 of taxable income after all deductions. A man who says that he is in a 50 percent tax bracket only has to pay 14 percent on the first $1,000, 15 percent on the next $1,000, 16 percent on the next $1,000, etc. If you examine the schedule, you will see that a property owner who says that he is in a 50 percent tax bracket does not pay half of his income in taxes. This man, filing a joint return with his wife, pays 50 percent only on that taxable income which exceeds $44,000. He does not pay 50 percent of the $44,000, or $22,000 in taxes, which he would pay if his 50 percent tax bracket meant that he must pay half of *all* the income that he reports to the IRS. Out of $44,000 in taxable income, he pays only $14,060. Why? Because he starts out, like everyone else, paying 14 percent on the first $1,000, and so on. A couple filing a joint return does not pay 50 percent on all taxable income until their income is $140,000 and their tax bracket is 66 percent. At that point, they will pay $70,380 in taxes, which is approximately one half of the $140,000 they are reporting.

After this brief discussion of the tax schedules, we can

Married Taxpayers Filing Joint Returns and Certain Widows and Widowers (See page 4)				Married Taxpayers Filing Separate Returns			
If the amount on Form 1040, line 50, is:		Enter on Form 1040, line 19:		If the amount on Form 1040, line 50, is:		Enter on Form 1040, line 19:	
Not over $1,000...14% of the amount on line 50.				Not over $500......14% of the amount on line 50.			
Over—	But not over—		of excess over—	Over—	But not over—		of excess over—
$1,000	$2,000	$140+15%	$1,000	$500	$1,000	$70+15%	$500
$2,000	$3,000	$290+16%	$2,000	$1,000	$1,500	$145+16%	$1,000
$3,000	$4,000	$450+17%	$3,000	$1,500	$2,000	$225+17%	$1,500
$4,000	$8,000	$620+19%	$4,000	$2,000	$4,000	$310+19%	$2,000
$8,000	$12,000	$1,380+22%	$8,000	$4,000	$6,000	$690+22%	$4,000
$12,000	$16,000	$2,260+25%	$12,000	$6,000	$8,000	$1,130+25%	$6,000
$16,000	$20,000	$3,260+28%	$16,000	$8,000	$10,000	$1,630+28%	$8,000
$20,000	$24,000	$4,380+32%	$20,000	$10,000	$12,000	$2,190+32%	$10,000
$24,000	$28,000	$5,660+36%	$24,000	$12,000	$14,000	$2,830+36%	$12,000
$28,000	$32,000	$7,100+39%	$28,000	$14,000	$16,000	$3,550+39%	$14,000
$32,000	$36,000	$8,660+42%	$32,000	$16,000	$18,000	$4,330+42%	$16,000
$36,000	$40,000	$10,340+45%	$36,000	$18,000	$20,000	$5,170+45%	$18,000
$40,000	$44,000	$12,140+48%	$40,000	$20,000	$22,000	$6,070+48%	$20,000
$44,000	$52,000	$14,060+50%	$44,000	$22,000	$26,000	$7,030+50%	$22,000
$52,000	$64,000	$18,060+53%	$52,000	$26,000	$32,000	$9,030+53%	$26,000
$64,000	$76,000	$24,420+55%	$64,000	$32,000	$38,000	$12,210+55%	$32,000
$76,000	$88,000	$31,020+58%	$76,000	$38,000	$44,000	$15,510+58%	$38,000
$88,000	$100,000	$37,980+60%	$88,000	$44,000	$50,000	$18,990+60%	$44,000
$100,000	$120,000	$45,180+62%	$100,000	$50,000	$60,000	$22,590+62%	$50,000
$120,000	$140,000	$57,580+64%	$120,000	$60,000	$70,000	$28,790+64%	$60,000
$140,000	$160,000	$70,380+66%	$140,000	$70,000	$80,000	$35,190+66%	$70,000
$160,000	$180,000	$83,580+68%	$160,000	$80,000	$90,000	$41,790+68%	$80,000
$180,000	$200,000	$97,180+69%	$180,000	$90,000	$100,000	$48,590+69%	$90,000
$200,000	....	$110,980+70%	$200,000	$100,000	....	$55,490+70%	$100,000

now consider the fifth tax, the capital gains tax, and its implications in estate planning. A capital gains tax is owed whenever you buy property, hold it for longer than six months, and then sell it for a profit. For example, you buy real estate for $30,000 and some years later sell it for $46,000. You have made $16,000, and any time you make money, the Internal Revenue Service wants part of it in the form of an income tax. But because you made it by the long-term profit route, you, the taxpayer, get a break. You may divide the profit in two and report only half of it as income to the IRS. This certainly gives you a tax break, for it is far better than having to report the entire profit.

The actual confusion that exists in regard to the capital gains tax lies in the fact that the maximum capital gains tax you have to pay is 25 percent.* Twenty-five percent of what? Of the profit, not of the entire sale. In the above $46,000 sale, you had a $16,000 profit; therefore, the maximum capital gains tax you would have to pay would be 25 percent of $16,000, or $4,000. Most people, however, do not report their capital gains tax this way. This is for the wealthy and is called the alternative method of reporting this tax, on Schedule D of the income tax return. It simply sets the *maximum* that would have to be paid.

Most people who realize a long-term profit divide it in half and treat it as income, like a raise in salary or an increase in profit from a business. They report it this way, because if they are in a tax bracket of less than 50 percent, and most people are, they do not have to pay the maximum tax of 25 percent of the profit.

It works this way. Let us say that you are reporting $8,000 in taxable income, and by consulting Schedule Y you see that your tax is $1,380 and that your tax bracket for anything earned above this amount would be 22 percent. In the above example you sold a piece of property for $46,000 and made $16,000, after having held it longer than six months. By dividing the profit in half you only have to report an additional $8,000, showing this amount on your return as increased income. This $8,000, when

---

* Married taxpayers filing a joint return have to pay 32½ percent, starting in 1970, and 35 percent in 1971 on any capital gains in excess of $50,000 in one year.

added to your other $8,000 of taxable income, would give you $16,000 of taxable income on which you now pay $3,260.

How much was the capital gains tax because of the sale? It was the difference between the $1,380 that you would have paid without the sale, and the $3,260 that you had to pay because of the sale. The difference is $1,880. This is certainly far less than the maximum tax of 25 percent on the $16,000 profit, or $4,000. It is actually 11.75 percent. This is why everyone who is in a tax bracket of less than 50 percent reports his long-term capital gain this way.

Many times a property owner feels that he is locked in because of the capital gains tax and can't sell, even though he would like to dispose of the property. He feels that it would cost him too much in taxes. This "locked in" feeling exists because he thinks that he would have to pay the maximum tax of 25 percent of the profit, and there are even some people who feel that the capital gains tax is 25 percent of the entire amount of the sale! Estate planning does not exist solely for the benefit of heirs; it is also for the benefit of the testator while he lives. Time and again property owners will retain low-income property during retired years, even though they are badly in need of more income, because of a misunderstanding of the capital gains tax.

Dr. and Mrs. Tole owned vacant land at a current market value of $30,000. It was purchased while the doctor was a practicing dentist, for speculation and a possible increase in value. The doctor was correct in his analysis, for he had purchased it for $20,000, and it had gone up in value 50 percent. He was now retired. He found himself with a $30,000 piece of property that was giving him no income; as a matter of fact, it was costing him money, for he was paying taxes on the vacant land every year. He needed more income but felt that he was locked in because of the capital gains tax. When he learned how to compute it correctly, he sold, investing the $30,000 (less the tax) at 6 percent and materially increasing his retirement income.

Sometimes gifts would not have been made had the capital gains tax been understood. For example, when a gift of property is made from the living estate to heirs, the cost basis of the property does not change. The donor's original cost basis is the one that is used in computing capital gains, not the market value of the property at the time of the transfer. If the donee should later sell the property, he has to take the donor's cost basis as the amount from which to figure his profits.

Mr. Thomas, a widower, owned three ranches, which he had inherited from his father many years before. One of the ranches was worth $250,000, and he erroneously decided to give it to his married son and pay the gift taxes. Since he had already used up his lifetime exemption and his annual exclusion for that year, the gift taxes amounted to $49,275 for the federal government alone. Four years later he died, and his son decided to sell the ranch. Because there had been no intervening death (that is, between the original evaluation and the time of the gift), and therefore no estate taxes had been paid, the son had to go back to the father's cost basis. The $250,000 ranch had been appraised in his grandfather's estate for a mere $30,000. The capital gains tax was 32½ percent of $220,-000, or $71,500. (See footnote on page 56.) Because the father did not fully comprehend the capital gains tax, his estate was needlessly subjected to both a gift tax and a capital gains tax instead of only death taxes.

On the other hand, full comprehension of the five taxes involved in estate planning can sometimes solve what seems at first glance to be an insurmountable problem.

Miss Murchison had worked for a national chain store for forty-five years, retiring at the normal age of sixty-five. She was now eighty-three and found to her private amazement, for she never had considered herself to be shrewd when it came to investments, that she was worth over $300,000. Early in her working years she had inherited a few thousand dollars and had proceeded to invest them in shares of the chain store and a few blue chip stocks. At the end of fifty years, what with stock splits and stock dividends and buying more shares with the dividends, she found herself with more wealth than she had ever dreamed of possessing. Since she had no near relatives, she was leaving the entire sum in her will to two second cousins, share-and-share alike. Both of them were married with three children. She wanted to help her cousins, who were not too well off, in the heavy expense of putting several children through college. Her problem was how to set up a fund to educate the six children while she was still alive and not have to pay too much in taxes. If she sold some of her chain-store stock, which was her major asset, the capital gains tax would be prohibitive, for the shares had cost her an average of only $2.00 per share, while they were currently selling at $62.00 per share. In addition the stock was paying a low dividend of just under 2 percent. With the help of expert estate planning advice she solved her tax problem this way.

Instead of selling the chain-store stock, she transferred $8,000 of the current value of the shares to each of the six children. By giving them the stock instead of selling it, she did not subject herself to a capital gains tax. She simply transferred the ownership to others. She did, of course, become subject to the gift tax rules.

It worked out this way.

She gave $48,000 from her living estate to the children of her heirs, who were classified as strangers under the tax laws. Three thousand dollars to each child times six, or $18,000, came under the annual exclusion of both the federal and state gift tax laws. Five thousand dollars times six amounted to $30,000, which qualified under her lifetime exemption for the IRS. The only gift tax owed was to the State of California, which amounted to $2,820, which she gladly paid out of her bank account. She had now successfully surmounted the capital gains tax problem and the gift tax problem, and had reduced her death estate by almost $50,000, an amount that she had decided she could well afford to give away, having made up her mind that at the age of eighty-three she wasn't going to spend the $300,000 she had accumulated.

She had one problem left. She did not want the children to own a growth stock earning 2 percent. She did not trust the parents' judgment either. She wanted the stock sold and put into a balanced mutual fund, for diversification and professional management plus a better income. This involved computation in advance of the capital gains tax problem imposed against each child. There had been no intervening death, therefore when each child sold his shares, his cost basis would still be the same as her cost basis, or $2.00 per share.

Each donee received a gift of 129 shares of the chain-store stock, resulting in a profit to each child of 129 shares times $60, or $7,740. When this was divided in half, each donee had to pay a capital gains tax on $3,870, now treated as straight income.

Every individual, whether he is a minor or not, has a $750 personal exemption plus a $300 standard deduction. According to Schedule X for single taxpayers, $3,870 minus $1,050 left a taxable income of $2,820, and the tax for each donee was established at $466. Each child, under an order from the probate court, was able to invest a net of $7,534 in a balanced mutual fund for his college education at a tax cost to Miss Murchison of $2,820 in state gift taxes.

Actually from an estate planning standpoint, it didn't even cost the $2,820, for this amount if left in the estate would have been paid in state inheritance taxes anyway. As we have seen, the California state gift tax and state inheritance tax are the same. The only difference was that Miss Murchison had to pay the $2,820 now as a gift tax instead of it being assessed against her heirs when she died.

Once the testator understands what is meant by probate, and understands taxes, he then is in a position to talk intelligently with an attorney about drawing a will. The legal language used by an attorney can understandably be very confusing at times to the average property owner. As one testator said: "I destroyed my last will and made a new one. There were too many 'whereases' to suit me." Yet wills and trusts must be drawn by the legal profession. It is the practical aspect of drawing wills, not how to draw wills, that will be the subject of the next chapter.

3

Wills

EVERYONE SHOULD have a will. If you do not have one, the law will dictate who gets your assets. No one really wants the state in which he is domiciled to determine who are his heirs and in what percentage they inherit, for this is what happens when you die "intestate" or without a legal will. Most people prefer to leave their estates to relatives and friends of their own choosing. Why then do people die intestate?

There are several reasons, but the main one seems to be inertia; they don't intend to die without having drawn a will, they just never get around to it. Most people do not like to make an important decision, particularly one that can easily be put off because there is no apparent reason for doing it now. No one plans on dying. Young people under thirty think they are immortal; older people know they are going to die someday and have philosophically learned to accept this fact, but this unhappy event is always at least ten years away, so there is plenty of time. As Bernard Baruch, the famous financier and adviser to presidents, once said: "Old people are those who are fifteen years older than I am," and this was true with him even in his eighties. This makes for a healthy mental attitude toward the golden years, but it is not conducive to the drawing of a will.

Another reason people die intestate is because they are superstitious. They feel that, if they have a will drawn, they will die soon afterward. Mr. Marks felt this way, and as a consequence he left no will. He died in Minnesota, and in that state, when there is no will, the widow receives one third and the children two thirds. As a result, his two sons could have claimed two thirds of the estate and left their mother in difficult financial circumstances. Instead Mr. Marks' two sons signed over everything to their mother, because they knew that was the way their father had wanted it.

Still another reason for not leaving a will is the argument by husband and wife that they have all of their assets in joint tenancy, and therefore the survivor of the two will automatically inherit from the other. This is true. When the first spouse dies, no will is necessary; but what is going to happen when the second spouse dies? Theoretically, after the first death the survivor can then draw a will. But if a married couple didn't bother when they were both alive, the survivor isn't liable to get around to drawing a will later. It is much better if a couple makes the decision on the eventual distribution of their estate while they are both living and have the advantage of a joint decision, rather than have the remaining spouse make the decision alone.

Everyone, therefore, should have a will. And it should be drawn by a competent attorney, for then it will hold up in probate court and be declared legal. But how to choose the attorney is often a problem. Many people are not in touch with a lawyer. They do not know one to go to, because it may have been years since they have found occasion to seek legal advice, and, surprisingly enough, many people have never seen an attorney for any reason.

If once upon a time they had an attorney, he may have retired or died, or they may have changed their residence and moved to another state. A great number of retired people move thousands of miles away from where they have lived most of their lives in order to be near their adult children and grandchildren. Or they may move in order to retire to a milder climate.

The choice of an attorney to draw your will is an important one. Lawyers specialize just as doctors specialize. You should not go to an attorney who has spent a lifetime in corporate tax law and ask him to draw your will. You should go to an attorney who is competent to solve your particular problem.

What then is the best way to choose an attorney to help plan your estate? One of the best ways is to ask the trust department of your bank. It will give you the names of three attorneys its probate department uses in its capacity as executors of wills. The bank knows they are competent in probate work, or it would not hire them. The bank must be careful, of course, not to play favorites, which is why it will give you the names of at least three different legal firms. It will give you the name of a large firm and a small firm, and sometimes even ask if you prefer to deal with an attorney of your own race or creed, such as black or white, Protestant, Catholic, or Jew. It will give you further information, too, if you ask, and you are then free to choose.

Another way to choose an attorney is to call the Attorney Reference Panel listed in the pages of your telephone book and ask them to recommend someone who is competent to draw a will. This service is available in over 250 cities in the United States. However, don't expect too much from this source. We checked out one personally in a large city and found it to be a telephone service only. The office was primarily in the business of providing secretarial and computer services; the name "Attorney Reference Panel" wasn't even printed on the door. The girl we talked to admitted that her service, which was only a sideline with her, consisted of giving a telephone caller the name of an attorney from a list she had. If you went to see the lawyer recommended, the cost would be $7.00, whether or not you engaged his services. Admittedly, however, it is better than picking a lawyer blind from the telephone book, for attorneys do list their specialties with the Panel. Lawyers cannot advertise, and can't even list in the yellow pages their particular branch of the law, which is strange because doctors, as professional men, can and do list their specialties such as internal medicine, general surgery, dermatology, etc.

You can also check the Martindale Hubbell Directory in your local library, which lists and rates U.S. law firms. Or you may have a friend who has lived in the same area for some time. You can ask him who drew his will, if he has one. However, despite care in your choice of an attorney, you can still choose the wrong one.

Dr. Elliot had become a millionaire by being an orthodontist to famous movie stars in Hollywood. He gave up the practice of dentistry in his fifties and moved to the northern part of the state where he lived handsomely retired for twenty years. He and his wife, when in their seventies, sought the advice of the head of the trust department of their bank in regard to estate planning, and in particular for the name of a competent legal firm to draw their will. Unfortunately, they chose a large firm in the financial center of the West, San Francisco. There was absolutely no question that the firm was competent. The mistake they made was in choosing a firm that was too big and too competent. Everything became settled in regard to the will among Dr. and Mrs. Elliot, the head of the trust department, and the attorney, except for one point. The Elliots had three children—two married daughters and a son. They insisted upon disinheriting their son, refusing to tell the attorney why they were disinheriting him except to say that he had disappeared for twenty years causing great mental anguish to his mother, not knowing whether he was alive or dead, and had only reappeared on the scene when he discovered that his parents had become millionaires. The Elliots insisted that the attorney put a clause in their will that the son should inherit one dollar, and no more.

The attorney insisted that the son should inherit fifty thousand dollars. Why? He was more interested in protecting his firm's famous reputation than in doing what the good doctor and his wife wanted. The lawyer was not going to be put on the witness stand, at some time in the future, and forced to admit that he had drawn a will that could be contested. He maintained, and rightly so for that matter, that if the son were left only one dollar, he would most certainly contest the will, protesting that his disinheritance was the result of undue influence under duress. If, however, he were left $50,000, the son would probably not risk a chancy lawsuit.

So, this prestigious law firm drew the will and trust agreement with the stipulation that the son receive $50,-000, unless he contested the will, and if he did and lost, he would receive one dollar. The good doctor and his wife were so incensed when they read the will that they tore it up and asked the law firm to send them a bill. Three months later, the doctor died intestate, leaving over one million dollars.

Dr. and Mrs. Elliot had chosen the wrong firm. What they should have done, when the impasse took place, was to go to a smaller firm. The smaller firm would have drawn the will the way they wanted it, and by the use of a trust agreement, a fortune would have been saved in federal estate taxes. Instead, through joint tenancy, Mrs. Elliot became the sole owner of the entire estate.

The effect of dying without a will can be disastrous, particularly when you consider the following nine different possible ways that an estate can be distributed when a property owner dies intestate.

1. Upon the death of husband or wife, where there are no descendants, parents, brothers, sisters, or their descendants—

> all property goes to the surviving spouse.

2. Upon the death of husband or wife, where there is one child—

> one half goes to the surviving spouse;
> one half goes to the child. *

3. Upon the death of husband or wife, where there are two or more children—

> one third goes to the surviving spouse;
> two thirds is divided among the children. *

4. Upon the death of husband or wife, where there are no descendants, but a father and mother—

> one half goes to the surviving spouse;
> one quarter goes to the father and one quarter goes to the mother; and if only one parent survives, then one half goes to the surviving parent.

5. Upon the death of a widow or widower or single person, where there are no descendants, but a father and mother—

> one half goes to the father;
> one half goes to the mother;
> and if only one parent survives, all the property goes to the surviving parent.

6. Upon the death of a widow or widower or single person, where there are no parents or descendants but brothers and sisters—

---

* Descendants of deceased child take deceased child's share. In community property states, all community property goes to the surviving wife or husband.

all property goes to the brothers and sisters;
descendants of deceased brother or sister take his
or her share.

7. Upon the death of husband or wife, where there are
no descendants and no parents, but brothers and sisters—
one half goes to the surviving spouse;
one half is divided among brothers and sisters;
descendants of deceased brother or sister take his
or her share.

8. Upon the death of widow or widower, where there is
a child or children—
the estate is divided equally among the children.

9. Upon the death of a widow or widower or single person where there are no descendants, parents, brothers, or
sisters, or their descendants—
all property goes to the next of kin.

To avoid one of the above arbitrary divisions of your
estate you should have a will, drawn by a competent attorney.

The correct choice of who will be your executor is sometimes more important than who will be your attorney. In
the first chapter we have seen that the executor is in charge
of the estate during probate. Certainly this is enough to
stress the importance of your choice. The person who will
manage the assets of an estate during the probate process
is called an executor, provided the testator named him in
his will. If the will does not provide for an executor, the
probate court judge will appoint someone to manage the
estate, and then he is called an administrator. Their function is the same. An administrator is appointed by the
court, an executor is named in the will.

An executor can be either an individual or a corporation.
This is the first important decision. As we have seen in
the chapter on probate, you shouldn't name a financially

incompetent or inexperienced member of your family to take charge of your estate simply because they will earn the executor's fee. The practical effect of naming an inexperienced individual is to have the attorney who drew the document act as both the executor and the attorney. The reason for this is fairly obvious. The inexperienced executor won't know the first step of the probate process, and therefore, out of necessity, he has to rely wholly upon the attorney. This was the problem when Aunt Mamie was named as executrix in Chapter One.

You might argue that naming an executor, who will simply rubber-stamp the attorney's decisions, is fine as far as you are concerned, for you have complete confidence in your attorney. But what if the attorney should die or retire, and your inexperienced executor now chooses a poor replacement? Now you have two people in charge of your hard-earned estate who are not knowledgeable. This could be very costly to your heirs and result in a drastic reduction of the future income and security of your family.

On the other hand you may well have a competent adult son or daughter in whom you have complete confidence in money matters, who can act as executor of your estate during probate. However, if you do not have such a member of your family, and there are many families who do not, then the second possibility of naming a corporate executor such as a bank should be weighed very carefully.

One of the principal arguments in favor of naming a corporation as an executor is that a corporation is a separate legal entity; it does not die. The death of any one individual makes no difference; another person will take his place. The next major reason in favor of a bank is competence. The trust department of a bank has a probate division that does nothing else every day but handle probate matters. The bank as executor will actually manage the estate and will hire and use the probate attorney for no

other reason than to prepare and make the necessary petitions to the court.

This does not mean that a bank will necessarily do a
better job than a good individual executor and his attorney. The length of time that the estate will be in probate
will be just as long, or longer, and in many cases the bank
will give out even less information to the heirs during
probate than would otherwise be the case. The corporate
executor will also be just as likely to ask the court for extraordinary fees for extra services if the bank feels they
are justified. While these extraordinary fees are usually
nominal, a few hundred dollars at best, nevertheless when
allowed by the judge they do add to the cost of probate.

After deciding on your attorney and your executor, the
next step is to arrange a conference with the lawyer. Here
is where a Confidential Inventory of Assets plays an important role. A copy of this inventory should be sent to the
attorney several days in advance of your meeting, because
if he has this vital information beforehand, it will considerably reduce the time you have to spend with him. If he
can have the family information on page one, and have a
complete inventory of your assets, he will have much of
the information that he would have to obtain from you by
tedious questioning. After all, he does charge by the hour
for his time, therefore his charges will be less. If you have
an existing will, drawn several years ago by another attorney, it would be of considerable help to him if you sent
this, too, along with the inventory of assets. This tells the
attorney quite a bit about your family and what would
have happened if you died yesterday. It also gives him an
insight into your thinking the last time you made a testamentary disposition. If there have been changes in your
family status since the last will, a covering letter to this
effect should be sent.

You should also be prepared to give him the exact ownership of your various assets. For instance, you can't will anything in joint tenancy, as we shall see later in the chapter on ownership. Your attorney must know what ownership you have on the assets in your estate, or he cannot draw a proper will. Again it will save time if you will examine the title to your assets in your safe-deposit box in advance. These have probably been acquired over a period of time, so that it may surprise you how many types of ownership you have, such as individual, joint ownership, beneficiary form, etc.

Once the attorney has drawn your will and sent you a copy, you should read it very carefully before you sign it, to be sure that there has been a complete meeting of the minds between you and your lawyer. Does he understand exactly what you are attempting to accomplish by this testamentary disposition of your living estate to your heirs? With a small estate and a simple will this should be no problem. A two-page document that says that you leave everything to your beloved spouse, both real and personal, and wherever situated; and if she should predecease you, then you leave your estate to your children share-and-share alike, certainly should not be misinterpreted between you and your attorney. In larger estates, however, particularly those involving trusts, the legal terminology can become quite technical, and therefore clear understanding as to what is being accomplished by this document is essential. Here is where a financial planning team is important, so that you can discuss the will before you sign it with your tax accountant, your investment representative, and your life insurance underwriter. The function of the financial planning team is discussed in Chapter Six.

All wills, however simple or complex, have certain essential phrases that lawyers use. It will be easier for you to comprehend your will if you understand the terms.

They are listed below in the usual order they appear in the average testamentary disposition.

1. "I hereby revoke all Wills and Codicils previously made by me." A codicil is an afterthought, and is added on to the will and signed separately, instead of having a whole new will drawn. You have changed your mind, let us say, and have decided to name your bank as executor rather than an individual member of your family. It hardly makes sense to draw a whole new will; your attorney simply adds on a codicil to this effect.

When drawing a new will, it is automatic that you should revoke all previous wills and codicils. Your attorney will insert this phrase even though you have assured him you have never had a will drawn before; after all, no harm is done, and it does revoke completely all previous testamentary documents. Sometimes people feel, when contemplating having a new will drawn by a different attorney, that they would rather not do it, because they will have to inform the first attorney that the will he drew is no longer valid. This is not necessary. Your new will automatically revokes the previous one, and that is that.

2. "I direct first that my executor shall pay all inheritance, estate, or other death taxes, all expenses of administration of my estate, and all legal claims against my estate." These first mortgage demands against your assets have to be paid, and then the residue can be distributed among your heirs. But how can your executor pay them if you state in your will that your heirs get their inheritance first, and everyone else—the government, your executor and the probate attorney, and your creditors—is paid out of what is left, when there may be nothing left? This is not possible, and could have the effect of causing your will to be declared invalid when your executor petitions to have it admitted to probate. Then you will die intestate, which is

exactly what you were trying to avoid when you had your will drawn in the first place.

3. "I have the following children," and then they are carefully named. Supposing you said in your will that you have several children, and they shall share-and-share alike if your wife predeceases you, but you did not name them? This is wrong as demonstrated in the following case.

Mr. Reese, who had seven children, left a will stating that they should share-and-share alike, but he didn't name them. His estate was sizable. He had married twice, having three children by his first wife, whom he divorced, and four children by his second wife, who died. When he divorced his first wife, he had been young and without money, but the court had awarded him the custody of his three children anyway. He found it financially impossible to take care of the youngest child, who was a daughter and only a year old, so he put her out for adoption, stipulating to the foster parents that he, the real father, would never contact her until she was twenty-one, or they had died. He kept his promise. But when his daughter's foster parents died while she was in her twenties, he contacted her and made himself known. This came as no great shock to his daughter, for she had been told that she was legally adopted and that her true father was still alive. However, many years later when Mr. Reese finally died, his will was contested by a woman living in Chicago, his former residence. She claimed through her attorney that she was one of the seven children mentioned in his will. The daughter who had been legally adopted by someone else was not meant as one of the seven, she maintained, but she, though illegitimate, *was* one of the seven! The claim was undoubtedly false, but it effectively tied up the estate in probate for five years. Finally, the executor settled out of court, paying her ten thousand dollars just to get rid of her, in order for him to be able to distribute the balance of the estate to the rightful heirs.

4. "If my executor shall fail, be unable, or cease for any reason whatever to act as executor hereunder I hereby appoint the following corporate executor." This is inserted when it is your desire to name an individual executor but you want a corporate executor to succeed him in the event that something should happen to that individual. You want to ensure competence in the eventual executor if this should prove to be necessary. It can, however, have unexpected results.

Mr. Gregory died, leaving his half of the joint estate owned by him and his wife in a bank trust, with income to be paid by the trustee to his wife during her lifetime, and then distributing the proceeds to several cousins who were twice, and thrice, removed. His purpose in setting up the trust on his half of the estate was to save death taxes, which was completely unnecessary for, if he had thought about it carefully, he really had no reason to reduce inheritance taxes upon his death when the only ones to benefit were his distant cousins whom he had not seen for many years. He should have been primarily concerned about himself and his wife.

Their joint estate was valued at $1,200,000, consisting of just three assets: one million dollars in one common stock, a $75,000 home, and the balance in cash. Before he drew his new will, all three assets were in joint tenancy, which meant that his wife would automatically inherit everything. By creating a trust, she not only lost control of his half, for by his will the bank took over as trustee, but she lost control of her half as well. Mr. Gregory, in his will, had named his wife as executrix, with the phrase that, if she were unable to serve, the bank would become the executor.

The bank put doctors on the stand in probate court that

caused the judge to rule that the widow was mentally incompetent, so the bank took over as executor. Then because she was legally declared incompetent, they petitioned the court to be the conservator of her half of the estate, which the court allowed. When probate was over, the bank was trustee on his half and conservator on her half, and she therefore lost control of the entire $1,200,-000. Remaining in joint tenancy, she would have inherited the entire estate.

5. "My executor shall have the right to dispose of any or all of my assets." This phrase is used so that your executor will be sure to have enough cash to pay death taxes, costs of administration, and legal claims. However, if you do not want all of your assets sold, this phrase should be carefully reviewed with your attorney, and perhaps changed to read that your executor shall have the right to sell only those assets that are necessary to pay these costs. You may prefer to pass on as many as possible of your carefully chosen investments to your heirs and not have your executor sell them and distribute cash. Giving your executor the right to sell all of your assets may be too broad a power and unnecessary in your case.

6. "If my wife and I should die as the result of a common accident, and she should survive me by a period of six months or less, it is presumed that she predeceased me." This is known as a common disaster clause, and is inserted by your attorney to avoid having your estate taxed twice within a short period of time. First in your estate because you died first, and then again in your wife's estate, because your will provides that she inherits from you. Some states have a Simultaneous Death Act which acts as a common disaster clause in the event that your will does not contain this provision, but it is good for only the first twenty-four hours.

7. "If my wife shall predecease me, then my estate shall

be distributed as follows." Many testators do not understand this phrase and fail to clear it up with their attorney.
Years ago it was common for attorneys to draw one will
for the husband and then have the wife sign a statement
that she concurred with its provisions. This is no longer
true. The modern method is for an attorney to draw a will
for each spouse. The provisions of the two wills are identical in most cases, except for the name of the testator,
which is the husband in one will and the wife in the other.
If the husband's will is being read, he is certainly dead.
"If my wife shall predecease me" means, therefore, that
they are both dead. By this phrase the entire estate is now
being distributed by the husband to the heirs.

8. "I give, devise and bequeath all of my property both
real and personal, and wherever situated." "Devise" means
to give real estate by will, and "bequeath" means to give
personal property by will. "Wherever situated" is certainly
an all-inclusive term. By this phrase you are willing, therefore, everything of which you die possessed.

The above practical explanation of frequently used
phrases in wills should enable you to read your will more
intelligently when it is presented by your attorney for
your signature.

Another reason for having a will drawn now, instead
of procrastinating indefinitely, is the possibility of living
so long that you arrive at the point where, because of age,
you are no longer capable of making the right decisions.
We are not speaking so much of senility here, for many
people live until they are ninety in full retention of all
their faculties. It is simply that they have outlived their
generation. They belong to another time. They refuse to
make decisions that are imperative, or make the wrong
ones, simply because they have lived too long.

Mr. and Mrs. Stevens had everything in joint tenancy
so that when he died his wife inherited everything. Mrs.

Stevens lived until she was ninety years old, remaining in remarkably good health, but drastic changes took place in the twenty years that she survived her husband. They had three married children, two sons and a daughter. The two sons and their wives died during that twenty-year period, and by the time Mrs. Stevens was eighty-five, her remaining child, her daughter, was already sixty.

In all that twenty years she held on tightly to a comfortable estate and gave nothing to her children. Of course, Mrs. Stevens had the right to retain the estate; it was hers; and if she wanted to keep possession of it until she was gone, it was nobody's business but her own. But by the time she was in her late eighties, it was certainly time to take cognizance in her will of the fact that her two sons had died. Finally at ninety she decided to make a change.

But the change she made was to virtually disinherit her only remaining child! She didn't like her son-in-law, and since she had already lost two children, she falsely reasoned that the third one would die relatively young, too. In this event, what property she left to her daughter would go to her husband, and she didn't want that. So she changed her will, leaving her daughter only $20,000 and placing the balance in a bank trust for the benefit of her six grandchildren. When she died at ninety-one, she left behind a very bitter daughter. Her husband had never made much money; he was retired now, and she saw her rightful inheritance left for the most part to grandchildren. Mrs. Stevens had lived too long to make a right decision.

In another case Mr. Rodney also lived to be over ninety and, because of joint tenancy, owned everything. He had been an engineer in China most of his adult life, and he and his wife had found it relatively easy to amass a fortune living in a land where the cost of living was very cheap. At ninety he was alert, his hearing was excellent, and he felt well enough to live alone in a great big house. His interest in national and international affairs, particularly since he had lived in Asia for so many years, was very keen. He was receptive to new ideas and took an avid interest in the death tax savings available through proper estate planning when these suggestions were made to him. But he had become too old, at ninety, to make a decision to implement any of the excellent suggestions made to him. His reply was always: "I'll think about it." He refused to face up to the reality of his great age. He was convinced that he would live to see a hundred, and more, but he was dead at ninety-two.

Living too long to make decisions cost his children dearly in unnecessary death taxes and probate costs. He should have made those decisions years before.

Two apparently minor, but important, items in regard to a will seem to puzzle most people. First, and the more important of the two, is how they should divide their assets. Should they leave each heir a specific dollar amount? Or if there are bequests, should these be made first and then the residue divided? Or what? The simplest and most effective method is to think of your estate in terms of percentages (the whole estate being, of course, 100 percent) and then dividing your assets by percentages instead of dollar amounts.

Mr. Bowman had an estate worth $40,000 which he was leaving to three sons. His youngest son was a high-school teacher with six children. Obviously the demands on his money were great. Financially, raising six children is a problem, much less being able to send them to college. Since Mr. Bowman's other two sons were fairly good money makers with small families, he decided to leave unequal shares to his children. He left 50 percent to the high-school teacher and 25 percent each to his other two sons.

This was the *correct* way to arrange the division of his assets in his will. Supposing, instead, his will had divided the $40,000 by dollar amounts, stating that the neediest son was to inherit $20,000 and that the other two sons would inherit the residue of his estate share-and-share alike. Now let's take a look at what could happen. First, he might have spent half of his estate by the time he died. Now the schoolteacher son would get $20,000, and his other two sons would receive nothing. Second, instead of spending part of his estate, let's suppose that, by sound investing, he had increased his estate from $40,000 to $80,000 by the time he died. Now the needy son would still inherit $20,000, but the other two sons would divide the remainder, or $60,000. Neither of these events actually took place because Mr. Bowman had wisely arranged for the one son to receive 50 percent of his estate no matter what happened. By the percentage method of division, the neediest son received half of his estate whether its value was $20,000, $40,000, or $80,000 by the time he died.

A word of caution. If you do leave uneven shares to children for some good reason, have your lawyer insert a clause in your will stating why you are dividing your estate in uneven shares. It will avoid ill feeling among your children later as to why you didn't treat them equally, share-and-share alike.

The second apparently minor, but important, decision is how to divide your personal belongings. Leaving your personal estate for your children to wrangle over can cause a lifetime of bitterness. In every household there are a few pieces of furniture and items of personal belongings that have an unusual monetary or sentimental value: a tea set that belonged to Grandma originally; a baby grand piano; an antique piecrust table over two hundred years old. These are called chattels by your attorney and consist of everything in your estate, except real estate, that has physical existence. Pick out these items and state in your will who gets them; or if you don't want to mention them in your will, use an old-fashioned method that isn't legal but still works. On the underside of each valuable article put the name of the heir who is to receive it. This clearly states your wishes, and most of the time your heirs will cheerfully abide by your thoughtful decisions. The balance of your personal estate will be divided without argument, or for that matter discarded or sold.

Mr. and Mrs. Page had three married sons and ignored the division of their personal estate. The sons didn't fight over who got what, but, believe me, their wives did! The grandfather clock was literally stolen by one daughter-in-law, according to the other two, just because she happened to be there first. And a very comfortable, brand-new bedroom set was bitterly wrangled over, but seized by the family that needed it the least, or so it was contended. The backbiting that went on eventually disrupted the three families to the point where the three sons seldom saw one another anymore.

Sometimes a personal estate partly consists of business furniture or equipment. It makes sense to leave farm equipment to your son who is managing the farm, not to your widow or to all of the children share-and-share alike. Also a business or professional man could better leave his office equipment to his business associates than to other heirs who would have little or no use for it.

One of the eventualities that should be avoided in your will is the possibility of ancillary administration. This is the probate of a part of your estate in another state besides the one in which you are domiciled, caused primarily by the ownership of real estate in that other state.

Mrs. Edie was a widow and retained ownership in her estate of a mountain cabin in an adjoining state, to which she retired every summer for about three months. She enjoyed the cabin immensely, but eventually she became too old to use it, so that her only son and his family were the ones who occupied it for the most part during his vacation each year. Mrs. Edie died still owning the cabin. She should have given it to her son during her lifetime, which would have avoided probate of the cabin in the adjoining state.

Sometimes, however, giving up ownership of real estate by the testator is not advisable. Then special arrangements can be made. Mrs. Woods lived in a large and expensive house in Philadelphia which had been her home for most of her adult life. For her security and protection she saw no alternative but to retain the ownership. She died, leaving her estate plus the house, to her only daughter who lived in New York. The daughter in turn died before her mother's estate was out of probate, leaving what she had inherited from her mother to her husband. Since the balance of Mrs. Woods's estate was solely in securities, the probate of her daughter's estate in New York presented no problem, but the ancillary administration of the house in Philadelphia became a headache and was not settled for several years, because the big, old home, though valuable, was a white elephant in the existing real estate market in Philadelphia. Mrs. Woods could easily have solved her problem by having her attorney arrange transfer of the property to her daughter while retaining a life interest in the property for herself, including the right to sell. This would have given her the security she needed and wanted, and at the same time would have avoided an expensive ancillary administration in Pennsylvania.

Ancillary administration is required for several reasons.

1. The state in which the property is located wants to be sure it collects its share of the inheritance taxes.

2. The creditors in that state have to be protected.

3. Heirs want to be sure that title to the real estate is not clouded, which could happen if probate of the property were not concluded in the state in which it is located.

Where assets other than real estate are held in another state, they should be physically brought into the state of domicile, particularly since some states require ancillary administration on all tangible personal property, and some even for stocks and bonds and bank accounts. The careless retention of a bank account in Vermont, for example, simply because you formerly lived there and go back to visit once in a while, could cause trouble, when it would be so simple to arrange for the physical transfer of that account to your new permanent home in Florida. Examination of the probate law of the State of Vermont is not necessary. To avoid any possible problem of ancillary administration of your estate, simply physically transfer the bank account into the State of Florida.

Real estate, as we have indicated, presents the major problem. There are actually five different ways to solve it:

(a) by an outright gift to your heirs
(b) by retaining a life interest in the property, including the right to sell
(c) by placing it in joint tenancy
(d) by placing it in a revocable living trust (discussed under trusts)
(e) by incorporating the property, if it is sizable. Now it is not real estate, but stock, which in most states would not make it subject to ancillary administration

Liquidity is another problem frequently not considered by the testator when drawing a will. An estate can be completely debt free, but in the next instant, because of death, be subjected to sizable bills. It costs money to die, as we have seen. Death creates immediate cash requirements for the following reasons:

(a) funeral expenses
(b) doctor and hospital bills
(c) administration costs
(d) cash bequests in the will
(e) federal estate taxes
(f) state inheritance taxes

An estate consisting entirely of real estate presents the biggest cash problem to an executor. The above obligations simply cannot be met except by mortgaging the property, or selling it in a hurry, usually at a sacrifice. An alternative method would be for the testator to carry an adequate amount of life insurance on his life. Most of the time this is not possible, however, for by the time the property owner has built a sizable estate, he is too old to pass a life insurance physical or, if healthy, has reached an age where the premium is too high. Still another method of solving the liquidity problem is to sell some of the real estate at a favorable price during the testator's lifetime.

Income taxes on your estate have to be paid during the time it is in probate. Be sure that your executor understands that he has a choice between electing a fiscal tax year or a calendar tax year. Let us say that death occurs on February 1. Your executor could choose a fiscal year and not owe any income taxes in the year of death, by transferring that obligation, very advantageously sometimes, to the following first of February. It is also possible, instead of the executor retaining the income from the estate during probate, for him to make a partial distribution of it to the heirs. It then becomes taxable in their individual income tax returns instead of being taxable to the estate as a whole, which may very well save on income taxes. Also your executor may charge the expenses of administration of your estate either against the Federal Estate Tax Return or the estate's Income Tax Return, whichever is more advantageous.

It is possible, but not advisable, to draw a will yourself and thereby avoid the expense of hiring an attorney. A handwritten will drawn by the testator is called a holographic will. The main objection to drawing your own will is the possibility that it will be declared illegal. It has to meet certain rigid standards, and even these can vary from state to state. Generally speaking, it must be written entirely in the testator's own hand on a perfectly plain piece of stationery; there can be absolutely no printing of any kind on the paper. It must be dated, of course, but it does not have to be witnessed. A handwritten will is drawn by a property owner because it is simple and it saves a fee.

Some attorneys will recommend a holographic will, under certain circumstances, as a stopgap device. A prospective client, for instance, might telephone in the middle of the night, upset over some unforeseen event because he does not have a will in force. It is not often possible for the attorney to see him immediately, so he may suggest, under these circumstances, that the testator write his own will, stating his wishes in regard to his estate. This will serve temporarily until a proper will is drawn, and is far better than dying intestate.

As we have stated, wills should be drawn by a competent attorney. However, for use in an emergency, reproduced below are two samples of holographic wills that were admitted to probate court and declared legal. Names, places, and dates have been changed. The wording used, however, is identical, including misspelling and bad punctuation.

San Jose, Calif.
March 14, 1971

I, Mae Morse, hereby make my last will—I, give all the property of which I die possessed to my husband George T. Morse—I appoint my said husband executor of this will without bonds. I give him power to sell all or any of my estate without an order of court I case my husband George T. Morse should die before I do—I want the estate to be divided into equal parts and given to each of my living sisters and brother.

I want Anna Jones to serve as executor of this will without bonds.

If any one contestes this will—they shall receive the sum of one dollar ($1.00)

This is my last will and declare this will is entirely written and dated and signed by my hand.

Mae Morse
45 N. Main St. San Jose, California

San Francisco, California
February 14, 1969

I, Mary Doe, being of sound mind and not acting under fraud menace, or the undue influence of any person do hereby make and declare this to be my last will and testament in the following manner: I give, devise and bequeath all of my property of every kind, nature and description and wherever situate to my brother, Thomas Doe.

I appoint as my executor to serive without bond James Doe of 100 Main Street, San Francisco, California.

I hereby affirm that this my last will and testament is entirely written by my own hand and signed by me.

Mary Doe

Whether your will is drawn by your own hand or by an attorney, it should be under periodic review. Too often a testator takes the attitude that once his will is drawn the job has been done. It has been, for the time being. But unfortunately assets entail responsibilities, and as far as your will is concerned, this means keeping it up to date. Any material change in circumstances should alert the property owner that perhaps his will should be reviewed.

Such a change would take place when there is a marriage, a divorce, or children or grandchildren born in your family. These events should serve as a red flag that perhaps your will should be reviewed. It would not necessarily need to be altered, but it's just as well to take it out of your safe deposit box and look it over to be sure.

Mr. Alexander owned 100 percent of the stock of a very profitable close corporation. He was a widower with an only daughter. His will provided that the business should be sold in the event of his death and the proceeds turned over to his only heir. Later, however, Mr. Alexander's daughter married and had two children, and Mr. Alexander took his son-in-law into the business. His daughter's husband proved to be, with time, a capable business executive. So Mr. Alexander changed his will. The business was no longer to be sold by his executor, but he provided instead that the stock of the corporation was to be placed in trust during his daughter's lifetime. By this method the son-in-law could manage and control the business for the benefit of the family, and in addition, when his daughter died, the business would not be taxed a second time in her estate.

The distribution of the death proceeds of life insurance are a part of a will review, so these valuable cash assets should also be considered because of changed circumstances.

Mr. Hammer's wife died, and he acquired their entire estate through joint tenancy ownership. His wife was named as the beneficiary on his life insurance policies, with his three children named as contingent beneficiaries. When his wife died, Mr. Hammer's death tax problem drastically increased. Upon review of his will, *and* his life insurance, he decided to change the beneficiary from his children to his estate, thereby making the death proceeds available to the executor. If the children had inherited the insurance proceeds outright, because of his increased death tax problem, there would not have been enough liquid assets available to the executor with which to pay them.

Quite often a will should be reviewed if an estate is reduced in size due to financial reverses. Now any cash bequests, for instance, could be eliminated because your principal beneficiaries will need the entire estate. A change in family or financial circumstances, therefore, is the key. Review your will automatically when this happens.

Sometimes a simple will, however, is not your answer. You need to have a trust drawn instead. Trusts and their uses are discussed in the next chapter.

4

Trusts

TRUSTS ARE created mainly because the property owner, for a very good reason, does not want his estate to be immediately inherited by his heirs. As we have seen, a will simply states who gets the assets, and when probate is over, title passes to the legal heirs. The new owners may then use these assets as they see fit. In a trust, title passes to a trustee who then administers the property according to the terms of the trust for the benefit of someone else. Disposition of the capital and/or the income for the beneficiaries of the trust usually takes place over a period of many years.

As a famous lawyer is fond of saying: "You can have a will instead of a trust, if you are willing to pay the price." In this chapter we will see how expensive a simple will can be in many cases.

When a trust is contemplated, most people are confused as to the difference between a trustee and an executor. An executor and an attorney are still necessary in a testamentary trust, because your assets still have to pass through the probate court. At the conclusion of probate, instead of your assets being given to your heirs, they are turned over by the executor to the trustee who then, and only then, starts functioning as your fiduciary agent. The trustee, in other words, takes over from the executor, and at that point starts managing your estate and handing out the income and/or the capital to the beneficiaries of the trust according to your clearly stated wishes as the grantor.

The trustee of a trust has three basic duties:

(a) to protect the property
(b) to carry out the terms of the trust
(c) to make fair and impartial decisions for the income beneficiaries, and for the remaindermen, who are the heirs who will eventually inherit the assets of the trust when it is terminated

Since the trustee takes title and is responsible for properly managing and investing the assets, great care must be taken in the choice of who will be trustee. A trust institution is usually chosen; witness the fact that trust departments of banks currently manage over 100 billion dollars. There is no question that banks know how to protect trust property, and, of course, they are completely reliable. However, a banker by his very training is ultra-conservative; the results, therefore, in the form of income and long-term growth are often disappointing. Not only that, but once a trust institution has been named trustee, it must be understood by the grantor that this corporate trustee will really "take charge" and will not relinquish control for any reason.

Mr. Turner, for tax reasons and upon the advice of his attorney, placed his half of the total estate that he and his wife had acquired over a lifetime in a testamentary trust. His bank was named trustee, with instructions to pay the income to his wife during her lifetime and, upon her death, to terminate the trust and divide the assets equally among his children. His wife made the same arrangement on her half. As an added precaution, each made the surviving spouse co-trustee with the bank. As it so happened, Mrs. Turner was the first to die, so Mr. Turner became co-trustee with the bank on his wife's half of the estate, which amounted to $100,000.

After a period of years Mr. Turner became completely dissatisfied with the way the bank was managing the money, and the poor return on it, compared to the income that he was receiving on his own $100,000, which he had placed in a mutual fund. He went to the head of the trust department and demanded that the bank place his wife's estate in the mutual fund also, agreeing that the bank could continue in their capacity as trustee and collect the trustee fee, despite the fact that they would no longer be responsible for any investment decisions. In two interviews Mr. Turner had with the head of the trust department, he brought his investment representative with him as an observer.

At the end of the first interview, in which the bank officers had done their best, without succeeding, to convince Mr. Turner that their performance on his wife's estate was satisfactory, the bank stated that they would submit the matter to a committee for a decision. The second interview was a repeat of the first interview, except that at its conclusion the bank stated that the committee's decision was a flat no.

At this point the investment representative spoke up for the first time. He reminded the head of the trust department that the $100,000 the bank was managing was actually Mr. Turner's money and not the bank's, and therefore his wishes should certainly be considered, particularly since he was co-trustee with the bank. He then proceeded to ask a direct question:

"As co-trustee with the bank on his own money, doesn't Mr. Turner have any rights?"

"Certainly" was the reply.

"What are they?"

"If he doesn't like our decision, he can sue the bank."

The result was that this trust institution continued to manage the money until Mr. Turner died.

The second duty of the trustee is to carry out the terms of the trust. This a trust institution will certainly do.

The third duty, which is to make impartial decisions in regard to the income beneficiaries, is something else again. Unfortunately, too many trust institutions take the attitude that they are working for the remaindermen and not for the immediate income beneficiaries of the trust. They are completely inflexible, and will pay out to the current beneficiaries only according to strict interpretation of the trust agreement.

Mrs. Wells, a widow, appealed to her investment representative for assistance in dealing with the trust department of her bank, which was administering a small trust of $50,000 set up by her and her deceased husband. Mrs. Wells had been a housewife all of her life, with no children, and was in complete ignorance about money matters. It was obvious to her representative why Mr. Wells, with his wife's consent, had placed their entire estate, both his half and her half, in trust. Many widows who are left estates outright are penniless within four or five years, and it was readily apparent that Mrs. Wells would have been no exception. Several years later, the property having been placed in trust, the $50,000 was still intact, but due to inflation, she could no longer live well on the income, and the bank refused to give her any more money.

Her representative read the trust agreement and informed her that the bank had complete discretion as to any payment of principal. However, he agreed to go with her to the trust department as her adviser, because he couldn't see any reason, with the events that had taken place since Mr. Wells's death, for the bank to continue to work for the remaindermen. The trust agreement provided, in the event of Mrs. Wells's demise, that the estate be divided among Mr. Wells's three brothers who were, like himself, all childless. But all of his three brothers, and their wives, had since died! In the event of this unlikely contingency, the agreement further provided that, upon termination of the trust, the $50,000 would go to a charitable school for boys.

However, despite the eventual distribution of the trust, the trustee, in his sole discretion, could provide any sum from principal each year that was necessary for his wife's proper support, care, and maintenance according to her accustomed manner of living. Again two interviews took place, this time with two minor employees of the trust department who were assigned to consider her request for a payment of some of the principal. They made Mrs. Wells bring in her checkbook and receipted bills, and they went over every penny of expense that she incurred. At the conclusion they informed her that she had fifteen dollars left over each month and that much extra money was enough!

Again the investment representative felt compelled to speak, bringing up the point that it had hardly been Mr. Wells's intention to deprive his wife of an adequate income. His main objective had been to protect her from bad investment decisions. Certainly he hadn't wanted her to live a penurious existence solely with the object of preserving the estate intact for the remaindermen, which in this case turned out to be a school for boys. Despite this sensible argument, however, they turned down her request for more funds.

What should have been done by the grantors in these two cases?

Mr. Turner should not have named a bank as co-trustee. Most people do not realize that they can be trustees of their own property, Mr. Turner should have named himself as sole trustee of his wife's estate, then there would have been no problem of appealing to a bank trustee in regard to investment decisions. Mr. Turner would simply have invested his wife's estate in a mutual fund.

Mr. Wells, however, had no alternative but to name a trust institution as trustee, because of his wife's incompetence in money matters. But he should have given her the right to invade some of principal each year at *her* discretion and not at the sole discretion of the bank. This right of withdrawal should have been given in the form of a percentage of the principal each year. Let us say that Mr. Wells wanted to protect his wife for a period of twenty years, which was well beyond her life expectancy. He could have given her the right to withdraw 5 percent of the principal each year, and if he had done so, she would not have had to go through the humiliating experience of begging the bank for a little of the principal of the estate that she and her husband had saved, only to be turned down in order to preserve the assets intact for a school for boys.

Whenever a bank trust is necessary, due to financial incompetence of heirs, the beneficiaries should be given the right by the grantor to invade a percentage of principal each year at *their* discretion. This discretionary withdrawal of principal will not necessarily be used, and can even expressly be made noncumulative by the grantor— if it is not used in any one year, it cannot be carried forward. Only the current year's percent may be used and that is all.

Until well into the twentieth century, property owners for the most part left their estates outright by will to members of their families. Death taxes and income taxes did not pose a threat to future family security. State laws were strict and inflexible, leaving little opportunity for the grantor to have his assets managed by the trustee other than in legalized investments, which were mostly fixed-dollar in nature, such as government bonds and real estate mortgages. However, with the increase in the income tax, and the advent of the Federal Estate Tax in 1916, taxes in estate planning have come to play a greater role as we have seen in Chapter Two. State laws have been liberalized, too, allowing latitude in investing, and attorneys have given increasingly broader powers to the trustee. In addition, inflation has tremendously increased the dollar value of estates, and when this is coupled with the lowering of the exemption amount, more and more people have been brought into the federal estate tax and state inheritance tax brackets. As a result of all these forces at work, trusts have come to play an increasingly important role in effective estate planning.

Today trusts are created for the following main reasons:

(a) to save taxes
(b) to protect beneficiaries
(c) to retain a business interest or a valuable piece of real estate intact
(d) to avoid probate
(e) to provide personal security to the grantor

In most trusts today the underlying motive of the grantor is to save taxes. Both death taxes and income taxes can be reduced by the use of trusts. By far the most common use of trusts for this purpose is the marital deduction trust between spouses to reduce the impact of the federal estate tax. Of course, not all married people should use trusts. A husband and wife should not consider a trust to save taxes for their heirs unless their estate exceeds $200,-000, because the estate tax saving is not large enough for those estates appraised below this figure. The surviving spouse, as the sole owner of a $200,000 estate, can make use of his or her annual exclusion and lifetime exemption to reduce taxes, if this is advisable. Also the income on $200,000 at 6 percent is only $12,000 a year, and this sum can easily be needed to support the survivor comfortably in today's economy of high taxes and inflation. At $300,-000, however, the use of a trust becomes attractive from a standpoint of death taxes. This can be demonstrated in the chart below. *D ɾɑɾh Tɑ+*

ɪɑ+

HIS	HERS
$150,000	$150,000
17,500 estate tax	150,000
	$300,000
	59,100 estate tax

When the husband dies leaving his half of their joint estate to his wife, you can see the serious escalation of the estate tax in the second estate when the survivor dies possessed of it all.

Supposing instead the following result could take place.

HIS	HERS
$150,000	$150,000
17,500 estate tax	17,500 estate tax

In this second example, by not allowing the husband's half to pile up in the wife's estate, each estate is taxed the same, resulting in an estate tax saving to the heirs of $41,600, which is the difference between $59,100 in example one and $17,500 in example two. Where children are the heirs, this is a very compelling reason for the creation of a marital deduction trust!

This estate tax saving is accomplished by each spouse leaving his or her half in trust for the children. The use of a trust saves as much in taxes as if the husband had left his half directly to the children. Obviously, if the children had inherited his estate upon his death, then upon his wife's death, taxes would be paid only on her half. Leaving an estate in trust instead of outright by will does not change this tax status. In addition his wife can be paid all of the income by the trustee, and when she dies, her husband's estate is not taxed again. The Internal Revenue Code also allows the wife to withdraw $5,000 or 5 percent of the principal per year, whichever is greater, from the half that is being held in trust. And besides that, if this is insufficient to maintain the standard of living to which she is accustomed, she can withdraw whatever additional amount is necessary to maintain that standard.

The chart, with these additional privileges, now looks like this:

HIS	HERS
$150,000	$150,000
17,500 estate tax	17,500 estate tax

$5,000 or 5 percent of the principal per year to the surviving spouse all income, plus

By this method the survivor is not financially hurt in any way. The widow has complete access to the capital on her half of the estate and may draw an additional $7,500 of capital per year from her husband's estate, plus more if necessary to maintain her standard of living. In the meantime she has the income from the entire estate, both from her half and from his half; the children as the eventual remaindermen do not enter the picture at all until their mother's death. Complete control of the estate can rest with the surviving spouse, if this is desired, for she can be named trustee so that she does not have to deal with a trust institution. Obviously, the same advantages apply to the husband, for the same results take place if his wife dies first.

It should be emphasized that use of this type of trust is not restricted to marriages that have lasted most of the adult lives of the two spouses involved. In these days of increasing longevity hundreds of thousands of people are marrying a second time after the death of their first spouse, and they too may make use of the marital deduction trust. Extra care must be exercised by the attorney in spelling out the power of appointment to the surviving spouse, however. He must be sure that all five conditions of the marital deduction rule are met that were outlined in Chapter Two.

Mr. Overman bought a ranch with his two brothers during World War II. It was a fortunate purchase, considering that they only paid $200,000 for it and that they sold it approximately twenty-five years later for over two million dollars! With his other holdings Mr. Overman found to his unfailing amazement that he was a millionaire. He had been a lifelong bachelor, but when he was almost seventy, he married a widow with three grown children. The marriage proved to be successful, so Mr. Overman decided to consult an attorney in regard to drawing a new will. His existing will provided that his two wealthy brothers should inherit from him share-and-share alike. The lawyer pointed out that this would simply compound the already serious death tax problem of his two millionaire brothers. He therefore suggested that a trust be created to take care of the problem.

Despite the fact that Mr. Overman's one million dollars was all his separate property, he had the right to leave half of his estate to his late-in-life wife in order to effect a tax saving, just as long as he gave her complete power of appointment to leave this half to whomever she pleased. Privately they agreed that she would probably leave it to her three married children, and this was all right with Mr. Overman, for his only heirs were nieces and nephews who were the adult children of his two wealthy brothers. The result was that only half of his estate would be taxed if he should die first. In addition, upon the advice of the attorney, he left the half that he did not will to his wife in trust for the *children* of his adult nieces and nephews, with the income going to their parents during their lifetime. By this method, death taxes would be paid on this half when Mr. Overman died, but no additional federal estate or state inheritance taxes would be paid when the trust finally terminated and was distributed to the remaindermen, which in this case were the grandnieces and grandnephews of the grantor.

Mr. Overman by his new will and a trust agreement accomplished several objectives at the same time. First, he did not disinherit his new wife. Second, he did not leave half a million dollars to each of his two millionaire brothers who did not need it and who would have had their already serious death tax problem unnecessarily compounded. Third, since the next generation below him would eventually become wealthy through inheritance from their parents, he bypassed them and left his half to the third generation instead. However, as his lawyer pointed out, Mr. Overman's nieces and nephews could use the *income* from his estate if Mr. Overman should die, even though from a long-term standpoint they did not need to inherit the principal. So the fourth objective he achieved was not to ignore his nieces and nephews, of whom he was very fond, but to leave them all of the income from his estate, which was all they needed anyway.

The federal estate tax savings alone for Mr. Overman's heirs were enormous. He was in an estate tax bracket of about 30 percent. Using approximate figures for simplicity, under his old will the estate tax would have been $300,000, leaving $700,000 to his brothers. When they died, another 30 percent tax would have been levied, leaving a net estate of $490,000. And when the nieces and nephews in turn died, and the estate was again taxed at 30 percent, there would have been left for their children a direct inheritance of $343,000 out of an original one million dollars! Under his new trust will the tax upon Mr. Overman's death would be $116,500, and the grandnieces and grandnephews would inherit the balance of the half million, or $383,500 tax free. In addition, the other half million that he left to his wife would be taxed the same way when she died, leaving her children the same amount, namely, a net of $383,500. By the use of a carefully worded trust, and taking full advantage of the marital deduction rule, Mr. Overman left several hundred thousand dollars more for the eventual enjoyment of heirs instead of to the Internal Revenue Service.

The above figures are approximate, and assume that only a federal estate tax would be owed. It must be understood that upon Mr. Overman's death, in most states, a state inheritance tax would have to be paid by his executor, which would be computed and levied against his grandnieces and grandnephews. When a trust is created, the state inheritance tax has to be paid upon the death of the grantor because the eventual remaindermen are considered to inherit upon the grantor's death, and not upon the death of the last surviving beneficiary, even though it may be twenty to thirty years or more before the corpus of the trust is distributed to them. However, at that time, the trust property will be turned over to the remaindermen death tax free. In Mr. Overman's case the remaindermen were so far removed they would be classified as strangers, so that the average state inheritance tax, levied against the grandnieces and grandnephews upon his death, would be approximately $40,000.

Trusts are used not only to save death taxes but also to save income taxes as well. The most common trust used for this purpose is the reversionary trust, also called the short-term or Clifford trust. This is a living trust, meaning that it goes into effect during the lifetime of the grantor, as opposed to the usual testamentary trust that does not come into being until the grantor dies. In a reversionary trust, as the name implies, the trust property reverts back to the grantor, because he is not wealthy enough to give away more than the income. This type of trust must last for a minimum period of ten years—or for the lifetime of the beneficiary. If the income beneficiary should die before the ten years are up, this certainly is not under the control of the grantor, and the trust is considered to have been set up in good faith.

Dr. Strum, a surgeon in his forties with a lucrative practice, had yet to build up a sizable estate. However, because he was in a 50 percent tax bracket, he had a serious income tax problem. Upon the advice of his attorney he placed $60,000 in common stocks in a ten-year reversionary trust, with the income being paid to his teen-age son, who was to follow in his father's footsteps and become an M.D. The income from the trust would help defray the costs of an expensive ten years in college and an internship. By shifting the trust income from his high income tax bracket to the low income tax bracket of his son, Dr.

Strum saved handsomely on his family income taxes. The son, by filing his own income tax return, had his personal exemption, a $100 dividend exclusion, and a standard deduction. The stocks were paying an average of 5 percent, or $3,000 per year. The son would have to report approximately $2,000 of taxable income, which would incur a tax liability of $200 per year. The father, however, in his 50 percent tax bracket, would have paid $1,500 per year. This family income tax saving of approximately $1,200 per year for ten years, or $12,000, would help pay for the son's expensive education. Since the surgeon was not wealthy, he would get the trust property back at the end of the ten years for his own retirement. In addition, Dr. Strum did not lose the personal exemption for his son on his own tax return, for he was still paying for the majority of his education.

Before a property owner places his estate in trust he should understand certain basic features of a trust agreement.

1. No trust is allowed to last forever; it must cease to exist sometime, at which time the trust property will be distributed to its eventual heirs. It cannot last perpetually. Unless sooner terminated, each trust created must terminate twenty-one years after the death of the last survivor of the grantor. In the example of Mr. Overman, where his survivors were his grandnieces and grandnephews, the maximum length of time the trust could have lasted would have been twenty-one years after the death of the last of the remaindermen. This could have been a very long time indeed, considering that most of his heirs were still minor children. Mr. Overman, when informed of this restriction against perpetuity, did not elect to have his trust last that long, which might well have been over a hundred years, but chose instead to have the remaindermen inherit outright upon the death of their parents. Nevertheless, under

the law, it could have lasted this long if that had been his desire.

2. The trustee has to be given the right to manage the property. Years ago the grantor was inclined to give only very restricted powers to the trustee in regard to how the property was to be managed. For instance, the trustee might be instructed to hold intact real estate left in the trust, with instructions that it could not be sold for any reason. It was discovered, however, that the heirs in such a trust could be disinherited over a period of time by such a limited power of investment. Shifts in population could occur, resulting in once high-income property turning into slum dwellings, where the income could not even pay the taxes and insurance, yet the trustee could not sell. The income beneficiaries would receive nothing under such an arrangement, and the eventual remaindermen would inherit property not worth the accumulated liens for back taxes. Attorneys today, therefore, give broad investment powers to the trustee in order to take care of unforeseen developments.

In creating them, however, lawyers for the most part do not draw their own broad trustee powers. Banks are the most frequent trustees named; therefore, each bank's trust department supplies printed copies to the legal fraternity of the trust powers they prefer to have delegated to them, which attorneys copy verbatim and insert into the trust agreements they draw for their clients. This is not usurping the duties of the legal profession. These broad powers have been worked out by the bank over a period of years, in which they have found certain ones to be most satisfactory. It just makes sense for the lawyer to take advantage of the trust institution's experience. Some lawyers, when an individual trustee is named, prefer to use a legal handbook, which again spells out the powers of a trustee, without the attorney having to do the research that would otherwise be necessary. Reproduced below are trust powers taken verbatim from a recent trust agreement drawn by a competent attorney experienced in estate planning.

Powers of Trustee. To carry out the purposes of any trust created under this Paragraph FIFTH, and subject to any limitations stated elsewhere in this will, the trustee is vested with the following powers with respect to the trust estate and any part of it, in addition to those powers now or hereafter conferred by law:

A. To continue to hold any property and to operate at the risk of the trust estate any business received or acquired under the terms of the trust by the trustee as long as the trustee shall deem advisable; provided, however, that unproductive or underproductive property shall not be held as an asset of the trust for more than a reasonable time during the lifetime of my wife without her consent: .

B. To manage, control, grant options on, sell (for cash or on deferred payments), convey, exchange, partition, divide, improve and repair trust property:

C. To lease trust property for terms within or beyond the terms of the trust and for any purpose, including exploration for and removal of gas, oil and other minerals; and to enter into community oil leases, pooling and unitization agreements:

D. To borrow money, and to encumber or hypothecate trust property by mortgage, deed of trust, pledge, or otherwise:

E. To carry, at the expense of the trust, insurance of such kinds and in such amounts as the trustee shall deem advisable to protect the trust estate and the trustee against any hazard:

. F. To commence or defend such litigation with respect to the trust or any property of the trust estate as the trustee may deem advisable, at the expense of the trust:

G. To compromise or otherwise adjust any claims or litigation against or in favor of the trust:

H. To invest and reinvest the trust estate in every kind of property, real, personal or mixed, and every kind of investment, specifically including, but not by way of limitation, corporate obligations of every kind, stocks, preferred or common, shares of investment trusts, investment companies and mutual funds, and mortgage participations, which men of prudence, discretion and intelligence acquire for their own account.

I. With respect to securities held in the trust, to have all the rights, powers and privileges of an owner, including, but not by way of limitation, the power to vote, give proxies and pay assessments; to participate in voting trusts, pooling agreements, foreclosures, reorganizations, consolidations, mergers, liquidations, sales and leases, and incident to such participation to deposit securities with and transfer title to any protective or other committee on such terms as the trustee may deem advisable; and to exercise or sell stock subscription or conversion rights.

J. Except as otherwise specifically provided in this will, the determination of all matters with respect to what is principal and income of the trust estate and the apportionment and allocation of receipts and expenses between these accounts shall be governed by the provisions of the California Principal and Income Law from time to time existing. Any such matter not provided for either in this will or in the Principal and Income Law shall be determined by the trustee in the trustee's discretion.

K. In any case in which the trustee is required, pursuant to the provisions of the trust, to divide any trust property into parts or shares for the purpose of distribution, or otherwise, the trustee is authorized in the trustee's absolute discretion, to make the division and distribution in kind, including undivided interests in any property, or partly in kind and partly in money, and for this purpose to make such sales of the trust property as the trustee may deem necessary on such terms and conditions as the trustee shall see fit.

When an individual trustee is named, these broad powers are conferred as a matter of protection in order to grant the widest possible latitude in investment decisions to the trustee. However, when a bank is named trustee, these broad powers can have an adverse effect, particularly if the grantor would like to see his assets remain in the trust. Too many banks will immediately sell the investments they receive and buy a whole new list, for they feel they know more about investments than any individual grantor. If the estate is over $100,000, they will buy individual stocks and bonds, but if the estate is below this figure, they usually will not manage it on an individual basis; instead, the assets will be sold and placed in the bank's common trust fund, which is similar in operation to a no load mutual fund. If the grantor is aware of this, and does not want his investments sold, he may state his wishes in this regard in the trust agreement. This does not guarantee to the grantor that the trust institution will not sell, but as long as the trustee feels that the investments are sound and meet the conditions of the trust, he will feel morally bound to hold them, although he is not legally bound to do so. Most trust officers feel that they should carry out the investment desires of the grantor if possible.

Mr. Boardman liked two stocks that he owned. He had held them over a period of thirty years, and through stock splits and stock dividends, his original four hundred shares had become four thousand shares, and the value of an original investment of just $8,000 had become worth over $165,000. The thought of a bank trustee selling these two stocks very much disturbed him, so his attorney suggested that he state in his trust agreement his desire that the bank not sell, unless in their considered opinion it was necessary for them to do so in view of sound investment practice. Mr. Boardman realized the logic in the argument that the bank had to be given broad powers, because of the possibility in the long term that his two stocks would not be as valuable an investment as they had been to him over the previous thirty years, but by stating his wishes that they not be sold, he obtained more peace of mind.

Many grantors also like mutual funds, and would not like to see them sold but held instead by the bank trustee.

Once again they may state their wishes in this regard. It used to be that trust institutions would not hold mutual funds in trust because they felt they were relinquishing their trust powers to the investment managers of the funds; however, most of them no longer feel this way. It is true that the professional managers of the mutual funds will make the investment decisions and not the trust department of the bank, but most trust institutions accept this fact, and some even welcome mutual funds as a part of the trust property, because they provide additional diversification and management.

Since the grantor usually has the choice of several banks from which to choose, if he is concerned about his investments being sold upon his death, he should talk with the vice-president of several trust departments and decide for himself which of them is the least likely to sell him out the minute they take control. He can then name that institution as trustee.

Nevertheless, power to sell trust assets should be expressly given in the trust agreement. In some states real estate cannot be sold unless the right to sell has specifically been given to the trustee, and some even require that he must also be given the right to decide on the terms and conditions of the sale. At the same time the trustee should also be given the right to retain any real estate, for if he is not given this right, some states require him to sell the property regardless of the implied wishes of the grantor and possibly the expressed wishes of the income beneficiaries and the remaindermen.

As many lawyers tell their testators when drawing a trust agreement, it is better to grant a power that is not needed than for the trustees to be without a power when it is needed. In paragraph G of the previously quoted trust the power was given "to compromise or otherwise adjust any claims." If this power is not given in some states, the trustee would have no other recourse but to resort to litigation to settle claims. Other powers that are better granted, than not granted, are the power to lease beyond the terms of the trust, the power to set up reserves (dependent upon state law), and the power to redeem close corporation stock. Powers can also be given to purchase nonliquid assets from the estate, thus providing cash for the executor, and the right to lend money to the estate.

3. Not all assets have to be placed in a trust. That little red wagon called a trust is a very convenient vehicle. Any assets may be put into it, and any assets may be left out of it. The most frequent asset not placed in trust is a home owned jointly by husband and wife. Since the survivor usually wants to occupy it for the rest of his or her life, this asset is kept in joint tenancy. A small joint bank account is frequently excluded, thereby providing immediate cash to the survivor. In the case of Dr. Strum, the only asset that he wanted in trust was the $60,000 that he owned in common stocks.

4. When contemplating a marital deduction trust, it is important for the grantor to know that physical segregation of the property is not required. If a hundred shares of General Motors stock are involved, for example, they may be retained in one stock certificate; two certificates, one in the name of the individual as trustee for that part that is being held in trust, and one in the name of the individual as sole owner, are not necessary. However, the trustee must keep separate accounts for the different undivided interests. Income, either distributed or left to accrue, must be shown as being attributed to the appropriate owners.

5. All trustees must make a fiduciary report once a year to the taxing authorities. They must be able to demon-

strate that the trust property is truly being held in trust for the benefit of the income beneficiaries and the eventual remaindermen, and that income taxes are being paid by the various beneficiaries and owners according to the Internal Revenue Code. In a marital deduction trust this is actually a simple matter and should not disturb the widow if she turns out to be the trustee. She merely turns the matter over to her accountant, just as she would her individual tax return.

6. When an individual trustee is named, a successor trustee should always be appointed, for as everyone knows, an individual can die at any time. A second individual trustee can usually be found that is satisfactory to the grantor, but settling on a final trustee, if both of the individual trustees first-named should be unable to serve, is very difficult. Most attorneys prefer to insert a bank as the eventual successor trustee, because there is normally no practical alternative, particularly if the trust will not terminate for many years. As we have stated before, a corporation never dies.

7. Corporate trustees are automatically bonded. Individuals are not; therefore, when no bond is required, the grantor must specifically state this in the trust agreement.

8. In community property states, to avoid the nuisance factor of having to change ownership on assets between husband and wife that are held in joint tenancy, a Property Status Agreement is quite often substituted by the attorney. The wording would be substantially as follows:

> This agreement is made between Clark Doe and Mary Doe, husband and wife, residents of ABC County, California, for the purpose of clarifying the ownership of their property.
>
> They therefore agree that all property now or in the future owned or held of record by them as joint tenants is and shall be their community property regardless of its record titling.

This agreement shall remain in effect until modified or revoked in writing by the parties, and shall be binding on their respective heirs, assignees and legal representatives.

Dated this   day of   , 197 .

_____

Clark Doe

_____

Mary Doe

9. A trust is a separate tax-paying entity. If income accrues to the trust because it is not paid out to the income beneficiaries, the trust itself must pay taxes. The trust enters the tax tables just as an individual taxpayer would—with, however, only a $100 deduction. In our previous example of Dr. Strum and his ten-year reversionary trust, he could not have arranged to escape paying income taxes on the trust property entirely (paying for his son's education out of his practice) by allowing the trust income to accumulate. He would not be taxed, as we have already pointed out, nor would his son be taxed if the income were allowed to accumulate in the trust, for the son each year would have nothing to report. But the trust would be taxed as a separate tax-paying entity, for it would be receiving the income. In addition, the difference between what the trust paid in income taxes, and what the son would have paid if he had received the income, would have to be paid by the son when the accumulated income was distributed to him at the termination of the trust.

10. A trust may be revocable or nonrevocable. Most trusts are of the former type, which means they may be revoked like wills. If the property owner changes his mind, he has the right to do so. He can either revoke the trust entirely and not draw a new one, deciding to distribute his assets by will, or he may draw a new trust agreement. Occasionally trusts are made irrevocable, usually for death tax reasons, as we shall see later.

11. Trusts may be testamentary trusts or living trusts. Most trusts are of the testamentary type, which means they do not go into effect until the grantor dies. In this respect they are similar to wills, and for that matter are quite often referred to as trust wills. Living trusts go into effect while the grantor is alive.

The second major reason grantors establish trusts is to protect their beneficiaries. An heir may be otherwise intelligent but simply not competent in money matters. The most frequently protected heir is a widow who has been a homemaker all of her life with no interest or experience in managing investments. Even in these days of excellent federal and state laws, unknowledgeable widows who are left estates outright are often destitute in four or five years.

Outright distribution to them, therefore, is not wise for the following good reasons:

1. The widow is presented with management problems and investment decisions that she cannot deal with intelligently.

2. She may have loan requests from relatives. She frequently does not know how to say no to these people, so the money is soon frittered away and never repaid, despite best intentions.

3. She has to deal with the conflicting interests of her children. One may be in bad need of funds, and the others well off, yet she feels she has to treat them all alike.

4. Advice on how to invest and when to invest is offered by well-meaning friends who have little to offer in the way of experience. Following this advice can be very costly.

5. And as we have seen with the marital deduction trust, outright distribution to the widow can result in unnecessary federal estate taxation.

But unknowledgeable widows are not the only heirs who need to be protected. Where minor children are involved, the only practical solution is a trust, normally with a bank acting as trustee. Trusts for minors usually extend beyond age twenty-one, for most grantors feel that outright distribution at this age is not justified, for it is too much to expect someone twenty-one to handle money properly. Lawyers usually recommend that one third be inherited at twenty-five, one third at thirty, and the balance at age thirty-five. It is a mistake for a grantor to try to protect his beneficiaries forever. If by the time children are thirty-five they have not learned to manage an estate, it is probably just as well to let them dissipate it entirely and start to learn the hard way about saving money.

Many families have a mentally or physically handicapped family member who must be protected by a lifelong trust, with the trustee being given full powers over the income and principal in order to meet the changing conditions that such a situation can present. In dealing with this kind of a problem, it is fortunate that bank trusts are available.

The third basic use of trusts is to protect a business or a valuable piece of real estate. Let's consider a business first, starting with those businesses that are incorporated.

Quite often ownership of close corporation stock is the major asset of an estate. A close corporation has been defined by the courts as "a corporation in which the stock is held in a few hands, or in a few families or one family, and wherein it is not at all, or only rarely dealt in." Quite often the owners, the directors, and the officers are all the same people, and they own 100 percent of the common stock. Family corporations, and corporations that have been formed by converting sole proprietorships or partnerships into the corporate form, are typical of the close classification. When 100 percent of the stock, or the majority of it, is held by one property owner, it can become a problem of how to will it.

Mr. Spencer, a widower, had three children and owned a very profitable business, possessing 100 percent of the close corporation stock. This stock was the major asset of his estate. His only son managed the business with him and was very competent; his two married daughters and their husbands, however, had no desire to enter the firm and help run it. Mr. Spencer wanted to treat all of his children alike, but if he left each of them one third of the corporation by will, he knew that the business would not long survive him, because if the stock were splintered up, no one, including his son, would have control. With the assistance of his attorney, he solved his problem by the use of a trust.

As grantor, he gave his son complete control of the business as trustee, with the right to vote the stock. His two daughters, although they each inherited one third of the corporation, were given no say in the management of the firm. However, Mr. Spencer recognized that there was still an unfair possibility in this arrangement, for the son as sole trustee could claim that all of the net profits were needed in the business and refuse in the future to pay any dividends on the corporation stock. This would result in no income being paid to his daughters while the son would be handsomely rewarded by his salary as president of the firm. So Mr. Spencer further stipulated in his trust agreement that his bank would be co-trustee with his son—with, however, only one specific power: the right to determine how much the dividends would be each year. The bank would annually determine the net income after taxes by using the services of an outside independent accounting firm. Now the corporation would be run for the benefit of all the family members, with each child inheriting one third.

Mr. Childs owned 100 percent of his close corporation, but he had a different problem and again solved it by the use of a trust. He was married, with two children, and wanted to make full use of the marital deduction in his estate to save estate taxes. He also wanted to preserve the voting unity of his stock. In addition, he wanted to retire and let the business be managed by his two competent sons who were respectively president and executive vice-president of the firm, but he could not retire unless he had the income from the company. His solution was re-capitalization of the corporation and the creation of a trust.

Preferred stock was issued, paying a 6 percent dividend, which included most of the former common stock. This stock was issued to Mr. Childs and his wife, and was declared by the Internal Revenue Service to be a tax-free dividend. In other words, the value of the preferred stock was not taxable to Mr. and Mrs. Childs as an income distribution. Upon the death of either of them, this preferred stock would qualify for the marital deduction and be owned outright by the survivor. A small amount of voting common stock (but still 100 percent) was issued and placed in trust in his estate, with his two sons as co-trustees. This gave them voting control of the corporation, with, however, all of the dividend income being paid to the surviving spouse.

By recapitalization and a trust agreement Mr. Childs accomplished several objectives simultaneously.

1. He gave himself and his wife adequate retirement income.

2. He gave complete control of the business, with power to vote the stock as they saw fit, to his two sons as co-trustees.

3. He saved substantially on estate taxes by not piling up 100 percent of the ownership of the corporation in the hands of the surviving spouse. Instead, the voting com-

mon stock, which was a growth asset, would be held in trust for the sons and would not be taxed again when the second spouse died.

4. The dividend from the preferred stock, and the dividend from the common stock, would be paid to Mr. Childs and his wife until they both died. The sons would be rewarded for running the corporation by their handsome salaries as president and executive vice-president of the firm.

Where unity of control of a valuable commercial or residential piece of property is desired, the same single ownership can be accomplished by the use of a trust. A corporation can be formed that will own the real estate, and the voting control can be passed by a trust agreement to a trustee. A trust should be created, of course, only for very valuable property. A trust should not be created, for example, for a duplex, simply to prevent the property from being inherited by three different people. It is true that any one of the heirs could force the sale of the property, even though the other two did not want to sell it. The possible loss to the estate, however, because of a forced sale when a small piece of property is involved is simply not great enough to warrant incorporation and the creation of a trust. Also there is the possibility that the two heirs who do not want to sell could buy out the third heir. There would not be much money involved, for one thing, therefore the other heirs may have it available, or if they do not, they could mortgage the property for the amount of the one-third interest of the heir who insists upon having cash for his share.

The fourth major reason for creating a trust is to avoid probate. This is accomplished by the creation of a revocable living trust, which is a trust created during the property owner's lifetime. It should be emphasized at once that a revocable living trust is never created for the purpose of saving estate taxes. It does not save estate taxes. Its major purpose is to avoid the expense, delay, and publicity of probate and is used only when a sizable estate is involved. As a rule of thumb, where estates are valued at less than $300,000, probate can better be avoided by having the correct ownership on the assets, rather than by creating a revocable living trust, as we shall see later in the chapter on ownership. But when death taxes are a serious problem, as they are in larger estates, avoiding probate and reducing estate taxes cannot be accomplished simultaneously except by the use of a trust.

Revocable living trusts should be used with extreme care even by the well-to-do and the wealthy. There are several reasons for this.

1. Most attorneys do not like revocable living trusts. Many lawyers have had no experience in drawing them, and many contend that they present too many problems when the sole desire of the grantor is to avoid the probate process. They feel that testamentary trusts should be used instead and the assets allowed to go through the probate court. Many attorneys feel that probate is the best way to pass on an estate to its new owners, for everything is then done with the approval of the judge. However, it must be admitted that they are not the heirs having to suffer through the probate process, which in larger estates can be for a period of several years.

2. Bank trustees should be avoided in revocable living trusts, because the property owner is usually knowledgeable, having built the sizable estate involved himself, and a bank trustee taking over the management of his assets while he is still alive can be very frustrating. Therefore, the grantor and his wife are usually named co-trustees of a living trust, and preferably the survivor of them is also the successor trustee. However, if husband and wife are

co-trustees, the assets should be relatively few in number and easy to manage, particularly since the wife may become the survivor and the successor trustee. If the assets are not simple and few in number, they should be rearranged accordingly before the trust is created.

4. Although tying up the assets in probate court is avoided, and therefore the successor trustee is immediately in possession of the assets upon the death of the first spouse, it must be understood that the successor trustee must still work with the attorney who drew the trust agreement, and an accountant, in solving the problems that death creates. The estate still has to be appraised, and federal estate and state inheritance tax returns prepared and the taxes paid. In some states, and in some counties within states but not in other counties, the state inheritance tax department will not go along with the living trust agreement and presents such problems in the appraisal and in the filing of tax returns that the successor trustee eventually wishes that he had gone through the probate process instead. Usually, however, if an attorney is willing to draw a living trust agreement, you can assume there will be no problem in this regard, particularly if the lawyer drawing the living trust is not alone in his law office but has partners. If the lawyer dies, one of his law partners can take his place, who, incidentally, will charge by the hour for the time involved and not the probate schedule of fees. When the same law firm is available that drew the living trust, the successor trustee should experience few problems.

When revocable living trusts are used between spouses to avoid probate, it should be understood that upon the death of the first spouse these trusts accomplish identically the same estate tax saving as marital deduction trusts. Upon the first death, half of the estate is held in trust for the eventual remaindermen, with all of the income plus

5 percent of the principal being paid to the surviving spouse.

Mr. and Mrs. Yates had a $700,000 estate, which they had built as the result of owning a profitable business in a small town. They had no children, so they decided their estate should eventually go to their favorite charities. They had been exceptionally frugal in building an estate of this size. As Mr. Yates said to his lawyer: "I am like a squirrel. I bury those nuts and I forget about them." As a consequence, no one in their small town had any more than an inkling of the size of their estate, and upon the death of the first spouse, the survivor wanted no one to know. When Mr. and Mrs. Yates found out about the glaring publicity of probate and that anyone could walk into the county courthouse when one of them died, ask for the probate file, and see down to the last penny what they were worth, they were appalled. Being frugal, they were equally appalled by the amount of the estate tax involved, especially if the survivor should live ten years and die possessed of the entire estate. Upon the advice of their attorney, they set up a living trust.

When Mr. Yates died, the complete lack of information as to the size of his estate so frustrated people that Mrs. Yates would be stopped on the street with a leading question, such as: "I assume that Jack left you pretty well off?" But she would just smile and walk on. If privacy in estate matters is desired, a living trust will guarantee it. Mrs. Yates, however, did experience considerable difficulty in settling the estate, because the attorney who drew the living trust had died, leaving no partner, and the local bar association and the state inheritance tax appraiser were both antagonistic to her living trust, maintaining that it was illegally drawn. Mrs. Yates eventually settled her problem by going to a sympathetic attorney in a nearby town.

Sometimes the desire for privacy originates in the fact that an estate has accumulated almost automatically. Perhaps the estate was originally inherited many years before, and through sheer passage of time and the soundness of the basic investments, assets have increased to a considerable size without the heirs materially raising their standard of living. As a consequence, heirs may be possessed of a sizable estate without their friends or relatives knowing anything about it, and the survivor wants to keep it that way.

Two maiden sisters inherited the trust income from a sizable estate left by their famous father. All the income was to be paid to them by a university trustee, until the death of the surviving sister, at which time the college would be the remainderman. But the estate was of such a size that the two daughters never did spend all of the income; in addition they successfully managed real estate which had been left to them outright. After forty years one of them was dying. The prospective surviving sister became almost panic-stricken at the thought of the publicity that would result when it became known that she and her sister had accumulated $600,000. A living trust, to avoid the publicity of probate and to save on estate taxes, was the only solution.

The fifth reason trusts are created is to provide personal security to the grantor. Managing assets of considerable size, particularly when compounded by the frailty of advancing years, can pose a problem, and can be solved by creating a living trust. However, while this is true, more and more attorneys recently are changing their thinking and, instead of suggesting living trusts to solve this problem, are recommending an agency account with the trust department of a bank instead. This accomplishes the same purpose of having the assets managed by professionals without the trouble of creating a trust and having a trustee named. Bank trust departments will take over all the problems of management by a simple written agreement, which is completely revocable at any time by a thirty-day written notice. It is hardly necessary to enter into a living trust agreement to accomplish the same objective. Besides, living trusts can also have disastrous results.

Dr. Frisbee had several heart attacks, the last one very severe. He made up his mind he was not going to recover permanently and, therefore, placed all of his sizable assets in a revocable living trust with his bank, giving the trustee complete discretionary power in dealing with his estate. Some two years later, to the doctor's amazement, he had recovered from his series of heart attacks to the point where he was again practicing medicine, and felt well enough to go to the trust department of his bank and ask them to return his assets to him, as he now wanted to continue to manage his own affairs. He anticipated no difficulty, because he had expressly made his living trust revocable at any time.

He found out to his dismay, however, that the bank had completely sold out the wonderful investments that he had spent a lifetime in accumulating. The new list was so poorly chosen that the trust department had lost him considerable money, and in addition the doctor was completely unfamiliar with the new portfolio! He was furious, but could do nothing about it for he had given broad trustee powers to the bank. An agency account would have served his purpose just as well, giving the trust department no authority to shift investments without his written consent.

Charitable trusts have been left to the last, because so few people use them. Most people do not have enough money to leave to anyone but a family member. Also, only the very well-to-do have such an income tax problem that charitable giving becomes attractive from an income tax standpoint. The property owner must have substantial means before considering these trusts, and he must have every intention (before creating the trust) of leaving the money to charity. The property owner shifts his charitable giving from outright distribution by will to a trust because of the tax advantages to the grantor himself and/or to his estate.

First the rules of charitable giving must be understood. The Internal Revenue Service recognizes the importance of charitable gifts by allowing tax benefits for those gifts that qualify. It is common knowledge today that colleges, churches, and hospitals are badly in need of funds due to inflation and the tremendous increase in the demand for their services. As a consequence, the IRS allows a deduction of up to 50 percent of the property owner's adjusted gross income for contributions *of cash* to public charities. These public charities are defined as churches, tax-exempt hospitals, educational institutions, and organizations that receive a substantial part of their support from the government or the public. This 50 percent is an *income* tax deduction and is deductible in the year of the gift.

If property is given, the limitation is reduced to 30 percent of the contribution base, which for all practical purposes is the property owner's adjusted gross income. But if the property has appreciated in value, the donor is given an added tax advantage, for he obtains an income tax deduction for the fair market value of the gift and not just a deduction for his cost. Also the trustee may sell the appreciated property, and reinvest it, with the donor not being subjected to a capital gains tax on the sale, and if the newly acquired property has a better income, the grantor also receives all of this higher income.

Charitable trusts take two main forms. They are either charitable income trusts or charitable remainder trusts.

A charitable income trust is usually a living trust created during the lifetime of the grantor. It in turn takes two forms. It may be either a trust with income being retained by the grantor, or a trust with the income going to charity, with the principal reverting back to the grantor or to some other member of his family at a later date.

A charitable trust is created with only the income going to charity, because the grantor wants the capital to be retained in his family. Mr. Jacobs arranged for the income from his charitable trust to go to his college for a period of ten years, but at the end of that time the property was to revert to his son. He had the satisfaction during his lifetime of seeing his college receive a sizable income over a ten-year period, and in addition, in the year that he created the trust, of being able to take a deduction on his income tax return of 30 percent of the value of the trust property. By this trust agreement Mr. Jacobs had, of course, deliberately made a gift to his son. The amount of the gift, however, was only 70 percent of the trust property for gift tax purposes, because charity would receive the trust income.

In the other type of charitable income trust, the reverse is true. Now the grantor wants to retain the income from the trust for himself during his lifetime, but upon his death have the principal go to charity. The charitable living trust is now made irrevocable, so there will be no federal estate tax owed upon the death of the grantor. There is no limitation on the amount of a charitable testamentary gift for federal estate tax purposes. The gift may be made either by will or in an irrevocable living trust; in either method the estate tax will be zero.

Mr. Pine was a widower who wanted to leave a substantial part of his estate to charity; however, he needed the income from the property during his lifetime. By establishing a charitable trust he actually increased his income during his lifetime, plus being able to assure the college of his choice in advance that he was making a substantial gift, for he made the trust irrevocable. His income was increased, because he was able to take a federal income tax deduction for the value of the remainder interest that he gave to the college. The value of the remainder interest is as follows:

> age 60–60   percent of the value of the trust property
> age 65–66.6 percent of the value of the trust property
> age 70–72.6 percent of the value of the trust property

As Mr. Pine continued to live, he planned to transfer property to his charitable trust each year and in this way achieve a regular income tax deduction on his tax return. His gross income each year would be the same as without the charitable trust, but his net income, after the remainder-interest deduction, would be considerably increased.

Charitable remainder trusts are testamentary trusts that do not take place until the grantor dies. Again the testator must have a sizable estate and the desire to leave a substantial benefit to charity.

Mr. and Mrs. Wilson had a million-dollar estate and no one to leave it to. Upon consulting an attorney they decided to establish two charitable remainder pooled-income trusts. Each arranged that his or her half of their combined estate would eventually go to charity, but the income would be paid to the survivor during his or her lifetime. This is similar to a marital deduction trust, with one important exception. The trust principal will go to charity and not to children, or another family member, upon the death of the survivor. As a consequence, when Mr. or Mrs. Wilson died possessed of half of their combined $1,000,000 estate, or $500,000, there would be an estate tax deduction of $363,000! This sizable deduction would be allowed because charity would eventually inherit the principal.

The actual amount of the deduction, which is called a charitable remainder, is computed by special tax tables of the Internal Revenue Service, and would be dependent upon the age of the first spouse to die. In this case it is assumed that Mr. or Mrs. Wilson would be age seventy upon the first death, and therefore the amount that charity would inherit, based upon the tables, would be slightly more than 70 percent of the value of the property put in trust. The purpose in creating this charitable remainder trust, instead of leaving the property by will to charity, was increased income to the survivor. The arithmetic looks like this:

With no charitable trust
$500,000 taxable estate upon the first death
$116,500 federal estate tax

With a charitable trust
$500,000 estate
$363,000 estate tax deduction
$137,000 taxable estate upon the first death
13,964 federal estate tax

The federal estate tax saving would be the difference between $116,500 and $13,964, or $102,536! This amount would be retained in the trust, and the income from it would substantially increase the income to the survivor.

Sometimes charitable income trusts are testamentary trusts. In these cases, not only are the parents wealthy, but the children are, too. The grandchildren are now the ones to be considered. $1,000,000 left by will, and not in a charitable income trust, will be subject to successive taxation of approximately 30 percent in two generations. This would leave only $500,000 to the grandchildren, which is a 50 percent reduction!

Mr. and Mrs. Eaton were each millionaires in their own right, and so were their children. Upon the advice of his attorney, Mr. Eaton established a testamentary charitable income trust. The income on his $1,000,000 would go to charity during the lifetime of his two children, who were about forty-five years of age. Upon the death of his children, however, his grandchildren would inherit the trust property. The value of the income interest passing to charity at the ages of his children would be about 65 percent, or $650,000. This huge deduction would leave a taxable estate of $350,000. Let's assume, for simplicity, that the tax on this amount of $73,300 would be paid out of other assets in the estate. Now when Mr. Eaton's children died, the grandchildren would inherit the entire one million dollars, including any growth in the trust assets in the meantime, and not $500,000 as they would have without the trust.

While charitable giving is not primarily motivated by tax saving, for it is the intention of the grantor for charities to benefit, nevertheless in sizable estates considerable tax savings can result by the judicious use of charitable trusts.

5

Ownership

THE CORRECT ownership of assets is one of the most important decisions in estate planning. Title may be held in
eighteen different ways; as a consequence, since most
people acquire their assets over a long period of time,
their ownership is quite often as varied as the property
they have acquired. Property which will pass by will is
called a probate asset, and that which will pass by operation of law is called a non-probate asset. What ownership
you have on your property, or how you hold title to it, is
the determining factor. Probate may be avoided by correct ownership.

However, this may not be the best way, or the wise way,
to transfer your assets to your heirs. It may be the testator's desire, in the best interests of his beneficiaries, or to
save death taxes, or both, to have his assets pass through
the executor's hands and be distributed according to his
testamentary disposition, whether it be by will or by trust.
This will not happen, however, if the property owner holds
title the wrong way; instead the ultimate disposition of
his assets will be by operation of law, and his testamentary document will have little or no effect on who inherits
the property. So ownership is of the utmost importance.

As we have seen, a will carefully drawn by a competent

attorney is the correct solution in most cases for determining who gets your assets. But unless all of the non-probate assets in your estate are properly coordinated with the assets that pass under your will, your estate plan may be completely disorganized and fall far short of accomplishing its objective. No one intentionally wants to take the time to understand probate, taxes, wills, and trusts, and then fail to solve his estate problem because he overlooked the primary importance of correct title. The solution is all the more complicated because property in a great many estates is held, and quite often should be held, in several different ways, comprising both probate and non-probate assets. To correctly understand how title should be held, the eighteen different kinds of ownership must be understood.

NON-PROBATE ASSETS

Non-probate assets are the most frequently owned; therefore, these nine ownerships will be considered first.

1. Joint tenancy with right of survivorship. This ownership is widely used, particularly between husband and wife. When title to property is held in this manner, the surviving joint tenant automatically inherits. A great many attorneys abhor this ownership, because property held in this way cannot be distributed by will or by trust. It doesn't make any difference what the will says, the survivor will own the property. If a married man says in his will, "I hereby leave the thousand shares of stock that I own to my friend, John Doe," it will not be inherited by John Doe, if the stock is held in joint tenancy with right of survivorship with his wife. It will be inherited by his wife. The will has nothing to do with it. It is a non-probate asset.

There are both advantages and disadvantages to this type of ownership.

Mr. Torrey was astonished to learn, when his wife died, that most of his $200,000 estate consisted of non-probate assets. He owned his home and other real estate, bank accounts, and most of his stock in joint tenancy with right of survivorship with his wife. Some of the stocks, however, he owned himself, and some of the stocks his wife owned. As a consequence, he found himself in probate court. (His attorney charged him probate fees only on the probate assets.)

The joint tenancy properties, as the attorney explained to Mr. Torrey, were non-probate assets; therefore, the ownership could be changed simply by dissolving the joint tenancy. This is a fancy term, which means removing the name of the deceased owner from the title to the property. (For this work the attorney charges by the hour.) However, the surviving joint tenant in many states can, if he prefers, dissolve the joint tenancy himself. Title to real estate can be changed at an abstract or title company; ownership of securities can be transferred by writing to the bank transfer agent named on the face of the stock certificate. In most states the primary documents required are a certified copy of the death certificate and an inheritance tax waiver. Those responsible for effecting the transfer want to know that the other joint tenant has died and that the taxes, if any, have been paid.

Mr. Torrey, when he found this out, was very pleased at the ease with which his attorney changed the joint tenancy property to his name, and very annoyed at the long delay of probate on the residue of his estate. In this case, since it was the desire of Mr. and Mrs. Torrey to have the survivor of them inherit all of the assets, Mr. Torrey could have avoided probate entirely by holding everything in joint tenancy. This would have avoided probate on all of the property and not on just part of it.

One of the disadvantages of this type of ownership occurs when separate property of a husband or wife is placed in joint tenancy. In that event, a gift tax may be incurred. This is because the non-contributing spouse now has an interest in the property that he or she didn't have before. The amount of the gift is one half of the asset transferred; it is not the whole amount, for the contributing spouse still owns the other half.

We said it *may* be a gift; it is not necessarily so. Depending upon the type of asset involved, the donor spouse has the option of treating a transfer of property into joint tenancy as a gift or not. When the gift consists of real estate, he has this choice. If the donor spouse decides not to treat the change of ownership as a gift, it will become a gift if and when the property is sold. Optional treatment is also available to the donor of government bonds and a bank account. Again, however, if the asset is not treated as a gift, it will become a gift should the non-contributing spouse cash any of the bonds or withdraw any part of the money from the bank. The gift will be the sum withdrawn or cashed. The option is available on these assets because either co-owner may cash out the bank account or the bonds at any time. If the donor spouse, who contributed his separate property to the joint tenancy, cashes all of the bonds or closes out the bank account, before the non-contributing spouse has received any money, then there has been no gift as far as the gift tax law is concerned. Securities, however, are a different matter. Since the non-contributing spouse has the right to dissolve the joint tenancy independently and take title to one half in his or her name at any time, a gift has taken place on the date of the transfer.

This merging of separate property into joint tenancy

with right of survivorship most frequently occurs when second marriages are involved, or when one of the spouses receives a gift or an inheritance.

Mr. Rothman was a widower, with no children, and recently remarried. He had known his new wife most of their adult lives, so the marriage was almost immediately a success. He wanted her to inherit his estate with the least trouble and expense, so he changed all of his assets into joint tenancy with right of survivorship to avoid probate, for he had just experienced the delay involved in probating his first wife's will. He also decided to resolve the question of gift taxes at the time of the transfer, although he was aware of the options available to him. His estate consisted of four assets—his home, government bonds, a bank account, and securities—with a total fair market value of $66,000.

They were divided as follows:

Home	$20,000
Government bonds	10,000
Bank account	6,000
Securities	30,000

By transferring all of his assets into joint tenancy, Mr. Rothman made a total gift to his wife of one half of the $66,000, or $33,000. Since this sum, for both federal and gift tax purposes, exceeded his annual exclusion of $3,000, Mr. Rothman had to file both federal and state gift tax returns.

The federal gift tax was due within fifteen days of the second month after the close of the quarter in which he made the transfer. On his federal return, Mr. Rothman deducted his annual exclusion of $3,000, and then claimed his lifetime exemption of $30,000. As a consequence, his federal gift tax was zero.

On his state gift tax return, due the following April 15,

the state in which he was domiciled allowed the $3,000 annual exclusion, but not the $30,000 lifetime exemption; they allowed $5,000 instead. Mr. Rothman, therefore, had to pay a state gift tax of 3 percent on $20,000 and 4 percent on $5,000, or $800.

Very simply stated, the arithmetic on the two gift tax returns looked like this:

United States Quarterly Gift Tax Return

Total value of the property at date of gift	$66,000
Less one half attributable to spouse	33,000
Balance	33,000
Less total annual exclusion	3,000
Balance	30,000
Less specific lifetime exemption	30,000
Amount of taxable gifts for calendar quarter	000

State Gift Tax Return

Total gross market value of gifts—one half	$33,000
Annual exemption	3,000
Balance	30,000
Less specific exemption	5,000
Amount of tax—3 percent on $20,000	600
4 percent on 5,000	200
Total tax	$ 800

Mr. Rothman had now left his entire estate to his wife, avoided probate completely, paid no federal gift tax, and kept his state gift tax down to $800, without having to remember the gift tax rules if an asset should later be sold or cashed. One word of caution: when real estate is the gift asset, an adequate appraisal must be made at the time of the gift by an expert acceptable to the taxing authorities, who is usually the state inheritance tax appraiser. In Mr. Rothman's case, he had an alternative fair market value available; he was allowed to use the appraisal in the probate proceedings on his first wife's estate because it was of such recent origin. If Mr. Rothman had inherited the $66,000 after he married his second wife, the same gift tax rules would have applied, for it would have been his separate property.

Assets placed in joint tenancy with right of survivorship can also have adverse death tax consequences. On large estates, leaving everything to the surviving spouse can badly escalate the federal estate and state inheritance taxes upon the second death, as we have seen in previous chapters; therefore, a trust is used instead. But even with a trust, a mixture of probate and non-probate assets is often advisable. Frequently it is the desire of the surviving spouse to continue to occupy the home; therefore, this asset is better left in joint tenancy; and the same thing applies to a small bank account, so the survivor can have access to immediate cash. As we have seen in the chapter on trusts, any assets may be placed in a trust, and any of them may be left out of it.

Another disadvantage of joint tenancy is the fact that heirs can be treated unfairly.

Mr. McAfee, a widower with three children, had married a second time to a widow who had one child. He was the 100 percent stockholder of a close corporation, which at the time of his second marriage did not have much value. He placed this stock in joint tenancy with his new wife. With the passage of many years, however, the corporation prospered, and the stock greatly increased in value. Mr. McAfee then died, and shortly thereafter his second wife died also. Now something happened, due to joint tenancy with right of survivorship, that neither one of them had intended. Mrs. McAfee inherited all of the stock, and in her will left everything of which she died possessed to her only child. Mr. McAfee's own three children were disinherited!

When all of the property is placed in joint tenancy, one fact must be clearly understood by both joint tenants. No part of the estate can be distributed under the will of the first spouse to die. The surviving spouse comes into possession of the entire estate by operation of law; therefore, it is the will of the survivor that will determine the ultimate disposition of the property. As we have seen in Chapter Three, the modern method is for each spouse to have a will; but the will of the first spouse to die is ignored when joint tenancy ownership is used. The survivor will not be in probate court, and an attorney does not have to be consulted in regard to the transfer of the assets, for, as we have said, the survivor may dissolve the joint tenancy by his or her efforts alone, if that is desired.

From a practical standpoint, if the husband survives he usually prefers to change title himself, because he is often the more knowledgeable partner. However, if the wife survives, and she has had little or no experience in money matters, she generally prefers to have the attorney who drew the will attend to the burdensome details of dissolving the joint tenancy. The choice is up to the surviving joint tenant. The main thing to understand and remember is that distribution of the assets cannot take place under the will of the first spouse to die.

Sometimes property that was previously held in joint tenancy is changed, so that it is now owned by the husband as an individual. The usual reason for dissolving the joint tenancy during the lifetime of the spouses is to permit the assets to be left in trust, instead of the survivor automatically coming into possession of the entire estate. Later, however, because of better information and different conditions, the married parties change their mind and want to return to joint tenancy. Under these circumstances, some trust officers will maintain that a gift tax liability has been incurred.

Mr. and Mrs. Norton had lived all of their married lives in the State of Minnesota. They could easily establish that they were broke when they were married, like most couples, and that neither of them after marriage had received anything by gift or inheritance; therefore, none of their assets was the separate property of either spouse. Upon advice of an attorney and a trust officer in Minnesota, they created a revocable marital deduction trust on their $150,000 estate in order to save death taxes for their only child, a divorced daughter with three small children.

Upon retirement, Mr. and Mrs. Norton moved to California to live near their daughter and their grandchildren. Several years later, they decided to review their estate plan with an experienced investment representative who had been handling their investments since they had arrived in California. He suggested that their estate of $150,000 was too small to have a serious death tax problem and that they had been poorly advised in creating a marital deduction trust in Minnesota. He wanted them to return to joint tenancy to avoid probate, since their primary objective in estate planning was to have as little trouble as possible for the surviving spouse. Before coming to a decision, Mr. and Mrs. Norton consulted the trust department of their bank in California, only to have the trust officer object to their transferring their property back into joint tenancy, on the grounds that a gift of one half of the trust assets would take place. The only way that Mr. and Mrs. Norton could resolve their dilemma, trying to decide between their investment representative's advice on the one hand and the trust officer's objection on the other, was to have an interview with the head of the State Inheritance and Gift Tax Department. He assured them that if they wanted to return their property to joint tenancy, a gift tax would not be incurred.

But despite all of the difficulties that can be encountered if property is placed in joint tenancy, it is still the best solution for most married couples with small estates that have no death tax problem. Like Mr. and Mrs. Norton, their main desire is to have the least possible delay and trouble if one of the spouses dies. The desire to avoid probate is widespread whenever the problem is understood and even when it is not understood. Joint tenancy positively avoids probate; however, the survivor should understand that he or she can't sit back and do nothing. Death creates costs and problems that did not exist before which must be solved, by the probate process or otherwise. But certainly they can be solved much easier, faster, and for less expense by dissolving a joint tenancy than by going through probate.

We have mentioned how to change the two major ownerships—real estate at an abstract or title company, and securities by writing the transfer agent. Bank accounts, and savings and loan accounts, can be transferred by the survivor with the two basic documents: a certified copy of a death certificate and an inheritance tax waiver; and savings bonds can be cashed by the same method. Car ownership can be taken care of at the motor vehicle bureau. Life insurance paid to a named beneficiary, usually the surviving spouse, can be handled easily by your life insurance underwriter, or by the local office of the company involved. Of course, if death taxes are owed, returns will have to be filed and the taxes paid. It is time consuming, but in small estates, sixty to ninety days should see an end to the problem of dissolving a joint tenancy.

2. Naming a beneficiary. This type of ownership is most commonly found in life insurance policies. It is particularly convenient in life insurance, for not only can one beneficiary be named, but contingent beneficiaries as well, in the event the first beneficiary should die before the

death of the insured. A typical example of this is where
a father, who is the insured, has a wife and three children.
The beneficiary designation can now read as follows: "To
Mary Doe, wife, if living; if not, to the lawful children of
the Insured and his Wife, Mary Doe, equally, the survivors
equally, or the survivor." Now all possible contingencies
have been taken care of without further changes in ownership, right down to the death of the last child.

While it is convenient and it avoids probate, there are
pitfalls in this ownership also. If most of the estate consists of life insurance, and the amount is sizable, which
can occur in young families where the breadwinner hasn't
had the time to build an estate except for large amounts
of decreasing term insurance, then outright beneficiary
designation might be a mistake for the same reasons as
outright distribution under a will. The death benefit could
soon be dissipated.

A beneficiary designation would also be wrong where
the proceeds of the policies might be needed by an executor to pay death taxes and other administration costs.
A frequent example of this is where most of the estate
consists of real estate and there is a liquidity problem. If
heirs receive the proceeds of the policies outright, this
money will not be available to the executor.

Mr. Leech was a widower in his late seventies with two
married children, a son and a daughter. He owned $300,-
000 worth of real estate which he had acquired many
years before. Through the passage of time it had greatly
increased in value; in addition, he had made full use of
the depreciation allowed by the Internal Revenue Service
in order to reduce his income taxes through the years. As
a consequence, his cost basis was very low, which prevented him from selling the property because of the huge
capital gains tax involved. He was also well aware, through
his auditor, of his death tax problem, which amounted to

over $70,000. However, despite this tax information, he ignored the urgent need for liquidity in his estate. In addition to his real estate, Mr. Leech owned a very important non-probate asset, a $100,000 life insurance policy. On this, he had named his minor grandchildren as beneficiaries! His purpose in doing this was to avoid the pyramiding of the death tax problem in the estates of the second generation. When Mr. Leech died, the executor was unable to pay the death taxes because of the lack of liquidity in his estate; he therefore had to sell some of the property at a sacrifice in order to pay the Internal Revenue Service. In this case there was a complete lack of coordination between the probate and non-probate assets.

If Mr. Leech insisted upon leaving the proceeds of his life insurance policy to his grandchildren, he should have changed the beneficiary designation to a life insurance trust. When this is done, the policies are placed in a living trust, with the death proceeds being made payable to a bank trustee. If other assets are available besides the insurance, such as securities, they are placed in the trust also, in sufficient amount that the dividends from the stocks can be used by the trustee to pay the premiums on the life insurance. If other assets are not available, the grantor simply continues to pay the premiums himself as he has in the past. In this latter case, the trust (even though it is in existence) is not actually activated until the insured dies. At that time the death proceeds are paid to the bank trustee, who then proceeds to use the cash available according to the instructions of the grantor as outlined in the trust agreement.

If the purpose of the trust is to make liquid assets available to the executor for the payment of taxes, the grantor has three options. First, the trustee can be given the right to pay the death taxes, which takes care of the problem. The balance of the money, if any, is held in trust for the beneficiaries. Second, the trustee can be given the power to purchase non-liquid assets from the estate; now the fair market value of the real estate is available to the executor instead of its having to be sold at a sacrifice. Finally, the trustee can be empowered to lend money to the estate, taking back a mortgage on the property, which will again give the cash needed to the executor. Often all three powers are granted, which gives complete flexibility to the trustee. Mr. Leech should not have named his grandchildren as beneficiaries, but should have created a life insurance trust instead, paying the premiums himself until he died, giving all three powers to the bank trustee to solve his liquidity problem.

A beneficiary designation is also allowed by some mutual funds. In these instances they use a revocable declaration of trust, which is outside of the will. It is not a formal trust document drawn by an attorney and does not cloud the title in the event the shares are used as collateral at a bank, for a special stock power can be used to revoke the trust temporarily until the loan has been paid off. This way, title to the stock does not have to be changed during the period of the loan. It should be emphasized that the mutual fund account is still owned by the grantor, and that the beneficiary designation may be changed by him at any time.

This method of naming a beneficiary will avoid probate on the mutual fund account, even though the balance of the property consists of probate assets. However, if this ownership is used, the mutual fund holder should understand that he should not attempt to obtain a loan at a bank himself. He should elicit the help of his mutual fund representative, or the local office of the fund, having one of them call the particular loan officer to whom he is going to apply for a loan.

The stock certificate on this type of ownership will read:

"Mr. Jones, as trustee for Mary Jones." As a consequence, unless the bank officer is acquainted with this type of ownership, and most of them are not, he will contend that the potential borrower is not the owner of the mutual fund shares. He will think that it is a formal trust created by an attorney, and therefore the trustee is simply acting in a fiduciary capacity for Mary Jones, and does not have the right to borrow, unless the trust instrument specifically provides for this.

If settlement options on life insurance are used in connection with a beneficiary designation, a different situation develops. Insurance is usually purchased on an installment basis over a long period of time. There are frequently several policies which have been purchased at different times for different purposes. Settlement options, which are mandatory for the beneficiary, may be put in force upon the death of the insured that no longer should apply. Such policies, therefore, should be frequently reviewed. The most common settlement options are:

(a) life income to the beneficiary, no refund
(b) life income, with refund
(c) life income, with ten, fifteen, or twenty years certain
(d) left on deposit with interest

In the first settlement option, a life income is paid to the primary beneficiary, with no refund to anyone. In the second option, that amount of the death benefit that the primary beneficiary has not received goes to his or her heirs. In the third settlement option, the heirs of the beneficiary are assured of the fact that at least ten years (or fifteen or twenty) of the life income will be paid to someone. If the primary beneficiary (who is usually a widow) does not live ten years, the secondary beneficiaries (who are usually the children) receive the balance. On the other

hand, if the primary beneficiary should live ten years or
longer, the secondary beneficiaries receive nothing. Because of the sheer lack of time, most life underwriters
cannot keep settlement options on beneficiary ownerships
up to date. As a consequence the modern method is to
choose option four, "left on deposit with interest." This
way the insurance death benefit starts earning interest
from the date of death, and the beneficiary is given the
right to choose the method of payment, either cash in a
lump sum, or an option.

3. A living trust. This is also a non-probate asset, as we
have seen in the chapter on trusts. Title to the property
passes immediately to the successor trustee; it does not
go through the executor's hands.

4. United States Government bonds held in co-ownership form. It takes the signatures of both owners to purchase these bonds originally but the signature of only one
owner to cash them out. Because of this feature, the survivor in most states owns them without probate. The ownership, however, cannot be changed. If the survivor wants
them in sole ownership, or wants to name a beneficiary,
the bonds have to be cashed and new ones purchased.

5. Pension and profit sharing plans and deferred compensation plans, not payable to the estate. These also pass
directly to a named beneficiary, like the death proceeds
of life insurance policies. They are a beneficiary form of
ownership but are mentioned separately because correct
ownership of them is frequently overlooked by the testator, and yet increasingly they are forming a sizable portion
of many estates.

Where a pension or profit sharing plan is sizable, careful
consideration should be given to whether or not a bene-

ficiary designation should be used. If taxes are a problem, it might be better to make the proceeds payable to the estate, so that the executor will have the cash available, the remainder being paid to the heir or heirs after probate is over. If taxes are not a problem, pension and profit sharing plans should be considered from the same point of view as lump sum payments from life insurance—is a beneficiary designation advisable in view of the financial responsibility or knowledge of the heirs? Many times, of course, a lump sum payment is desired. However, in some plans it is expressly provided that a beneficiary may receive only a monthly income, in which case a beneficiary form of ownership cannot be used; it has to be changed so that the proceeds are made payable to the estate.

6. Joint tenancy as a matter of convenience. This is joint tenancy with right of survivorship, but with a tax difference. The joint tenants are not spouses. It is most frequently used by a widow or a widower and one or more of his or her children. The purpose of this ownership is to avoid probate, but since one joint tenant originally owned all of the property and continues to receive all of the income, the asset is 100 percent taxed in his or her estate.

Mrs. Crane was a grass widow for twenty years and decided to place the property she had acquired as a schoolteacher in joint tenancy with her spinster daughter, who had followed in her mother's footsteps and had become a teacher, holding a Ph.D. and a full professorship in an endowed college. By placing her assets in joint tenancy, Mrs. Crane was not trying to reduce death taxes—her estate was not large enough to have a death-tax problem —but she did want to avoid probate, and joint tenancy achieved this. Since Mrs. Crane received all of the income from her assets, and her daughter admittedly received none, it was a joint tenancy of convenience. Court proceedings were avoided on Mrs. Crane's subsequent death, but the entire property was included in her estate for death tax computations.

7. Tenants by the entirety. This is another form of joint tenancy. It may be used only by a husband and wife and, when used, can apply only to real estate. The advantage to be derived from this type of ownership is that the property cannot be attached by a creditor of either the husband or the wife alone. Upon the death of either spouse, title rests with the survivor. This ownership is used most frequently by retired people with meager resources, where one spouse may not handle money wisely. The creditor of the financially irresponsible spouse cannot have recourse to legal action to collect his money from property that is held this way.

8. Claiming the premises as a homestead. This is allowed in many states and can be used only between husband and wife, and then only on their home. It is accomplished by filing a declaration of homestead with the county recorder and paying the appropriate fee. Once the property is so recorded, by file, book, and page number, a photocopy is made, and the original is returned to the married parties to be placed with their other valuable documents. Preparation and filing of a declaration of homestead should be done by an attorney to be sure that it is legal. Property is homesteaded for virtually the same reason that tenancy in the entirety is used. Now, however, instead of protecting the property from the rash financial actions of one of the co-owners, the home is now protected from seizure as the result of judgment being obtained against either or both of the joint tenants because of an unpaid obligation. A lien can be obtained on the home,

but the property cannot be taken away from the owners to satisfy that lien. If the property is sold, of course, the lien or liens must be satisfied. Where available, like tenants in the entirety, it is used by many couples as a prudent precaution against possible future financial reverses, and by many more couples as an immediate protection because of present financial difficulties. It is not a protection, however, against two possible creditors—the holder of the mortgage on the property and the Internal Revenue Service. As a practical matter, however, the IRS is loath to move against a married couple, taking their home away from them by legal action and putting them out on the street, though they have the legal right to do so.

9. Gifts during life that are still taxable in the deceased's estate. The most frequent example of this are gifts made under the lifetime exemption that do *not* escape federal taxation because of the three-year contemplation of death rule. If the donor dies within three years of making the gift, this amount is taxable in his or her estate. These gifts, however, are non-probate assets, for they are excluded from probate as far as change of ownership is concerned, title having been transferred to the donee or donees. The new owners are enjoying the use of the property and receiving the income, and they own it. The executor or trustee simply has to include the fair market value of the gifts on the federal estate tax return and pay the appropriate tax.

PROBATE ASSETS

When title to property is held so that it is a probate asset, the property will pass through the executor's hands and be distributed according to a will or a trust agreement. There are nine different ownerships that are subject to probate.

1. Tenants in common. This ownership is used when both owners want to have their names on the asset, yet each desires to distribute his or her half by will. Like joint tenancy with right of survivorship, it is most commonly used between husband and wife. Escalation of federal estate and state inheritance taxes in the estate of the survivor is one of the primary reasons for not using joint tenancy but tenants in common instead. Sometimes individual ownership is used instead of tenants in common, but this would place entire control of a joint estate in the hands of the husband during life, which gives the wife a feeling of insecurity. Like joint tenancy, tenants in common requires the signatures of both parties to dispose of the property, or to change the ownership. It is true that quite often the husband makes all of the investment decisions for the married parties, and this type of joint ownership (against holding all of the assets in the husband's name alone) limits his freedom of action, for he has to obtain the signature of his wife every time a change is necessary; but this is a minor inconvenience when it is balanced against the wife's desire to know what is taking place in regard to their estate. Most assets, including securities, may be held in this form of ownership.

2. Individual ownership. This is most widely used among single persons who want their assets to pass by will. The simplest way for a single person to distribute his or her assets is to own them as an individual and have them disbursed according to a will drawn by a competent attorney. An exception to this statement involves a widow or a widower with children. Now the desire to avoid the expense and delay of probate is very strong; therefore, where feasible, ownership is held so that it is a non-probate asset, usually in joint tenancy or beneficiary form. There are millions of single people who have never married. Most of them, however, have families which consist of

brothers and sisters, nieces and nephews, cousins, aunts and uncles, or any combination of these people. The distribution of an estate to these relatives is usually to several of them, and then not in equal amounts; as a consequence, a will, using percentages, is the simplest solution. Likewise there is little desire upon the part of such an individual testator to avoid probate or to reduce the impact of death taxes, if the estate is of such a size that taxes are a problem. "Let the ax fall where it may" is the general attitude.

3. A testamentary trust. As we have seen in the last chapter, property left in this manner goes through probate as do assets left by will. Nothing takes place until the testator dies, at which time the executor takes over as the fiduciary agent of the property owner and passes on the assets to the trustee at the conclusion of probate.

4. As community property. This type of ownership is used only in community property states and then only between married parties. Title is held as follows: "John Doe and Mary Doe, husband and wife, as community property." The married parties want to go through probate, but they also want no misunderstanding either about the fact that their estate is all community. In that event, only one half of the estate of the first spouse to die will be subject to the federal estate tax, for by community property law the husband or wife dies possessed of only half of the joint estate. Likewise in most community property states, the assets are not subject to a state inheritance tax; therefore, the surviving spouse is not taxed at all.

Community property is the least understood of all the ownerships. Yet it is important that its complexities be grasped, for over forty million people, which is 20 percent of the population of the United States, live in states where community property is the law, and millions more will at some time or other move into those states.

The eight community property states are Arizona, California, Idaho, Louisiana, Nevada, New Mexico, Texas, and Washington.

You are considered to be living in a community property state if you have your domicile there. You can have only one domicile, although you may have more than one residence. Your domicile is a place of abode fixed and permanent, or at least of indefinite duration. The question of domicile is one of intent; you intend a given state to be your permanent home in order to claim it as your domicile. A temporary residence may be a matter of months or even years, while a domicile may be established the first moment you occupy the property. Also the domicile of a wife is, generally speaking, the domicile of her husband.

California, Nevada, New Mexico, Arizona, and Texas were once part of Mexico, which before that belonged to Spain. Therefore, the common law in these states goes back to Spain, where community property has always been recognized. Louisiana was originally French territory, so its state law reflects the community property law of France. Washington and Idaho simply adopted community law. All the other states in the Union, however, go back to the common law of England, where the husband has always died possessed of the entire estate and is taxed accordingly.

Community property is all property, not falling within the definition of separate property, acquired by husband and wife during their marriage while they are domiciled in a community property state. The husband and wife each have a half interest in all such property, according to state law. Death of either spouse dissolves the community, and an absolute decree of divorce also dissolves it.

In Louisiana, however, it is dissolved by a separation from bed and board, while in Arizona, community property may be divided upon grant of a divorce "*a mensa et thoro*," which for all practical purposes is synonymous with the Louisiana definition.

Separate property is all property owned separately by the spouses prior to their marriage, and all property that is acquired after marriage by one spouse, as a gift, devise, or inheritance.

It wasn't until the serious escalation of the federal estate tax during World War II that the rest of the country became aware of the community property law and the advantage, say, of dying in California, with the husband being taxed on only half of the estate, as against dying in New York, for instance, where he was taxed on it all. The outcry when this became widely known was justifiably great, and Congress eventually had to take recognition of this injustice in the tax laws by passing the marital deduction rule in 1948.

As we have seen, by qualifying for the marital deduction, people dying in non-community property states have the same estate tax advantage as those who die owning community property, for only one half is taxed upon the death of the first spouse. It must be stressed, however, that the tax advantage is for a different reason. It is because of a law passed by Congress, and not by the common law of a state in which you happen to be domiciled.

The five conditions of the marital deduction rule, of course, have to be met. The marital deduction law may also be used by those living in the community property states, for it applies equally to all fifty states; therefore, where it is necessary, because separate property is involved, those domiciled in community property states can invoke both the common law of community property and

the marital deduction law passed by Congress, in order
to have only one half of their property taxed upon the
death of the first spouse.

We have seen in previous examples that a husband marrying late in life, and owning sizable separate property in
a community property state, can still die possessed of only
one half by drawing a new will, leaving one half of his
community property, if any, and one half of his separate
property to his wife—being sure, however, to abide by the
marital deduction rule by giving her all of the income
plus the right to leave her half to whomever she pleases.

Residents of community property states still retain one
tax advantage. This is in regard to computing the capital
gains tax. Ordinarily, the cost basis of property which you
have acquired is the amount you paid. However, if you
inherit property, its cost basis is the fair market value at
which it is appraised in the estate of the person who died.
This is not true in a community property state. If at least
half of the community property is includable in the decedent's estate (whether or not the estate is required to
file a return), the fair market value of the community
property at the date of death becomes the basis of *both
halves* of the estate. What does this mean? It means that
the surviving spouse in a community property state may
sell property which has increased in value during his or
her married years and not have to pay a capital gains tax
at all, on either his half or on her half. The entire property
takes on a new cost basis for capital gains tax computations and not just half of the property that belonged to
the spouse who died.

Considerable argument against the soundness of this
statement is often raised in community property states.
To satisfy these dissenters, the following is a verbatim
quotation from a bulletin entitled *Community Property,*

Document No. 5192 (12–65), U.S. Treasury Department, Internal Revenue Service, published by the U.S. Government Printing Office, Washington, D.C.

> Example. You and your wife bought securities in 1954 with community funds for $50,000. When your wife died in January 1965 the securities had a value of $100,000, and such value was included in her estate tax return. Your basis for your half of the securities after her death is $50,000 (not $25,000—your half of the cost). Also, the basis of half of the securities to your wife's heirs is $50,000. If you are your wife's heir, your basis for all the securities is $100,000.

It should be made clear that it is not necessary to hold title to your property as "John and Mary Doe, husband and wife, as community property" in order to achieve community property status. If joint tenancy with right of survivorship between husband and wife is not so classified in a community property state, what is? Community property does not achieve its status because of the type of ownership; it achieves it because of how and where it was acquired. If a husband and wife were broke when they were married and lived all of their lives in a community property state, and neither one of them inherited anything or was given anything, then their property is community regardless of the ownership in which they choose to hold their assets.

Quasi-community property. This is not a form of ownership; it is an interpretation. It simply means that assets will have community property status even though they are acquired in a non-community property state. This is to take care of those couples who move into such a state and establish domicile with assets earned elsewhere. If the estate which they bring in was acquired under conditions which would have made it community had they acquired it in a community property state, the assets will be ruled as quasi-community property, and the estate will have all the advantages of community status. This applies even though the assets which were brought into the state, such as securities, have considerably appreciated in value.

Sometimes poor advice is obtained by married couples who live in community property states who hold their assets in joint tenancy. They rush down to their stockbroker and demand that the ownership be changed to husband and wife as community property, feeling that over the years they have been given incorrect information on ownership when the assets were originally purchased.

Mr. and Mrs. Cross were one such couple. They lived in a community property state and had been told that joint tenancy with right of survivorship was not community property and that therefore, to achieve this status, all of their assets had to be changed, the main reason being given that no state inheritance taxes would then have to be paid. The bugaboo of taxes had been raised, which was enough for Mr. and Mrs. Cross to become upset, although their estate was small, only $70,000. How much could be saved in inheritance taxes, however, had not been made clear to them.

Fortunately the investment representative they consulted was an expert. He agreed with them on only one point—that if their assets were declared as community property upon the death of the first spouse, there would be no state inheritance taxes. But he suggested that, before they made a hasty decision and changed their ownership, they should look at both sides of the problem. First, if their advice had been correct, how much would be saved by changing from joint tenancy to community property? If they remained in joint tenancy, and their assets were declared as separate property, half of the separate property, plus $5,000, would be exempt, which would subject the remainder of their $70,000 estate to a state inheritance tax of $700. In order to avoid this small tax, they were going to dissolve their joint tenancy and go through probate, which would incur administration expenses equal to the inheritance taxes they were trying to save. Besides that, their investment representative told them, they had been misinformed. Joint tenancy with right of survivorship *was* community property, and state inheritance taxes would not be owed. Mr. and Mrs. Cross went away relieved, leaving their property in its existing ownership.

5. Co-ownership. This is a favorite way for two persons to own a bank account, and it is very commonly used with E and H bonds issued by the United States Government, as we have previously mentioned. Most of the time this is a probate asset. This ownership requires the signatures of both parties to enter into it, but either one may cash it out. There is no protection, therefore, for either party against adverse action that might be taken by the other co-owner. As one investment representative, who is a wag, is fond of saying with a good-natured grin: "Are you sure, Mr. Jones, that you still have those government bonds in your safe deposit box? Maybe your wife has sneaked down there and cashed you out!" Which brings home the point on co-ownership: it takes two signatures to buy, but only one signature to cash out. When this ownership is used on E and H bonds, it is a non-probate asset. When it is used on bank accounts, it usually results in probate of these accounts.

6. Outright ownership by a minor. This is treated separately, though it is another form of individual ownership. Assets owned outright by a minor come under the jurisdiction of the probate court; they cannot be sold or transferred without a court order. This is for the protection of

minor children, for without it many of them would be victimized by their more knowledgeable adults.

It used to be that minor children's funds could only be invested in legalized investments such as bank accounts, government bonds, and mortgages. In recent years the courts have become more lenient, particularly in those states that have passed the Prudent Man Rule, which allows fiduciaries to invest in common stocks, including, of course, mutual funds. This rule has been adopted by at least forty states. It lays down broad principles by which fiduciaries can invest money that is entrusted to their care. The Prudent Man Rule states in part:

> All that can be required of a trustee . . . is that he shall conduct himself faithfully and exercise a sound discretion. He is to observe how men of prudence, discretion, and intelligence manage their own affairs, not in regard to speculation but in regard to the permanent disposition of their funds, considering the probable income as well as the probable safety of the capital to be invested.

Assets will be more inclined to be left outright to children, rather than in trust, when the protection to minors on individual ownership is understood. If parents (who are the natural guardians of their own children), or guardians of minors legally appointed by the court, desire to change the minor's funds from one asset to another, they have to petition the court through an attorney for permission to do so. In those states, however, that have passed the Prudent Man Rule, a petition for the child to own securities or mutual funds receives almost automatic approval by the judge. The attorney simply sees the clerk of the court, who obtains the judge's signature on a standard form. The whole procedure usually takes only a few minutes. If the minor should die, his property is inherited by his estate and passes by operation of law. It is therefore a probate asset.

7. A guardian. Guardians are appointed by the court, or in a will, to handle the affairs of people who are financially incompetent for mental or physical reasons, or both. Minor children, the elderly, the physically handicapped, and the mentally impaired all fall into this category. An individual may be named guardian of the person, or guardian of the property, or both. When a guardian is named in a will, it is because a personal relationship is desired, and therefore the guardian is usually placed in charge of both the person and his assets. Where protection and payment of property only is required, the testator normally creates a trust instead.

Mrs. Greenfield was appointed by the court to act as guardian for her widowed sister. Years before, her sister had fallen on her head, and the injury had so damaged her brain that eventually she could no longer take care of herself or her affairs, and had to be placed in a mental institution. Mrs. Greenfield, as guardian, not only managed her assets and paid all her bills for several years until she eventually died, but also took care of her personal wants and needs as well, such as overseeing a practical nurse when she was still at home, and buying her clothes and personal necessities. During this time she opened a separate fiduciary account in a bank and hired a public accountant to keep books and prepare an annual report to the court of her guardianship. When her sister died, Mrs. Greenfield took over as executrix, and eventually distributed the assets according to her sister's will.

8. Conservator. This is also a fiduciary ownership like a guardianship. However, a conservator is more likely to be appointed in place of a guardian where an adult is the

owner of a sizable estate and has been declared legally incompetent by the court. Now the estate must be conserved against the rash acts of the present owner for his or her protection, as well as conserving the estate for its eventual heirs, who will inherit the property either through the operation of law or by a will of the owner drawn before he or she was declared incompetent. Frequently, a spouse is named as conservator of that half of the estate owned by the other married party when he or she becomes incompetent through senility or a stroke.

Mrs. Alderman was named conservator for her husband on their joint estate because he had become senile. As far as she was concerned, this was just the same as if she had inherited the entire estate, for she now had to make all the investment decisions. It is quite a responsibility, and many wives because of their background are not able to assume it. Mrs. Alderman felt this way, even though she was named conservator by the court, so she sold all of their securities and put them into a balanced mutual fund on a monthly payout. As a fiduciary agent for her husband's half, she acted in a sensible manner, particularly since she lived in a Prudent Man Rule state. She did not have to obtain a court order to change the assets. She already had one, appointing her as conservator. All she had to do was to supply the transfer agent with a certified copy.

In the case of Mrs. Peck, an attorney was appointed as conservator of her estate when she was declared incompetent by the court. She was worth almost one million dollars, which would eventually be inherited by distant relatives according to her will. In this case a disinterested professional man was chosen by the court as conservator to lessen the possibility of any future legal action by the heirs claiming mishandling by the conservator because of the amount of money involved.

9. Custodian under the Uniform Gifts to Minors Act. This act allows outright gifts of any kind of property to minors, using an adult as custodian, without the custodian later having to resort to a court order to withdraw the funds. For years, about the only asset that could be owned by a minor to pay for his college education eventually, without a guardian having to appeal to the probate court to withdraw the money prior to the child's majority, was life insurance. This was seriously objected to, and was successfully contested by banks and stockbrokerage firms, until it resulted in the passage of the Uniform Gifts to Minors Act. Now securities, bank accounts, savings and loan accounts, and mutual funds may be held in this ownership. When the money is needed, the company involved is empowered to honor the redemption request over the signature of the custodian without the custodian having to obtain a court order.

As a result of the passage of the Uniform Gifts to Minors Act, there has been widespread use of this type of ownership. Many parents and grandparents prefer to build a college education fund through the means of an equity investment, and its concomitant opportunity for gain, rather than through the medium of a fixed-dollar asset, as long as it may be withdrawn when needed without a problem. It must be understood by anyone using this form of ownership, however, that it is an outright gift to the minor, and as such is a part of the minor's estate, and if not used, it will become the property of the minor when he or she becomes legally of age. If the custodian dies, a successor custodian may be named simply by notifying the company involved.

As with many ownerships, there are adverse features.

If the donor names himself as custodian, and he should die, the gift will be taxed in his estate. If the donor has a death tax problem, he should, therefore, name some other member of the family. This presents no problem where a grandparent is the donor, for he or she simply names one of the child's parents as custodian. Another adverse feature is that the asset cannot be transferred into another type of security. Where mutual fund shares are involved, as part of a group of funds under the same management that allows a free transfer privilege, this rule results in a sale and a new purchase, with a new commission, which can be prohibitive.

Probate, as we have said, is a matter of ownership. There are three basic ways to avoid probate, and they all involve the correct title to your assets:

(a) joint tenancy with right of survivorship
(b) naming a beneficiary
(c) a living trust

If you hold your assets in joint tenancy with right of survivorship, you do not have to go through probate; you simply dissolve the joint tenancy. To repeat, the two main documents required are a certified copy of a death certificate and an inheritance tax waiver.

Naming a beneficiary will avoid probate. Most people own life insurance and are therefore familiar with this, for the life insurance company will pay directly to the named beneficiary, ignoring the will, if any. The death benefit will have to be included by the executor for computation of death taxes, but the beneficiary will receive the proceeds without their having to pass through the executor's hands. Whether the beneficiary will pay his proportionate share of the taxes depends upon the provisions of the will. The testator may provide that the beneficiary must pay his share of the death taxes, or the property

owner may specifically state that the beneficiary inherits
the death proceeds tax free, in which event all of the taxes
will have to be paid by the residuary legatees. Many
people are under the mistaken impression that life insurance is nontaxable because of this very ownership feature.
The beneficiary designation avoids probate, and if the
beneficiary himself doesn't pay taxes, the insurance proceeds are considered to be tax free. But this is simply
not so.

A living trust to avoid probate is used only on large
estates where a death tax problem prohibits outright inheritance by the surviving spouse. Joint tenancy can't be
used, for it would result in serious escalation of death
taxes in the estate of the survivor. However, because of
the desire to avoid the delay, the expense, or the publicity
of probate, or any combination of the three, a living trust
is created. Upon death the assets pass directly to the successor trustee. A living trust should be approached with
caution, even by the well-to-do, for the reasons stated
earlier.

It is true that the six other ownerships that have been
discussed earlier as non-probate assets also avoid probate;
but the other six are special situations where a particular
ownership is allowed because of the nature of the asset
involved, or is required because of a different objective
on the part of the testator, other than the basic one of
avoiding probate.

Formerly, ownership of a bank or savings and loan account resulted in the automatic probate of that account.
This was because the ownership could only be in the name
of an individual, or in the names of two people as co-
owners. Recently, however, these institutions are permitting joint tenancy with right of survivorship, and a beneficiary form as well. The practice widely varies from state
to state, so the new account department of your institution

should be consulted if you desire to make a change. Banks still feel that they should not advise a customer in any way as to what ownership he should use, but if the customer decides, independently of the bank, that he wants a certain type of ownership, many of them are perfectly willing to register regular savings accounts, time certificates of deposit, and checking accounts in any one of several different ways.

As you can see from the eighteen different ownerships, title is important and varied. One ownership is sometimes sufficient, such as joint tenancy with right of survivorship between married parties when the estate is small. On the other hand, on large estates many ownerships can be involved, and even a mixture of both probate and nonprobate assets might be advisable, and almost always a trust is involved. Non-probate assets, it should be remembered, are usually assets without a plan, quite often acquired hit-and-miss over a period of years, and they will pass directly to your heirs by operation of law. Probate assets on the other hand must pass through the executor's hands. The testator should review the various titles to his property, and look upon them, not as individual assets, but as part of an economic whole if he expects his overall estate plan to accomplish its objectives.

6

The Financial
Planning Team

IN EVERY area where advice is sought, only proven experts should be consulted, and nowhere is this axiom more important than when applying it to the members of your financial planning team. Most of the time four experts are needed for effective estate planning: an investment representative, an attorney, a life underwriter, and an accountant. Sometimes it is necessary to consult a trust officer as well, particularly on large estates. But often on smaller estates only the first two are needed, the investment representative and the attorney, especially if the investment specialist is dual-licensed, as so frequently occurs today, and is therefore an expert on life insurance as well.

As we emphasized in Chapter One, it is difficult to obtain accurate information on estate planning. It is hard to find someone who has a broad enough background so that he is equipped to advise you on all phases of the problem. Analyzing your assets, and determining what you want to accomplish in your overall estate plan (made all the more difficult because quite often you are not sure yourself), is not easy. Many experts are in possession of estate planning principles, but they are unable to provide a solution that particularly applies to you. After all, it is your estate and your heirs that you are trying to protect, and though you want to know as much as you can about probate, death taxes, wills, trusts and ownership, nevertheless, the crux of the matter is how can this information be best applied to you.

The one expert who should act as the financial planning correlator for your estate plan is the investment representative. Quite often the attorney is looked upon as the captain of the financial planning team, and it is his advice, as against the others (for many times there is a conflict), that is followed. This is often a mistake, because it is your property that you are trying to protect and conserve for your heirs, and taxes that you are trying to reduce; you are not too concerned with the framework of the law. The investment representative is often the catalyst that caused you to think of estate planning in the first place. It is he, more than the other experts, who is responsible for the inventory of your assets, the overall suggestions, and seeing to it that the plan is carried through to its conclusion. The investment specialist cannot draw wills and trusts, and your accountant is more familiar than he with your tax problems; and if he is not a life underwriter, your insurance agent should be consulted in regard to your life insurance program. However, it is only after the investment specialist has reviewed your estate and provided most of the solution that you consult the other specialists for their particular knowledge.

In preadministering your estate and consulting with the financial planning team, you are anticipating the problems that will be encountered by your executor, the trustee (if any), and your heirs. You are dealing with uncertainties, but those who follow behind you will be dealing with facts—and facts that cannot be changed, for now it is too late.

Procrastination is one of the main stumbling blocks to effective estate planning, and can cause more hardship and loss of property and future family security than any other prime cause. Delay in most cases is costly, but nowhere is it more expensive than in failure to arrange for the proper settlement of your estate. Daily urgent problems are apparently more important than that which may or may not happen tomorrow; the estate tax due some time in the future is of less importance in the mind of the average property owner than the income tax that is due today. But it should be remembered that a lifetime of effort, thought, and self-denial has gone into the building of a living estate; therefore, a few hours spent on arranging the death estate is more than just time well spent; it is a must.

Pre-will planning has three objectives:

(a) the future security of the family members
(b) the protection and conservation of the property
(c) the reduction of death taxes by utilizing the provisions granted under the Internal Revenue Code

Let's admit that each member of your financial planning team has an axe to grind. They are all in business to make money. This is why there is quite often a conflict in their suggestions. But the testator has been accustomed to this in building his living estate, and therefore it should not confuse or upset him in planning his death estate. In the last analysis the decisions have to be his.

After you have decided that you must do something about estate planning, what exactly do you do? There are nine steps to take in planning your death estate.

1. A complete and careful Confidential Inventory of Assets should be filled out. An outline of such an inventory was given in Chapter One. The testator must be very

frank in listing all of his assets and his liabilities, if any. Failure to disclose all of the facts, or withholding any unpleasant information, such as the spendthrift tendencies of a daughter-in-law, or that one of your children is mentally retarded and therefore must have a carefully drawn trust for his or her protection, can defeat the overall purpose of your estate plan. Careless listing of the ownership on your assets—relying on memory, rather than taking the time to actually check the titles—can result in lack of coordination between your probate and non-probate assets. There is natural reluctance to divulge this information. Your money and the interplay of family relationships have been your private concern in building your living estate, and therefore putting this information down in black and white to hand over to an investment specialist, a non-member of your family, so that he may properly plan your death estate, is not easy. But it has to be done. Confidence in your estate planning correlator, with full understanding between you that the information is strictly confidential, and will remain that way, is essential.

2. The investment representative, after carefully reviewing your confidential inventory, will make his suggestions as to what you should do. These should be in writing, and they should be reviewed carefully one at a time, so that you understand each suggestion and the reasoning behind the recommendation. No decision should be made at this meeting. The property owner has learned in building his living estate that hasty decisions are often a mistake. But don't procrastinate. No one makes a hurried decision if he sleeps on it. Certainly one week should be a sufficient length of time in which to consider carefully the suggestions that have been made.

3. Frequently a recommendation is made for you to sell some of your assets. If you agree, you should sell them before you see your attorney in regard to drawing a new

will and/or trust agreement. The lawyer should not be asked for his opinion in regard to this part of your estate plan. You did not consult him on the assets you acquired in building your living estate, so why should you consult him now in regard to the assets that should be held in your death estate? Lawyers are notoriously poor investors, like most professional people, because they are not business-men. You do not ask a lawyer or a doctor about how to invest; you go to him because he is a specialist in medicine or the law. Likewise your attorney can better discuss your will if he has a list of the assets that you intend to keep, not a list on which you plan to make a change. So you have a second meeting with your financial planning cor-relator to decide at this conference what assets you are going to sell or not sell.

4. If a suggestion has been made to change your life insurance, you quite frequently have to see your insurance agent. You have confidence in him or you would not have followed his suggestions in the past. Here you may en-counter your first conflict of interest, because your life underwriter is in the insurance business, and he believes in it. Likewise he is inclined to be slightly resentful of an outsider making suggestions on policies that he sold and on which he is supposed to be the specialist. However, if he understands that this is part of an overall estate plan and that in your opinion the suggestions that have been made are sound, he will go along with your thinking.

5. The most frequent suggestion in estate planning in-volves taxes. Before assets are sold, your auditor should be consulted as to any capital gains tax implications. If gifts are to be made, he should agree as to the amount of the gifts and the amount of the tax, if any. If the will is to be changed, he should fully concur with the estimated amount that will be saved in death taxes, both federal and state. Certainly there will be attorney's fees if a new legal

document is contemplated; therefore, he should agree that the money is available for this or any other suggested expenditure.

6. Mail your finalized Confidential Inventory of Assets to your attorney and set up an appointment with him to draw the necessary legal documents. The ordinary request will be for a will; but on larger estates, of course, a trust will often be necessary. When you meet with the attorney, you again have to be prepared for a conflict of interest.

The lawyer, by training, wants you in probate court. Most lawyers honestly feel that this is the best way to pass on your assets to your heirs, for then everything will be done with the approval of a judge. An attorney is also a technical man who frequently uses legal language that is completely foreign to the average layman; therefore, the tendency is to become hopelessly confused and throw up your hands and say, "Draw the will whatever way you feel is best." This is a mistake. You should decide before you go to the attorney what you want done, and you should insist that he do it.

For instance, if you and your other three specialists have agreed that you can and should avoid probate, and because of this you want all of your assets in joint tenancy, you should not let him persuade you to the contrary, with a lot of whereases and what if this happened and what if that happened. You came to him to have a new will drawn, or an old one brought up-to-date, to be used only upon the second death. If he doesn't want to draw it that way, there is always someone else.

Let's face the facts. A lawyer does not make money drawing wills and trust agreements—his fee is too small. He is willing to work for a small fee today on the assumption that on some tomorrow he will be chosen as the probate attorney. Nevertheless, small fee or not, how much he will charge for his services should be agreed upon in advance. Most people are horrified at this suggestion, but it is simply a matter of business. After all, you insist upon knowing beforehand how much you have to pay for everything else, why not the fees of a professional man? As a matter of fact, most lawyers do not object to this.

At the conclusion of this first conference, another appointment will have to be arranged, unless you are asking for a simple two-page will; but by the end of this second interview you and the attorney should be in complete agreement as to all the provisions of your legal document. At this point you should ask him to mail a preliminary draft to you, and also to send a copy to your investment representative. You must ask him to do this, because the correlator cannot, and the attorney, if he mailed a copy of your will to anyone but you, without your specific instructions, would be violating his code of ethics. Sometimes the property owner wants his investment representative with him when he sees the attorney. If he does, the testator should understand that he is now destroying the confidential relationship between a lawyer and his client. An attorney does not have to divulge what was said during an interview, even on a witness stand in court, but an investment representative does. This fact should be clearly understood by the testator, but despite this, many property owners want to have the correlator with them.

7. After a draft of the proposed legal document has been received by you and your investment representative, and both of you have had time to review it, you should have a third meeting with him. A will or a trust is difficult to understand. The correlator has read so many of them, he can reduce to plain English what the lawyer has had to couch in legal terms. In other words, the testator quite often will not fully understand what he is signing without the correlator's explanation. It should be remembered that the executor and the heirs are going to have to live with

the provisions of the will. Penciled notations should be made by the testator in the margin of this preliminary draft of the will for anything that he does not understand so that he and the investment specialist can discuss them in detail.

8. Any proposed changes in the legal document should be discussed with the attorney over the telephone, or personally if necessary, and then the final document should be drawn.

9. Sign the revised will and/or trust agreement when you receive it. This is the final act, but an important one.

Mr. Freeland told his investment representative that he had received the final version of his trust agreement and that he had signed it. The ownership of his assets was therefore changed from joint tenancy to tenants in common so that he could distribute his half by will. But he never did sign it! As a consequence, instead of his wife automatically inheriting everything because of joint tenancy with right to survivorship, Mr. Freeland died intestate, with his assets being distributed according to state law.

The best way to understand how to take advantage of estate planning is to review several actual confidential inventories and the suggestions finally adopted by the testator after careful review of his estate plan with his financial planning team. In these case histories, you will find that the information on page one is sketchy, containing only the necessary family information to understand the problem. The individual testator, of course, should complete this page in detail. Certainly addresses and telephone numbers, Social Security information, exact birth dates, and the names and addresses of the testator's financial planning team are not germane to an estate planning solution, but this is vital information for the eventual executor or trustee.

CASE ONE

Mrs. Gray's second husband had died, and after a year and a half, his estate had been settled and was out of probate. Mr. Marcus Gray, having had no children by his first marriage, had left his separate property to his second wife, which consisted entirely of securities. Mrs. Gray was seventy, and by her own admission was getting a little infirm and slightly forgetful. She had two married sons by her first husband, Mr. Nelson, and four grandchildren. She lived in an apartment and wanted to continue to live alone and be independent of her sons and their families. Having been through probate twice, she was aware of the problems involved, except for taxes. She did not realize, now that she had inherited from her second husband and had substantially increased her estate as a consequence, that she had a serious death tax problem, until her financial planning correlator pointed out to her that her federal and state taxes would amount to approximately $40,000. It was at this point that she made out the following inventory, asked for the investment representative's comments, and requested that her two sons be present when he returned with his written suggestions.

A CONFIDENTIAL INVENTORY OF ASSETS

name ____Mrs. Katherine Gray____ age __70__ birthday _____

wife's name _____ age ____ birthday _____

address _____ telephone _____

city_____ state _____ zip code_____

Social Security number _____

total value of the estate ____$201,998_____

1. names of children (include name of spouse if child
   is married) birth dates—residence
   Norman Nelson   Age 51
   George Nelson   Age 50
   both married

2. names of grandchildren—birth dates—residence
   (if not living with parents)

   Norman   two children
   George   two children

3. last will and testament—date—where kept
   Yes—up-to-date—safe deposit box

4. your advisers: name—address—telephone
   lawyer
   life underwriter
   accountant
   investment representative

5. business address and telephone

Signature   date

Assets

	present value	ownership
1. checking accounts	$ 2,000	individual
2. bank savings	8,000	
3. savings & loan associations		
4. credit unions		
5. securities (see pages 12 & 13)	191,998	
6. mortgages and trust deeds		
7. notes receivable		
8. home		
9. other real estate		
10. life insurance death benefit		
11. business equity (see page 5)		
total assets	$ 201,998	

Liabilities

	amount
1. mortgages or trust deeds	$
(a) home	
(b) other	
2. notes payable	
3. other liabilities	
total liabilities	$ none

total assets	$ 201,998
total liabilities	$ none
net value of the estate	$ 201,998

Marcus Gray (Deceased)

Securities

common stocks

no. shares	company	current value
111	Bank of Tokyo	$ 4,200
204	Chemical New York Corporation	12,138
100	Southern Company	1,950
200	Warner Lambert	13,850
256	Kimberly Clark	11,575
600	Standard Oil of California	33,200
259	Pacific Gas & Electric	7,700
200	Pacific Lighting	4,000
50	General Electric	5,200
	Total value	$ 93,813

preferred stocks

no. shares	company	current value
42	Cincinnati Gas & Electric	$ 2,800
55	American Home Products, conv.	6,300
85	Tenneco, Inc. 4.92% conv.	7,600
	Total value	$ 16,700

municipal bonds

face amount	description	current value
$5,000	State of California 4% Series C dated 12-1-59 due 6-1-78	$ 4,050
5,000	State of California 4% Veterans Bond Act 1958 Series U due 2-1-82	3,900
5,000	Texas Turnpike Authority, Dallas-Fort Worth Turnpike due 1-1-95	2,150
	Total value	$ 10,100
	Total value in securities	$ 120,613

Katherine Gray

SECURITIES

common stocks

no. shares	company	current value
	Putnam Investors Fund	$ 25,000
	American Mutual	25,000
410	American Telephone & Telegraph	18,860
39	Pacific Gas & Electric	1,170
10	United States Steel	230
20	Pacific Power & Light	400
105	Texas Capital Corporation	500
10	Boeing	225

Total value $ 71,385

Current Income

bank accounts	$ 70.00
savings & loan	
credit unions	
mortgages and trust deeds	
notes	
securities	110.00
mutual funds	500.00
real estate income	
salary or business income	
company pensions	234.00
other pensions	
Social Security	140.00
annuities	337.00
other	

total monthly income $1,391.00

(This was after correlator's suggestions were adopted.)

COMMENTS BY THE
INVESTMENT CORRELATOR

1. At your age you have too many securities to manage. You should sell seven of the individual stocks that you inherited from your second husband. They took on a new cost basis upon his death, they have not increased in value since the appraisal in his estate, and therefore there is no capital gains tax problem.

2. You should also sell four of the stocks that you own yourself in order to reduce the number of your investments. On these you would have a slight loss.

3. If you add $50,000 from the sale of these securities to your existing two fund accounts, you can receive a monthly income from each fund of $250, or a total of $500 per month. These checks can be sent directly to your bank for deposit to your checking account.

4. Since the total sale of the securities would amount to $60,000, you would have $10,000 left after the mutual fund purchases. This sum should be put in the bank. At the present time, since you want to travel, you don't have enough cash.

5. You have a death tax problem. Your estate is valued at $200,000, on which your taxes would be about $40,000. You should reduce these taxes by immediate gifts to your two sons by giving them the preferred stock, the municipal bonds, and the six hundred shares of Standard Oil. The transfer to your heirs of this $60,000 in securities would save $16,720 in federal estate taxes and $3,710 in state inheritance taxes, for a total tax saving of $20,430. It should be remembered, however, that only $6,000 of the $60,000 in gifts would come under the annual exclusion, and that only $30,000 would come under the lifetime exemption; therefore, the balance would be subject to federal and state gift taxes which would reduce your death tax savings of $20,430 by about $3,000.

6. You would not be hurt financially in any way by these gifts, for you would still be worth $140,000 and have an income of $1,391.00 per month.

7. Future gifts should be made sparingly, but if your bank account builds up by the end of the year, indicating that you are not spending all of your income, you should give the excess away each year under your annual exclusion.

8. Your revised assets would be very simple and easy to manage. You would have left in the estate the mutual fund accounts, two utility stocks—American Telephone and Telegraph and Pacific Gas & Electric—and your bank savings.

EXPLANATION OF THE COMMENTS BY THE CORRELATOR

1. The seven stocks to be sold included everything except Standard Oil of California and Pacific Gas & Electric. Mrs. Gray already owned in her estate thirty-nine shares of P. G. & E., and she liked the stock. The combined holdings would give her a total of 298 shares. As a matter of fact, she bought two more shares in order to own three hundred. It is easier to compute the dividend and the current value on multiples of a hundred shares, and if sold, no odd lot transaction is involved.

2. The four stocks sold in her estate consisted of U.S. Steel, Pacific Power & Light, Texas Capital Corporation, and Boeing. The market value of all four stocks amounted to only $1,355. A seventy-year-old widow should not bother retaining four different stocks for this small amount of money. They were sold to get rid of a nuisance factor. She also sold ten shares of A. T. & T. for the same reason she bought the two shares of P. G. & E.

3. A systematic pay-out from a mutual fund will be discussed in Chapter Seven.

4. Mrs. Gray wanted to take an expensive trip with a friend, but because she had only $8,000 in the bank she was wondering if she could afford it! Sometimes objective estate planning places assets in their proper perspective. Certainly at the age of seventy, and worth $200,000, Mrs. Gray could afford to go where she pleased! Even when her assets were reduced to $140,000 to save death taxes, the same principle applies.

5. Since both estates were now in her name, giving part of the securities to her two sons was the only way the testator could reduce her death taxes. Her auditor was consulted for the exact amount of the tax savings.

6. $140,000 was enough capital because she was infirm and seventy years old; it would not have been enough if she were well and twenty years younger.

7. The testator still had a death tax problem with an estate valued at $140,000. But at this point she had to consider her own position. Future gifts would further re duce taxes, but some taxes would inevitably have to be paid if she were to maintain her financial independence. Each year the state of her finances, her age, and her general health would be reviewed, and a decision made as to what part of her annual exclusion, if any, she would use rather than forever lose the gift privilege for that calendar year.

8. Simplicity was a major part of the overall estate plan. Mrs. Gray was getting too old to manage her affairs, so if her assets could be placed in a position where she had to make no decisions, this would give her much less trouble and more peace of mind. Her sons preferred it this way, too, rather than having to make decisions for her, for they readily admitted they knew very little about investments. As a matter of fact, both sons sold the preferred stock and the municipal bonds they received from their mother and put the proceeds into a maximum capital

appreciation fund, both for management and the probable better long-term results, thinking in terms of their own retirement, retaining only the Standard Oil stock.

CASE TWO

Mr. and Mrs. Roger Matthews had been married for over forty years and lived in a community property state. The total value of their estate was $300,000, which they held in joint tenancy with right of survivorship. In addition to this community property, Mrs. Matthews had inherited a portion of her sister's estate, which amounted to $30,000, which she kept in her name in a savings and loan institution. Mr. Matthews was seventy years of age and had been retired for several years; Mrs. Matthews was sixty-nine. They had two married sons in their early forties and three grandchildren. They were both in excellent health and didn't appear to be within ten years of their actual ages.

A CONFIDENTIAL INVENTORY OF ASSETS

name ____Roger Matthews____ age _70_ birthday _____

wife's name ____Helen Matthews____ age _69_ birthday _____

address _____ telephone _____

city _____ state _____ zip code _____

Social Security number _____

total value of the estate ___$329,731_____

1. names of children (include name of spouse if child
   is married) birth dates—residence
   Two married sons in their forties

2. names of grandchildren—birth dates—residence
   (if not living with parents)
   Three grandchildren, two by the elder son, one by the
   younger son

3. last will and testament—date—where kept
   A simple will made many years ago, kept in the safe deposit
   box.

4. your advisers: name—address—telephone
   lawyer
   life underwriter
   accountant
   investment representative

5. business address and telephone

Signature   date

Assets

	present value	ownership
1. checking accounts	$ 1,500	joint
2. bank savings	15,150	joint
(Mrs. Matthews' separate prop.)		
3. savings & loan associations	30,000	single
4. credit unions		
5. securities (see page 6–21)	149,681	joint
6. mortgages and trust deeds	30,900	joint
7. notes receivable		
8. home		
unimproved land	50,000	joint
9. other real estate	42,500	joint
10. life insurance death benefit	10,000	(cash value $7,700)
11. business equity (see page 5)		
total assets	$ 329,731	

Liabilities

	amount
1. mortgages or trust deeds	$
(a) home	
(b) other	
2. notes payable	
3. other liabilities	
total liabilities	$ none

total assets	$ 329,731
total liabilities	$ none
net value of the estate	$ 329,731

Securities

common stocks

no. shares	company	current value
100	American South Africa	$ 4,760
400	American Radiator	10,300
200	American Tel. & Tel. Co.	10,200
139	Commonwealth Edison	3,352
250	General Motors	21,739
200	Flying Tiger	4,968
60	I. B. M.	20,669
100	Liberty Loan Corporation	2,084
725	Occidental Petroleum	14,681
200	Reynolds Industries	12,750
204	Standard Oil of New Jersey	16,677
200	Texaco	7,600
200	Fleetwood Enterprises	3,968
	Total value	$ 133,748

utility bonds

face amount	description		current value
$2,000	Southern Bell Telephone	9.05%	$ 2,000
1,800	American Tel. & Tel. deb.	8¾%	1,800
4,000	Mountain States Telephone	8½%	4,000
4,000	New Jersey Telephone	9.0%	4,000
4,000	Pacific Tel. & Tel.	9½%	4,133
	Total value		$ 15,933
	Total value in securities		$ 149,681

Current Income

bank accounts	$ 50
savings & loan	65
credit unions	
mortgages and trust deeds	150
notes	
securities	571
mutual funds	
real estate income	
salary or business income	
company pensions	
other pensions	
Social Security	304
annuities	
other	

total monthly income $ 1,140

COMMENTS BY THE INVESTMENT CORRELATOR

1. You each need a new will.

2. Your estate is large enough so that federal estate taxes pose a serious problem. These taxes on half of the estate, or on $150,000, would be $17,500. But there is a big escalation if the survivor dies possessed of $300,000, for the estate taxes would then be $59,100.

2. This escalation can be avoided by each of you leaving your one half in a testamentary trust to your two sons. This way the estate taxes against the estate of the survivor would be $17,500 and not $59,100, which is a tax saving of $41,600. In addition, the surviving spouse can receive all of the income from the trust, plus be given the right to withdraw 5 percent of the principal each year. Complete

control of the entire estate can rest with the survivor by having him or her named trustee.

4. All of your assets don't have to be placed in trust; some of them may be left out if you desire. For instance, your home could be left in joint tenancy.

5. Mrs. Matthews' separate property, consisting of the $30,000 savings and loan account, should be given to your two sons immediately in order for death taxes to be no more than the calculation in paragraphs two and three.

6. The survivor could further reduce death taxes by a judicious use of gifts. The annual exclusion should be used first and then the $30,000 lifetime exemption. It should be remembered, however, that part of the lifetime exemption of each of you will have been used already if Mr. Matthews joins in the gift to your sons of Mrs. Matthews' separate property.

7. Your life insurance policy should be reviewed.

8. You could consider disposing of the unimproved real estate. It is not producing an income. You should not be trying to increase your estate at this time through rising land values, but enjoying the income from investments instead.

9. If you decide not to sell the land, you could increase your income by investing another $25,000 in 7½ percent utility bonds.

EXPLANATION OF THE COMMENTS BY THE CORRELATOR

1. The existing will was out of date, and in addition a trust was needed in order to save taxes.

2 and 3. Any estate of this size, if left entirely to the survivor, will result in serious escalation of taxes in the estate of the surviving spouse. However, when a married

couple reach the ages of Mr. and Mrs. Matthews, before a trust is created to reduce death taxes, their state of health should be considered, because there is a sizable tax credit allowed against the first estate if the survivor should die in a relatively short period of time. In this case both testators were in excellent health, so it was possible that the survivor would live many years, and as a consequence, very little credit would be available. A testamentary trust, therefore, was drawn by a competent attorney.

4. They agreed, and left their home in joint tenancy.

5. It was decided that Mrs. Matthews should give her inheritance to their two sons. Mr. Matthews, however, would also sign the gift tax return forms in order to make both of their annual exclusions and lifetime exemptions available. This way they could each give $3,000 to each of their sons, making a total of $12,000. The balance of $18,000 would also be divided between their lifetime exemptions, so that each would have $21,000 still available in the future if needed.

6. Gifts would be used by the survivor only if he or she should live for a period of years; otherwise the tax credit against the first estate would be sufficient to reduce taxes.

7. The life insurance policy was analyzed by the investment representative because he was dual licensed and was therefore a life underwriter. The testators were not paying premiums on this insurance, because it was a participating policy that had been in force for over forty years, so that the dividends each year were slightly greater than the premiums. However, the amount of insurance was low, which was the difference between the cash value of $7,700 and the $10,000 face amount, or $2,300. Although it was costing nothing to carry the policy, it was Mrs. Matthews' decision (for she would be the loser) on whether or not they should enjoy the lower cash value of $7,700 now (by cashing the policy) or she should later enjoy the higher

death benefit of $10,000 alone. Her decision was further complicated by the fact that the estate, which would eventually be owned by the sons, could also be considered to be the loser if Mrs. Matthews should predecease her husband. After careful thought she decided to cash the policy and invest the money.

8. Their two sons were called in when the unimproved real estate was discussed. If income was not a consideration, they said, they preferred to inherit the property, rather than some other investment, because of its excellent long-term growth potential.

9. This was actually a part of decisions six and seven. Mr. and Mrs. Matthews said they could use a little more income, but instead of selling the unimproved property, because their sons preferred they did not, they decided to sell enough of their lower-paying common stocks, which when added to the cash value of the life insurance would give them $25,000 to invest elsewhere. This amount they invested in utility bonds paying 8½ percent, which increased their monthly income by approximately 10 percent.

CASE THREE

Mrs. Alice Little was a widow, age sixty-seven, with no children, with a $415,500 estate which she acquired herself working as a minor office employee in a five-and-dime store chain. Her husband died shortly after their marriage, and she had never married again. Most of her assets were in securities. She paid $25,714 for them, and forty years later she found to her amazement that they were worth $380,500, of which well over half was in S. S. Kresge common stock. Half of her original cost was inherited money; the balance she saved herself.

Her only heirs were two married nieces, each with four

children. She was very fond of both families, and they of her, visiting them frequently, although they both lived hundreds of miles away in another state. Her older niece was married to a successful businessman who was very well off. The younger niece was married to an engineer on a modest salary.

Mrs. Little was frugal. As a consequence she was willing to listen to suggestions on estate planning, even though she had no immediate heirs.

A CONFIDENTIAL INVENTORY OF ASSETS

name ____Mrs. Alice Little____ age__67__ birthday_____

wife's name_____ age_____ birthday_____

address_____ telephone_____

city_____ state_____ zip code_____

Social Security number_____

total value of the estate ___$415,500_____

1. names of children (include name of spouse if child
   is married) birth dates—residence
     No children
     Heirs—two married nieces, each with four children

2. names of grandchildren—birth dates—residence
   (if not living with parents)

3. last will and testament—date—where kept
     Yes—in safe deposit box—recent

4. your advisers: name—address—telephone
     lawyer
     life underwriter
     accountant
     investment representative

5. business address and telephone

Signature   date

Assets

	present value	ownership
1. checking accounts	$	
2. bank savings	4,000	
3. savings & loan associations	11,000	
4. credit unions		
5. securities (see page 4)	380,500	
6. mortgages and trust deeds		
7. notes receivable		
8. home	20,000	
9. other real estate		
10. life insurance death benefit		
11. business equity (see page 5)		
total assets	$ 415,500	

Liabilities

	amount	
1. mortgages or trust deeds	$	
(a) home		
(b) other		
2. notes payable		
3. other liabilities		
total liabilities	$ none	

total assets	$ 415,500
total liabilities	$ none
net value of the estate	$ 415,500

Current Income

salary or business income	$ _____
bank accounts	17
savings & loan	46
credit unions	_____
securities	600
mortgages and trust deeds	_____
real estate income	_____
notes	_____
securities	_____
company pensions	_____
other pensions	_____
Social Security	75
other	_____

total monthly income $ 738

Securities

common stocks

no. shares	company	cost basis	current value	date acquired
175	Allied Chemical	$ 2,719	$ 54,000	1934
100	Chesapeake & Ohio	5,141	6,500	'35–'44
800	General Electric	3,313	48,000	'34–'42
600	General Motors	4,070	50,400	1936
2,600	S. S. Kresge	6,500	190,600	1933
200	Standard of California	1,093	10,000	1941
300	Standard of New Jersey	2,878	21,000	'35–'37
	Totals	$25,714	$380,500	

COMMENTS BY THE INVESTMENT CORRELATOR

1. You have a serious death tax problem. On an estate of $415,500 the federal estate tax is over $92,000, and your state inheritance tax, because nieces are your heirs, is ap-

proximately $30,000. When administration expenses of $16,000 are added to these figures, the grand total of taxes and costs would be $138,000. As a single person, you have only one method of reducing these taxes, and it can be stated in just nine words—give part of your estate away before you die.

2. You have twelve heirs, when you consider that you have a niece, her husband, and their four children in each family. You can give $3,000 to each one of these twelve under your annual exclusion, or a total of $36,000, and another $30,000 under your lifetime exemption. You should do both, which will immediately transfer $66,000 to your heirs at a saving of $19,008 in federal estate taxes, and $9,240 more in state inheritance taxes.

3. Despite the tax savings in paragraph two, you would still have a $94,000 tax problem; therefore, you should decide each year if you want to give any more away under your current annual exclusion.

4. You need a new will. Your present one leaves your estate outright to your two nieces, share-and-share alike. In your new will you should still leave one half of your estate outright to your younger niece; but you should not compound an already serious death tax problem of your older niece and her husband, who are very well-to-do, by leaving this niece the other half. You should create a testamentary trust, with the trustee being instructed to pay the income during her lifetime to your niece. By the use of a trust, this one half will not be taxed again when your niece dies, but will go tax free to her children.

5. It has to be your decision as to which stock you should transfer to your heirs. The obvious asset, however, would be part of your Kresge stock, since this comprises over half of your estate. You should not give one half of your lifetime exemption, however, to your older niece, for once again she doesn't need it. You should give each of her four children $3,750 instead.

6. There will be no capital gains tax on the gift of this stock, but if the donees should sell, since there has been no intervening death, their cost basis is what you paid for the stock, not its value on the date of the gift. You should caution your heirs on this, because the cost basis of your Kresge stock is only $2.50 per share.

EXPLANATION OF THE COMMENTS BY THE CORRELATOR

1. In most cases people who have no children, whether married or not, are not interested in estate planning. They feel that their heirs are lucky to inherit at all, without leaving them more by determining how to reduce taxes and administration costs. Mrs. Little, however, felt differently. Her state inheritance taxes would amount to as much as $30,000 because she wasn't leaving her estate to children, but to nieces, whose individual exemption was only $2,000, and to whom tax rates on the first $100,000 were 6, 10, and 12 percent.

2. The testator admitted that a lifetime of frugality would not allow her to spend a good part of $400,000, that as a matter of fact she had come to the realization that at the age of sixty-seven she would probably spend very little of it during the balance of her lifetime. Sizable gifts would not, therefore, deprive her of anything, so it was time that she seriously considered giving part of her estate away. She agreed to transfer $66,000 to her heirs.

3. Mrs. Little also agreed that each year she would consider additional gifts. However, she did not want to become involved in the future with gift taxes, or with gift tax returns (as she was the first year because of her lifetime exemption), so in later years she would stay within her annual exclusion.

4 and 5. Alice Little was so intrigued by these suggestions that, before she saw her attorney about a new will, she paid a visit to her older niece and her husband and

told them what the correlator had suggested in regard to gifts and a trust. They wholeheartedly agreed, stating they had no idea she was worth so much money, and that they had actually at one time discussed the possibility of having to support her in her old age. The three of them had quite a good-natured laugh over this.

6. The older niece's husband was aware of the fact that the cost basis of the Kresge stock, if sold, would be the price that Mrs. Little paid for it. He was surprised, however, that her original cost was so low; he was glad to have this information for it would have a distinct bearing on any future sale by members of his family.

CASE FOUR

Mr. and Mrs. Virgil had been married for forty years and had amassed an estate of $600,000. Mr. Virgil had been retired for several years, having made his money in the building-material and hardware business, selling out for cash to a national concern at age sixty-five. He was now seventy-two, and so was his wife. When he retired, they invested $300,000 in a balanced mutual fund on a systematic payout of $1,500 per month, on the theory that, even though they lost the balance of the money, this would be enough capital and income, conservatively invested and managed, to make them comfortable for the rest of their lives.

Mr. and Mrs. Virgil wanted to conserve their estate for their only child, a daughter, who had four children and was married to a man on a low salary without very good prospects. They lived modestly in a small town, perfectly content with their friends and their daughter and her family who lived nearby.

They had an up-to-date will, with a testamentary trust to reduce estate and inheritance taxes.

A CONFIDENTIAL INVENTORY OF ASSETS

name _____Howard Virgil_____ age _72_ birthday _____
wife's name _____Alice Virgil_____ age _72_ birthday _____
address _____ telephone _____
city _____ state _____ zip code _____
Social Security number _____
total value of the estate _____$606,500_____

1. names of children (include name of spouse if child
    is married) birth dates—residence
      One married daughter

2. names of grandchildren—birth dates—residence
    (if not living with parents)
      Four grandchildren

3. last will and testament—date—where kept
      Yes -safe deposit box—up-to-date

4. your advisers: name—address—telephone
    lawyer
    life underwriter
    accountant
    investment representative

5. business address and telephone

Signature   date

Assets

	present value	ownership
1. checking accounts	$	
2. bank savings	43,000	
3. savings & loan associations	45,000	
4. credit unions		
5. securities (see page 4)	312,000	
6. mortgages and trust deeds	61,500	
7. notes receivable		
8. home	50,000	
9. other real estate	40,000	
10. life insurance death benefit	55,000	
11. business equity (see page 5)		
total assets	$ 606,500	

Liabilities

	amount
1. mortgage or trust deeds	$
(a) home	
(b) other	
2. notes payable	
3. other liabilities	
total liabilities	$ none

total assets	$ 606,500
total liabilities	$ none
net value of the estate	$ 606,500

Securities

common stocks

no. shares	company	current value
_____	Commonwealth Fund	$ __300,000__
__300__	General Electric ____	__12,000__
_____	_____	_____
_____	_____	_____
_____	_____	_____
_____	_____	_____

total value $ __312,000__

preferred stocks

no. shares	company	current value
_____	_____	_____
_____	_____	_____

total value $_____

industrial and municipal bonds

face amount	description	current value
_____	_____	_____
_____	_____	_____

total value $_____

government bonds

face amount	description	current value
_____	_____	_____
_____	_____	_____

total value $_____

total value in securities $_____

Current Income

bank accounts	$	200
savings & loan		190
credit unions		
mortgages and trust deeds		500
notes		
securities		50
mutual funds		1,500
real estate income		
salary or business income		
company pensions		
other pensions		
Social Security		300
annuities		
other		

total monthly income $ 2,740

COMMENTS BY THE INVESTMENT CORRELATOR

1. You should explore the advantages of a living trust with your attorney. You have a strong desire to avoid the publicity of probate, particularly since you live in a town of only 15,000 people, with no one aware of the fact that you are worth $600,000.

2. It should be understood that the establishment of a living trust will not further reduce your death taxes, for your estate will receive the same tax treatment as with your present testamentary trust.

3. You now have a bank trustee; you should name the surviving spouse instead. Both of you know how to manage money, and you have no management problems anyway. You have made up your minds, except for your securities and your 4-plex, to remain in a fixed-dollar position, and the bank could still be instructed to act as your

agent in collecting the mortgage payments, if that is desired. The survivor could feel very frustrated in having to deal with the bank as trustee on one half of the estate, possibly for a period of years.

4. As an only child, your daughter will some day own your entire estate according to your present will. You are very fond of your son-in-law, even though he is not a money maker. You should leave him $50,000 in your new will.

5. Although you have helped your daughter financially from time to time, you have no program of gifts. You should start transferring your assets to her now by giving her the $40,000 apartment house. It will relieve you of a management headache, give your daughter more income from the net rents (which she can use), and further reduce your death taxes.

6. You should take out two insurance policies, one for $100,000 on the life of your daughter, and one for $50,000 on the life of your son-in-law. The spouse who is not the insured should be the owner of each policy, and you should pay the premiums.

EXPLANATION OF THE COMMENTS
BY THE CORRELATOR

1. Mr. and Mrs. Virgil could not avoid probate by the two most common methods, joint tenancy or naming a beneficiary, because of their severe death tax problem on $600,000. Since they wanted to avoid the publicity of probate, their only recourse was a living trust.

2. Upon the death of the first married party, the tax treatment would be exactly the same as with a testamentary trust. The difference between the two trusts was solely in the avoidance of probate. Instead of the assets passing first through the hands of an executor, they would pass directly to the successor trustee, thereby avoiding

the probate process. The trustee would arrange for the appraisal of the estate and the payment of the taxes, but there would be no information of any kind recorded in the county courthouse.

3. There is nothing wrong with naming a bank as trustee, if there is a management problem or the heirs are financially incompetent. In this case there was nothing to manage, and the heirs didn't need any help in money matters.

4. The son-in-law should be left $50,000 so that he would also be financially independent. A penniless husband with a wife worth several hundred thousand dollars is inviting marital difficulties.

5. Despite the tax savings through a trust, death taxes were still a problem and should be further reduced by gifts.

6. The two insurance policies were taken out for two different reasons.

(a) The $100,000 whole life policy on the life of the daughter was for her death taxes some day when she came into possession of a net estate, after taxes and costs, of several hundred thousand dollars.

(b) Mr. and Mrs. Virgil could not see the need for a $50,000 insurance policy on the life of their son-in-law until it was explained to them by their insurance agent. Both parents were healthy, and therefore one of them could survive the other a long time, in which event the daughter would not inherit from them for many years. If her husband should die and his salary be gone, she would be hard-pressed to raise four children and put them through college without appealing to her folks for help. She would be financially independent of them, in raising the children, if she should receive the death proceeds on a $50,000 life insurance policy on her husband. Also, as a corollary benefit, Mr. and Mrs. Virgil would not be financially responsible for raising their grandchildren. When it was explained to them this way, they readily agreed to take out the insurance on their son-in-law.

(c) The premiums on both policies were substantial, and, of course, the son-in-law could not afford to pay them. The Virgils readily agreed to bear this expense while they were alive, and after that their daughter could afford to pay the premiums, for she would then own the estate. With the opposite spouse from the insured being the owner of each policy, the death proceeds would be estate tax free.

These four examples, then, demonstrate how previously discussed estate planning information can be used to improve both the living estate and the death estate of the property owner. By making up a Confidential Inventory of Assets beforehand and thinking about how you can improve your individual estate, you can better evaluate the suggestions that will be made when you call in your own financial planning team.

7

Estate Planning Principles

IN ADDITION to the testator's estate plan, embodied in his final legal document, there are estate planning principles which the property owner should use if he is going to obtain the maximum enjoyment from his living estate, and if his heirs are to be protected and have the maximum income from the estate they will inherit.

There are twelve estate planning principles which, when applicable, can be of immense help to the testator in his estate planning, for they provide simplicity, add cash flow, improve investments, further protect the heirs, and ensure future growth to protect the estate from the inroads of inflation. These twelve principles, not necessarily in the order of their importance, are as follows:

1. When retired, take an income from all of your assets. The habit of a lifetime of saving is hard to break. It is surprising how many people, for instance, will hold a substantial amount in E bonds, even though they are retired. E bonds do not pay a current income, for they automatically compound the return every six months. Retaining them after retirement is simply saving interest for your heirs. If you have quit working, now is the time for you to enjoy the income from all of your assets, for isn't this why you saved your estate in the first place—to enjoy it

now? Let's face the fact that life expectancy at age sixty-five is just fifteen years. The property owner should not, out of habit, continue to save money at this point in his life.

Mr. and Mrs. Stroop were in their late sixties and worth $300,000. They had too much in their checking account, by their own admission. When their investment representative asked them how much it was, they said it was about $50,000! They admitted, laughing at the correlator's surprise, that it had been in their checking account just a short time as the result of a sale of a piece of property. At his suggestion, they invested $40,000 in securities, holding them in a street name at the brokerage house. When asked if they wanted to receive the dividends, Mr. Stroop said they didn't need them, that they would probably just pile up in the bank; therefore, why not reinvest them and buy more shares? However, they took the dividends when their correlator pointed out to them the fundamental estate planning principle of receiving all of the income from their estate now that they were retired. If they did not spend all of the dividends, they could use their annual exclusion and give away the excess at the end of the year to their heirs.

Dr. Heller, a dentist and a bachelor, retired early at age sixty-two. He lived in a $70,000 home which, in a way, he couldn't afford; but he loved the old homestead and refused to sell. He had $10,000 in the bank and $100,000 in a balanced mutual fund from which he was taking only $300 per month; in addition he received $220 per month from Social Security. He maintained that he didn't need any more money, that he was getting by on his monthly income. His representative persuaded him to take $500 per month instead of $300 per month from his mutual fund, pointing out to him that, based on the doctor's average cost per share and the previous ten-year record of dividends and capital gains, the fund should be able to pay 6 percent. To the dentist's surprise, he did enjoy the extra income, living much better as a consequence. Sometimes it takes the objective thinking of an outsider to evaluate what you are doing with your estate, and particularly to persuade you, if this is necessary, to take an income on all of your assets when retired.

2. If you are receiving all of the income from your estate, but still need more money, spend part of your capital so you can live better. Don't hang on to all of your assets for dear life, just to leave them intact to someone else. The majority of retired people could increase their standard of living and enjoy their retirement years more if they would use this principle. It takes a lot of money to live well today. Assets totaling $60,000 invested at 5 percent produce $250 per month, which is not much income. So what should you do about it? You should spend part of your capital each year in order to increase your standard of living. Certainly a couple will live better if they spend $400 per month instead of $250 per month from $60,000. It is difficult for retired people to adopt this estate planning principle, because they feel they should spend only the income from their accumulated capital, for this way the money will always be there. This line of thinking, however, should be abandoned in today's economy of high taxes and inflation.

There are several ways that you can invest money, and simultaneously spend part of the capital and all of the income.

You can invest in a mutual fund and take a systematic payout. This method is widely used by thousands of mutual fund owners today. The shareholder simply elects what percentage he wants to receive, and the fund's disbursing agent sends him a check each month, selling a sufficient number of shares and fractional shares to equal that month's payment. The usual amount withdrawn is 6 percent, which on a $30,000 account would be $150 per month. A shareholder, however, who needs or wants more income than this usually takes 8 percent, or $200 per month. At this rate of return he would be selling $2,400 of his shares a year, and returning part of this to his fund account by reinvesting all of the dividends and the capital gains, if any, in shares at asset value, or no load. If the shareholder receives 8 percent in the form of twelve monthly checks by selling his shares, and reinvests 5 percent, he would be spending 3 percent of his capital. If all he spent was an average of 3 percent per year (more some years and less other years depending upon the investment performance of the fund) the account would last 33⅓ years. The average testator at age sixty-five will readily agree that he will probably have passed on to his reward long before he is ninety-eight years of age!

On a systematic payout from a mutual fund the testator does not have any kind of a contract where he must receive the percentage he has chosen. He may change the percentage, stop receiving checks altogether, or cash his account at any time for its then current value. If he should die, the remaining shares will be inherited by his heirs. Many property owners who are retired find this an ideal way to spend all of their income and part of their capital on a controlled basis. In addition, since a mutual fund is a cross section of securities managed by professionals, it is a way, too, of providing management and diversification for eventual heirs.

Another method used by some testators is to place a part of their estate in a mutual fund and deliberately dissipate it to zero in ten years. By using this method the shareholder receives a relatively high payout—in excess of 10 percent—with the guarantee that, regardless of the amount being sent to him by the fund each month, the shares in the account will not be dissipated before the ten years have elapsed. If $12,000 is placed in a safe deposit box, the property owner can spend 10 percent per year, or $100 per month, knowing that he cannot spend all the $12,000 in under a decade. If the $12,000 is invested instead, he can spend the same 10 percent, plus the dividends, plus the growth, if any, with this amount being actuarially computed by the fund each month.

Mr. and Mrs. Noyes owned a valuable commercial property on which they had unfortunately signed a low-income lease many years before. Since the time they had first signed the lease, the county in which they lived had become one of the fastest growing communities in the United States, causing the property to increase tremendously in value. They desperately needed more income, for the taxes had correspondingly increased. They wanted to retain the property, not only for themselves, but for their children as well, but they were going to lose it unless something was done. Fortunately they had some money which they could invest. Their correlator suggested they place this sum in a mutual fund and deliberately dissipate the account to zero, to coincide with the termination of the low-income lease. This saved the property for the heirs.

Mr. and Mrs. Grand, each age sixty-six, had a different problem. He had retired from running a small business because of chronic poor health, and his wife also was not well. Their total income, including Social Security, was only $450 per month. Fortunately their small home was free and clear, but they badly needed more income. Their investment representative tactfully inquired into their state of health, and when he found that neither one of them thought they would live too many years longer, he suggested that they invest $10,000 in a balanced mutual fund and take a payout to zero in ten years. When the survivor died about seven years later, the fund was paying at the rate of 17 percent per year, and during the preceding seven years Mr. and Mrs. Grand had the assurance that, regardless of the amount being paid to them, the fund's shares would not be exhausted in less than ten years.

Another method of spending capital, as well as income, is a fixed dollar annuity issued by an insurance company. This method should be used with care, with the complete understanding by the testator that he is now using an annuity principle based on life expectancy, with capital and income both being spent to zero. Even if a refund annuity is chosen, if the annuitant lives long enough to receive the return of his money, the heirs receive nothing.

Mrs. Hampton was a widow, age sixty-eight, who elected a lifetime income with no refund on $25,000, arranging for the first payment of $200 per month to start when she became seventy years of age. When her only daughter found out what her mother had bought, she called her investment representative, who was dual licensed, and asked his help in cashing the policy, feeling that the entire $25,000 could be refunded since the first monthly payment had yet to be paid. When she was told that, if her mother should die, the entire $25,000 would be gone because she had purchased a no refund policy, the daughter almost went through the roof of her modest home. Mrs. Hampton, however, was not disturbed, for the policy had been carefully explained to her, and she had what she wanted, which was a guarantee of $200 per month for life so she would be financially independent of her daughter. Fortunately for the daughter's peace of mind, her mother had another $25,000 which she was perfectly willing to invest in securities. By buying blue chip stocks and reinvesting all of the dividends, the correlator pointed out, the original $50,000 in the estate could probably in time be recovered.

Mrs. Hawks, a widow, and her spinster sister were both

retired and lived together out of financial necessity because Mrs. Hawks's sister was completely without funds. Mrs. Hawks was barely able to pay their bills, even though they lived frugally. When an investment representative was consulted to determine if the situation could be improved financially, he found out they were living so poorly because they were not receiving all of the income from Mrs. Hawks's assets, and, of course, they were not spending any of the capital, even though Mrs. Hawks's only heir was her sister. Her assets consisted of $100,000 in securities at an average return of 3 percent, $10,000 in cash in a checking account at no interest, and $25,000 in matured E bonds. When Mrs. Hawks was asked why she was trying to get along on $300 per month in dividends, she replied that she didn't know what else to do, for these were the assets her husband had left her, and she knew that if she spent only the income, the capital would still be there.

By using principles one and two, the correlator was able, with Mrs. Hawks's delighted consent, to alter the two sisters' way of life completely. He had Mrs. Hawks cash the $125,000 in securities and E bonds, and invest $110,-000 in 8 percent utility bonds, which gave her an income of $8,800 per year. He then suggested that she spend the remaining $15,000. Over the years since her husband had died her apartment had become so shabby she was ashamed of it, so she spent $5,000 refurnishing it, and with the other $10,000 she booked herself and her sister on a world cruise! This is a drastic example, but it clearly demonstrates how principles one and two can be used to an advantage by retired people.

3. Don't leave your heirs too much cash. "Easy come, easy go" is an old expression, but still a true one; as a consequence, cash will too often be spent. Your heirs are normally much younger and less experienced than you,

and therefore you should exercise your mature judgment and invest the money. If heirs are left a sound investment, with a good income, they are more inclined to leave it alone. If your heirs don't spend the cash, but through lack of experience make bad investments instead, the money will again be gone, and this way more tragically dissipated because no one will have actually enjoyed it. It is true that decisions are always difficult, and when you are older and retired, and are getting along on what you have, it is easier to do nothing; but in the best interests of conserving your estate, you should make the decision and invest your excess cash.

Mr. and Mrs. Hoving had accomplished the difficult task of accumulating an estate of $100,000, made particularly noteworthy because neither one of them had gone beyond the sixth grade in school, and Mr. Hoving had never made much money. They had one son, who unfortunately had not inherited his parents' acquisitive instincts, and in addition was a ne'er-do-well who couldn't seem to hold a job much longer than six months. Mr. and Mrs. Hoving's estate, outside of their home, was entirely in cash. Repeated efforts by both their bank's trust department and an investment representative to have them either invest the money or create a trust for their son's protection were to no avail. When the son eventually inherited the estate, it was all gone within two years. This seems almost impossible today with the wonderful laws, both federal and state, that protect the investor. However, since the son knew nothing about money, he was an easy prey for an unscrupulous real estate promoter. The scheme was underfinanced, and eventually was declared bankrupt, with the result that the boy lost in a very short time an estate that took a lifetime to build.

4. If you need more income, stop paying premiums on permanent life insurance when you are retired. Whole life

insurance has a cash value which should be used at retirement, when needed, in one of three ways, called nonforfeiture options by the insurance company.

(a) You should take the cash, as Mrs. Matthews decided to do in the last chapter, because your potential
widow would rather have both of you enjoy the lower
cash value together, than to have her enjoy the higher face
amount of the policy alone.

(b) Take the reduced paid-up option with the cash.
This way a policy for a lesser sum than the face amount
will be in force for life; however, you will stop paying
premiums. On a whole life policy for $10,000 taken out
at age thirty-five, the reduced paid-up policy would have
a death benefit of approximately $7,500.

(c) Take the extended term option with the cash. By
this method the entire face amount of the policy will be
in force for a certain number of years and days, with no
further premium payments. In our typical policy for $10,-
000 at issue age thirty-five, the full amount of the policy
would be in force at age sixty-five for almost thirteen
years. At age seventy-eight, however, the insurance would
terminate.

If your decision is not to use option one and take the
cash, you would elect option two if your health were excellent, but option three if it were not. In most states,
when using the last two options, the remaining cash value
in the policy is still available if you change your mind. In
any event, no matter which of the three options is used
in regard to the cash, the property owner's income is increased by the amount of the saved premiums. The death
estate, however, would be reduced by using options one
or two, and by the full amount of the policy by using
option three if the insured were to outlive the extended
term insurance.

Mr. and Mrs. Roosa were retired, trying to get along on

$500 per month, and having a difficult time of it, because they were living in one of the highest cost-of-living areas in the United States. Mr. Roosa was still paying premiums on three small whole life policies totaling $13,000. When he called in his life underwriter to see what could be done, the agent suggested that they write the three insurance companies involved for the necessary information. They found out that the combined cash value of the policies was $10,000, that the reduced paid-up amount was $11,400, and that the extended term insurance would last for twelve years. Since Mr. Roosa's health was apparently excellent, the extended term insurance for the full $13,000 was ruled out. The reduced paid-up insurance was high, and would not mean much of a loss to Mrs. Roosa if her husband should die, and in addition no further premium payments would be necessary. After much discussion, however, Mrs. Roosa decided to take the cash. She fully understood that if her husband should die, she would lose the difference between the cash value of the three policies and the face amount, or $3,000. But she decided they would rather enjoy the income on $10,000 now, rather than for her to enjoy the $13,000 alone. So they cashed the policies, only to have Mr. Roosa drop dead of a heart attack ninety days later; but the widow did not make one complaint to her life underwriter, for she had fully understood her decision.

5. If income real estate is presenting such a management problem that you cannot retire and enjoy your golden years, you should sell it and invest the money elsewhere. Real estate has been an excellent estate building vehicle for a great many people; however, in too many cases today it is not a good retirement investment, and the reason for it stems from the times. Retired people who no longer want the management headache, or who are physically incapable of taking care of real estate them-

selves, cannot call in a plumber or a painter every time an apartment has to be redecorated or a leaky faucet repaired, for the high cost of these services will reduce their net income to a very low figure indeed. It might be advisable, under these circumstances, to review your real estate, sell it, and invest the money where it does not require your personal daily attention. You should realize that you are not truly retired if you are still managing property.

Mr. and Mrs. Beard owned a sixteen-unit apartment house in a metropolitan area. They had purchased it many years before with a small down payment, and after years of effort had succeeded in paying off the mortgage. Mr. Beard was now sixty-seven years old and had a bad back, which his doctor kept reminding him might be improved if he would move to a warmer climate. They lived in one of the sixteen apartments in the building and managed the property themselves, very pleased that some day their only son would inherit a fine piece of residential real estate. With considerable persuasion on his part, a friend succeeded in arranging an appointment with an investment correlator. The representative suggested, as one of his recommendations, that Mr. and Mrs. Beard, now that they had reached normal retirement age, should spend the income on a $20,000 investment they owned rather than reinvest the dividends, which, based upon the record of their account, would give them about $1,200 per year.

"But if we received the money," Mr. Beard objected, "we couldn't spend it."

The correlator was surprised. "Why not?" he asked.

"Because we are tied down to this apartment house seven days a week, that's why," Mr. Beard replied. "We don't have time to spend money. As a matter of fact, I shouldn't be talking to you right now, because if I don't repair the lock to the hall door on apartment fourteen before dark, that spinster lady will move out!"

Mr. and Mrs. Beard estimated that their building was worth $160,000. His health was poor, and his doctor kept urging him to move to a warmer climate. They had $20,000 in securities, $10,000 in cash, a son who was married and doing well, and who had no interest whatsoever in owning or managing an apartment house. Yet Mr. Beard was still working seven days a week! After two years of discussing it, they finally sold their apartment house for a $40,000 down payment, taking back a $120,000 mortgage at 6 percent. By investing the down payment, they now had $60,000 in securities and a $120,000 first mortgage on an excellent piece of property, giving them an income of over $10,000 per year, plus Social Security. They moved to a warmer climate, and Mr. Beard stopped working. His back improved, and they started enjoying their retirement years.

6. If you own securities and you have inexperienced heirs, either create a bank trust or start training them immediately how to manage your investments. It is surprising how different your stocks and bonds look to you when viewed as being in the hands of your heirs. Many a testator will have to admit that the future management of his investment portfolio is a dim prospect indeed. If this is true, in your case, you had better create a testamentary bank trust; or better yet, transfer some of your securities to your heirs and observe how well they handle them. They may surprise you, and if they do, or if they learn under your direction, then a trust will not be necessary, and they can inherit the investment outright, which is the best possible solution.

7. Don't own too many assets. They present a management problem to you in your living estate, and extra work

for your executor in your death estate. A testator simply cannot keep effective track of, say, thirty different securities. If you will review them with your broker, you should be able to reduce your portfolio to a manageable number of ten or twelve stocks and bonds that meet your overall objective, and this might even improve your investment results as well.

Mr. Falk owned over forty stocks and bonds, three mutual funds, several parcels of real estate, and his own business. He was successful and had amassed a sizable estate. Since his results had been excellent, he felt that he was doing a good job of managing his living estate, until his investment representative complained to him that over the past two or three years he had not made one investment decision. Mr. Falk was so busy keeping track of what he owned, he no longer had time to improve his portfolio, or to follow through on several excellent suggestions that had been made by his advisers. When this was pointed out to him, and particularly when he realized the unnecessary work that he was presenting to his executor, with the concomitant long delay in settling his estate, he drastically trimmed his investment portfolio.

8. Don't keep assets that have a small monetary value. They simply clutter up your living estate and your death estate. Five shares of a $5 stock are worth $25.00, and one matured E bond for which you paid $75 is now worth $100. Such small assets are hardly worth keeping in your estate, yet people do retain them. They should be sold and the money put in a bank—for the same reasons, actually, as in rule number seven: they present an unnecessary management problem to both you and your executor. Small assets that are acquired over a lifetime are often retained through sheer inertia on the part of the property owner, and frequently he has forgotten how he happened to acquire them in the first place.

9. Be chary of making gifts. You should enjoy your living estate, and remember that any taxes saved by making gifts benefit only your death estate and your heirs. Gifts should be made where there is a serious death tax problem that cannot be sufficiently reduced by creating a trust, but the donor should always be sure that he is not hurt financially in any way. He should at all times have enough capital and income to remain financially independent of his heirs.

Mrs. House, a widow, was well-to-do with an only son who was an auditor. She owned sizable real estate holdings which, of course, made her completely independent. Over the course of several years, her auditor son persuaded her gradually to dispose of all of her property and invest the money in securities in his name only, in order to avoid probate and to save death taxes. Eventually he placed her in a retirement home, at the relatively young age of sixty, after which he condescended to see her only once or twice a year. Mrs. House, while not in want, became a very unhappy and lonely woman. She should have made substantial gifts, for she was worth that kind of money; but she should not have reduced herself to a point of financial dependence upon her son.

10. Don't make yourself financially responsible for your grandchildren. You don't have to put yourself in this position if your son or son-in-law is insurable. If your son-in-law, for instance, does not believe in life insurance and refuses, therefore, as the breadwinner to protect his young family through an adequate life insurance program, you should take out the insurance on his life and pay the premiums. Life insurance is the only way that a sizable estate can be created for a widow and dependent children where the head of the family hasn't had the time or the inclination to save. You may not object to acting as a baby sitter if your son-in-law should die, but you shouldn't put

yourself in the position of reducing your living estate in order to help your daughter out financially or send your grandchildren through college. A $100,000 reducing term policy for twenty years at a premium of around $30 per month (depending upon the age of the insured) is a lot easier to pay than $100,000 in cash.

11. Even a small estate can benefit from estate planning. Testators and heirs alike, through lack of information, worry about probate, taxes, delay, and costs, even though they may be nonexistent.

Mrs. Thurber was seventy-four, a widow with two married daughters. Her total estate consisted of $24,000 in a savings and loan account. Her two daughters and their husbands, and Mrs. Thurber, became concerned as to what was going to happen to her estate when she was gone. They had read about probate in their local newspaper, and a recent account of the taxes and costs involved triggered them into asking for a conference with an investment representative who was experienced in estate planning.

He met with all five of them one afternoon, with everyone crowded around the kitchen table of Mrs. Thurber's modest rented apartment. They were worried about many things—probate, lawyers' fees, death taxes, delay—but mainly they were concerned that there would be nothing left of the $24,000 after Mrs. Thurber was gone. The correlator was able to allay their fears by giving them the information they so badly needed. He told them that a will could be drawn for a small fee, but this would not be necessary if they followed his suggestions and used both a beneficiary and joint tenancy form of ownership in order to avoid probate.

With everyone's enthusiastic consent, he placed $20,000 in two separate $10,000 mutual fund accounts, with each daughter as a beneficiary, giving Mrs. Thurber a flat 6 percent return from each account in the form of a monthly check. The $4,000 that remained in the savings and loan account he placed in joint tenancy with Mrs. Thurber and the older daughter, after satisfying himself that this was a closely knit family, with everyone having complete trust in the others. Upon Mrs. Thurber's death, each fund account would be transferred to the appropriate daughter, and the older child would divide what was left of the savings and loan account with her sister after paying final expenses.

The correlator showed them from his tax tables that there would be no federal estate tax because of the $60,000 exemption against every estate, and that state inheritance taxes, because of a $5,000 exemption for each daughter, and then a 3 percent rate, would be only $420. The suggestions were finalized, as far as Mrs. Thurber was concerned, when the representative pointed out to her that the group of funds in which she would be invested had a free transfer privilege, so that upon her death each daughter could transfer her account to an all common stock fund (from the balanced fund that she would own) and that within ten years—going by past performance, and if the dividends and capital gains were compounded, each daughter would have twice what she left them. The conference broke up with everybody in the family tremendously relieved, and with a sincere thanks to the correlator for his information and suggestions.

In addition to these eleven estate planning principles, there are fundamental rules to follow that have been brought out in the preceding six chapters, which should be emphasized here in order for the testator to arrive at some broad conclusions.

It must be understood by everyone who saves money that two estates are built during a lifetime—a living estate and a death estate. Too often the living estate receives all of the attention, and the death estate receives none, which is a mistake, for because of it a great deal of property and future family security are sacrificed when property owners die. People just do not know about the complex problems that are created when they transfer their property to their heirs, but they should learn about them, so that those who take over from them won't feel that, in their case at least, probate was the most expensive undertaking establishment in the world.

It is true that your assets cannot be left intact to someone else. Death creates debts that did not exist before, and these first mortgage demands of death taxes and administration costs must be met before the heirs can inherit anything. The long delay of probate can be very frustrating, and when your assets are listed down to the last penny as a matter of public record, the resulting lack of privacy can be nerve-racking, at least for many people. You can avoid probate if you like, and how you can avoid it is simply a matter of correct ownership—joint tenancy with right of survivorship, naming a beneficiary, or creating a living trust, the last one being used only where large estates are involved because of the death-tax problem.

Everyone should have a will drawn by a competent attorney, even though, when joint tenancy is used, the will is ignored upon the first death; and on large estates, a trust has to be created as well if death taxes are to be reduced.

Only proven experts should comprise your financial planning team, but when making your decisions based upon their advice, don't take the attitude that you are going to live forever. Be chary of gifts, yes, for your own protection and your financial independence, but remember, too, that there is a lot of truth in the old cliché that nobody lives longer than rich relatives. If this is true, let the younger generation enjoy now some of the fruits of your lifetime of labor.

Once you have drawn your estate plan, don't mistakenly feel that the job has been done. Resolve to review your plan periodically, particularly when there has been a marriage, a death, or a birth in your family.

And remember that estate planning is a must if you are to transfer your assets to your heirs with the least trouble and expense.

Appendix Commentary

THE FEDERAL Estate Tax Return is the fundamental document to be filed in the settlement of all estates in excess of $60,000. By completing this return your executor, administrator, or trustee can determine the amount of your taxable estate. The schedules on which he lists your assets and takes your allowable deductions are not only simple, but opposite the schedules are clear and concise instructions on how to fill them out. Any testator who will take the trouble to become acquainted with this return will be much better equipped to make decisions in regard to his own estate planning. General information is listed on pages 3 and 5. Schedules A through I list the assets in the estate, and schedules J through N the allowable deductions. Schedule O provides a simple recapitulation of these schedules, and from this, in just five lines, the taxable estate can be determined from Schedule P. Page 40, the last page, provides tables from which to compute the estate tax, which is entered on line 1, page one.

The tax tables on page 40 can be a confusing part of the return. This is because Table A has already taken into consideration the $60,000 exemption, and so has Table B. For example, Table A states that if the taxable estate is $100,000 the estate tax is $20,700; while Table B states that if the taxable estate is $100,000, the maximum credit for state death taxes is $400 on $90,000, plus 1.6 percent of the excess over this amount. This results in an estate actually valued at $160,-000 being taxed for $20,700, minus a state death tax credit of $540, or for a net of $20,140. It is suggested that the reader refer to the estate tax table in Chapter Two which shows on one line that a total estate of $160,000 is taxed for $20,140.

The result is the same without the reader being confused by Tables A and B, page 40. This is because the table in Chapter Two includes the entire estate (without first deducting the $60,000 exemption) and is also automatically adjusted to include the state death tax credit.

Because of its importance, the Federal Estate Tax Return should be reviewed carefully in its entirety by every testator. Copies are available at most banks.

STATE INHERITANCE TAX RETURNS

Most states impose a death tax, and therefore the testator should be familiar with the inheritance tax return in the state in which he is domiciled. Brief information is given on four states: California, New York, Pennsylvania, and Texas. Sixty million people, which is approximately three tenths of the population of the United States, live in these four states. California and New York are the most populous, each with twenty million people; also, California is a community property state while New York is not. Pennsylvania was chosen as a demonstration of high tax rates, and Texas because it is an example of how death taxes are imposed in a community property state other than California.

State returns tend to follow the format of the Federal Estate Tax Return. The exemptions allowed and the tax rates, however, are entirely different. The various states tax the heirs, not the deceased; therefore, most states separate heirs by classes, with Class A having the highest exemption and the lowest death-tax bracket. Class A heirs are usually the spouse, ascendants and descendants, brothers and sisters, and sons-in-law and daughters-in-law of the deceased. Class B are all other heirs. Some states, however, like Texas, also have Classes C, D, and E, with the last class being strangers to the testator. Some states do not tax the surviving spouse at all; others do, but give her a substantial exemption. The usual exemption for Class A heirs, others than the spouse, is $5,000, and after that they are taxed all the way from 1 percent to 6 percent on the first $100,000.

The other main difference between federal and state death tax returns is the taxation of life insurance. Usually there is an exemption of the first $50,000 to $100,000 payable to named beneficiaries. However, if the death benefit is made payable to the estate most states will tax the entire amount. At the other extreme, for example, is Pennsylvania which does not tax life insurance at all, no matter to whom it is paid.

The testator is urged to consult the death tax laws of the state in which he is domiciled. If a letter is written to that department in your state that has jurisdiction, you should receive a reply at no cost, enclosing a digest of the inheritance tax laws of your state, the accompanying instructions, and the necessary filing forms.

THE U. S. QUARTERLY GIFT TAX RETURN

Gifts play an important part in estate planning of large estates. When gifts are made that exceed the $3,000 annual exclusion, a federal gift tax return has to be filed, even though no gift tax is owed, because the Internal Revenue Service wants to know when your $30,000 lifetime exemption has been exhausted. It is well for the property owner to become acquainted with this form and the accompanying instructions. It should be remembered that the three-year contemplation of death rule applies to all gifts that exceed the annual exclusion. State gift taxes are also imposed by many states, but these vary so widely the testator should consult the state gift tax law, if any, of the state in which he is domiciled.

FORM **706** (Rev. Jan. 1966) **U. S. TREASURY DEPARTMENT** Internal Revenue Service	**UNITED STATES** **ESTATE TAX RETURN** Estates of nonresidents not citizens of the United States may generally file on Form 706NA instead of this form. For details see page 39.	**DO NOT WRITE IN SPACE BELOW** Date received

Decedent's first name and middle initial	Decedent's last name

Decedent's social security number	Employer identification number for estate

Date of death	Citizenship (nationality) at time of death

Residence (domicile) at time of death

Did the decedent die testate? ☐ Yes ☐ No	Were letters testamentary or of administration granted for this estate? ☐ Yes ☐ No	Date granted

Case No.	Name of court	Location of court

To whom granted? (Designate whether executor, executrix, administrator, or administratrix. Explain if different from the person or persons filing return)

NAME	DESIGNATION	ADDRESS (Number, street, city, State, and Postal ZIP code)

COMPUTATION OF TAX
(See instructions on page 38)

Taxable estate (Item 5, Schedule P, or Item 9, Schedule Q, whichever is applicable) . . . . $_____

PART I

1. Gross estate tax (use table A, page 40). . . . . $_____
2. Credit for State death taxes (use Table B, page 40) . . . .
3. Gross estate tax less credit for State death taxes (item 1 minus item 2). This is the net amount payable unless credit for Federal gift taxes, tax on prior transfers, or foreign death taxes is claimed in Part II. . . . . $_____

PART II

4. Credit for Federal gift taxes. . . . . $_____
5. Credit for tax on prior transfers. . . . .
6. Credit for foreign death taxes. . . . .
7. Total of credits under Part II (total of items 4, 5, and 6). . . . .
8. Net estate tax payable (item 3 minus item 7). . . . . $

(SPACE FOR USE OF INTERNAL REVENUE SERVICE)

	Assessments				Payments		
Type of assessment (tax, interest, etc.)	Amount	List	Page	Line	Date	Principal	Interest
	$					$	$

DETERMINATION BY INTERNAL REVENUE SERVICE

GENERAL INFORMATION

1. Address of decedent at time of death (Number, street, city, State, and Postal ZIP code)

2. State in which domiciled at time of death

3. Year in which this domicile was established

4. Place of death

5. Cause of death

6. Length of last illness

7. Decedent's physicians

NAMES	ADDRESSES (Number, street, city, State, and Postal ZIP code)

8. If decedent was confined in a hospital during his last illness or within 3 years prior to his death, give name and address of hospital

9a. Date of birth

9b. Place of birth (City and State or country, if other than United States)

10a. Business or occupation

10b. If retired, state former business or occupation

10c. Business name

10d. Decedent's employer identification number, if any

10e. Business address (Number, street, city, State, and Postal ZIP code)

11. Marital status of decedent at date of death

☐ Married   ☐ Single   ☐ Legally separated   ☐ Widow or Widower   ☐ Divorced

12a. Name of surviving husband or wife

12b. Social security number of surviving husband or wife

12c. Date of marriage to surviving husband or wife

12d. Domicile at date of marriage to surviving husband or wife

13a. If decedent was a widow or widower, give name of deceased husband or wife

13b. Date of death of deceased husband or w

14. Individuals who receive benefits from the estate (do not include charitable beneficiaries shown in Schedule N or any heir receiving l than $1,000)

Name.—Enter the name of each individual who receives benefits from the estate directly as an heir, next-of-kin, devisee or legatee or indirectly (for example, as beneficiary of a trust, shareholder of a corporation or partner of a partnership which is an heir, etc.).

Social Security Number.—If the individual has no social security number, use his taxpayer account number.

Age.—On the date of the decedent's death.

Relationship.—Include relationships by blood, marriage, or adoption or indicate NONE.

Amount.—Value all interests on the date of death or the altern valuation date, whichever is used for estate tax purposes. The terest of each beneficiary should be valued in the same manner it would be valued for estate or gift tax purposes. Where prec values cannot readily be determined, a reasonable approximat should be entered. The sum of the values of the interests of unborn or otherwise unascertainable beneficiaries should be sho on the last line (all unascertainable beneficiaries).

Name	Social Security Number	Age	Relationship to Decedent	Amount

All unascertainable beneficiaries..

ESTATE OF _____   Page

GENERAL INFORMATION—Continued

a. Did the decedent at date of death own property in any State or country other than that of his last domicile?
If "Yes," state place of ancillary probate proceedings ☐ Yes ☐ No

b. Name of ancillary administrator or executor

c. Address of ancillary administrator or executor (Number, street, city, State, and Postal ZIP code)

a. Did the decedent at the time of his death have a safe deposit box held either alone or in the joint names of himself and another?
If "Yes," state location ☐ Yes ☐ No

b. If held jointly, give the name of the joint depositor

c. Relationship of joint depositor to decedent

d. If the decedent had a safe deposit box at the time of his death, indicate by schedule and item number under what schedules in this return the contents are listed

e. If any of the contents of the safe deposit box are omitted from the schedules, explain fully why omitted

. Did the undersigned person or persons filing return make diligent and careful search for property of every kind left by the decedent? ☐ Yes ☐ No

. Did the same undersigned make diligent and careful search for information as to any transfers (other than outright transfers not in trust) of the value of $5,000 or more made by the decedent during his lifetime without an adequate and full consideration in money or money's worth? ☐ Yes ☐ No

. Did the same undersigned make diligent and careful search for the existence of any trusts created by the decedent during his lifetime or any trusts created by other persons under which the decedent possessed any power, beneficial interest, or trusteeship? ☐ Yes ☐ No

a. Name of attorney representing estate, if any

b. Address (Number, street, city, State, and Postal ZIP code) | **20c.** Telephone No.

ALTERNATE VALUATION

hese instructions apply only if alternate valuation is elected. For further information on this subject, see **General Instructions on page 4**)

. An election to have the gross estate of the decedent valued as of the alternate date or dates is made by entering a check mark in the box set forth below.
The executor elects to have the gross estate of this decedent valued in accordance with values as of a date or dates subsequent to the decedent's death as authorized by section 2032 of the Code.

TATE OF --- Page 5

SCHEDULE O

RECAPITULATION

Sched-ule	Gross estate	Alternate value	Value at date of dea
A	Real estate	$	$
B	Stocks and bonds		
C	Mortgages, notes, and cash		
D	Insurance		
E	Jointly owned property		
F	Other miscellaneous property		
G	Transfers during decedent's life		
H	Powers of appointment		
I	Annuities		
	TOTAL GROSS ESTATE	$	$

Sched-ule	Deductions	Amount
J	1. Funeral expenses and expenses incurred in administering property subject to claims	$
K	2. Debts of decedent	
K	3. Mortgages and liens	
	4. Total deductions (Items 1 thru 3)	$
	5. **NET TAXABLE ESTATE** (TO BE DISTRIBUTED UNDER SCHEDULE R, PAGE 27)	$

ESTATE OF

DECLARATION

Under penalty of perjury, I declare that this return, including any accompanying statements, has been examined by me, and s, to the best of my knowledge and belief, a true, correct, and complete return, made in good faith pursuant to the Internal tevenue Code and the regulations thereunder.

| ------------ | -------------------------------------- | ------------------------------- |
| (Date) | (Signature of executor, administrator, etc.) | (Address) |

DECLARATION OF ATTORNEY OR AGENT PREPARING RETURN

Under penalties of perjury, I declare that I prepared this return for the person or persons whose signature(s) appear(s) above nd that this return, including any accompanying schedules and statements, is, to the best of my knowledge and belief, a true, correct nd complete return based on all the information relating to the matters required to be reported in this return of which I have any nowledge.

| ------------ | -------------------------------------- | ------------------------------- |
| (Date) | (Signature of preparer (individual or firm) other than executor, administrator, etc.) | (Address) |

TABLE A

COMPUTATION OF GROSS ESTATE TAX

Taxable estate equal to or more than—	Taxable estate less than—	Tax on amount in column (1)	Rate of tax on excess over amount in column (1)
(1)	(2)	(3)	(4)
			(Percent)
0	$5, 000	0	3
$5, 000	10, 000	$150	7
10, 000	20, 000	500	11
20, 000	30, 000	1, 600	14
30, 000	40, 000	3, 000	18
40, 000	50, 000	4, 800	22
50, 000	60, 000	7, 000	25
60, 000	100, 000	9, 500	28
100, 000	250, 000	20, 700	30
250, 000	500, 000	65, 700	32
500, 000	750, 000	145, 700	35
750, 000	1, 000, 000	233, 200	37
1, 000, 000	1, 250, 000	325, 700	39
1, 250, 000	1, 500, 000	423, 200	42
1, 500, 000	2, 000, 000	528, 200	45
2, 000, 000	2, 500, 000	753, 200	49
2, 500, 000	3, 000, 000	998, 200	53
3, 000, 000	3, 500, 000	1, 263, 200	56
3, 500, 000	4, 000, 000	1, 543, 200	59
4, 000, 000	5, 000, 000	1, 838, 200	63
5, 000, 000	6, 000, 000	2, 468, 200	67
6, 000, 000	7, 000, 000	3, 138, 200	70
7, 000, 000	8, 000, 000	3, 838, 200	73
8, 000, 000	10, 000, 000	4, 568, 200	76
10, 000, 000	------------	6, 088, 200	77

TABLE B

COMPUTATION OF MAXIMUM CREDIT FOR STATE DEATH TAXES

Taxable estate equal to or more than—	Taxable estate less than—	Credit on amount in column (1)	Rate of credit on excess over amount in column (1)
(1)	(2)	(3)	(4)
			(Percent)
0	$40, 000	0	None
$40, 000	90, 000	0	0. 8
90, 000	140, 000	$400	1. 6
140, 000	240, 000	1, 200	2. 4
240, 000	440, 000	3, 600	3. 2
440, 000	640, 000	10, 000	4. 0
640, 000	840, 000	18, 000	4. 8
840, 000	1, 040, 000	27, 600	5. 6
1, 040, 000	1, 540, 000	38, 800	6. 4
1, 540, 000	2, 040, 000	70, 800	7. 2
2, 040, 000	2, 540, 000	106, 800	8. 0
2, 540, 000	3, 040, 000	146, 800	8. 8
3, 040, 000	3, 540, 000	190, 800	9. 6
3, 540, 000	4, 040, 000	238, 800	10. 4
4, 040, 000	5, 040, 000	290, 800	11. 2
5, 040, 000	6, 040, 000	402, 800	12. 0
6, 040, 000	7, 040, 000	522, 800	12. 8
7, 040, 000	8, 040, 000	650, 800	13. 6
8, 040, 000	9, 040, 000	786, 800	14. 4
9, 040, 000	10, 040, 000	930, 800	15. 2
10, 040, 000	------------	1, 082, 800	16. 0

ESTATE OF _____

STATE OF CALIFORNIA

STATE CONTROLLER'S OFFICE
INHERITANCE AND GIFT TAX DIVISION

INHERITANCE TAX INSTRUCTIONS

These instructions have been prepared for the purpose of assisting in the proper completion of the Inheritance Tax Declaration, Form IT-22, and the Marital Property Declaration, Form IT-3. The declarations and other information submitted therewith are strictly confidential and cannot be divulged except to local, state or federal tax officials or as may be necessary for the enforcement of the Inheritance Tax Law.

1. General Instruction

All questions must be answered except as indicated. If the space furnished is not sufficient, additional sheets should be attached, making reference to the question being answered. The Inheritance Tax Declaration, Form IT-22, may be completed by anyone having a general knowledge of the decedent and his financial affairs. The Marital Property Declaration, Form IT-3, should normally be completed by the surviving spouse.

The forms are designed so that they may be signed under penalty of perjury. However, since the "penalty of perjury" provision is not effective unless executed within the State of California, the forms must be notarized if executed outside California in order to be acceptable.

A. Inheritance Tax Declaration, Form IT-22

The California death tax is an inheritance tax. As such, it is levied on the right of each beneficiary to take (see rate chart at end of instructions). It applies equally to inheritances and transfers made in lieu of inheritances such as joint tenancies, life estates, gifts in contemplation of death, certain trusts, etc.

This form is designed to provide the basic information from which the inheritance tax can be determined. In order to avoid unnecessary correspondence, delays and the possibility of an unfavorable interpretation, it is important to answer all questions completely and clearly.

The following documents are generally required to be submitted with the Inheritance Tax Declaration, form IT-22:

(a) *Will and Codicils*. Legible copies of decedent's last will and codicils thereto whether or not there is to be a probate proceeding.

(b) *Trust documents, etc.* See questions 6 (b), (c), (d).

(c) *Blood tracing, etc.* See question 7 (a).

(d) *Deeds or deed information*. See Instruction 7 (a).

(e) *County real estate tax bills*. See Instruction 8 (c).

2. When Inheritance Tax Declaration Form IT-22, Required

(a) *Resident Decedents*. When a person who was residing in California at the date of death had interest in any type of property or who, during lifetime transferred by gift any property.

(b) *Nonresident Decedents*. When a person who was not residing in California at the date of death had an interest in any tangible personal or real property located in California or who, during lifetime transferred by gift any such property.

(c) *Estate Administered in California*. In all cases where there is a court proceeding in California to probate an estate, terminate a joint tenancy or life estate, or to determine inheritance tax.

3. Time and Place for Filing

The process of determining the amount of tax due cannot begin until the required forms have been filed. The forms must be filed with the Inheritance Tax Appraiser, if one has been appointed, otherwise with the nearest office of the State Controller, Division of Inheritance and Gift Tax. There is no penalty for late filing. However, interest is due at the rate of 6% per annum on any unpaid tax beginning two years after the date of death. A 5% discount is allowed against the inheritance tax when it is paid within six months of the date of death.

4. Safe Deposit Boxes (Question 3)

Every safe deposit box *must* be examined by the County Treasurer of the county in which it is located. If the box has not been examined by the County Treasurer, arrangements should promptly be made to do so. If the box was entered after death and prior to examination by the County Treasurer, form IT-34 "Declaration Re Entry" must accompany the Inheritance Tax Declaration, Form IT-22.

5. Proof of Relationship to Decedent (Questions 4a, 7a, 8a, 9c, 10b)

The amount of exemption and the rate of tax depend upon relationship to the decedent (see rate chart at end of instructions). Beneficiaries not related to the decedent by blood other than spouse, son-in-law, daughter-in-law, adopted or mutually acknowledged child or issue of same, should be designated as "stranger," even though they may be related by marriage or may have been close friends of the decedent.

6. Previously Taxed Property (Question 7e)

Where the decedent acquired, within five years of his death, assets taxed to him as a transfer from a spouse, lineal issue, lineal ancestors, adopted child or adopted child of lineal issue, a previously taxed property credit may be allowable against the inheritance tax. (Revenue and Taxation Code, Section 14071)

7. Description of Assets (Questions 4a, 10b, 13)

A complete description of each asset should be provided.

(a) *Real Estate.* Describe and identify so that it may be readily located for inspection and valuation. If a Certificate of Release of Inheritance Tax Lien is desired, it is necessary to submit the date of the deed, date of recordation and book and page number of record. This may be done by a separate attachment or by submitting a copy of the deed which includes the recording information stamped on the deed by the County Recorder.

(b) *Promissory Notes.* State (1) name of maker, (2) date of note, (3) face value, (4) rate of interest, (5) unpaid balance at date of death (principal and interest), and (6) names of payees (beneficiaries) and manner in which title to note held. If note was secured by a trust deed or mortgage, give brief description of the property securing same.

(c) *Bank, Checking, Savings and Certificate Accounts.* State name and branch of bank or savings institution, account number and nature of account (checking, savings, time deposit, etc.).

(d) *Stocks.* State exact name of corporation, number of shares and class or series.

(e) *Bonds.* State quantity and denomination, name of obligor, kind of bond, date of maturity, interest rate and interest due dates. For U.S. Savings Bonds also state year and month of purchase.

(f) *Miscellaneous Assets.* Jewelry, furs, automobiles, art objects, livestock, leaseholds, judgments, growing crops, etc. should be described with sufficient precision to readily permit identification. General descriptions are not sufficient.

(g) *Fractional Interests.* If decedent was the owner of an undivided (fractional) interest in any asset as a co-tenant with any other person(s) state (1) name of co-tenant(s), (2) relationship of co-tenant(s), if any, to decedent, (3) the percentage or fraction of each interest, and (4) source from which the co-tenant(s) acquired his interest.

8. Value of Assets (Questions 4a, 10b, 13)

The value to be reported is the fair market value as of the date of death, except for the third column of Question 10b which asks for the date of transfer value.

(a) *Bank, Checking, Savings, Certificate Accounts.* The balance including any unposted interest. This amount can be verified with the bank or savings institution.

(b) *Promissory Notes.* The outstanding balance, including any accrued interest, should be shown. This amount is normally available from the payment schedule or book or from the collection agent if one has been used.

(c) *Real Property.* The fair market value of the property, not just the equity should be shown. Any encumbrance should be listed as a deduction in Question 15. Unless recently purchased or sold, the value shown should be the declarant's own opinion of value. *In all cases where no Inheritance Tax Appraiser has been appointed, a copy of the county property tax bill for the year of death or as close thereto as possible should be attached for each parcel of property.*

(d) *Stocks, Bonds, Other Securities.* The value of securities traded on the open market can be ascertained from any reputable stock broker, if not readily available in the newspapers. For closely held securities (family corporations, etc.), copies of the income statements and balance sheets for the three years immediately preceding death should be furnished.

(e) *Miscellaneous Assets.* The declarant's opinion (and in appropriate cases an expert's opinion) of value of jewelry, furs, furniture, automobiles, mobile homes, tools and equipment, etc., should be furnished. For insurance on the life of another person (Question 13), IRS Form 938 should be obtained from the insurance carrier. For partnership interests and sole proprietorships, the income statements and balance sheets for the three years immediately preceding death should be furnished.

9. Contribution (Questions 4b, 6a)

Proof of contribution, as explained in the note to Question 4b, is vital to the determination of whether any joint or "trustee" asset is wholly or partially exempt from inheritance tax. In certain cases, the proof of contribution to a joint tenancy will result in the requirement that the survivor file a gift tax return for the creation of the joint tenancy asset. For proof of contribution by the survivor to real property or bank accounts, forms IT-16 (real property) and IT-15 (accounts) may be used.

10. Value or Percentage of Interest in Estate (Question 7a)

The inheritance tax is based upon the amount which passes to each individual. Therefore, the answer to this question should indicate the approximate amount or percentage of the estate going to each heir, beneficiary or transferee. Statements such as "see will" or "see trust" are not helpful since they do not indicate the declarant's opinion of the proper distribution to be made under the will or trust.

11. Trusts, Life Estates, Powers of Appointment (Question 6)

(a) Question 6a refers to bank and/or savings and loan accounts that are titled, for example, "X in trust for Y." These accounts will pass to the beneficiary by the contractual provisions designated.

(b) Question 6b refers to trusts, other than trustee accounts, established by the decedent.

(c) Question 6c refers to interests of decedent in trusts established by other persons for his benefit.

(d) Question 6d refers to a power or authority given to the decedent to distribute property or income therefrom or to control assets.

12. Gifts and Transfers (Question 10)

This question requires a scheduling of *all* gifts by decedent, not just gifts made within three years of death. Only minimal gifts should be excluded from the schedule. The value of each transferred asset both at the date of gift and at the date of death is required. If the asset was sold by the transferee prior to death, the date of sale, amount and subsequent disposition of the proceeds of sale should be shown. (See also Instruction 8)

13. Deductions (Question 15)

Itemization must be made for deductions in excess of $1,000, except as noted on the declaration. This does not mean deductions of less than $1,000 should be omitted. Where no court proceeding is pending, use only subdivision (a); where there is a probate proceeding, use all subdivisions; and where there is a court proceeding other than a probate, use only subdivisions (a) and (c).

Real property taxes become a lien as of the first day in March. Therefore, if the decedent died after the first day in March and before any installments have been paid, the entire amount of the tax is deductible. If the decedent died after the first installment was paid but before the second, the amount of the second installment only is deductible. If the decedent died after the first day in March, but before the second installment of the prior year's tax has been paid, the full year's tax for the year of death plus the unpaid second installment from the prior year are deductible.

Only the ordinary expenses of administration are deductible for inheritance tax purposes. These include filing fees, publication of notice to creditors, cost of executor's or administrator's bond and the Inheritance Tax Referee's fee. Extraordinary expenses and cost of property upkeep during administration are not deductible even though they are valid administration expenses.

Under subdivision (c), fees claimed must be only for those services which are specified in Revenue and Taxation Code, Section 13988.1, and the character of each such service should be set forth with the amount of fee allotted to it.

B. Marital Property Declaration, Form IT-3

This form is designed to provide information in order that the character of assets held by the spouses or either of them may be determined.

In California, assets may be separate property, community property or quasi-community property in nature. Separate property generally is property owned before marriage and property acquired during marriage by gift or inheritance. Community property generally is property acquired during marriage through personal effort of the spouses while residing in California. Quasi-community property generally is property which was acquired by the spouses while residing outside California which would have been community property had the spouses been residing in California at the time of acquisition.

The distribution of the estate and the amount of tax may vary considerably depending upon the character of the assets. Therefore, it is important that care be taken in completing this declaration.

14. When Marital Property Declaration, Form IT-3, Required

When a decedent is survived by a spouse and an Inheritance Tax Declaration, Form IT-22, is required (Instruction No. 1)

5. Description of Assets (Questions 2, 5b)

See also Instruction 7. A conscientious effort should be made to adequately describe and value the assets owned by decedent at marriage or acquired by gift, devise, descent or joint tenancy survivorship thereafter. The answer to Question 2 must be considered in connection with Question 3. An explanation will be required if the decedent's occupation or net worth appears to be inconsistent with the answers regarding assets owned at the date of marriage.

6. Valuation of Assets (Questions 2, 5b)

See also Instruction 8. The values given should be as of the date of marriage or date of receipt as indicated. For real property owned by decedent at date of marriage, in addition to the market value, indicate the original purchase price and any balance owing at date of marriage.

7. Accounting for Separate Property (Questions 6, 7)

Both of these questions require either specific designation of the assets previously reported in Questions 2 and 5b (Question 6) or a tracing of their disposition up to the date of death (Question 7). The burden of tracing is, by law, placed upon the declarant and general claims of "commingling," "disposed of before death," etc., will not relieve this burden. In absence of such a presentation, the continued existence of the proceeds of such separate property and any increase in the value thereof as part of the decedent's assets will be presumed.

18. Accounting for Quasi-Community Property (Question 8)

The answers to this question are important in determining what portion of the estate is community property and what portion is quasi-community property. Quasi-community property is property acquired during marriage while the spouses were residing outside California which would have been community property had the spouses been residing in California at the time of acquisition. The answers must be consistent with those given to Questions 9 and 10, regarding the spouses' business careers or occupations. Where these answers are contradictory, an explanation will be required.

The burden of tracing the subsequent disposition of quasi-community property is, by law, placed upon the declarant and general claims of "commingling," "disposed of before death," etc., will not relieve this burden. In absence of such a presentation, the continued existence of such quasi-community property and any increase in the value thereof as part of the decedent's assets will be presumed.

19. Business Careers and Occupations of Spouses (Questions 9, 10)

The answers to these questions should be set forth as complete as possible, in chronological order, starting with the date of marriage. The employer, position, approximate annual income and dates should be specified. Relatively inconsequential jobs held early in the marriage may be lumped together. The answers to these questions are helpful in establishing the net worth of the spouses when they became California residents.

CALIFORNIA INHERITANCE TAX RATES AND EXEMPTIONS
Effective as to decedents dying after 7:00 p.m., July 29, 1967

CLASSIFICATION		EXEMPTION	Rate of tax on amount left after deducting exemption from $25,000.00	$25,000 to $50,000	$50,000 to $100,000	$100,000 to $200,000	$200,000 to $300,000	$300,000 to $400,000	Over $400,000
Husband or Wife	Decedent's Separate Property only [1]	One-half of Separate property [2] Plus $5,000.00							
Minor Child (Includes Adopted)		**12,000.00**	3%	4%	6%	8%	10%	12%	14%
Adult Child, Grandchild, Parent, Grandparent (Relationship may be by Blood or Adoption) **Mutually Acknowledged Child** **Descendant of Mutually Acknowledged Child**		**5,000.00**							
Brother, Sister (Excludes Brothers- and Sisters-in-law) **Descendant of Brother or Sister** (Includes Descendant by Adoption or Acknowledgment) **Wife or Widow of Son, Husband or Widower of Daughter**		**2,000.00**	6%	10%	12%	14%	16%	18%	20%
Strangers in Blood and Relationships Not Specified Above		**300.00**	10%	14%	16%	18%	20%	22%	24%

[1] COMMUNITY PROPERTY passing or given to a spouse is exempt from inheritance tax except that (effective September 17, 1965): (1) decedent's half is subject to inheritance tax to the extent that a power of appointment therein is given to the surviving spouse and (2) decedent's half resulting from separate property conversions is treated as separate property in computing inheritance tax.

[2] MARITAL EXEMPTION. One-half of separate property is exempt in computing inheritance tax.

Table of Contents

STATE OF CALIFORNIA
INHERITANCE TAX DECLARATION, FORM IT-22

ANSWER ALL QUESTIONS. If space is insufficient, attach 8½ x 11 sheets showing decedent's name, social security number and question number.

Full Name of Decedent. (Show all names ever used)	Date of Death	Social Security No.
		Date of Birth

Place of Death. (Last usual address)	Cause of Death	Length of Last Illness

Attorney for Estate	Address	Telephone No.

Type of Court Proceeding	Case No.	Name of Executor/Administrator, If Any, and Title	
☐ Probate ☐ Other ☐ None	County and State	Address	Telephone No.

1. RESIDENCE OF DECEDENT AT TIME OF DEATH
   County   State

   NOTE: If it is claimed that decedent was not a California resident, attach completed form IT-2, Declaration Concerning Residence.

2. Did decedent leave a will? ☐ Yes ☐ No   If yes, attach copy of will and any codicils.

3a. Was decedent a tenant of a California safe deposit box? ☐ Yes ☐ No   If yes, give location of box. (See Instruction 4)

3b. Has box been opened by County Treasurer? ☐ Yes ☐ No   If yes, give date inventoried.

3c. Are any assets in box on date of death not reported on this form or a probate inventory? ☐ Yes ☐ No   If yes, explain in attachment.

4a. JOINT TENANCIES. Did decedent, at date of death, hold any assets in joint tenancy or joint tenancy form? ☐ Yes ☐ No   If yes, include **all** jointly held personal property (including stocks, bonds, mortgages, checking and savings accounts, etc.) wherever located, and California real property. Full amount must be shown, although portion has been released or transferred after death, and all assets must be included even if tax release or consent is not required.

Item No.	Name of surviving joint tenant	Relationship to decedent (See Instr. 5)	Description of each asset (See Instruction 7)	Market value at date of death (See Instr. 8)	FOR STATE USE ONLY

4b. Does surviving joint tenant **claim** any contribution to any of the joint tenancy assets? ☐ Yes ☐ No   If yes, give full particulars tracing source of funds, values, dates, etc., in attachment. (See Instruction 9)

NOTE: **Survivor's burden of proof of claim of contribution:** All joint tenancies are presumed to have been created from assets originally belonging to the decedent and subject to tax in full to the surviving joint tenant, except to the extent that the survivor can prove that the assets, or a portion, originally belonged to the survivor or that the survivor furnished consideration which was never received from the decedent. (Revenue and Taxation Code Sec. 13671)

I DECLARE UNDER PENALTY OF PERJURY THAT THIS DECLARATION, INCLUDING ANY ATTACHMENTS, HAS BEEN EXAMINED BY ME AND TO THE BEST OF MY KNOWLEDGE AND BELIEF IS TRUE, CORRECT AND COMPLETE. IF PREPARED BY A PERSON OTHER THAN THE DECLARANT, HIS DECLARATION IS BASED ON ALL INFORMATION OF WHICH HE HAS ANY KNOWLEDGE.

Signature	Date	At (County and State)	Address
Relationship to Decedent			
Signature of Person Preparing This Declaration	Date	At (County and State)	Address

THE INHERITANCE TAX APPRAISER MUST HAVE THIS FORM TO BEGIN DETERMINATION OF THE TAX. Send this form and all attachments to the **Inheritance Tax Appraiser**, if one has been appointed, otherwise to STATE CONTROLLER, Division of Inheritance and Gift Tax.

P. O. Box 1019	107 South Broadway	785 Market Street
Sacramento 95805	Los Angeles 90012	San Francisco 94103

5. **ASSETS OUTSIDE CALIFORNIA.** Excluding assets listed at item 4a, did decedent own tangible or intangible personal or real property outside of California?	☐ Yes ☐ No	**If yes,** describe property and give estimated value. (If probate is pending in another state, also attach copy of inventory.)
6a. **TRUSTS, LIFE ESTATES, POWERS OF APPOINTMENT.** Was decedent a trustee or beneficiary of a "trustee" bank or savings and loan or similar account?	☐ Yes ☐ No	**(See Instructions 7, 8, 11)** **If yes,** attach a list of accounts giving balances at date of death, sources of funds and exact title in which each was held. **(See Instruction 9)**
6b. Did decedent enter into a declaration of trust, written or oral, or join in a trust agreement during his life time?	☐ Yes ☐ No	**If yes,** attach copy of trust document or proof of the oral agreement, and a list of trust assets at date of death and estimated market value of each.
6c. Was decedent beneficiary of a trust not created by him?	☐ Yes ☐ No	**If yes,** attach copy of trust documents and a list of assets at date of death and estimated market value.
6d. Was decedent a donee of a power of appointment?	☐ Yes ☐ No	**If yes,** attach a copy of document creating power of appointment and a list of assets at date of death and estimated market value.

7a. **HEIRS, BENEFICIARIES, SURVIVING JOINT TENANTS AND TRANSFEREES.** List all even if there is no court proceeding.

Item No.	Name	Date of Birth	Full Address	Relationship to decedent (See * below and Instr. 5)	Approximate value of interest or percentage of estate (See Instr. 10)

* **Relationship must be by blood,** except for surviving spouse, son-in-law, daughter-in-law, adopted or mutually acknowledged child or issue of adopted or mutually acknowledged child. List all others who are not blood relatives as "strangers".

* **Attach blood tracing** for niece, nephew, uncle, aunt, cousin, grandniece, grandnephew, great grandniece or great grandnephew.

* **Adoption or mutual acknowledgment of child.** Affidavit or other proof is required for transferee claiming through adoption or mutual acknowledgment of child. (Revenue and Taxation Code Sections 13307, 13310)

7b. Did any beneficiaries named in will predecease decedent?	☐ Yes ☐ No	**If yes,** list names, and if blood relatives list names of their children.
7c. Did decedent have any predeceased spouses? (Probate Code Sections 228, 229)	☐ Yes ☐ No	**If yes,** give name, county of residence and date of death of each.
7d. Is any divorced spouse claiming an interest in or is a creditor of decedent or his estate?	☐ Yes ☐ No	**If yes,** attach a copy of final decree and any property settlement agreement.
7e. Is California **previously taxed** property credit claimed?	☐ Yes ☐ No	**If yes,** give name, county of residence and date of death of prior decedent. **(See Instruction 6)**
8a. **LIFE INSURANCE.** Was there life and/or accident insurance in force on life of decedent?	☐ Yes ☐ No	**If yes,** list below.

Item No.	Insurance Company	Type of policy (term, endowment, mortgage, etc.) and face amount	Owner of policy (See * below)	Beneficiary receiving proceeds and relationship to decedent (See Instruction 5)	Mode of payment and amount of proceeds received

* If owner was other than decedent or total proceeds exceed $50,000, or if decedent irrevocably selected mode of settlement, attach copy of IRS Form 7 obtainable from insurance company.

ANNUITIES, SUPPLEMENTAL CONTRACTS AND DEATH BENEFITS

9a. Was decedent owner of annuity policies or supplemental contracts? ☐ Yes ☐ No   If yes, list under 9c.

9b. Did decedent have any interest in a "death benefit", "retirement plan", "profit sharing plan" or "stock purchase plan" or were any payments made under such plans by virtue of decedent's death? ☐ Yes ☐ No   If yes, list under 9c.

9c. Item No.	Company, or issuer of annuity, supplemental contract or death benefit	Type of policy or death benefit	Beneficiary and relationship to decedent (See Instruction 5)	Mode of payment	Lump sum or commuted value

9d. Is any item in 9c claimed to be nontaxable? ☐ Yes ☐ No   If yes, explain below or in attachment.

GIFTS AND TRANSFERS

10a. Did decedent, transfer, **at any time during his life,** any real or personal property (stocks, bonds, notes, savings accounts, etc.) for other than money, for less than market value, or without any payment or consideration (including withdrawals or transfers from joint tenancy bank or savings and loan accounts)? ☐ Yes ☐ No   If yes, list under 10b and answer 10c through 10g. **(See Instruction 12)**

10b. Item No.	Name of transferee and relationship to decedent (See Instruction 5)	Date of transfer	Description of property and estimated market value at date of transfer (See Instructions 7, 8)	Market value at date of death (See Instr. 8)	FOR STATE USE ONLY

10c. Did decedent continue to receive all or part of the income after transfer, or continue to use property (including residing on real estate)? ☐ Yes ☐ No   If yes to 10c, 10d or 10e, explain below or in attachment.

10d. Was deed to any real property listed under 10b recorded after decedent's death? ☐ Yes ☐ No

10e. Was any restriction imposed by decedent on transfer of any property listed under 10b? ☐ Yes ☐ No

10f. Is it claimed that any property listed under 10b is not subject to inheritance tax? ☐ Yes ☐ No   If yes, explain below or in attachment. ("Payment of gift tax" or "exemption under Gift Tax Law" is insufficient.)

10g. Were California gift tax returns filed for any of the transfers listed under 10b? ☐ Yes ☐ No   If yes, identify transfer and give amount of gift tax paid (including penalties and interest).

11. Was decedent survived by a spouse? ☐ Yes ☐ No   If yes, attach completed form IT-3, Marital Property Declaration.

12. Will Federal Estate Tax Return, Form 706, be filed? ☐ Yes ☐ No   **If already filed,** attach copy of page 1 of Form 706.

Federal Estate Tax	$	☐ Estimated	☐ Paid
Maximum allowable credit for State death taxes	$	☐ Estimated	☐ Determined

13. **ASSETS NOT OTHERWISE LISTED.** Assets standing in decedent's name alone, or in bearer form, including real property, stocks, bonds, mortgages, judgments, notes, accounts and loans receivable, cash, business or partnership interests, autos, farm equipment, interests in retirement funds, stock purchase plans or other employee benefits, furniture, furnishings, personal effects, insurance owned by decedent on life of any other persons, amounts due including tax or other refunds, and any other type of property. Also include assets in name of the surviving spouse which are community property. **(Probate cases.** If all property is listed in Inventory and Appraisement, do not list but make reference to Inventory and Appraisement.)

Item No.	Description of assets not otherwise listed (**See Instruction 7**)	Market value at date of death (**See Instr. 8**)	FOR STATE USE ONLY

14a. Was probate homestead granted or statutory homestead confirmed or exempt personal property set aside by probate court? ☐ Yes ☐ No   **If yes,** attach copy of court order.

14b. Was a family allowance ordered by probate court? ☐ Yes ☐ No   **If yes,** list persons receiving, amount of monthly allowance and duration.

14c. Has there been litigation affecting the estate as to distribution, entitlement or value? ☐ Yes ☐ No   **If yes,** attach copies of court orders. If litigation is pending, give case title, number, relevant issues and facts.

ALLOWABLE DEDUCTIONS (**See Instruction 13**) Any deduction over $1,000 must be itemized.

15a. All Cases

Expenses of last illness (paid after death by transferee or estate, net after any insurance reimbursement) ....

Funeral expenses (net after burial insurance, social security or other reimbursement) ....

Debts of decedent (**if probate,** list only allowed claims) ....

Encumbrances on real property (state exact balance for each parcel) ....

Liens or security agreements on personal property (state exact balance for each asset) ....

Taxes a lien or due and unpaid at death: Income tax (net due at death) ....

Real property (state exact balance for each parcel) ....

Other taxes (itemize and explain) ....

Other deductions (itemize and explain) ....

15b. Probate Cases Only

Other debts (itemize and explain) ....

Ordinary attorney's fees ☐ Statutory ☐ Other ☐ Not claimed ....

Ordinary executor's/administrator's commission ☐ Statutory ☐ Other ☐ Not claimed ....

Costs of administration (filing fees, notices, etc.) ....

15c. Additional Professional Fees—Probate and Other Court Cases. (Show basis: tax work, joint tenancy, etc. Include only fees allowed under Revenue and Taxation Code Sections 13988.1)

Executor/Administrator ....

Attorney ....

Accountant ....

Itemization and detail of items under 15a, b, c.

STATE OF CALIFORNIA
MARITAL PROPERTY DECLARATION, FORM IT-3

ANSWER ALL QUESTIONS. If space is insufficient, attach 8½ x 11 sheets showing decedent's name, social security number and question number.

Full Name of Decedent	Social Security No.	Date of Death

1. DECEDENT AND SURVIVING SPOUSE WERE MARRIED ON	Date	In City of	In State of

2. Did decedent own any real or personal property at date of marriage?   ☐ Yes ☐ No   **If yes,** list below. (Also attach real property tax bill for year of marriage, if available)

Item No.	General description of each asset (**See Instruction 15**)	Approximate market value at date of marriage (**See Instr. 16**)

3. Decedent's occupation at date of marriage	4. Decedent's net worth at date of marriage

5a. Did decedent receive any real or personal property **after** date of marriage by gift, bequest, devise, descent or joint tenancy survivorship?   ☐ Yes ☐ No   **If yes,** complete 5b, 5c and 5d.

5b. Item No.	General description of each asset (**See Instruction 15**)	Full name and relationship of person from whom received	Date received	Approx. value on date received (**See Instr. 16**)

5c. IF CALIFORNIA INHERITANCE TAX DETERMINATION WAS MADE	Name of estate	Court case No. (if any)	County

5d. IF RECEIVED BY GIFT	Item No.	State of residence of donor at date of gift

6. Are any assets listed under 2 or 5b now on inventory of decedent's estate or included in Inheritance Tax Declaration, Form IT-22? (**See Instruction 17**)   ☐ Yes ☐ No   **If yes,** specify where each such item is shown on inventory or Form IT-22.

7a. Were any assets listed under 2 or 5b **transferred** to anyone (including decedent's spouse) during decedent's lifetime? (**See Instruction 17**)   ☐ Yes ☐ No   **If yes,** complete 7b and 7c.

7b. ANY SUCH ASSETS SOLD	Item No.	Date of sale	Proceeds received	Subsequent disposition of proceeds	

7c. ANY SUCH ASSETS TRANSFERRED WITHOUT FULL CONSIDERATION	Item No.	Date of transfer	Names & addresses of persons to whom transfers made	Consideration, if any

I DECLARE UNDER PENALTY OF PERJURY THAT THIS DECLARATION, INCLUDING ANY ATTACHMENTS, HAS BEEN EXAMINED BY ME AND TO THE BEST OF MY KNOWLEDGE AND BELIEF IS TRUE, CORRECT AND COMPLETE. IF PREPARED BY A PERSON OTHER THAN THE DECLARANT, HIS DECLARATION IS BASED ON ALL INFORMATION OF WHICH HE HAS ANY KNOWLEDGE.

Signature	Date	Relationship: ☐ Spouse of decedent ☐ Representative of spouse
		If not spouse, explain in attachment:
		a. Why spouse is not signing,
At (County and State)	Address	b. Declarant's relationship or connection with decedent and
		c. Basis of knowledge required to provide necessary information.

Signature of person preparing this declaration	Date	At (County and State)	Address

Send this form and all attachments to the **Inheritance Tax Appraiser,** if one has been appointed, otherwise to STATE CONTROLLER, Division of Inheritance and Gift Tax

P.O. Box 1019	107 South Broadway	785 Market Street
Sacramento 95805	Los Angeles 90012	San Francisco 94103

| 8a. Did decedent and surviving spouse reside outside California during marriage? (See Instruction 18) | ☐ Yes ☐ No | If yes, complete 8b, 8c and 8d. |

8b. States in which resided, including California, after marriage	Inclusive dates (month and year if known)		Combined net worth of spouses upon taking up residence in each state (include value of all assets, including cash)
	From	To	

8c. Does net worth at date of last arrival in California include any separate property of either spouse?   ☐ Yes ☐ No   **If yes, state source and value.**

8d. Trace subsequent disposition of combined net worth of spouses after last arrival in California.

9. Brief history of **decedent's** business or occupational career from marriage to death, showing dates. **(See Instruction 19)**

10. Brief history of **surviving spouse's** business or occupational career from marriage to decedent's death, showing dates. **(See Instruction 19)**

11. Did either spouse receive damages or a settlement for a personal injury after September 11, 1957?   ☐ Yes ☐ No   **If yes, show dates, amounts received and subsequent disposition.**

12. Did decedent and surviving spouse ever enter into any written or oral agreement concerning the status of their property as community or separate?   ☐ Yes ☐ No   **If yes, attach copy of agreement or affidavit proving oral agreement.**

13. Did spouse ever obtain a legal separation (separate maintenance) or an interlocutory divorce?   ☐ Yes ☐ No   **If yes, attach copy of decree and any property settlement agreement.**

Date of reconciliation, if any.

14. Give on attachment any additional information bearing upon the separate or community status of decedent's property.

NOTE: *It is vital that all pertinent information be given. Under the inheritance tax law there is no presumption that property acquired after marriage is community property; the burden of proof is upon the person so claiming.* (Revenue and Taxation Code Sections 13556, 13556.5)

FORM NO.	COMPTROLLER OF PUBLIC ACCOUNTS	DO NOT WRITE IN SPACE BELOW
30-4.01	STATE OF TEXAS	Date received
Revised 1-69	**INHERITANCE TAX RETURN**	
INHERITANCE TAX	(RESIDENT)	

Decedent's name

Residence (domicile) at time of death | Date of death

Did the decedent die testate?
☐ Yes ☐ No
If "Yes" attach copy of will

Were letters testamentary or of administration granted for this estate?
☐ Yes ☐ No

Date granted

Case No. | Name of Court | Location of Court

To whom granted? (Designate whether executor, executrix, administrator, or administratrix)

NAME	DESIGNATION	ADDRESS (Number, street, city and state)

INHERITANCE TAX DUE

PART I

Basic inheritance tax (Brought forward from Schedule R)............................ $

PART II

Federal credit for state death tax (Brought forward from Schedule S).............. $

INHERITANCE TAX DUE (PART I OR PART II, WHICHEVER IS THE GREATER)............. $

(SPACE FOR USE OF COMPTROLLER OF PUBLIC ACCOUNTS)

Type of assessment (tax, interest, etc.)	Assessments		Payments		
	Date	Amount	Date	Tax	Interest
		$		$	$

GENERAL INFORMATION

1. Address of decedent at time of death (Number, street, city, State, and Postal ZIP code)

2a. State in which domiciled at time of death	2b. Year in which this domicile was established

3. Date of marriage to surviving spouse	4. Domicile at date of marriage to surviving spouse	5. Citizenship (nationality) at date of death

6a. Place of death	6b. Cause of death	6c. Length of last illness

7. Decedent's physicians

NAMES	ADDRESSES (Number, street, city, State, and Postal ZIP code)

8. If decedent was confined in a hospital during his last illness or within 2 years prior to his death, give name and address of hospital.

9a. Date of birth	9b. Place of birth (City and State or country, if other than United States)

10a. Business or occupation	10b. If retired, state former business or occupation

10c. Business address (Number, street, city, State, and Postal ZIP code)

11. Number of children

12. Marital status of decedent at date of death
☐ Married   ☐ Single   ☐ Legally separated   ☐ Widow or Widower   ☐ Divorced

13. If decedent was a widow or widower, give name of deceased spouse	13a. Date of such spouse's death

14. Did the decedent at date of death own real property in any State other than that of his last domicile? ☐ Yes   ☐ No
If "Yes" state place of ancillary probate proceedings.

15. Name and address of ancillary executor or administrator

16. Did the decedent at time of his death have a safe deposit box held either alone or in the joint names of himself and another?
☐ Yes   ☐ No   If "Yes" state location

17. Name of attorney representing estate, if any

18. Address of attorney (Number, street, city, state and ZIP code)	19. Telephone No.

ALTERNATE VALUATION

20. An election to have the gross estate of the decedent valued as of the alternate date or dates is made by entering a check mark in the box set forth below:

☐ The executor elects to have the gross estate of the decedent valued in accordance with values as of a date or dates subsequent to the decedent's death as authorized under Article 14.11, Chapter 14, Title 122A, Taxation General.

ESTATE OF ....   Page 3

SCHEDULE O
RECAPITULATION

Sched-ule	Gross estate	Alternate value	Value at date of death
A	Real estate..	$...................	$...................
B	Stocks and bonds..	....	....
C	Mortgages, notes, and cash..	....	....
D	Insurance...	....	....
E	Jointly owned property..	....	....
F	Other miscellaneous property..	....	....
G	Transfers during decedent's life..	....	....
H	Powers of appointment...	....	....
I	Annuities...		
	TOTAL GROSS ESTATE...	$	$

Sched-ule	Deductions	Amount
J	1. Funeral expenses and expenses incurred in administering property subject to claims..	$...................
K	2. Debts of decedent..	....
K	3. Mortgages and liens..	
	4. Total of items 1 through 3..	$............
	5. Allowable amount of deductions from item 4 (see note*)................	$...................
L	6. Net losses during administration......................................	....
L	7. Expenses incurred in administering property not subject to claims......	....
	8. Total of items 5 through 7..	$...................
M	9. Bequests, etc., to surviving spouse....................................	$...................
	10. Adjusted gross estate (see note**)....................................	....
	11. Net amount deductible for bequests, etc., to surviving spouse (item 9 or one-half of item 10, whichever is smaller)...	....
N	12. Charitable, public, and similar gifts and bequests....................	
	TOTAL ALLOWABLE DEDUCTIONS, except exemption (totals of lines 8, 11, and 12)......................	$

*Note.—See paragraph 1 of the instructions.

**Note.—Enter at item 10 the excess of "TOTAL GROSS ESTATE" over item 8, if the decedent and his surviving spouse at no time held property as community property. If property was ever held as community property, compute the "Adjusted gross estate" (item 10) in accordance with the instructions and example on page 32, and attach an additional sheet showing such computation.

ESTATE OF ....   Schedule O—Page 33

o59—16—77750-1

INSTRUCTIONS FOR SCHEDULE R

DISTRIBUTION OF NET TAXABLE ESTATE AND BASIC INHERITANCE TAX THEREON

THE NET TAXABLE ESTATE (LINE 5 SCHEDULE 0—RECAPITULATION) MUST BE DISTRIBUTED UNDER THIS SCHEDULE.

If the decedent died testate, a copy of the last will and testament must be attached to this return. If the decedent died intestate, an affidavit of heirship must be attached to this return.

The basic inheritance tax is computed by the use of Table I shown below:

TABLE I
COMPUTATION OF BASIC INHERITANCE TAX

Classification of Beneficiaries	Value of Share of Net Taxable Estate		Tax on amount in Column (1)	Rate of tax on excess over amount in Column (1)
	Equal to or more than (1)	Less than (2)	(3)	(4)
CLASS A Art. 14.02—Husband or wife, or any direct lineal descendant of husband or wife, or any direct lineal descendant or ascendant of the decedent, or to legally adopted child or children, or any direct lineal descendant of adopted child or children of decedent, or to the husband of a daughter, or the wife of a son.	0 $ 25,000 50,000 100,000 200,000 500,000 1,000,000	$ 25,000 50,000 100,000 200,000 500,000 1,000,000 ———	Exempt ——— $ 250 1,250 4,250 16,250 41,250	0 1% 2% 3% 4% 5% 6%
CLASS B Art. 14.03—If passing to or for the use of the United States, to be used in Texas.	Same as Class A	Same as Class A	Same as Class A	Same as Class A
CLASS C Art. 14.04—Brothers, sisters or their descendants.	0 $ 10,000 25,000 50,000 100,000 250,000 500,000 750,000 1,000,000	$ 10,000 25,000 50,000 100,000 250,000 500,000 750,000 1,000,000 ———	Exempt ——— $ 450 1,450 3,950 12,950 30,450 50,450 72,950	0 3% 4% 5% 6% 7% 8% 9% 10%
CLASS D Art. 14.05—Uncles, aunts or their descendants.	0 $ 1,000 10,000 25,000 50,000 100,000 500,000 1,000,000	$ 1,000 10,000 25,000 50,000 100,000 500,000 1,000,000 ———	Exempt ——— $ 360 1,110 2,610 6,110 46,110 106,110	0 4% 5% 6% 7% 10% 12% 15%
CLASS E Art. 14.06—If passing to any other person, organization, or institution not included in any of the classes mentioned in the preceding Articles or unless specifically exempted.	0 $ 500 10,000 25,000 50,000 100,000 500,000 1,000,000	$ 500 10,000 25,000 50,000 100,000 500,000 1,000,000 ———	Exempt ——— $ 475 1,375 3,375 8,375 56,375 131,375	0 5% 6% 8% 10% 12% 15% 20%

Example showing the computation of the basic inheritance tax showing use of the above table

Value of share of net taxable estate in the amount of $160,000 passing to a surviving wife:

Tax on amount in Column (1) CLASS A $1,250

Rate of tax on excess over amount in Column (1) $60,000 x .03= 1,800

Basic inheritance tax $3,050

The value of life estates can be computed by use of Table II, Page 30.

SCHEDULE R
DISTRIBUTION OF NET TAXABLE ESTATE AND
BASIC INHERITANCE TAX THEREON

Name of beneficiary and address	Relationship of beneficiary to decedent	Age of beneficiary at date of death of decedent	Value of share of net taxable estate	Basic inheritance tax

SCHEDULE S
COMPUTATION OF FEDERAL CREDIT
FOR STATE DEATH TAX

Has a Form 706, U. S. Estate Tax Return been filed with the Internal Revenue Service?   ☐ Yes   ☐ No

1. Total gross estate (Schedule O, U.S. Estate Tax Return) . . . . 1. $

2. Value of Real Property Located Outside the State of Texas (Itemize under schedule below)

3. Texas gross estate (Item 1 minus Item 2) . . . .

4. Percentage of Texas gross estate to total gross estate (Item 3 divided by Item 1) . . . . %

5. Funeral, administration expenses, debts of decedent and mortgages and liens (Schedules J & K, U. S. Estate Tax Return) . . . . $

6. Other deductions (Total of Schedules L, M and N, U. S. Estate Tax Return) . . . .

7. Specific exemption 60,000.00

8. Total deductions plus exemption . . . .

9. Taxable estate (Item 1 minus Item 8, also Schedule P, U. S. Estate Tax Return) . . . . $

10. Maximum Federal Credit for State Death Tax (Part I, Line 2, Page 1, U. S. Estate Tax Return) . . . . $

11. Portion of Federal Credit for State Death Tax allocated to the State of Texas (Item 10 multiplied by Item 4) . . . . $

12. Total Federal Credit for State Death Tax due the State of Texas (Either of Item 10 or 11) (TO BE CARRIED FORWARD TO PAGE 1, PART II) . . . . $

Real Property Located Outside the State of Texas

Description	Value used in U.S. Estate Tax Return

RECONCILIATION SCHEDULE

Item

1. FEDERAL TOTAL GROSS ESTATE *(From Federal Schedule O)* $ _____

2. Less: Real or tangible personal property
   having an actual situs outside
   New York $ _____

3. Item 1 less item 2 $ _____

4. Plus: Limited Powers of Appointment *(ScheduleII)* $ _____

5. NEW YORK GROSS ESTATE
   (Item 3 plus item 4) $ _____

---

6. Total of deductions allowed under Federal
   Schedules J, K and L
   (Item 8 of Federal Schedule O) $ _____

7. Less: Expenses, etc., specifically
   attributable to property
   described in item 2 $ _____

8. Item 6 less item 7 $ _____

9. New York adjusted gross estate
   (Item 5 less item 8) $ _____

10. Bequests, etc., to surviving spouse
    (Item 9 of Federal Schedule O) $ _____

11. Less: Property in item 2 included in
    amount in item 10 $ _____

12. Item 10 less item 11 $ _____

13. New York marital deduction
    *(Item 12 or ½ of item 9
    whichever is smaller)* $ _____

14. Federal charitable, public, and similar
    gifts and bequests
    (Item 12 of Federal Schedule O) $ _____

15. Less: Property in item 2 included in
    amount in item 14 $ _____

16. New York charitable deduction
    (Item 14 less item 15) $ _____

17. TOTAL NEW YORK ESTATE TAX DEDUCTIONS
    (Totals of items 8, 13 and 16) $ _____

---

18. NEW YORK TAXABLE ESTATE
    (Item 5 less item 17) $ _____

TAX COMPUTATION SCHEDULE

1. NEW YORK TAXABLE ESTATE *(Item 18 of Reconciliation Schedule)* $ _____

2. New York gross estate tax computed
   from table .... $ _____

3. Credit for personal and insurance
   exemptions if any *(Schedule VII)*

       a. 2% of first $50,000 exempt,
          if any .... $ _____
       b. 3% of next $100,000 exempt,
          if any .... $ _____

4. Total credit for personal and insurance
   exemptions *(Item 3a plus item 3b)* .... $ _____

5. Credit for tax on prior transfers, if
   any *(Schedule VIII)* .... $ _____

6. Total credits *(Sum of items 4 and 5)* .... $ _____

7. NEW YORK NET ESTATE TAX
   (Item 2 less item 6) .... $ _____

NOTE: If the difference between the amounts at item 2 and item 4 is $40 or less, the estate
is exempt from tax under Section 952 (b) of the Tax Law.

NEW YORK TAXABLE ESTATE

Over	Not Over	Tax		
$0	$50,000		2% of New York taxable estate	
50,000	150,000	$1,000 +	3% of excess over	$50,000
150,000	300,000	4,000 +	4% of excess over	150,000
300,000	500,000	10,000 +	5% of excess over	300,000
500,000	700,000	20,000 +	6% of excess over	500,000
700,000	900,000	32,000 +	7% of excess over	700,000
900,000	1,100,000	46,000 +	8% of excess over	900,000
1,100,000	1,600,000	62,000 +	9% of excess over	1,100,000
1,600,000	2,100,000	107,000 + 10% of excess over		1,600,000
2,100,000	2,600,000	157,000 + 11% of excess over		2,100,000
2,600,000	3,100,000	212,000 + 12% of excess over		2,600,000
3,100,000	3,600,000	272,000 + 13% of excess over		3,100,000
3,600,000	4,100,000	337,000 + 14% of excess over		3,600,000
4,100,000	5,100,000	407,000 + 15% of excess over		4,100,000
5,100,000	6,100,000	557,000 + 16% of excess over		5,100,000
6,100,000	7,100,000	717,000 + 17% of excess over		6,100,000
7,100,000	8,100,000	887,000 + 18% of excess over		7,100,000
8,100,000	9,100,000	1,067,000 + 19% of excess over		8,100,000
9,100,000	10,100,000	1,257,000 + 20% of excess over		9,100,000
10,100,000		1,457,000 + 21% of excess over		10,100,000

(Last Name)   (First Name)   (Initial)

REPORT OF INHERITANCE TAX APPRAISER

I, the undersigned duly appointed Inheritance Tax Appraiser in and for the County of _____
Pennsylvania, do respectfully report that I have appraised the real and personal property as reported in the foregoing return
the values set forth opposite each item in the last column to the right in Schedules "A", "B", "C", and "E".

Dated: _____

_____
INHERITANCE TAX APPRAISER

REPORT OF THE REGISTER OF WILLS

I, the undersigned duly elected Register of Wills in and for _____ County, Pennsylvania, do resp
fully report that I have allowed deductions in the amounts claimed by deponent, except as to those items where a greater or
lesser amount is set forth in the last column to the right in Schedule "F", which greater or lesser amount represents the su
allowed as a deduction.

Dated: _____

_____
REGISTER OF WILLS

INVENTORY	VALUE AS REPORTED	VALUE AS APPRAISED	VALUE AS REAPPRAISED
Real Property (Schedule A)	$	$	$
Personal Property (Schedule B)			
Transfers (Schedule C)			
Joint - Held Property (Schedule E)			
TOTAL GROSS ASSETS			
Less Debts and Deductions			
(SCHEDULE F)			
CLEAR VALUE OF ESTATE			

Valuation of life estates or annuities	$		
ESTATE TAX ASSESSMENTS	$		

FOR USE OF REGISTER ONLY

COMPUTATION OF TAX

Tax on $ _____	2%	$ _____
Tax on $ _____	6%	$ _____
Tax on $ _____	5%	$ _____
Tax on $ _____	10%	$ _____
Tax on $ _____	15%	$ _____
Exemptions _____	*	
Total Estate _____		

(*) As evidenced by Charitable Exemption Certificates issued by the Secretary of Revenue.

TOTAL TAX $ _____

Less tax previously paid $ _____
BALANCE $ _____
Less 5% of tax if paid within
3 months after death $ _____

BALANCE OF INHERITANCE TAX DUE $ _____
Add interest at rate of 6% from
_____ to _____ $ _____
AMOUNT OF ESTATE TAX ASSESSED $ _____
Estate tax paid $ _____
BALANCE DUE $ _____
Add interest at rate of 6% from
_____ to _____ $ _____
TOTAL TAX BALANCE $ _____
PAID _____ $ _____

FOR USE OF REGISTER ONLY   ADJUSTMENTS
NOTE: Where subsequent adjustments are made to the above computation of tax by the Register of Wills, for proper reason
same should be noted below, with short explanation.

orm **709**
Rev. March 1971)
epartment of the Treasury
nternal Revenue Service

United States Quarterly Gift Tax Return

Calendar quarter ending (month and year)

onor's first name and middle initial	Donor's last name	Social Security Number
address (number and street)		Residence (domicile)
city, State, and ZIP code		Citizenship

A. Have you (the donor), during the calendar quarter indicated above, without an adequate and full consideration in money or money's worth, made any transfer exceeding $3,000 in value for the calendar year (or regardless of value if a future interest) as follows? *(Check whether "Yes" or "No.")*

	Yes	No
1. By the creation of a trust		
or the making of additions to a trust previously created		
in either case for the benefit of a person or persons other than yourself, and with respect to which you retained no power to revest the beneficial title to the property in yourself or to change the beneficiaries or their proportionate benefits; or by relinquishing every such power that was retained in a previously created trust		
2. By permitting a beneficiary, other than yourself, to receive the income from a trust created by you and with respect to which you retained the power to revest the beneficial title to the property in yourself or to change the beneficiaries or their proportionate benefits		
3. By the purchase of a life insurance policy		
or the payment of a premium on a previously issued policy		
the proceeds of which are in either case payable to a beneficiary other than your estate, and with respect to which you retained no power to revest the economic benefits in yourself or your estate or to change the beneficiaries or their proportionate benefits; or by relinquishing every such power that was retained in a previously issued policy		
4. By permitting another to withdraw funds from a joint bank account which were deposited by you		
5. By conveying title to another and yourself as joint tenants		
6. By conveying title to your spouse and yourself as tenants by the entirety or as joint tenants with right of survivorship . . . . *(If "Yes," see section 9 of the instructions.)*		
7. By the exercise or release of a power of appointment, except as provided in the Gift Tax Regulations		
8. By any other method, direct or indirect		
If the answer is "Yes" to any of the foregoing, such a transfer (other than the creation of a joint tenancy with your spouse in real property with right of survivorship, or addition thereto, which you do not elect to treat as a gift) should be fully disclosed in Schedule A.		

B. Gifts of husband and wife to third parties.—Do you consent to have the gifts by both you and your spouse to third parties during the calendar quarter considered as having been made one-half by each of you? (See section 8 of instructions.) . . *If the answer is "Yes," the following information must be furnished and the consent shown below signed by your spouse.*

1. Name of spouse	**1a.** Social Security Number

2. Were you married during the entire calendar quarter? . . . .
3. If the answer to 2 is "No," check whether ☐ married, ☐ divorced, or ☐ widowed; and give date ▶
4. Will a gift tax return for this calendar quarter be filed by your spouse? . . . .

Consent of Spouse

I consent to have the gifts made by both me and my spouse to third parties during the calendar quarter considered as having been made one-half by each of us.

Signature of spouse .... Date ....

Computation of Tax

1. Enter the amount from line j, Schedule A	$	
2. Enter the amount from line c, Schedule B		
3. Total (item 1 plus item 2)	$	
4. Tax computed on item 3 (See "Table for Computing Gift Tax" in separate instructions.)	$	
5. Tax computed on item 2 (See "Table for Computing Gift Tax" in separate instructions.)		
6. Tax due (item 4 minus item 5)	$	

Under penalties of perjury, I declare that I have examined this return, including any accompanying schedules and statements, and to the best of my knowledge and belief it is true, correct, and complete. If prepared by a person other than taxpayer, his declaration is based on all information of which he has any knowledge.

_____   _____
(Signature of taxpayer)   (Date)

_____   _____
(Signature of preparer other than taxpayer)   (Date)

_____
(Address of preparer other than taxpayer)

SCHEDULE A—Total Gifts During Calendar Quarter and Computation of Taxable Gifts

Item number	Description of gift, and donee's name and address	Donor's adjusted basis of gift	Date of gift	Value at date of gift
		$		$

(a) Total gifts of donor . . . . $...................

(b) Less one-half of items .... to .... attributable to spouse (see section 11 of instructions) . . . . . .

(c) Balance . . . . $...................

(d) Gifts of spouse to be included (from line b of spouse's return) (see section 11 of instructions) . . . .

(e) Total gifts for calendar quarter . . . . $...................

(f) Less total exclusions not exceeding $3,000 for the calendar year for each donee (except gifts of future interests) . . . . .

(g) Total included amount of gifts for calendar quarter . . . . $...................

(h) Deductions (see sections 16, 17, and 18 of instructions):

(1) Charitable, public, and similar gifts (based on items .... to ...., less exclusions) . |$...................

(2) Marital deduction (based on items .... to ....) . . . . |...................

(3) Specific exemption claimed . . . .

(i) Total deductions (total of lines 1, 2, and 3) . . . .

(j) Amount of taxable gifts for calendar quarter (line g minus line i) . . . . | $

SCHEDULE B—Returns, Amounts of Specific Exemption, and Taxable Gifts for Prior Periods

1. Have you filed Gift Tax Returns for prior periods? . . . . ☐ Yes ☐ No

If "Yes," follow section 19 of instructions in completing Schedule B below.

Calendar years (prior to 1971) and calendar quarters (1971 and subsequent years)	Internal Revenue office where prior return was filed	Amount of specific exemption	Amount of taxable gifts
		$	$

(a) Totals for prior periods (without adjustment for reduced specific exemption) . . . . . | $ | $...................

(b) Amount, if any, by which total specific exemption, line a, exceeds $30,000 (see section 19 of instructions) . . . . .

(c) Total amount of taxable gifts for prior periods (total, last column, line a, plus amount, if any, line b) . . . . . | $

(If more space is needed, attach additional sheets of same size)

Index

ership, 146; on federal inheritance tax return, 37–39; and preferred stock, 113; and trusts, 97–99. *See also* Marital deduction trust

Marital deduction trust, 94, 107–8, 133; compared with revocable living trust, 116–17; and second marriages, 97–99

Martindale Hubbell Directory, 65

Mental incompetence rulings, 75

Mentally or physically handicapped, and trusts, 111

Minnesota, inheritance laws of, 63

Minor children. *See* Children

Miscellaneous property, in Federal Estate Tax Return, 36

Mortgages, as inheritance tax deductions, 5, 37, 72

Mutual funds: beneficiary designation ownership of, 137; and custodianship under Uniform Gifts to Minors Act, 155; held by bank trustee, 105–6; investment in, 198–201; and outright ownership by minor, 151

Nonforfeiture insurance options, 204

Non-probate assets, 126–42; and claiming premises as homestead, 141–42; definition of, 125; and gifts during life, 142; and joint tenancy as matter of convenience, 140–41; and joint tenancy with right of survivorship, 126–34; and tenants by the entirety ownership, 141; and U.S. government bonds held in co-ownership, 139

Non-spouses, and joint tenancy as matter of convenience, 140–41

Ownership of assets, 70–71, and avoidance of probate, 125, 155–57, 212; and beneficiary designation, 134–39; and joint tenancy as matter of convenience, 140–41; and joint tenancy with right of survivorship, 126–34; and living trusts, 138; and probate assets, 142–57

Partial distribution method, 22, 83–84

Pensions, as non-probate assets, 139–40

Personal belongings, division of, 79–80

Petition: for appointment of inheritance tax appraiser, 20; for hardship cases, 22; for hearing on will, 20; for partial payment of attorney fees, 22–23

Powers of appointment, 36

Preferred stock, in trust, 113–14

Privacy: and Confidential Inventory of Assets, 161; and revocable living trusts, 117

Probate: conclusion of, 23; costs of, 24–25; definition of, 3; delay during, 4–5, 22–23, 27–28; and liquidity problems, 82–83; notice of hearing, 20; as public record, 25–26, 117; for trusts, 88. *See also* Probate assets; Probate avoidance

Probate assets: as community property, 144–48; and conservator, 152–54; co-ownership of, 150; custodianship under Uniform Gifts to Minors Act, 154–55; definition of, 125; guardianship of, 152; individual ownership of, 143–44; outright ownership by minor of, 151–52; quasi-community property ownership of, 148–50; tenants in common ownership of, 143; and testamentary trusts, 144

Probate attorney: choice of, 5, 8–9; fees of, 22–23, 24–25; rela-

JEAN PLAIDY

Myself My Enemy

For a complete list of
books by Jean Plaidy
please see pages 383 and 384

JEAN PLAIDY

Myself My Enemy

G. P. PUTNAM'S SONS
New York

Library of Congress Cataloging in Publication Data

Plaidy, Jean, date.
Myself my enemy.

Bibliography: p.
1. Henrietta Maria, Queen, consort of Charles I,
King of England, 1609–1669—Fiction. 2. Charles I,
King of England, 1600–1649—Fiction. I. Title.
PR6015.I3M9   1983   823'.914   83-9684
ISBN 0-399-12877-8

Printed in the United States of America

Contents

MYSELF MY ENEMY

This is the story of a tragic queen told as though by herself, during what is undoubtedly the most turbulent period of English history.

Henrietta Maria's father was murdered a few months after her birth and she grew up in a court of intrigue which was constantly on the verge of conflict until the arrival of the future King of England on a romantic visit to Spain.

Eventually Henrietta Maria herself was betrothed and embarked on the stormy years of a marriage which seemed doomed to failure overshadowed as it was by the malevolent Buckingham.

But out of these tempestuous beginnings grew one of the greatest love stories of all times and Henrietta Maria fiercely loyal in love, impetuously ruthless in hatred, stood beside her husband through his tragic progress. This is an account of a most successful yet disastrous marriage between a man of honour determined to do his duty as he saw it, and a woman entirely devoted to helping him. Blindly they blundered through the years, watching the fall of Strafford and the rise of men such as Cromwell, Hampden and Pym, unaware even of the spies in their own household; and so came the inevitable march towards war, Englishman against Englishman, Cavalier against Roundhead, the sequel of which was played out on a cold January day in Whitehall.

At the centre of the disaster stand the King with his unswerving belief in the Divine Right of Kings and his Queen, warmhearted, passionate Henrietta Maria who was her own greatest enemy and that of those whom she loved best.

There is that other Charles, witty, calm, inscrutable refusing to be influenced by his mother, coming back to claim his rights; there are Mary, James, Henry and Henriette all determined to go their own way; and so Henrietta Maria must retire to the *château* of Colombes, a lonely doubting woman to brood on the past and ask herself How much was I to blame?

The Dowager Queen

When I sit here alone in my *château* of Colombes, which I inhabit by grace of my nephew that great and glorious ruler whom they call The Sun King, I often think back over my life—one which has had more than its fair share of sorrow, humiliation, intrigue and tragedy. I am old now and my word stands for little, but though no one listens to me, I am allowed my comforts, for after all they must remember that I am the aunt of one King and the mother of another; and kings and queens never forget the deference due to royalty, for if they did not show it to others a day may come when it is not shown to them. Royalty is sacred to royalty – though not always so, alas, with the people. When I think of the manner in which the people of England treated their King – the wickedness, the cruelty, the bitter, bitter humiliation – even now my anger rises to such heights that I fear I shall do myself an injury. I should be old enough to restrain my temper now; I should remind myself that I have my silent accusers who would say that if the King had not had the misfortune to marry me, he would be alive and on his throne at this moment.

That is all in the past . . . all dead and gone. It is a new world now. There is a King on the throne of England for the Monarchy has been restored. The people love him, I am told; and indeed I was aware of this when I paid a visit to England not long ago. My dearest Henriette – the best-loved of all my children – glows when she talks of him. She always loved him dearly. He is witty, they say; he loves pleasure but he is shrewd. He is his grand-father – the father I never knew – all over again. He has charm though he is ugly. He was born ugly – the ugliest baby I ever saw. I remember when they first put him into my arms, I could not believe that this little unprepossessing thing could possibly be the child of my handsome husband and myself – for in spite of my small stature and certain defects, I was regarded in those days –

even by my enemies – as having a goodly share of physical charms.

Are the troubles over? Is this the end of the nightmare which overshadowed England for all those years? Have people learned their lesson? With flowers and sweet music they welcomed Charles when he returned and there was rejoicing throughout London and the whole of England. They had done with the hideous Puritan rule. For ever? I wonder.

So Royalty has come back into its own. But it is too late for me. I am here, grateful to be in my small but beautiful *château* during the summer days, and in the winter, if I wish to go to Paris, my nephew has put the truly splendid Hôtel de la Balinière at my disposal.

He is kind to me – my glorious nephew. I think he has been a little in love with my sweet Henriette. And my son is kind, too. He always was – in that careless way which makes me think he would do anything for peace. I pray he will hold the crown. Louis respects him for all that he seems to devote himself to pleasure, and his great preoccupation would appear to be with the next seduction.

He looked at me so wisely when I was last in England. I begged him then to come to the true Faith, and he took my face in his hands and kissed me, calling me 'Mam' as he used to when he was a little boy. 'When the time is ripe,' he said enigmatically.

I never did understand Charles. I only know that he has this power to win people to him. He has grace for all his height, and charm which outshines his ugliness. If he could but get a child all would be well for England – as well as it could be, that is, unblessed by the true Faith as it is. And that may come. It has been my hope for so many years that it will.

Charles's wife, dear Catherine, is so docile and so much in love with him. How can she be when he parades his mistresses before her and refuses – though in that charming, lighthearted way of his – to give up his profligate way of life?

I tried to talk to him when I was there – though more of religious matters, I must admit, than the need to get an heir. Catherine must be at fault. God knows he has enough bastards scattered throughout his kingdom, and he distributes titles and lands among them with a free hand. One of his courtiers said that a time will come when almost every Englishman, even from the remote corners of the country, will claim to be descended from Royal Stuart. And he cannot get one legitimate heir!

Life is strange. And I am now near to the end of mine. I think often of my dear husband Charles – of his saintly goodness, his gentleness, his loving kindness, and most of all the love which grew between us, though we had many a disagreement in the beginning, and in those early days there must have been times when he wished he had never been persuaded into the marriage, for all the good it was said it would bring to our two countries.

I dream of him now . . . going to his death on that cold January day. They told me he had said: 'Give me an extra shirt. It is cold and I could tremble from the wind, and those who have come to see me die would think I trembled in fear of death.'

Nobly he went out to die. I see him in my dreams and I say to myself: 'What did I do? If I had been a different woman, is it possible that this great tragedy, this murder, need never have happened?'

I want to go right back to the beginning. I want to think of everything that happened. And then I want to find the answer.

Could it have been different? Is it really possible that it need not have happened the way it did?

One cannot call the man who wielded the axe the murderer. But what of those cold-eyed men who passed the sentence?

I hate them. I hate them all.

But was I the one to blame?

The Early Days

I was born into a troubled world and when I was only five months old my father was murdered. Fortunately for me at that time I was in my nursery and knew nothing of this deed which was said to have had such a disastrous effect not only on our family but on the whole of France.

Everything I knew of him was through hearsay; but I was one to keep my ears and eyes open, and for a long time after his death, he was talked of, so that by cautious questioning and alert observation, in time I began to learn a great deal about the father who had been taken from me.

He had been a great man – Henri of Navarre, the finest King the French had ever known – but of course the dead become sanctified, and those who are murdered – particularly those in high places – become martyrs. My own dear Charles . . . but that was a long way ahead in the future. I had much to endure before I was overwhelmed by the greatest tragedy of my life.

So my father died. There he was one day in good health – well, as near good health as a man of fifty can be who has lived a life of much indulgence – and the next a corpse brought home to the Louvre and laid on his bed in his closet there while the whole country mourned and the ministers guarded the palace and us children, particularly my brother Louis, who had then become King. And all the time I was sleeping peacefully in my cradle unaware of the action of a maniac which had robbed France of her King and me of my father.

There were seven of us in the nursery at that time. The eldest was Louis, the Dauphin, who was eight when I was born. After him came Elizabeth, who was a year younger than Louis. There was a gap of four years between Elizabeth and Christine and then the family increased with rapidity. There had been the little Duc d'Orléans who had died before there was time to give him a name, and after that Gaston and then myself, Henriette Marie.

My mother may have been unsatisfactory in the eyes of many but she certainly filled the nursery and that is said to be the first and most important duty of a queen. The people disliked her as much as they loved my father. For one thing she came from Tuscany, being the daughter of Francis the Second of that land; and the French had always hated foreigners. Moreover she was fat and not very handsome and was of the Medici family. People remember that other Italian woman, wife of Henri Deux, towards whom they had shown more venom than to any other monarch, blaming her for all the misfortunes of France, including the Massacre of St Bartholomew and the deaths by poison of many people. They had made a legend of her – the Italian poisoner. It was unfortunate that my mother should bear the name of Medici.

However, while my father had been there my mother was unimportant. She had had to accept his infidelities. He was a great lover of women. The Evergreen Gallant, the people called him, and right up to his death he was involved with women. The Duc de Sully – his very able minister and friend – had deplored this characteristic; but it was no use. Great king that he was he was first of all a lover and the pursuit of women was to him the most urgent necessity of his life. He could not exist without them. While this is doubtless a great weakness in a king, it is a foible which people indulgently shrug aside and indeed often applaud. 'There is a *man*,' they say, with winks, nods and affectionate smiles.

Even at the time of his death he was involved in a romantic intrigue. I learned all about it from Mademoiselle de Montglat, who was the daughter of our governess and who, because she was so much older than I, had been set in charge of me by her mother. I called her Mamanglat as at first she was like a mother to me and later like an elder sister; and I was more fond of her than anyone I knew. Mamanglat became affectionately shortened to Mamie, and Mamie she remained to me forever.

We were all terrified of Madame de Montglat, who was always reminding us that she had the royal permission to whip us if we misbehaved, and as we were the Royal Children of France, higher standards had been set for us than for all other children.

Mamie was not a bit like her mother. Although in a way she

was a governess, she was more like one of us. She was always ready to laugh, tell us the latest scandal and to help us out of those scrapes into which children fall and which would have brought down the wrath of Madame de Montglat on our heads if they had come to her knowledge.

It was from Mamie that I began to understand what was going on around me, what it meant to be a child in a royal nursery, the pitfalls to be avoided – the advantages and the disadvantages. It seemed to me that there were more of the latter and Mamie was inclined to agree with me.

'Your father loved you children,' she told me. 'He used to say you were all beautiful and he could not understand how two such as the Queen and himself could have begotten you. I used to have to peep out at you because my mother forbade me to appear before the King.'

'Why?'

'Because I was young and not ill favoured – good looking enough to catch his eyes, she thought.'

Then Mamie would be overcome with laughter. 'The King was like that,' she finished.

Being very young and ignorant of the world I wanted to ask a great many questions, but did not always do so being afraid of exposing my ignorance.

'You were his favourite,' said Mamie. 'The baby – the child of his old age. He was proving, you see, that he could still get beautiful children – not that he need have worried. There was constantly some woman claiming that her child was his. Well, what was I saying? Oh . . . you were the favourite. He was always fond of little girls and weren't you named for him . . . well, as near as a girl could be. Henriette Marie. Henriette for him and Marie for your mother. Royal names both of them.'

From Mamie I learned the gossip of the Court – past and present – much that was necessary for me to know and more besides. I heard from her that before he had married my mother, my father had been married to La Reine Margot, daughter of Catherine de Medicis – one of the most mischievous and fascinating women France had ever known. My father had hated Margot. He had never wanted to marry her and it was rather dramatically said that their marriage had been solemnized in blood, for during the celebrations the most terrible of all massacres had taken place – that which had occurred on the Eve of St Bartholomew; and it was because so many Huguenots had been in Paris to attend the marriage of their leader's son to Catholic Margot that they had been conveniently situated for destruction.

I supposed something like that would haunt a bride and bridegroom for ever. It was a mercy that my father escaped. But all his life – until the last fatal moment – he had had a knack of escaping. He had lived his life dangerously and joyously. Often careless of his royalty he had had an easy familiarity with his men. No wonder he had been popular. He had done a great deal for France too. He cared about the people; he had said he wanted every peasant to have a chicken in his pot on Sundays; moreover he had brought about a compromise between the Catholics and Huguenots and that had seemed an impossible task. He himself had paid lip service to the Catholics with his famous quip of Paris being worth a Mass when he had realized the city would never surrender to a Protestant.

He had been a wonderful man. When I was very young I used to weep tears of rage because he had been taken from me before I could know him.

He had been a good soldier, but it was said that he never let anything – not even the need to fight an enemy – stand in the way of his love affairs.

The object of his passion at the time of his death had been the daughter of the Constable de Montmorency. She was only sixteen years old but no sooner had my father set eyes on her than he declared she must be his 'little friend'.

Mamie loved to tell these stories. She had a certain histrionic talent, which she loved to display and which often made me helpless with laughter. She could never tell anything dramatic without acting it. I remember her explaining, dropping her voice to conspiratorial confidence.

'However . . . before presenting his daughter Charlotte to Court, the Constable de Montmorency had betrothed her to François de Bassompierre who was a very magnificent gentleman of the House of Cleves – handsome, witty, and as he was also a Gentleman of the King's Bedchamber, he was much sought after. Monsieur de Montmorency thought it an excellent match.

'But when the young lady came to Court and the King saw

her, that was the end of her romance with François de Bassompierre.'

How I loved to listen to her as she threw herself into the part she was playing for me!

'The King was determined that Bassompierre should not have her because he was a passionate young man and deeply in love with her and therefore could not be expected to become the kind of accommodating husband whom the King favoured because they were always willing to stand aside when the need arose. One morning – so the story goes – when the King was about to rise from his bed, he sent for Bassompierre – remember he was a Gentleman of the Bedchamber. "Kneel Bassompierre," said the King. Bassompierre was astonished for the King was never one to stand on ceremony, but if you wish to present some suggestion which may not be acceptable it is always best to reduce the person whom you intend to deprive or displease by stressing your own superiority.'

I nodded. I could understand that.

'The King was full of guile. He knew men well and that meant he could usually wriggle satisfactorily out of awkward situations.' Mamie had thrown herself upon my bed and assumed an air of royalty. ' "Bassompierre," said the King, "I have been thinking a good deal of you and I have come to the conclusion that it is time you were married." ' Mamie leaped from the bed and assumed a kneeling position beside it. ' "Sire," said Bassompierre. "I should be married now, but the Constable's gout has been troubling him of late and for this reason the ceremony has been postponed." ' She was back on the bed, royal again. ' "I have just the bride for you, Bassompierre. What think you of Madame d'Aumale? When you marry, the Duchy of Aumale shall come to you." "Sire," said Bassompierre, "have you a new law in France? Is a man then to have *two* wives?" ' She was back on the bed. ' "Nay, nay, François. In Heaven's name, one is enough for a man to manage at a time. I will tell you all. I know of your commitment to Mademoiselle de Montmorency but the truth is that I myself have become madly enamoured of her. If you married her I should begin to hate you . . . especially if she showed any affection for you. Now I am fond of you, Bassompierre, and I know you would be the last one to wish for a rift in our friendship. Therefore I cannot see you married to this girl. I

shall give her to my nephew Condé. That will keep her near me
. . . in the family . . . and she can comfort my old age. Condé
likes hunting better than women. I shall make him an allowance
as compensation. Then he can leave the delightful creature to
me." '

Mamie looked at me and raised her eyebrows. She was a little
breathless jumping off and on the bed and having to play the two
parts in the drama.

'Poor Bassompierre!' She was herself now, the wise story
teller. 'He saw that it would be impossible to go against the King's
wishes, and when he told Mademoiselle de Montmorency what
was planned she cried: "Jesus. The King has gone mad!" But very
soon she grew accustomed to the idea and after a while she quite
liked it. The whole Court was talking about the change in bridegrooms, and very quickly Mademoiselle de Montmorency
became the Princesse de Condé.

'Now this led to other complications. The Queen accepted the
fact that the King must have many mistresses but she hated there
to be one who could influence him so much. She had never been
crowned and a monarch always feels insecure until the crown has
been placed on his – or her – head in solemn ceremony. So the
Queen cried: "I want to be crowned!" and because of the guilt he
felt about Charlotte de Montmorency the King, who had brushed
aside this matter of the Queen's coronation whenever it was
raised, had to give way to save himself from violent recrimi-
nations. Then to make matters worse, the Prince de Condé
became so enamoured of his wife that he decided that he would
no longer stand aside. She was after all *his* wife, and he secretly
left the Court with the new Princesse and took her to Picardy, and
since that might not be far enough he carried her on to Brussels.

'The King was desolate. He was mad with grief and threatened
to follow her. Now a King cannot move far without everyone's
knowing, and who would have believed that a King who had
been on most excellent terms with so many women at the same
time, should take such steps for one. People were saying that it
was a secret move to go to war. So the King found himself in the
centre of a controversy. The Duc de Sully was worried and he told
the King that his conduct over the Princesse de Condé was
destroying his reputation . . . not his reputation for being a rake
. . . that was unimportant and he already had that in any case. It

was only when his amours intruded into statecraft that there was danger.

'The affair had made the Queen more restive than ever. She was demanding her coronation, and the King, feeling he owed her some recompense, at length agreed that it should take place.

'Now at this time the King had a strange presentiment. Kings' lives are always in danger so perhaps it is natural for them to have presentiments. Well, some time before, the King had been told that he would only survive a few days after the Queen's coronation, and it was for this reason that he had never wanted her to be crowned; and if it had not been for his guilt about the Princesse de Condé, he would never have agreed to it. However, now that she was to be crowned, the feeling of disaster grew and grew and he became so certain of his imminent death that he went to see the Duc de Sully about it, which shows how strongly he felt, for the Duc was not the man even a king would go to with a story like that.

'So the King went to the Arsenal where the country's weapons were stored and where the Duc de Sully had his apartments.' She was acting again; the same role for the King, but Bassompierre had been replaced by the Duc de Sully. ' "I don't understand this, Monsieur le Duc, but I feel in my heart that the shadow of death is right over my head." "Why, Sire, you alarm me. How can this be? You are well. Nothing ails you." The Duc de Sully had had a special chair made for the King to sit in when he visited him. It was low and very regal. The King sat in it, and looking very grave, he said: "It has been prophesied that I shall die in Paris. The time is near. I can sense it." '

'Did he really say that?' I asked. 'Or are you making it up?'

'It is all true,' Mamie assured me.

'Then he must have been a very clever man to see into the future.'

'He *was* a very clever man, but this is apart from cleverness. It is the special gift of clairvoyance, and magicians and sorcerers had been saying that the King would meet his death in Paris, and if ever the Queen was crowned, then the blow would fall.'

'Then why did he allow my mother to be crowned?'

'Because she would give him no rest until he did; he felt guilty about the Princesse de Condé; and he hated to deny a woman anything – even the Queen. He thought: Once I have given the

Queen her coronation – which is what she wants more than anything – she will leave me to pursue my heart's desire.'

'But if the prophecy was coming true how could he have his heart's desire with the Princesse de Condé?'

'I can tell you no more than what happened. In fact, the Duc de Sully was so impressed that he declared he would stop the preparation for the Queen's coronation as the thought of it so filled the King with foreboding. The King said: "Yes, break if off . . . for I have been told that I shall die in a carriage, and where could it be more easily done than at such a ceremony?" The Duc de Sully gazed earnestly at the King. "This explains much," he said. "I have often seen you cowering in your carriage when you pass certain places, and yet I know that in battle, there is not a braver man in France." '

'But they did not stop the coronation,' I pointed out, 'for my mother *was* crowned Queen of France.'

Mamie continued with her narrative. 'When the Queen heard that the coronation was to be cancelled, she was furious.' Mamie did not attempt to imitate my mother. She would not dare go as far as that. But I could imagine my mother's rage.

'For three whole days the matter was disputed. There will be a coronation. There will not be a coronation. And at last the King gave way in face of the Queen's demands and the coronation was fixed for the thirteenth of May at St Denis.'

'Thirteenth,' I said with a shiver. 'That is unlucky.'

'Unlucky for some,' agreed Mamie portentously. 'So she was crowned and it was arranged that on the sixteenth she should make her entry into Paris. Now. . . .'

She paused and I watched her with rounded eyes for I had heard the story before and I knew that we were approaching the terrible climax.

'Now . . . on Friday the fourteenth the King said he would go to the Arsenal to see the Duc de Sully. He was not sure whether he wanted to go or not. He hesitated. First he would go and then he thought he would not . . . but in the end he made up his mind. It was just to be a short visit after dinner. "I shall soon be back," he said. When he was about to get into his carriage, Monsieur de Praslin, Captain of the Guard, who always attended him even on the shortest journeys, came forward. "No need," said the King. Mamie waved her hand imperiously. "I don't want any attendance today. It is just to the Arsenal for a brief visit." Well, he got into the carriage and sat down with a few of his gentlemen. There were only six of them, not counting the Marquis de Mirabeau and the equerry who sat in the front of the carriage.

'Now comes the dramatic part. As the King's carriage came into the Rue de Ferronnerie close to that of St-Honoré, a cart came into the road, and because this blocked the way a little, the King's carriage had to go near to an ironmonger's shop on the St Innocent side. As the carriage slowed down a man rushed forward and hoisted himself onto the wheel and trust a knife at the King. It entered right here. . . .' She touched her left side. 'It went between his ribs and severed an artery. The gentlemen in the carriage cried out in horror as the blood gushed forth. "It is nothing," said the King. Then he said that again so quietly that it could scarcely be heard. They took him with all speed to the Louvre. They laid him on his bed and sent for the doctors – but it was too late. To the sorrow of France, the King passed away.'

I had heard the story many times and it never failed to move me to tears. I knew how the Duc de Sully had made everyone swear allegiance to my brother and how the entire country mourned, and that the mad monk Ravaillac was caught and torn apart by four wild horses to whom his body had been attached before they were sent off in different directions.

I knew that my mother had become Regent of France because my brother was only nine years old and too young to govern.

Had my father survived the assassination everything would have been different. As it was, I, a baby in her nursery, was to live my early years in a country torn by strife.

I attended a great many ceremonies of which I was unaware. Mamie told me of these later. Sometimes I tried to delude myself that I remembered – but I could not have done so. I was far too young.

The whole of France was mourning my father and calling vengeance on the madman who had killed him. There must have been a certain relief that he was a madman and that no revolutionary coup was intended. France had been satisfied with her King while he lived and when he was murdered he became a near saint. That was good because it augured well for my brother who

was such a boy at the time, and ministers are always afraid of boy
kings. They mean too many people near the throne jostling for
power.

I was taken in the procession with my brothers and sisters.
People wept, I was told, when they saw us. It was the impression
the Duc de Sully wished to create. He was one of the greatest
statesmen in the country and my father had recognized him as
such. Now all his allegiance was for my brother who had slipped
from the rôle of Dauphin to that of King.

How maddening it is that I cannot remember anything of what
pased and had to rely on Mamie's accounts. She made me see it
clearly but I was never sure that she was absolutely accurate; but
it is the custom for children, however young, to be present at
their dead parents' obsequies and naturally I, as one of the
Children of France, must have been there. 'You rode in the
carriage in the arms of my mother,' Mamie told me; and I could
imagine that child sitting there held firmly by a stern-faced
Madame de Montglat and later being with her at the bier on
which my dead father lay.

Madame de Montglat would have guided my hand while I
sprinkled holy water on my dead father's face. I hoped I performed the act with dignity, which must have been rather
difficult in the arms of Madame de Montglat; but presumably I
made no protest which was surely all that could have been
expected of me.

My next public appearance was at my brother's coronation, but
as I was then only eleven months old I remember nothing of that
either. The ceremony in the Cathedral of Rheims must have been
very impressive. Louis was nine years old then and a boy king is
always so appealing. I never really knew Louis well for he was no
longer in our nursery after he became King. Even my elder sister
Elizabeth was almost a stranger to me. Christine was with us for a
while, but Gaston and I were closer than any of the others
because we were near in age of course.

Mamie told me afterwards that on the great occasion I was
carried by the Princesse de Condé who, now that the King was
dead, had been allowed by her husband to return to Court.

So these great happenings took place when I was too young to
know what was going on. It was a little frustrating afterwards to
have known I was there and have no recollection of it.

But I was not going to remain a baby forever and I began to grow up in the nursery which I shared with Gaston and Christine, presided over by the stern Madame de Montglat and with Mamie there to bring laughter into our days.

My first real memory is of going to Bordeaux with a great cavalcade led by my mother to deliver my eldest sister Elizabeth to the King of Spain that she might marry his son and heir. At the same time she was to receive Anne of Austria, the daughter of the King of Spain, who was to marry our brother Louis. The importance of this occasion can be imagined, but at six years old this was just an exciting adventure to me. I did not know, of course, that the country was seething with discontent.

I loved ceremonies – all the pomp and glitter and the fine clothes, even though these were often uncomfortable to wear. I can remember Gaston often tore off his ruff and cried because it hurt his neck. He was severely beaten by Madame de Montglat who made him wear even stiffer ruffs to teach him a lesson. All people must be taught discipline, said Madame de Montglat, and none more so than royal children.

Poor Gaston! He was very rebellious in those days but I was even worse and gave way to my infantile furies by kicking, screaming, biting any hand that came near me, and lying on the floor and kicking.

'Disgraceful!' said Madame de Montglat. 'What would the Queen say?'

Those words could always sober us. 'I am afraid,' Madame de Montglat would warn, 'that if your behaviour does not improve I shall have to tell the Queen.'

The Queen paid visits to the nurseries very rarely and when she did it was a great occasion. She seemed enormous to me and was like a great battleship – invincible. One knew that she was the Queen as soon as one set eyes on her. When she arrived everybody changed – even Madame de Montglat – and became watchful, making quite sure they observed every trick of etiquette. They dared not forget for one instant that they were in the presence of the Queen. Not that she would let them! Gaston and I would come forth and bow low. She would incline her head, accept our homage and then take us onto her ample lap and kiss us.

Sometimes we thought she loved us dearly. She would ask what we were learning and remind us that we must never forget that we had had the good fortune to be brought up in the Holy Catholic Faith. I learned later that there was trouble in the country between the Catholics and the Huguenots and that when my father had been alive he had held that trouble in check. Now that he was dead the same leniency was not shown to Huguenots and in view of the fact that the country was less prosperous than it had been – owing to my mother's less effective rule – trouble loomed.

But what did a six-year-old girl sheltered in her royal nursery know of these matters?

Gaston and I would vie for our mother's interest while she was with us, and talk about her for days after her visit; we looked up expectantly every time a visitor came but after a while we ceased to expect her. I never did understand my mother. She was fond of us that was clear – but whether as her children or the Children of France, I was never quite sure. But I was fascinated by her – and Gaston was too. She was the Queen as well as our mother and we saw the effect she had on everyone in the nursery and we thought it must be wonderful to have people bow when you came into a room and show such respect for you.

It was always impressed on us that we must not forget that we were the children of a King and a Queen – and a King of France at that. Royal dignity must be maintained throughout our lives; and we must never forget that we were Catholics and we must uphold the true Faith wherever we found ourselves.

In our games we played Kings and Queens, and Gaston and I used to fight over which one should sit on the throne – an improvised chair – and receive the homage of the other.

'A King,' said Gaston, 'is more important than a Queen. In France a Queen cannot be Queen in her own right, because of the Salic Law.'

I was not going to allow that.

'A Queen is more important,' I said.

'No, she is not.'

My temper flared up. There were times when I hated Gaston. Madame de Montglat said I must learn to curb that temper of mine or it would destroy me one day. That made me think. I wondered what it was like to be destroyed. She made it sound terrible and sometimes when I remembered her words they did sober me a little – but not for long. I could never resist the joy of letting myself fall into a rage. It was the only way I could express my anger.

But I had an irrefutable case on this occasion and I let my rage simmer. 'What of our mother, eh? She is a Queen and the most important person in the land. She is greater than the Duc de Sully who used to be so important and is no longer so. Why? Because our mother does not like him. A Queen can be as great as a King . . . greater perhaps. What about wicked Queen Elizabeth of England who defeated the Spanish Armada?'

'You mustn't speak of her. She was a. . . .' He put his lips to my ear and whispered the terrible word: 'Heretic!'

'Queens can be as good as Kings and this is my throne so kneel to me or I shall send you to the torture chambers. But first I will tell our mother that you think Queens are of no importance.'

It would have been wiser to play at puss-in-the-corner or blind-man's-buff.

But for all our quarrels we were fond of each other.

Monsieur de Breves, who was a very learned man, came each morning to give us lessons in the nursery. These were for my elder sisters Elizabeth and Christine, but Gaston and I took part. Perhaps Monsieur de Breves was too learned to understand young children; perhaps Gaston and I were incapable of giving our minds to anything for long. (My sister Elizabeth said our minds were like butterflies flitting here and there and seemed incapable of settling anywhere long enough to absorb everything.) In any case Gaston and I were not academically inclined and while we sat listening to Monsieur de Breves and making futile attempts to grapple with the problems he set us, we were waiting impatiently for the time when we could go off to our dancing lessons.

At least our dancing master was pleased with us – and particularly with me. 'Ah, Madame Henriette,' he would cry folding his arms across his chest and raising his eyes to the ceiling, 'but that was beautiful . . . beautiful. Ah, my dear Princesse, you are going to enchant the Court.'

I was never happier than when dancing – unless it was singing.

I noticed one day when we were in the schoolroom listening – or trying to listen – to Monsieur de Breves, and I was thinking how pretty Christine's dress was and wondering whether I might ask Madame de Montglat if I could have one like it, that Elizabeth was looking rather sad and very preoccupied and was not paying any attention at all to Monsieur de Breves.

I thought: I believe she has been crying.

How strange! Elizabeth was seven years older than I. She and Christine were great friends although Christine was a good deal younger than she was. Elizabeth had always treated Gaston and me with a kindly tolerance. She had always seemed far beyond us – almost grown up. It was difficult to imagine her crying. But yes. Her eyes were red. Something had happened. I wondered what.

Monsieur de Breves was standing close to me and had picked up the paper on which I was supposed to have written something – I was not sure what and I had been so concerned with Elizabeth that I had not thought to look at Gaston's and copy his, although this was always risky for what he wrote invariably displayed as great an ignorance as mine.

'Ah, Madame la Princesse,' said Monsieur de Breves sadly, shaking his head, 'I fear we are never going to make a scholar of you.'

I smiled at him. I had for some time realized that when I smiled in a certain way I could melt the anger or disappointment of a number of people. Alas, neither my mother nor Madame de Montglat was among them.

I said: 'No, Monsieur de Breves, but my dancing master says that my dancing will delight the Court.'

He smiled faintly and patted my shoulder. That was all. No reprimand. What a smile could do! If only I could turn the magic on Madame de Montglat.

My thoughts went back to Elizabeth and later on I came upon her sitting alone.

She had gone back to the schoolroom expecting no doubt to find no one there at this hour, and she was sitting on a window seat, her hands covering her face.

I was right. There were tears.

I put my arms about her neck and kissed her.

'Elizabeth,' I said. 'Dear sister. What ails you? Tell Henriette.'

There was a brief silence during which I thought she was about to order me away angrily. I gave her my conquering smile and suddenly she put her arms about me.

'There!' I said. 'There!' I patted her back, marvelling that I, the baby, should be comforting my elder sister.

'Dear little one,' said Elizabeth, more kindly than she had ever spoken to me before – not that she had ever been unkind, only seeming to be unaware of my existence.

'You are unhappy. What is wrong?'

'Oh, you wouldn't understand.'

'I would. I would.'

Elizabeth sighed. 'I am going away . . . away from you all.'

'Away? Why? Where?'

'To Spain.'

'Why are you going to Spain?'

'To marry the King's son.'

'The son of the King of Spain! Oh, Elizabeth, when the King dies you will be the Queen of Spain!'

'Does that surprise you?'

'No,' I said. 'I know we all have to marry. What surprises me is that you are sad when you are going to be Queen of Spain.'

'And you think that is worth . . . losing everything else for?'

'It must be wonderful to be a Queen.'

'Oh, Henriette, what of your family? Suppose you had to go and leave us all . . . go to a new country. . . .'

I considered it. Giving up everything . . . Mamie, Gaston, Madame de Montglat . . . my sisters . . . my mother. . . . And all in exchange for a crown!

'You are too young to understand, Henriette,' went on Elizabeth. 'It will come to you one day. You must be prepared for it.'

'When?'

'Oh there is a long time to wait yet. How old are you? Six. I am seven years older than you. In seven years your time will come.'

Seven years! It was too far in the future to be considered. It was longer than the time I had been on Earth.

'Louis will be married too,' said Elizabeth. 'Lucky Louis, he will not have to leave his home.'

'Do you hate going so much?'

'I don't want to leave my home. To go into . . . I do not know what. It's frightening, Henriette. It will be easier for you. You will have seen my going . . . and Christine's before your time comes, so it won't be such a shock.'

She set me down and blinked away the tears.

'Don't tell anyone that you found me like this. Not even Mamie or Gaston.'

I promised.

'Our mother would be angry. She thinks it is wonderful that she has brought about this match with Spain. Some of the people are not too pleased.'

'Who isn't pleased?'

'The Huguenots.'

'Huguenots! What concern is it of theirs?'

She took my face in her hands and kissed me. It was rare affection from Elizabeth.

'You are so young,' she said. 'You don't know anything of what is going on outside.'

'Outside where?'

'In the world . . . beyond the Court. Never mind. You will in time.'

She had stood up and, straightening her dress, became the Elizabeth I knew, inclined to be disdainful of her little sister's youth.

'Run along now, dear,' she said, 'and forget what I have said.'

But of course I was not going to forget. Many times I was on the verge of telling Mamie or Gaston. I felt it very difficult to restrain myself for I should have felt very superior for once to have discovered something they did not know. But I remembered my promise.

I did not have to wait long, for a few days after my encounter with Elizabeth our mother arrived in the nursery. Gaston and I did our ceremonious bows and when she held out her hand to us we approached and stood one on either side of her. I found myself staring at her bosom, which always fascinated me. It was one of the biggest bosoms I had ever seen and very different from that of Madame de Montglat, which was almost non-existent.

'Now, my children,' she said. 'I have come to tell you some very good news. Your dear brother the King is about to be married.'

I gasped and stopped myself just in time from blurting out: 'But I thought it was Elizabeth who is going to be married.'

We saw little of our brother Louis. Now that he was the King he was too important to be in our nursery and had to be taken away to have special tuition.

The Queen went on: 'His dear little wife will come here to be with you for a while . . . but only until she is old enough to go to her husband. We are going to Bordeaux where we shall meet the new little Queen of France, whose father is giving her into our care. She is to be married to your brother. And now that we are taking his daughter from the King of Spain we think he might be a little unhappy so we are giving him our Princess Elizabeth. She is to be the wife of the son of the King of Spain. You were both at the proxy ceremony. You don't remember. You were too young. It took place three years ago at the Palais Royal. You were only four then, Gaston, and you were three, Henriette.'

'I remember,' cried Gaston. 'There was dancing and a banquet. . . .'

'I remember too,' I put in, although I did not, but I was not going to be outdone by my brother.

'Well, that is good,' went on our mother. 'There will be a real marriage now. So we are all going to Bordeaux and I have decided that it will be good for you children to come too.'

Our mother drew away to look at us closely.

I could see the questions trembling on Gaston's lips, but he was always afraid to speak too freely in our mother's presence.

The Queen went on: 'It is a most happy occasion. It is an alliance with Spain. The daughter of a Spanish King will be a Queen of France and our daughter a Queen of Spain. Fair exchange, eh? Spain will be our ally and my daughter . . . Queen of Spain. She has married well, and what delights me as much as her crown is that she is going into a Catholic country.'

I was afraid then that our mother was going to ask how we were getting on with our religious instruction and I was just as scatterbrained with that as I was with other subjects.

But, however, she did not. She was clearly too excited by the marriages she had arranged.

'There will be many preparations to be made,' she said. 'You will have new clothes.'

I clasped my hands in joy. I loved new clothes and I knew that those we would have to attend a grand wedding would be very grand indeed.

The preparations for this great occasion went on. I learned

afterwards that there were murmurings in the streets against my mother but I did not know of them then.

We seemed to spend long periods being fitted. I laughed at Gaston in his scarlet velvet coat and broad-brimmed beaver hat. He looked like a miniature cavalier. And I was like a lady of the Court in my puffed sleeves and wide cuffs, looped-up skirts and laces and ribbons. Everyone in our household came in to admire us and we loved our clothes – apart from the ever-present ruffs. 'I shall never get used to them,' I declared; and Gaston hated them even more than I did.

Elizabeth's gown was more glorious than anything we had ever seen. I heard my mother say that she must impress the Spaniards with our infinitely better taste. Poor Elizabeth, in spite of the fact that she was going to be a Queen in a Catholic country she stood with a look of cold indifference on her face while she was fitted with the most sumptuously trimmed gowns; and I could not forget the sight of her sad face above all that splendour.

In due course we left for Bordeaux. On some occasions I rode on one side of my mother, Gaston on the other.

I heard two people whispering. I think they were minor attendants. 'She thinks the people will so like those two pretty children that they will forget how much they dislike her.'

And there was no doubt that the people liked us. I smiled and lifted my hand in acknowledgement of their cheers just as I had been taught to do.

They cheered Louis too. After all he was the King, and I heard Elizabeth say to Christine that he was too young to have done anything the people did not like.

'All their blame is for our mother and the Maréchal d'Ancre,' said Elizabeth.

I wanted to know more. Why should they blame my mother, and who was the Maréchal d'Ancre, that Concino Concini about whom I had heard people whispering?

Although I hated to learn lessons I was avid to gather information about what was happening around me. The trouble is that when you are six no one considers you seriously enough to talk to you.

We stayed at castles and great houses on the way to Bordeaux and there we were entertained lavishly. Gaston and I were allowed to dance on certain occasions and I sang, for singing was another of my accomplishments and my singing master said I had the voice of a nightingale.

My mother was very pleased with us, and I kept wondering whether it was because she loved us or because it was necessary to make the people pleased with the children she had brought into the royal nurseries so that they would forget those mysterious things she appeared to have done which annoyed them.

However neither Gaston nor I was given to introspection – certainly not at the ages of seven and six; and we were going to enjoy ourselves.

'This is an exciting life!' I said to Gaston; and he agreed wholeheartedly.

In due course we reached Bordeaux.

We were not present at the important ceremony of handing over the two Princesses, but we did dance at the celebrations which followed; and when we left Bordeaux we had lost our sister Elizabeth and had gained a sister-in-law who was known as Anne of Austria and, as she was married to our brother Louis, she was Queen of France.

When we returned to Paris the excitement increased. We had to show Anne of Austria and her attendants how much more cultured we were in France than they were in Spain.

As we came into the city, the narrow streets were crowded with people who had come to see the new Queen. Nobody loves pageantry more than the Parisians and they evidently liked the look of Anne as she rode beside Louis at the head of the cavalcade. She was a tall girl with a good figure and as fair as I was dark. Moreover she was young – just about the same age as Louis. She had beautiful hands, which she was fond of bringing into display, and she seemed very sure of herself. I thought we might get on well together for I had already discovered that she was not very good at learning but enjoyed singing and dancing as much as I did.

We rode past the new house of the Place Royale and the Place Dauphine which my father had caused to be built. I had been watching Anne to see if she was impressed by our grand city. My father had believed in building and he had made great improvements in Paris.

'Ah, Madame la Princesse,' the old ones used to say, 'you are lucky to live in such a city. In my day it was a very different place. Thanks to your great father we have now the finest city in the world.'

I had heard how he had completed the old Arsenal – that building to which he had been making his way when he was murdered – and he had built the Hôtel de Ville also. I had been taken to see them on one occasion and I had been completely overawed by the magnificent staircase, the moulded ceilings, the sculptured doors and the most wonderful fireplace in the throne room.

My father had done all that. People constantly said, when speaking of him: 'What a tragedy! Oh what a tragedy for France!'

And sometimes I felt a flash of uneasiness because I realized that criticism of the present rule was implied – and present rule was, of course, my mother, for Louis was too young to be blamed for anything.

I was so proud as we approached the Louvre. We called it the New Louvre because the ancient one had become so unhealthy and decrepit that François Premier, who had loved fine buildings, had decided to rebuild it. It was hardly begun when he died, but the next King, Henri Deux, and his wife Catherine de Medicis also loved fine buildings and they went on with it. I, too, love beautiful things and until the day I left France I was always thrilled by that glorious façade of Jean Bullant and Philibert Delorme every time I went past the New Louvre.

Now the celebrations began in real earnest. We could be so much more lavish in Paris than they could be in provincial towns, and we were going to show these Spaniards how rich and clever we were.

For a while everyone must forget his or her grievances and enjoy the occasion. I had rarely seen my mother so happy. She was so pleased with the marriages. Later she began to imbue me with a firm belief in the true Faith and the determination to preserve it wherever I was. There were two precepts which must be upheld at all cost: the true Faith and the determination to enforce it on all people for their own good; and the other was the importance of Royalty, the right to rule which had been bestowed on kings and queens by God: The Divine Right of Royalty.

But stern as she was on these two points, she did enjoy

feasting, banquets and fêtes; and she was determined to indulge these pastimes no matter what old Sully would say. Not that that mattered. He could grumble away to his heart's desire in retirement. He had been shown the door as soon as he had lost his master.

No expense was to be spared. Everyone was going to rejoice in the marriage which she – the Queen Mother now that there was a new Queen – had brought about.

For me it was a wonderful time. I forgot lessons, the dull routine, the admonitions of Madame de Montglat – they were all in the past. Here we were celebrating the marriage of our King, and I was going to enjoy every minute of it.

I danced. I sang. 'What an enchanting creature little Madame Henriette is!' I heard that more than once and I was quick to see the pleasure in my mother's face.

Such happiness! I prayed that it would go on for ever.

There was Spanish influence in quite a number of our entertainments – in honour of the Queen, of course. Some of our gentlemen performed the Galanterie Castellane and there were quadrilles and Spanish dances. Gaston and I learned a little Spanish *pas de deux* which we performed together to the delight of everyone at Court. Some of the company dressed up as gods. I sat round-eyed watching while Jupiter led in Apollo and Diana; and then came Venus, who knelt before our young King and Queen and chanted verses about La Belle Espagnole. Poor Louis hated it all and found it very hard to smile and pretend he was happy. Perhaps he had not wanted to marry and was a little worried about all it entailed . . . just as Elizabeth had been. The Queen however threw back her long fair tresses and flourishing her pretty hands quite clearly enjoyed it.

At one point my hand was taken by an old woman who made me sit beside her.

I did not know who she was at first but I was intrigued by her and considerably overawed. She had a regal air so I guessed she was of importance but I could not think what she could want with me.

Her old hands clawed mine and she studied me intently. I could not take my eyes from her. Her face was wrinkled; her eyes were deeply shadowed; but she wore so much rouge and white lead that from a distance she might have been quite young. She had a wig of luxuriant black curls, and her clothes struck me as belonging to an earlier age. Her gold-braided houppelande was certainly out of date.

She said: 'So you are the little Madame Henriette.'

I agreed that I was.

'And how old are you?'

'Six years.'

'A baby,' she commented.

'Indeed not.'

She laughed and touched my cheek. 'Beautiful soft skin,' she said. 'Mine was like that . . . once. When I was your age I was the prettiest girl in the whole of France . . . and I was the cleverest, too. I was old for my years, they said. Are you, little one?'

'I don't know.'

'Then you can't be, can you? Little Margot knew everything. She was born with knowledge.'

'Are you . . . La Reine Margot?'

'Ah, so little Madame Henriette has heard of me! Yes, you might have been my daughter – think of that. I was your father's wife before he married Marie de Medicis.'

I was overawed. I had heard of her, of course, but never had I thought I would meet her. She had been notorious in her youth . . . and after.

She said: 'Your father and I hated each other. We fought like two wild cats. Then we divorced and he married your mother. If he had not, *you* would not be here, would you? What a calamity! Can you imagine a world without Madame Henriette?'

I remarked that it would be rather difficult for me to do that if I were not here.

She laughed.

"He hated me, but he hated his second wife even more, they say. Strange is it not, that a man who loved women more than any other man in France should have had two wives whom he hated.'

'You should not talk about my mother like that.'

She came close to me. 'La Reine Margot always says what she means and cares not whom it may offend. So do you think little six-year-old Madame Henriette will stop me?'

'No,' I answered.

'I like you,' she said. 'You are very pretty. I will tell you

something. You are prettier than the new Queen. I don't think
our lord Louis is very impressed with her, do you?'
    'My mother would not wish me. . . .'
    'To give an opinion? But, little Henriette, when you grow up
you are going to state your opinions whether people like it or not.
Don't you agree with me?'
    'Yes, I expect I shall. But I have to get a little older first.'
    'You are getting older every minute while you talk to me. Oh,
little one, do I look very old to you?'
    'Very old.'
    'Look at my beautiful skin. Look at my lovely hair. You do not
know what to say, do you? Once I had beautiful luxuriant hair.
Many men loved me. Oh yes, I have had many lovers . . . and still
do. But not so many now. I don't remember ever having been
innocent as you are, my beautiful child. When I married your
father I was not innocent. It was an ill-fated marriage. The streets
ran with blood. Have you ever heard of the Massacre of St
Bartholomew's Eve?'
    I said I had.
    'Catholics and Huguenots – and your father coming very near
to death then. They meant to get him. But he survived. He
would. Like a country boy, he was . . . crude . . . rough . . . no
mate for an elegant Princesse . . . not cultured as I was. We
disliked each other from the start. Catholic and Huguenot . . . I
wonder if they will ever live in harmony.'
    'I hope that the Huguenots will give up heresy and come to the
true Faith.'
    'You are repeating what you have heard, little one. Don't do
that. Think for yourself as I always did. Do I frighten you?'
    I hesitated.
    'I do,' she went on. 'Well, now go, little one. You are a beautiful
child and I hope you will have as vivid a life as I have had.'
    I said: 'I like sitting here talking to you.'
    The hand pressed mine and she smiled.
    'You must go. Your mother would not wish you to talk too long
with me. I think she has noticed us . . . or one of her spies has.
The King is her son but I have as much right as anyone to be here
when there is a wedding in the family.'
    A young man was approaching and I saw her interest in me
fade.

He came and bowed before her.

'*Ma belle Margot!*' he said softly and she smiled and held out her hand.

I knew it was then time for me to leave.

I never forgot her and was extraordinarily moved when a year later I heard that she had died. She was sixty-three years old then and I found it hard to believe that anyone could live so long. When Mamie came to us she told me lots of stories about La Reine Margot; her life seemed to have been one long succession of lovers and wild adventures. I was surprised to hear that she and my mother had been quite friendly.

'I should have thought she would have hated my mother who took her place,' I commented to Mamie.

'Oh no,' Mamie corrected me. 'She liked her because of it. Every time she saw her she would say how lucky she was to be rid of your father. And your mother was in sympathy with her because they had both had to – as they would say – "put up with him" and knew what a troublesome matter that could be. It made a bond between them.'

So she was dead and that wild and exciting life was over for ever.

Those celebrations were certainly an important event in my life. I ceased to be a child during them. For instance it was the first time I saw the Maréchal d'Ancre about whom people were constantly talking. Christine pointed him out to me. 'Look,' she said, 'there is the Maréchal talking to our mother. I don't think our brother likes him very much.'

'Why not?' I asked.

Christine was about to speak when she looked at me and I guessed she was reminding herself that I was only a child.

'Oh, he has his reasons, I'll swear,' she said and then she left me.

I noticed my brother, the King, was sitting looking at the proceedings with a disconsolate air. His Queen was beside him, smiling, fluttering her fan and now and then putting up one of her hands to touch her mantilla – not to adjust it but to bring her pretty hands into prominence. She looked very Spanish and I wondered whether the people were going to like that. Louis spoke very little to her. He stammered quite a bit when he was in a temper or alarmed about something. I suspected he was in one of his stammering phases now.

Then he was smiling suddenly because Charles d'Albert had come to sit beside him and it was immediately clear that he enjoyed the company of Charles d'Albert better than that of his Queen.

I knew a little about Charles d'Albert because there was a great deal of talk about him around the nurseries.

'Another of those Italians,' I heard one of the attendants say. The man was standing beneath my window at the time and even though I had to take a few paces back to hide myself, I was able to hear what was said.

The man to whom he was talking replied: 'We have had our fill of them since the King went to Italy for a wife.'

'And married one of the Medicis at that! It would have been better if he had stayed with La Reine Margot.'

They said something about La Reine Margot which I did not understand and they laughed heartily. I could tell by the sound of their feet on the gravel that they were pushing each other to make their point.

'Well, we wouldn't have had a new King if he had not married her.'

'No, no. For all her tricks Margot was no hand at producing the goods.'

More laughter and jostling.

'They say he's getting a real hold on the young King. . . .'

'Won't do him much good with Maman in control. Concini will see to that.'

'Another Italian! Isn't it time France was for the French?'

'Yes, I agree. But don't worry about Albert. The King is in leading strings and likely to remain there as far as I can see. He's no Henri Quatre.'

'Ah, there was a man!' There followed what I guessed to be more shuffling and jostling, but to my chagrin they moved away. I should have liked to hear more about Charles d'Albert.

I was interested though and kept my ears open. It was no use asking questions – everyone either considered I was too young to understand or they did not want to waste time on me.

So I listened and at the time of the wedding I did know that Charles d'Albert was originally Alberti and he had come to France from Florence to make his fortune. When he found he could do this he decided to become French and changed his name to Albert. He came to the King's notice because he was clever with birds and trained hawks. He loved to hunt with them and as the King did too that made a bond between them and they soon became very friendly. My brother made him his very special falconer and they were constantly in each other's company training birds and making nets and thongs for hawking. Albert could train other birds and he was very clever with little sporting birds like *pies grièches* which, I discovered later, in England, were called butcher birds.

It was very interesting to see the young man of whom I had heard so much. He was considerably older than my brother Louis and he had certainly made his fortune at the Court of France. He had married, through the King's graces, Mademoiselle Rohan Montbazon, who was recognized as one of the beauties of the Court.

Watching them now it was easy to see that he was on very familiar terms with the King.

I sat on a stool close to them. It was sometimes an advantage to be so young that one was ignored. I listened to their talk. They were discussing hunting and Albert was asking the King to come as soon as he could to see a new falcon which he had acquired and of which he had high hopes.

They talked of falconry for some time and then Albert said suddenly: 'Look at Concini over there. What airs that man gives himself!'

'You are right,' said my brother. He was not stammering now that he was talking to Albert which was a sign that he was completely at his ease.

'Your royal mother seems besotted by the man. I believe he thinks himself more royal than she is.'

'I dislike him, Charles. He tries to tell *me* what to do.'

'What impertinence! You should not allow that, Sire.'

I looked up and saw the pleased look on my brother's face. He loved people to recognize his royalty. They did in the streets, of course, and cheered him as the King out of loyalty to our father, Christine said; but there were always those to tell him what to do. It must be a trial to be a King in name and not old enough to be one in fact.

'There'll come a time,' said Louis.

'And I pray the saints it will not long be delayed,' added Charles d'Albert.

'Concini and the Queen Mother will delay it as long as possible you may be sure.'

'Indeed they will. They want to rule, and how can they do that if the King is in his rightful place?'

'I won't always be a boy.'

'If you will forgive my saying so, Sire, you have the attributes of a man already.'

I could see why Louis was fond of Albert. This was the way he liked people to talk to him. 'The time will come . . .' he said.

'Soon, Sire, soon.'

Someone had come forward and was bowing to Louis. I slipped away.

I realized later that I had been listening to the beginning of a plot.

Those wedding festivities were a turning point in my life. My mother seemed to realize that I was growing up, and because I was dainty and pretty and could sing and dance well, the people liked me. It was necessary for her to be seen with us children because the people always cheered Gaston and me and she could pretend the cheers were for her. In fact the only way she could get the people to cheer when her carriage rode by was to have us in it.

My mother loved displays of any sort – banquets, ballets, any kind of dancing and singing; she loved fine clothes too and was determined to have them because she believed that entertainments of a lavish nature made the people forget their grievances. It was no wonder that she had forced the Duc de Sully into retirement. He would have been horrified to see the exchequer, which he had always kept under his control and that of my father, dwindling away.

Paris was becoming a very beautiful city; and my mother liked to call attention to all that she and the late King had done to make it so. She wanted to give balls and fêtes throughout Paris. This she did and the people certainly loved to see the carriages passing through the streets and to catch glimpses of the nobility in all their splendour. On summer evenings the whole Court would go to the Place Royale where my father had begun to build what he intended to be a bazaar, lined with shops rather like St Mark's in Venice. My mother was very enthusiastic – possibly because of its Italian associations, and as my father had died before it was completed, she had had it finished in time for the wedding. There was a promenade known as the Cours de la Reine because she had planted several rows of trees along it and in an attempt to win the people's favour had opened it to the public.

They thronged there and were delighted to catch glimpses of the grand seigneurs and ladies walking in the gardens.

Alas, it needed more than that to win the people's favour, and even if my mother had been the best of rulers, she could not have hoped for great popularity because she was an Italian.

Many of the nobles lived in the houses of the Place Royale and they all had magnificent gardens with wonderful examples of the skill of topiary, and the sculptured figures and glistening fountains were a splendid sight.

'See what a wonderful city we have given you!' That was what my mother was saying.

But the people continued to dislike her and they complained bitterly about the rise of Concini.

It was about this time that Mamie was brought into the nurseries to help her mother with the children. That meant chiefly Gaston and me, for Christine was at that time nine years old and so considered herself to be very grown up.

Mamie did not seem old to me although most people over fourteen usually did. She was even older than that – in her middle teens, I believe – and I loved her from the moment I set eyes on her.

She exuded an air of wisdom; she was serene; and she did not treat me as a child, so that I could ask her questions without fearing to expose my ignorance as I did with most people.

Then there was Anne, the new Queen, who was only thirteen and not quite old enough to be a wife, so I saw a great deal of her too.

We liked each other in a mild kind of way – not as I liked Mamie, of course, but although Anne gave herself certain airs and was a little coquettish in a rather prim way, she was not clever and hardly ever looked at a book, and this endeared her to me; she was lazy and did all she could to evade lessons; and she loved dancing and singing and we discussed ballets and danced and sang together; and she, with Gaston and me, arranged a

dance which we said we would perform together whenever we
had the opportunity to do so.

So I had two welcome additions to my life in Anne and dear
Mamie. The days seemed to have become full of pleasure. I had
no notion of the storms which were gathering in the country.

Then I began to learn, through Mamie, something of what was
going on.

'You should know,' she told me. 'It is a time of great events and
as the daughter of a King you may well have your part to play in
it.'

That made me feel very important.

It was then that she told me about the murder of my father and
that ever since his death my mother had been Regent and would
doubtless remain so until it was considered that my brother Louis
was of an age to rule.

'When will that be?' I asked. 'Poor Louis. He is not much like a
king.'

'It might be sooner than you think.'

She pursed his lips and looked mysterious, glancing over her
shoulder in a manner which I found most exciting. That was
Mamie's way. She created intrigue and made mystery around it.

I remember flinging my arms about her – it must have been
some six months after she had come to the nursery – and making
her promise that she would never go away.

She had stroked my hair and rocked me to and fro. 'I'll never go
until they force me to,' she promised.

For all her exciting outlook on life, Mamie was a realist. 'It could
be that the time will come when I shall have to go. But for now
. . . we are safe. I don't think anyone wants to part us. To tell the
truth my mother finds me too useful here with you children.'

'Gaston loves you too,' I told her. 'And Christine also . . .
although she doesn't show it as I do.'

'Poor Christine! She thinks a great deal about the Princesse
Elizabeth, and she fears that one day what has happened to her
sister will happen to her.'

'Will it?'

Mamie nodded slowly. 'Almost certainly,' she said. 'Princesses
usually marry.'

'I am a Princesse. . . .'

'A little one. You have a lot of growing up to do.'

She was comforting me, but I knew what was in store for me although it had not yet appeared on the horizon. But it would come, because it came to all Princesses.

'We shall always be together,' I said fiercely.

And she did not deny that we should.

She changed my life for me. Although it would soon have changed after the wedding in any case, she put something beautiful into it. I realized for the first time that I wanted a mother – someone to care about me, to scold me at times, to tell me about life, to comfort me when I needed comfort, someone who was the most important person in the world to me – and I to her. I felt I was beginning to get somewhere near that relationship with Mamie. And how strange it was that only then I knew that I had missed it.

She began to make me aware. She told me what was happening all around me. It was by no means what it seemed, and sometimes it was a little frightening, but as conveyed by Mamie always exciting.

'Who is Concini?' I asked, and instead of telling me it was no concern of mine, and that I should know all I needed to know when I was older, she told me.

My mother had brought Italians with her when she came to France. It was inevitable. Usually attendants were dismissed when a young princess came into a new country, but Marie de Medicis had kept some of hers, and many were saying that it was to the detriment of France.

'She brought with her Elenora Galagaï,' Mamie told me, 'who was the daughter of her nurse and who had been brought up with her. They grew up to be very fond of each other . . . like two sisters.'

'As we are . . . you and I, Mamie,' I put in.

'Yes,' agreed Mamie. 'It is very like that. Well, when she came to France to marry the King, your mother refused to be parted from Elenora Galagaï and brought her with her. Then because she wanted to see her settled she arranged for her to be married to a man for whom she had the greatest regard. This was another Italian who had come with her to France – Concino Concini. He was the son of a notary from Florence and she had made him her secretary. They were married and, of course, being such favourites of the Queen, they planned to make their fortunes.'

'And did they?' I asked.

'My dear Princesse! Did they indeed! Concini became the Maréchal d'Ancre. You know of him.'

'I saw him at the wedding celebrations with my mother. Charles d'Albert, who was with my brother, did not seem to like him very much.'

'Oh Charles d'Albert! It is said that the King listens to him more than he does to his mother.'

Gradually I began to learn more and more of what was going on outside the nursery. Mamie was such a vivid talker and I never ceased to marvel that she had made me her special friend. That honour might so easily have been reserved for Christine who was so much older than I, or even Gaston who could give me a year. But no! *I* was the one, and for that I promised myself that I would be grateful to her for ever more.

'At times,' she said, 'I forget how young you are. Never mind,' she went on as though to excuse herself. 'You will have to play a part in all this one day so it is as well that you should be pre-pared.'

I remember the great excitement just after the wedding. The Prince de Condé was at the centre of it. Mamie had already told me how he had married Mademoiselle de Montmorency when my father had wanted her to be his 'little friend' and how the Prince had turned out to be not quite the indifferent husband my father had hoped he would be. Apparently when my father had died, the Prince had brought his wife back to Paris because there was no need then for him to keep her hidden away.

'It had been a very stormy marriage,' Mamie told me. 'Many marriages are.'

I was not surprised to hear this and remembered what I had heard of my father's marriages to La Reine Margot and to my mother.

'The Princesse was very angry because he had taken her away from Court. She had quite looked forward to being your father's 'little friend'. She would have had all the advantages of being a queen and none of the disadvantages. And what had Henri de Condé done? Dragged her away. For what? His indifferent attentions? She has held that against him ever since.'

I had seen them at one of the *fêtes* at the time of the wedding. The Princesse was very beautiful and I could understand why my father had been attracted by her.

A week or so after the wedding festivities the Prince de Condé was arrested.

'He has plotted to overthrow the Maréchal d'Ancre,' said Mamie, 'and has tried to assemble the nobles of France against the man he calls the Italian Schemer.'

'Arrested!' I cried. 'But he is a royal Prince!'

'Royal Princes can be arrested for plotting against the Queen Mother.'

'He has really plotted against my mother?'

'Dear Princesse, he has plotted against the Maréchal d'Ancre, and that can be said to be plotting against the Queen Mother. There is a great deal of excitement in the streets. They are saying that a great many wish the plot had succeeded. But the Italian is too wily for that.'

'What will happen to the Prince?'

'I doubt they will dare execute him. He may well be sent to prison.'

'At least,' I said, 'the Princesse de Condé will be rid of him now.'

She hugged me suddenly. 'Oh, my dear Princesse, we live in dangerous times.'

Everybody was talking about the coup that had failed and there was a surprising sequel. The Prince was exiled to Vincennes and instead of congratulating herself that she was rid of him, the Princesse de Condé declared her intention of joining him there in captivity and living with him as his faithful wife.

'People are very strange,' commented Mamie. Then she laughed and kissed me. 'It is good that they are,' she went on. 'It makes life more interesting.'

About this time Mère Magdalaine, a Carmelite nun, was chosen to look after my spiritual welfare. I spent long sessions with her; we prayed together; we asked for help; and she made me realize – as my mother did – that the most important motive in one's life was to promote the Catholic Faith, bringing all those who were outside it to the Truth.

The days sped by . . . religious instruction from Mère Magdalaine, lessons from François Savary de Breves, playing games with Gaston and the children of noblemen, dancing, singing, happy hours with Mamie . . . they were the pleasant days.

It was only just beginning to occur to me that they could change.

There was more talk than ever about Concini after the Prince de Condé went into confinement.

'There is a great deal of dissatisfaction with Concini,' Mamie told me, 'and the King is getting older. He is with Charles d'Albert more than ever, but Albert is only as powerful as the King is, whereas Concini walks with the Queen Mother.'

'You talk as though my mother and the King are enemies.'

'Perhaps that is because they are,' said Mamie.

Then she went on to tell me about Concini's vast possessions. 'He has several beautiful *châteaux* in the country as well as two in Paris. He has vineyards and farms. They say he is one of the richest men in France and the people do not like that because they say that when he came here he had nothing.'

'He has worked hard for my mother,' I said.

'And for himself,' added Mamie.

One day, in an unguarded moment, she said: 'There is something in the air. I feel it in the streets. There are two factions now: the King with Charles d'Albert and the Queen Mother with Concini. Albert and Concini . . . both Italians . . . and the people don't like either of them.'

'Well,' I pointed out. 'My mother is Italian so both I and my brother are half Italians.'

'You are French,' cried Mamie fiercely. 'You are your father's children and he was one of the greatest Frenchmen who ever lived.'

It was all very puzzling to me but I enjoyed hearing the news and I must confess to a certain disappointment when life continued smoothly. Sometimes I felt I wanted things to happen, and even tragic horrible things were better than nothing. They brought excitement into the monotony of my daily life.

'Concini and his wife are shipping their wealth to Italy, so I heard,' Mamie told me one day. 'That looks to me as though they intend to flit. It would be a wise thing for them to do that from what I hear in the streets. The people are gathering against them . . . sharpening their knives. . . .' She laughed at me. 'Oh, I did not mean that literally, my child. I mean they are preparing to drive him out of the country.'

It could only have been a few days after that when the trouble started. Secretly Charles d'Albert had been plotting with the King and their idea was to get rid of Concini, for without him the Queen Mother would be powerless. She was not interested in statecraft – which had been obvious since the Regency – and she looked to Concini to see to all that for her – with the aid of his friends, of course. She liked food and had grown fat; she liked gaiety, religion, and parading her royalty. People said unkindly that that was all that could be expected of a banker's daughter.

It seemed that Charles d'Albert had decided that the moment had come to strike. The King was growing up. He should exert his rights or he would remain a puppet for years.

The King signed a warrant for Concini's arrest, which was delivered by six of the King's guards. I can imagine Concini's astonishment when he – who had been supreme – was suddenly confronted by the King's men. He must have wished that he had followed his inclination and left for Italy. We learned afterwards that he would have gone but for his wife who had insisted that the time was not yet ripe and that there were many more pickings to be had and thus they could augment their wealth.

Elenora Galigaï was proved wrong.

It was natural that such an important person as the Maréchal d'Ancre should demand to know on what grounds he was being arrested, and that when he was told to be silent and that they must leave right away, he should resist arrest. He drew his sword and that was the signal for which they had all been waiting. The guards fell upon him with their daggers and within seconds it was a bleeding corpse which lay at their feet. In the meantime, having seen the guards going into the residence of the mighty Maréchal d'Ancre, a crowd had gathered and when the guards appeared on the balcony dragging out the dead body of the once-powerful Maréchal, the mob became frenzied with excitement.

One of the guards cried out: 'Here is the body of the Italian Concini, Maréchal d'Ancre, for whose pleasure you have been paying dearly through your taxes.'

With that they threw the body over the balcony and the mob seized it, savagely mutilating it, calling vengeance on all Italian schemers, and declaring that from henceforth France was to be for the French.

That was the signal. The people had spoken.

'Now,' prophesied Mamie, 'there will be change.'

How right she was! My brother lost no time in appointing Charles d'Albert as Chief Minister and created him Duc de Luynes. Concini's wife was arrested. The rumour was that she was a sorceress for only such a person could have such complete control over the Queen Mother. Mamie said it was a waste of time to make her stand trial for her judges had already decided on the verdict beforehand. The charge against her was that only by spells could she have wielded the influence she had had over the Queen Mother.

'There were no spells,' was her rejoinder. 'If I have had the power to influence the Queen, it is that of a strong mind over a weak one.'

My mother would not have liked to hear that, of course, but she had already been sent into exile and was more or less a prisoner in the *Château* of Blois.

Poor Madame la Maréchale, as they called her. She did not long survive her husband. She was judged guilty, and in accordance with the law against sorceresses was beheaded and her body condemned to the flames.

'At least,' said Mamie, 'they did not burn her alive. She was lucky in that.'

Lucky! Poor Elenora Galigaï who had enjoyed such favour and amassed such wealth and power. What were her thoughts when they led her to the scaffold? How she must have reproached herself, for if it was indeed true that her husband had wished to leave France, and it was she who had persuaded him to remain a little longer to make themselves more wealthy, she was certainly in a way responsible.

I remembered well the pall of smoke which hung over the Place de Grève. I thought then how short a time ago it was when we were all rejoicing there among the crowds who had come to see the processions. Now it had become a place of horror. I had never actually seen La Maréchale but I could imagine her horrible death.

I forgot her after a while but I remembered her later, and when I was lonely and filled with remorse, certain incidents from my childhood would flash into my mind and I would see those events more clearly than I had done at the time when they happened.

Louis was now sixteen years old. He had changed. He had looked so happy when my mother was leaving the Court for Blois. He really had been greatly in awe of her and she had never won his affection. He had never forgiven her for being so strict with him when he was a boy for often she had given orders that he was to be whipped for some trivial offence. Kings, she had said, had to be brought up very carefully; they must be chastised more severely than ordinary people. Sometimes she even administered the cane with her own hands. He had hated that more than ever. And when after my father died and she became Regent and he was King and yet not King and so much restraint was put on him, he blamed her for that. I could understand why he responded to people like Charles d'Albert.

So I suppose it was not surprising that he had been so pleased on the day she left for Blois.

He lost his stammer and I heard him say in a clear loud voice, full of the utmost satisfaction: 'Enfin me voici Roi!'

The nobles gathered round the King, and it was clear that they approved of what had happened. The Prince de Condé was released from confinement and he came to Paris to be with my brother.

There was another matter of significance which I think perhaps none of us realized at the time. The Bishop of Luçon, Armand du Plessis, who had held office with the Maréchal d'Ancre, hastily left for Avignon and declared he intended to occupy himself with study and writing.

After all the excitement we settled down to a normal routine again. I did not miss my own mother, for, in fact, she had never given me much loving attention.

'It was very interesting while it lasted,' said Mamie.

Queen Anne had joined her husband and was living with him now. Louis had grown up overnight when my mother was removed from Court. There were fewer entertainments now because it had been my mother who had loved them. Louis had never greatly cared for them, preferring his horses and dogs and hunting. Anne loved dancing so she was not very pleased by the change, and I believed she preferred being a juvenile in our nurseries to wife to Louis.

In her rather impulsive way Mamie whispered to me that they were not really suited to each other and it was not a happy marriage; and then she put her fingers to her lips and said: 'Forget I said that.'

That was the sort of thing which endeared her to me. We grew more and more friendly and I often felt that I was in a cosy cocoon guarded by my dear Mamie. Since she had come, Madame de Montglat had more or less passed me over to her, only making sure that I attended my lessons and was getting my religious instruction. She did not mind so much about Monsieur de Breves. The most important duty was religious study; I had to learn to be an unswerving Catholic, to believe blindly in the Faith and to remember, no matter what happened, that I was the daughter of a King and Queen and that such a state was bestowed by God.

Sometimes I went to Court to enjoy some ball or entertainment devised by Anne. She and I often danced together for we made a very successful pair.

I was to wish in later life that I had paid more attention to Monsieur de Breves and that I had had more than superficial knowledge of the history of my country and of the world. If I had had this I might not have made so many miscalculations. Often in my days of loneliness I look back and think how much I could have learned from the experiences of those who went before me.

But I was impatient with serious matters for I was frivolous by nature and my mind was filled with the tune of a new song or an intricate dance step.

Two years passed. My mother was still at Blois and Armand du Plessis was acting as a sort of go-between. He had been my mother's adviser until the death of Maréchal d'Ancre, and after a spell in Avignon he had emerged and was now professing a desire to serve the King. He was endeavouring to bring about a reconciliation between my mother and Louis. Du Plessis was a brilliant man. We did not realize how brilliant then, but in later years when he became the Duc de Richelieu and later Cardinal, he made his mark on the history of France.

It was two years after Louis' marriage that Christine left us to become the Duchesse de Savoy. She had grown so accustomed to the idea of leaving home that she did not seem to mind as much as Elizabeth had done. There were festivities and banquets, but they were not as grand as those with which we had celebrated Louis' wedding – naturally not, I supposed, because he was the King, but the real reason was that they lacked my mother's extravagant hand.

I was now ten years old – getting alarmingly near that time when my own future would be decided. I fancied that I was beginning to be noticed more. I was next in line for a husband and I began to dream romantically of what he would be like. I should like a king if possible. Elizabeth was Queen of Spain, Christine only Duchess of Savoy. What would be the fate of Henriette Marie? I talked about it with Mamie. We used to conjure up bridegrooms for me. It was a great game of mine and I always ended by saying, 'And where I go, you shall be with me.'

'But of course,' Mamie always said.

I saw less of Gaston now. At eleven years old he was quite a little man. He was as indolent as I was and liked to be near the King. Louis was quite tolerant to him and Gaston was longing to cast off his youth – even as I was.

There was an uneasy situation in the country as I suppose there always is with a king who is young and inexperienced and who has favourites jostling for the highest posts. The bitter Catholic–Protestant antagonism had been kept in check by my father but it was always simmering near the surface and ready to break out at any moment.

It was disturbing to have a Queen Mother in captivity and a young King dominated by a minister who had been born Italian and was beginning to give himself far too many airs – as such people always did. The people were getting as irritated with the Duc de Luynes as they had with the Maréchal d'Ancre.

Soon after Christine's wedding there were rumours and whispering throughout the Court, so I knew something was happening, and heard what it was eventually from Mamie.

'The Queen Mother has escaped from Blois!' she said in a hushed whisper. It was like Mamie to get the utmost drama out of a situation. She described it to me graphically. 'The Queen Mother could no longer endure captivity and with the help of her friends, she made a plan of escape. How could this be brought about? There were guards all over the place. Well, she had made up her mind that she was going to try and you know that when your mother decided on something it was as good as done. A

ladder was placed up against her window and she alighted to a
terrace. But you know Blois. She was still very high up. So they
got another ladder to take her to the next terrace. She was so
exhausted by the first descent that she would not undertake the
second so they let her down by means of a rope. At last she
reached the ground, but she still had to get out of the castle, so
she wrapped herself in a cloak and marched right past the
sentries between two equerries. The equerries winked at the
sentries and whispered something. . . .'

'What did they whisper?'

'That the woman had come in to provide a little light entertainment for some of the men. So as they winked and nodded
and made a few crude remarks, the Queen Mother passed on.
The Duc D'Épernon had a carriage waiting for her and they sped
away to Angoulême.'

'But what does this mean?'

'That your mother is no longer a prisoner. Something will have
to be done now or there will be war.'

'War between my mother and my brother! That's impossible.'

'Nothing is impossible in France . . . or anywhere else for that
matter, little Princesse. Always remember that.'

How her words had a habit of coming back to me during my
troubles. It was no use saying: That could never happen. She had
been right. Anything could happen in France . . . or in England.

We did not know very much of what was taking place in the
Angoumois. It was a very uneasy time. The last thing my brother
wanted was to be at war against his mother and I am sure she did
not want to be at war with him. Fortunately Richelieu was able to
convince them both that what the people wanted was a reconciliation. There were a few skirmishes and a great deal of nego-
tiation and in time a meeting between my mother and brother
took place in Paris. It was an occasion. The people did not want a
civil war. My brother embraced my mother publicly to the
people's cheers and it was another excuse for balls and banquets.

My mother declared that she was delighted to see me and
kissed me more fervently than ever I remember her doing before.
Then she looked at me speculatively.

'You are growing out of girlhood, Henriette,' she said.

I knew what that meant, and the prospect excited me while it
filled me with apprehension.

Elizabeth gone. Christine gone. It must be my turn next.

I was nearly fifteen when I first became aware of the existence of the Prince of Wales. It came about in an unusual way.

Queen Anne was devising a ballet as she so often did and as she and I danced well together she was arranging for a part to be written in for me. I was always excited at the prospect of a new dance and called in the seamstress to make a dress for me which would be suitable for the occasion.

Anne and I practised together and each complimented the other on the lightness of her step and the grace with which she twirled. Earnestly we discussed how we could make the dance more beautiful as – so Mamie said – two generals might plan a campaign which was going to result in the conquest of the world.

I laughed at her. One of the few things about me which she did not fully understand was my passionate commitment to dancing.

We rehearsed together and each time we were more enchanted by our performance. As we neared perfection we would sometimes have an audience from people who could persuade or bribe the guards to let them into that part of the palace where we were dancing.

I enjoyed an audience; so did Anne; so we looked forward to these rehearsals almost as much as we did to the grand performance in the presence of the King.

I did not know at that time that there was anything unusual about that performance, but it seemed that all the Court was laughing about it and in due course Mamie told me what had happened.

'The audacity!' she cried. 'Guess who was in the audience at your rehearsal?'

'Many people it seemed.'

'There were two gentlemen there calling themselves Tom Smith and John Brown. They asked the Queen's Chamberlain so pleadingly to be given seats for the ballet and, because they were English, he let them in. He said he thought it only courteous to show hospitality to foreigners, and he was so proud of the way in which his Queen danced that he wanted foreigners to see it for themselves. So they came. They applauded the ballet, but

somehow it became known who they were. Now, Henriette,
guess who our discreet visitors were.'

'How should I know? What did you say their names were? Tom
. . . Smith and John what . . .?'

'Their *assumed* names. The gentlemen masquerading under
those very undistinguished names were none other than the
Prince of Wales and the Duke of Buckingham.'

'Why did they not come as what they are and be treated with
the respect due to them?'

'Because, my Princesse, that is exactly what they did not want
to do.'

'But why not?' I cried. 'Why did they come?'

'To see the Queen.'

'But they did not make themselves known to her. She would
have received them warmly.'

'They did not want to make themselves known and now that
the secret has leaked, it is really very romantic. The Prince of
Wales is to marry the Infanta of Spain. She is the Queen's sister.
He is on his way to woo her because he believes that husbands
and wives should know each other before marriage. He thinks
they should not be thrust at each other without having a chance
to see whether they can like each other or not.'

'*I* think that is right. Elizabeth might have been much happier if
she could have seen her husband first.'

'Well, the Prince of Wales was on his way to Spain, and of
course he must pass through France and the romantic young
gentleman could not resist the temptation of getting a glimpse of
the Queen, but he did not want her to know for what purpose. He
thinks that her sister must be a little like her, and if the Queen is
beautiful, her sister might have a good chance of being so too.'

'Was he . . . satisfied?'

'He must have been because he has gone on to Spain.'

'It sounds very romantic. I wish I had been able to catch a
glimpse of him.'

'He caught a glimpse of you no doubt.'

'He wouldn't be looking at me, would he? All his attention
would be for Anne.'

'You're pretty enough for him to take a second look.'

The incident was talked of for some time. Everyone was
amused by it and thought it was a very daring thing to do.

Anne mentioned it to me when we were at our next rehearsal. She said: 'Did you hear about the outrageous behaviour of the Prince of Wales and the Duke of Buckingham?'

'I did,' I answered. 'Everyone is talking about it.'

'He will now be in Madrid.' Anne looked a little wistful. She enjoyed her position here in France but I sometimes thought she was a little homesick. 'Somehow,' she went on, 'I don't think this marriage will come to anything.'

'Oh surely it will. Such a bold young man will surely succeed with your sister.'

'It is not a matter of succeeding with *her*. I agree she may like him well enough. But nothing is likely to come of this. In the first place the Prince is a heretic from a heretic country. My sister is deeply religious – far more so than I ever was – and one of the terms of the marriage is to restore the Palatinate to Frederick who is the son-in-law of the King of England and brother-in-law to this Prince Charles. They ask too much, and I will tell you something: the Parisians may laugh at two young men who come in disguise on a romantic mission, but the Spaniards will not. They are very formal. No, I feel sure this is a mission doomed to failure.'

'It seems a pity. But you never know what governments will do. They take the strangest decisions sometimes. I think it is rather charming and romantic to come in disguise to court a lady.'

'Oh, I can see he has taken your fancy. It is a pity he did not come to court *you*.'

'Me? What *do* you mean?'

'Well, we shall have to find a husband for you, and don't forget that whoever marries that young man will be the Queen of England.'

'But you just said your sister could not marry him because he is a heretic. I am Catholic too.'

Anne crossed herself. 'As all right-thinking people are. But – apart from his religion – he is the most eligible bachelor in Europe . . . at least one of them. He has a crown to offer. Oh, I wish he had seen you better. The light wasn't very good and he would have been seated rather far away. I wish I had known who they were. . . .'

'But, Anne, he is going to woo your sister. I am only fourteen.'

'I was married when I was fourteen.'

I shivered slightly but I thought that if ever I was married I should like the young man to take the trouble to come and court me.

I often wondered what the Prince of Wales had thought of the Infanta and what happened to him when he reached Madrid. It was strange – almost as though I had a presentiment of what was to come – but I could not get him out of my mind.

War had broken out in France – the sort of war everyone dreaded – with Frenchmen fighting against Frenchmen. When my father had been alive he had appeased both Catholics and Huguenots. It was different now.

The war was remote from Paris and I thought little about it. I was so completely involved with my singing and dancing. I did gather that the King's armies were winning, but as long as what was happening outside did not interfere with my pleasure I dismissed it from my mind.

But there was change in the air and in time even I could not ignore it.

Charles d'Albert, Duc de Luynes, died . . . but not in battle, although he was in camp at Longueville when he was struck down by a malignant fever.

He had been so powerful and so eager that everyone should know how important he was – as people often are when they have risen from small beginnings to high honours. And now he was dead.

I heard that he had been very ill for three days and during that time, because they knew he was dying, his attendants had not bothered to come to his aid. So, as he had been no longer in a position to do them harm or good and was obviously close to death, he was ignored and left to die in agony with no one to give a hand to help him.

I felt rather sorry for the Duc de Luynes.

When he died they put his body on a bier to carry it away and so little did they reverence him that some of the servants actually played piquet on his bier while they waited for their horses to be watered and fed.

Of course his death changed everything. Louis was too weak to reign on his own. My mother came back into power and with her came Richelieu who had done so much to keep the peace between my mother's party and that of my brother.

My mother was jubilant. She saw herself holding the reins again and ruling, with the help of Richelieu.

What she did not see was that in Richelieu, who had now become a Cardinal, she had found a man who was determined to take complete charge and guide a weak King in the way he should go.

It was a blow for my mother, but good fortune for France. But that was later, of course.

In the meantime envoys from the King of England had arrived in France and what they proposed was of the utmost importance to me.

Betrothal

It was a rather bleak February day. I would not be fifteen until the following November so was still very young. Mamie, who was by nature curious and particularly so about matters which concerned me, was the first to tell me about our visitor.

'My Lord Kensington has arrived,' she said, 'and I have heard that he comes to France on a very special mission.'

I replied that when foreign noblemen came to Court it was usually on some special mission.

'I believe he is a great friend of the Duke of Buckingham, and as the Duke of Buckingham is the first favourite of the King of England and known to be a crony of the Prince of Wales, does that suggest anything to you?'

'That his visit might be more than just for personal pleasure.'

'The Prince of Wales is of an age to marry.'

'I believe so and it was for that purpose that he went courting in Spain. Perhaps Lord Kensington calls on us now as the Prince of Wales and Duke of Buckingham did when they were on their way to Spain.'

'The Spanish arrangement no longer exists. The Prince and Duke were not pleased with their reception in Spain.'

'You mean he is not going to marry the Infanta?'

'I do mean that. It is said that he looks elsewhere for a bride.'

I felt myself go cold suddenly, as though – as Mamie would say – someone were walking over my grave.

'Who?' I heard myself whisper.

Mamie took me by the shoulder and replied, smiling: 'Who else?'

From then on my thoughts were in a turmoil. I quickly realized that Mamie's surmise was not without foundation.

I was torn by contrasting emotions. There was pleasure . . . excitement . . . but always apprehension. He had decided against the Princess of Spain. What if he should do the same in the case of the Princess of France.

I knew there was no doubt of what was afoot when my mother sent for me.

All the way to her apartments I tried to tell myself that she wanted to see me about a masque which Anne was devising and in which I was to play a prominent part. As we had a visiting lord from England it might be that she wished us to perform something special.

But, of course, it was nothing to do with the masque.

I curtsied to my mother, who beckoned me to come closer. She laid her hands on my shoulders and said: 'You have grown into a very pretty young woman, Henriette. I am glad. That will please your husband.'

I did not answer and she went on: 'I have good news for you. It may well be that you will be the bride of the Prince of Wales. You understand what that means? You will, in due course, be Queen of England.'

I tried to look greatly impressed but I was only extremely nervous.

'I always wanted crowns for you children. Elizabeth has hers, and now it is your turn, my daughter . . . although of course it is not yet yours. I want you to do all you can to please Lord Kensington who will carry back a report to his master. You are to have a miniature painted and he will take it back with him to England. I am sure we shall get a lovely picture. Stand up straight, child. It is a pity you do not grow a few more inches.' She looked at me critically. I had always been a little self-conscious about my height for I was an inch or so shorter than most people of my age. Mamie used to say: 'Little and good. You are dainty and feminine. Who wants to be a strapping hoyden?' But I could see that my mother did not agree with that and was regretting that my lack of height might be a handicap in the matrimonial stakes.

I tried to stand as tall as I could.

'That's better,' she said. 'Now when you meet Lord Kensington make sure you hold yourself erect. Talk to him confidently. Do not mention that you know about the trip to Spain. It is better to say nothing of that. But it is a stroke of luck for us that it was not successful and it leaves the Prince of Wales free for us.'

I was dismissed and went immediately to Mamie to report the conversation.

'It seems very certain that there will be an offer of marriage,' she said.

'If I go to England you are coming with me.'

'Of course I shall come with you. I'll be the chief maid of honour. You couldn't go without me.'

'I wouldn't go at all . . . unless you came too.'

'There!' said Mamie, speaking more lightly than she felt; knowing the world far better than I she could see difficulties looming ahead, but I did not understand all this until later. 'It will be interesting to be in England,' she said quickly, 'if we go that is . . . to be among strange people. We'll find lots to amuse us, I don't doubt.'

She discovered that Lord Kensington was staying with the Duc and Duchesse de Chevreuse. I liked the Duchesse very much; she was very beautiful and vivacious and had a reputation for being what was called "a little naughty".

'I'll swear my Lord Kensington is enjoying his stay with the Duc and Duchesse,' said Mamie. 'With the Duchesse in any case . . . so rumour has it.'

She made a point of discovering all she could about Lord Kensington, so that when I met him I should not be at a disadvantage. He was Henry Rich, the son of Penelope Rich who was the daughter of the Countess of Leicester – so his stepgrandfather was the famous Leicester who had become notorious as the favourite of Queen Elizabeth. Lord Kensington was an extraordinarily handsome man – tall, with very gracious manners, and I could see why he was a temptation to the Duchesse's not very strict morals.

My mother presented me with a certain pride, and he took my hand and, bowing very deferentially, kissed it.

I must forgive him, he said, if he appeared dumbfounded. I might have retorted that he did not appear in the least so. But he was overwhelmed by my charms. He had heard of my beauty but no accounts could do justice to the reality.

Such fulsome flattery should, of course, have irritated me but it did not. I delighted in it and I conversed with him for fifteen minutes before my mother broke up the meeting. She was smiling benignly and I was not quite sure whether this meant that she was pleased with my performance or whether it was merely the facial expression politeness demanded. If it were not the former, I had no doubt that I should hear in due course.

At the masque I had an opportunity of speaking to the Duchesse de Chevreuse who was present with her husband and Lord Kensington. I danced with the Queen and we were very loudly applauded, but I was most eager to have a word with the Duchesse about Lord Kensington.

I said to her: 'Lord Kensington seems to be a very happy guest.'

The Duchesse laughed. It seemed to me that she was constantly laughing; she had reason to be content; she was very pretty and had something beyond prettiness. I noticed how her eyes sparkled as they rested on certain gentlemen, and I was aware of the warm responses she had from them.

'Oh, Madame Henriette, I assure you he is a most contented guest.'

'Does he talk to you much of the English Court?'

'Constantly. He is devoted to Prince Charles and the Duke of Buckingham.'

'So he talks of them?'

'Most glowingly. He says that the Prince of Wales is the most cultivated and handsome gentleman he ever set eyes on.'

'Does he mention that journey to Spain?'

'Oh that. A fiasco . . . nothing more. My Lord Kensington says he is grateful for it. If it had succeeded that would have been an unhappy day for the Prince.'

'Is that what he truly says?'

'Yes . . . now his envoys have come to France. I can tell you this: the Prince is very handsome.'

'How can you know? Did you see him when he came here as Tom Smith or was it John Brown?'

'No. But I have seen a miniature of the Prince, which Lord Kensington keeps on a ribbon about his neck. It is hidden by his coat.'

'But you have seen it!'

She laughed and put her lips to my ear. 'Many times,' she whispered. 'I say to my lord: "Let me see the picture." I declare he grows quite jealous. He demands to know whether I think the Prince more handsome than he is.'

'And do you?'

'Strictly for your ears . . . yes. Though of course the Prince is young but my Lord Kensington is a man well practised in the ways of love.' She evidently thought she had betrayed too much for she put her hand over her lips and giggled.

I was not very interested in her affairs, but I kept thinking about the miniature which hung round Lord Kensington's neck. I longed to look on the face of Prince Charles.

I told Mamie what the Duchesse had said and she herself asked Lord Kensington to show her the miniature. This he did readily and Mamie said that it was indeed a handsome face depicted there. She told me that he withdrew the ribbon from where it was hidden and displayed the miniature to several of the ladies who had gathered round.

'It seems,' I said coldly, 'that everyone has seen this picture except me.'

'I think,' replied Mamie, 'it would be considered unseemly if you showed a great interest in the picture at this stage.'

'Yet how I long to see it. I think I should be the one to see it first.'

'As soon as there has been agreement between the English ambassadors and your mother, you can ask to see it. But I think you can hardly show a great interest before that.'

I grew angry to think that all my ladies knew what he looked like and that I did not, so I decided to act. When I next saw the Duchesse de Chevreuse, I asked her if she could procure the portrait at the right moment . . . and bring it to me.

The Duchesse, who loved intrigue, swore she would do it. 'The very next time he takes it off,' she said, 'which he does . . .' she smiled at me, 'on occasions. . . .'

Within a day or so the portrait was in my hands.

My fingers trembled as I opened it for it was in a gold locket. And there he was! My heart leaped as I looked at it. He was handsome, yes, but there was a fineness – a refinement – about his features . . . something almost ethereal, which I found enchanting.

I could not stop looking at it, and I held it in my hands for the best part of an hour until I knew every part of that handsome face, and the more I looked the happier I felt.

When I gave the picture back to the Duchesse I thanked her for her help. She said that Lord Kensington had missed the locket and she had told him where it was.

'It did not seem to disturb him in the least. In fact I think he was very happy about the matter. He assured me that the Prince of Wales is even more handsome than his portrait.'

Matters were progressing very fast and Lord Kensington asked my mother if she would permit him to have a private interview with me.

After some hesitation she allowed this and I spent a pleasant half hour in the company of the man who, everyone was saying, was not only the English envoy but the lover of Madame de Chevreuse.

He was very courteous to me and implied again that he thought me very pretty. He said he would go back to England and tell his Prince what a charming Princess I was, and that any man who had the good fortune to marry me would be very lucky.

This was the sort of talk which delighted me.

'Doubtless you have some growing to do yet,' he said, and that was the only allusion to my somewhat short stature.

Then he told me about the Court of England. 'Less elegant, I fear, than yours here in Paris, but we manage to enjoy life.'

I replied that I could well imagine *he* did that wherever he went.

He told me that he very much hoped to complete his mission successfully. 'My Prince is a very impatient man where some matters are concerned,' he said, his eyes twinkling.

I liked him very much and during those days I lived in a whirl of excitement.

It was Mamie who told me that everything was not going as smoothly as they had at first expected.

'If you married Prince Charles there would have to be a dispensation from the Pope,' she said, 'because of the difference in religion. Catholic France and Protestant England.'

'If ever I became Queen of England I should try to save my subjects from damnation,' I replied firmly.

'Yes,' said Mamie lightly, 'but what if they should determine to save you?'

'How could they? I am a Catholic and therefore saved.'

She looked at me with her head on one side as she did sometimes but she did not pursue the matter; but when I had interviews with my mother which I did constantly at this time, she impressed on me the need to remember always that I was a Catholic and that it was my duty to bring people to the true Faith.

But Charles, the handsome young man in the miniature, what of him?

"It is the English,' my mother explained. 'They insist on their Kings being Protestant. It is very misguided of them and your first task will be to bring *him* to the true Faith . . . if there should be a marriage.'

I thought about it and burned with zeal. I imagined Charles in time thanking me. 'But for your coming I should have died in ignorance. I should have spent eternity burning in hell.'

It was a pretty picture.

Then there was Mère Magdalaine who was constantly advising me. If it should be God's will that I should go to England I must not give myself up to frivolous pleasures. I must remember that I had a duty there.

There came a time when it seemed that the marriage might not take place. There were too many difficulties, but the main one was the difference in religion. The English were very reluctant to accept a Catholic Queen. They had deplored the idea of a Spanish marriage – for they saw the Spaniards as their greatest enemies; but because an alliance with that country through marriage had been mooted and had come to nothing they were so pleased and almost ready to accept the French proposition as the lesser of two evils. But, of course, the religious aspect still persisted, and it was growing to such proportions that the Duke of Buckingham – who was in charge of negotiations and eager to see them successful – came to the conclusion that Lord Kensington, suave and charming court gallant though he might be, was not capable of handling complicated politics. So he sent out Lord Carlisle.

It was some time afterwards that I discovered why the marriage almost did not take place.

The matter of Frederick and the Palatinate which had put an end to the Spanish negotiations cropped up again. King James wanted the Palatinate restored to his son-in-law, but the French had no wish to support Germany, which was staunchly Protestant.

There was another reason for delay. The French wanted King James to promise to protect Catholics in England and without his promise they refused to conclude a marriage treaty so it certainly seemed at one point that marriage negotiations were about to be broken off and I should have to forget the handsome face in the miniature, which had haunted my dreams since I had seen it.

I suppose my brother and my mother thought that if this marriage did not come about it might be difficult for me to find another opportunity as good as this one and decided that it was better to be a little lenient if by being so they could get me to England where I might be instrumental in doing good work for the Catholic cause.

A great deal of all this I learned later but the fact was that my brother and Lord Carlisle talked together privately and my brother hinted that the English King need not take the religious controversy too seriously. If he would just give his word that the Catholics might practise their religion privately all might be well.

Both sides hesitated. But the English, no less than the French, were eager for the marriage and finally they decided to make concessions to each other.

I was to have full freedom to worship in the true Faith; I was to be given control of the religious instruction of any children I should have up to the age of thirteen; I was to have my own chapel wherever I was, together with my priests and almoners and chaplains.

The next step was to get the dispensation from Rome.

It came at length and with it was a letter for me written by the Holy Father himself. I felt weighed down with responsibility when I read it.

It was simply because I was going to be Queen of a heretic country that he was giving the dispensation. I should have power – perhaps even over my husband – and it would be my duty to devote myself to the salvation of him and his poor sad subjects. I had the opportunity of being like Queen Esther – the Jewish virgin – who was chosen to be his Queen by the Persian King Ahasuerus and who brought about the deliverance of her people, or like Bertha who married Ethelbert of Kent – in that very country to which I was going – and converted him and spread Christianity among the Anglo Saxons. The eyes of the Catholic world would be turned on me.

My fingers shook as I penned my reply to the Holy Father. I assured him that I was aware of the great task which lay ahead of me and that I would endeavour with all my heart to carry out the work assigned to me by Heaven, and to raise my children in the Catholic Faith.

After I had written that letter I knelt and prayed that God would give me the strength to do what I had to do.

So with the Pope's dispensation, there was no longer need for delay. Preparations for the proxy wedding began. It was decided that May would be the best month. It was then March.

News came from England that King James was ill. No one thought he was near to death so therefore it was a shock when on that cold March day news came to Paris that he was dead and his son, my bridegroom-to-be, was King Charles the First of England.

It was a beautiful May morning when I was escorted to the episcopal residence where I was dressed for my wedding. It would only be a proxy wedding and it seemed very strange to be married to a man whom I had never seen, although such an arrangement was commonplace in royal circles. At least I had seen a miniature of him. I wondered if he were thinking the same of me. But perhaps he would have other matters than his wedding with which to occupy himself as he had, only two months before, become a King.

I stood very still while they dressed me. I could not help feeling happy to wear such clothes. Clothes always had an effect on me and I believe I could not have been completely unhappy while I was wearing a beautiful gown. Of course I was very young then and perhaps more thoughtless and frivolous than many of my age. Now I stood patiently while they put on my gown. It was made of cloth of gold and silver and the material was spattered with golden fleur-de-lys and here and there diamonds twinkled on it. My mother had said I must have the most elaborate of dresses to match the Duke of Buckingham, who would most surely be elegantly attired. At that time it had been thought that he would be my proxy bridegroom but he had been unable to leave England because his presence was necessary there on account of the death of the late King.

Strangely enough the choice of proxy had fallen on the Duc de Chevreuse because he was a distant connection of King Charles. I wondered fleetingly if he would be reminded of his own wedding and whether he regretted having married his fascinating wife, who seemed to create scandal wherever she was.

Mamie hovered about me while they placed the little crown on my head. It was very becoming.

'Crowns suit you,' she said.

I smiled happily. I should have to go away but as she would come with me my qualms were considerably reduced.

The morning slipped quickly away and I was glad when we set out for Notre Dame. It was a very slow procession that passed to the west door of Notre Dame for we were to be married outside the cathedral as La Reine Margot and my father had been because marriage in which one of the participants was a Protestant could not take place inside.

The Swiss guards and trumpeters were followed by a great assembly of knights, heralds and marshals. Then I came in my beautiful glittering dress with Louis on one side of me and my brother Gaston on the other – followed by my mother and Queen Anne.

As we neared the platform, which had been placed at the west door, and I stepped under the canopy, my brother Louis stood aside and the Duc de Chevreuse came to stand beside me. He looked very handsome in black velvet with slits in his jacket to show a lining of cloth of gold. Across his chest was a sash covered in diamonds, and as diamonds also sparkled on his coat he glittered almost as much as I did.

So I was married – albeit by proxy – to the King of England.

After the ceremony I went into the cathedral to celebrate Mass with my family, but the Duc de Chevreuse, as proxy for King Charles, did not join us and went off with Lord Kensington, as Charles would have done had he been present. This incident called attention to the differences in my religion and that of my bridegroom and I felt a little sad while I burned with zeal to begin his conversion.

After Mass I could return to the episcopal residence and rest awhile before the banquet began. I spent the time with Mamie, who chattered excitedly about the ceremony and the splendour of my diamonds and those of the Duc de Chevreuse.

It was a merry banquet which took place that evening. I sat at the head of the table on the right-hand side of my brother, and my mother was on the other side of me. I noticed that they paid a

new deference to me. I was no longer little Madame Henriette; I
had become a Queen.

Afterwards I danced with the Duc de Chevreuse as my partner
and I tried to see, instead of his face, the one in the miniature;
then I danced with Louis and after that Anne and I did one of our
special ballets. I felt excited dancing with Anne because I could
remind myself that we were now of equal rank.

It was not an unhappy day by any means though an exhausting
one, and I was really rather glad to get out of my splendid gown
and lie down to sleep.

'This is my wedding night,' I said to Mamie.

She plumped up the pillows and said: 'It will not be long before
you sleep with your bridegroom beside you.'

I was thoughtful and she suddenly put her arms about me and
held me tightly.

'He has a kind and gentle face,' she said reassuringly.

And that was my wedding night.

Lord Kensington was made Earl of Holland as a reward for
having brought about the marriage and two weeks after the
ceremony the Duke of Buckingham came to France. He created
quite a stir. He was so debonair and so handsome; and he
brought with him a most magnificent wardrobe. 'All the clothes,'
said Mamie, 'that he had intended to wear as proxy bridegroom.'

When he was first presented to me he was dressed in white
satin covered with diamonds. Mamie heard that the suit alone –
considering the number of precious stones on it – was valued at
twenty thousand pounds. And that was just one outfit. He loved
diamonds and everything he possessed was decorated with them;
they were in his hat and even the feather was decorated with
them; and they were on the hilt of his sword and on his spurs.

It was as though he wanted everyone to know how rich and
important he was. In fact, it has been said that he was the most
important man in England. King James had doted on him – but
then King James was apt to dote on handsome young men; and
now he had become the close friend and adviser to Charles. He
had arrived ostensibly to escort me to England but Mamie
believed he might have other motives as well. He wanted to make
an alliance with my country against Spain.

However, there he was in all his glory and glitter, behaving as though he was an equal of my brother, my mother and the young Queen. There were great festivities to honour him, for we were still celebrating the wedding and it had been decided that after a week of entertainments for the Duke, we should begin the journey to England.

I was not to be torn completely from my family just at first, for my mother with Louis, Anne and Gaston were to accompany me as far as the coast. There I should leave them and cross the Channel in the company of the Duke of Buckingham, and Kensington – now Earl of Holland. The Duc de Chevreuse as my proxy bridegroom was to stay with me until I was passed over to my real one; and as the Duc came, so did his flighty Duchesse. I was quite reconciled to leaving my country – after all none of my family had been very affectionate towards me – as long as I was accompanied by Mamie as my chief lady in waiting.

It was a merry party and as we passed people came hurrying out of their houses to cheer us. There was intrigue afoot – romantic intrigue. This would always occur where the Duchesse de Chevreuse happened to be. What could be more exciting for her than to have a lover actually in the party.

Mamie said that she and the Earl of Holland were quite blatant and she wondered the Duc de Chevreuse was not aware of the flagrant immorality of his wife.

It was not long before the behaviour of another couple in our entourage began to demand our notice. Mamie mentioned it to me.

We had ridden far and she was helping me to bed one night when she said: 'Have you noticed the Duke of Buckingham and the Queen?'

'What of them?' I asked.

'It would seem that the Duke is romantically inclined towards the Queen.'

'Anne!'

'Anne indeed. I must say it does not surprise me. Louis is a most negligent husband.'

'The Duke just admires her.'

'And she likes to be admired.'

'You're imagining this. I believe you do imagine things.'

'Perhaps . . . a little. But I have a sharp pair of eyes.'

We talked of other things, but the next day when we continued our journey I did notice that Buckingham contrived to ride beside the Queen and engage her in conversation. There was a great deal of laughter, and Anne's eyes sparkled with delight while my Lord Buckingham appeared to be very pleased with himself.

So although I lacked a husband in the flesh, what with the accomplished affaire of the Duchesse and Holland, which was carried on quite blatantly in the presence of the cuckolded husband, and the aspirations of the Duke of Buckingham towards the Queen, I was beginning to learn a great deal about existing morals.

We had not gone very far – Compiègne as a matter of fact – when Louis began to have one of his shivering fits. Our mother was greatly concerned and insisted that we stop while physicians were called. This threw a slight gloom over the proceedings and several of the festivities which had been arranged for us were cancelled. I was not very disappointed about this, much as I loved dancing and singing and all that went to make up these entertainments, for it was rather refreshing to have a few quiet evenings in Mamie's company.

My mother came to my room in the morning looking rather grave.

'The King is suffering from fever. I don't think it would be wise for him to continue with his journey,' she said.

I could not believe she was worried about Louis for himself. They did not like each other. That had been obvious when the Maréchal d'Ancre had died. At the same time Louis' death or long illness would plunge the country into disorder. There was no child of the King's marriage, and I did not know how my mother felt about my brother Gaston who would be the next in line to the throne. However, for whatever reason, there was no doubt that she was deeply concerned about my brother's health.

'I shall rely on what the physicians have to say,' she went on. 'If they advise him to rest here, the question will be whether to wait with him or pursue our journey, but I do think it is necessary for you to get to England as soon as possible.'

I bowed my head. I wondered why she was saying this to me. It was not as though my opinion would count. But I had forgotten. I was a Queen now.

'So . . .' went on my mother, 'if the physicians think it is wise

for him to remain in Compiègne, the rest of the party will continue the journey.'

'Yes, Madame,' I said.

'Perhaps a good night's sleep will cure him.'

It did not. And during the next day it was decided that the
journey should continue without Louis.

When we came to Amiens, my mother was very tired and
admitted that she found the journey exhausting. It was not only
the arduous travelling conditions which she had to endure, but
there were the festivities which had been arranged in the villages
and towns through which we passed. She looked very pale and
when we arrived at the *château* where we were to spend the night,
she fainted.

There was no doubt that she was ill. We called the doctors and
the verdict was the same with her as it had been with my brother.
Rest was needed.

There followed a conference. The Duke of Buckingham seemed
to welcome a little delay, which I was sure had something to do
with his pursuit of the Queen, and he said there was no need for
great haste. He would send messengers to the King to explain
why our progress was interrupted. He was of the opinion that we
should not proceed without the Queen Mother, for we had
already shed the King on the way and it would seem as though
the journey were ill-fated if we had to go on without another such
important member of the party.

The Earl of Holland warmly agreed with this. Their reasons
were identical, but the Duke of Buckingham's were more urgent
than those of the Earl of Holland for the latter's mistress would
accompany the party to England so he would not be deprived of
her company for some time. It was different with Buckingham;
the Queen would leave us when we sailed; and he still had his
courting to do, it seemed.

'At least,' commented Mamie, 'we hope so. I would not like to
think that the royal House of France might have a little cuckoo in
the nest . . . even though the little bird had the blood of such a
noble Duke.'

'For shame!' I cried.

And she laughed at me. Her attitude had changed since 'my

marriage'. She referred to me often as 'Your Majesty' and 'the
Queen,' and she behaved as though I had suddenly become
experienced of the world, which was far from the truth of course.

However we stayed at Amiens and, without the strict supervision of the Queen Mother, morals became more lax than usual.

Ladies and gentlemen paired off and not always with their
legal partners. We were lodged in a large mansion surrounding
which were beautiful grounds and in which there was a walled
garden. It was rather overgrown but there were paths through
the trees, and it soon became the favourite haunt of lovers.

One of my mother's elderly women brought this to her notice
and as a result orders were given that this garden should be kept
locked at night. This could be quite easily managed for there was
a gate leading to it. The key of the garden was left with the
Captain of the Guard, who was ordered to make sure it was
locked at dusk and not opened until the morning.

I did not know what happened exactly, but it appeared that one
night the Queen with some of her ladies ordered the Captain of
the Guard to give her the key of the garden. He did not know
what to do. The Queen Mother had said he was to keep it in his
possession, but here was the Queen ordering it to be given up.
Anne cajoled – she could be very persuasive – she threatened and
she could be ominous. Poor man, he did what most men would
have done in the circumstances; he gave up the key.

Several ladies with their gallants were in the garden that night
and among them was the mischievous Duchesse de Chevreuse
with the Earl of Holland. In fact it was she who had put the idea of
getting the key into Anne's head. The Duchesse was a woman
who lived dangerously, and like so many of her kind, not content
with going the way she wanted to, she was anxious that others
should follow her example. I believed she had urged the Queen
to encourage Buckingham while her lover Holland did all he
could to help the Duke to success with the Queen.

I was not present on this occasion, of course. Why should I
want to walk in the darkening gardens? I was in my bed so only
heard of the incident from my usual source; but I could be sure
Mamie would get the entire story.

'It was like this,' she said. 'The ladies and gentlemen were in
the garden walking through the paths to sequestered spots
where they settled down to rest for a while. The Queen soon

discovered that the Duke of Buckingham was her companion. Imagine them . . . wandering in the darkness. He would put his arm through hers and tell her how beautiful she was and mention that it was a great shame that the King should be so neglectful and seem unaware of her dazzling charms.'

'Anne would like to hear that,' I commented.

'Most young people would – particularly those who have an indifferent husband. The Queen is very young and my Lord Buckingham . . . well, he is not so young. He is thirty-three if he is a day and experienced in all ways of making love, so I have heard. Therefore one would have thought he would have been more subtle on this occasion. He had misjudged his . . . I was going to say victim . . . but perhaps it is *lèse majesté* to talk thus of the Queen.'

'Oh, get on with the story,' I cried impatiently.

'Well, suddenly a shrill scream rent the air. Imagine it! A moment of silence and then all the attendants running to the spot where the Queen stood . . . wide-eyed, hands across her breast as though to protect herself . . . and standing close by looking as near sheepish as such an arrogant Duke could look . . . my Lord Buckingham.'

'What did it mean?' I asked.

'It could mean only one thing. Our Duke made a mistake. He must have attempted to force his attentions on the Queen. He did not realize that all she wanted was words . . . gestures . . . certainly not actions. I will tell Your Majesty something: This will be the end of that little affaire. Perhaps it is as well that it was only a little one. Queens, Your Majesty, must be beyond reproach.'

The next day everyone was talking about the scream in the garden. I was glad no one mentioned it to my mother. I wondered what would have happened to the Captain of the Guard who had relinquished the key if she had known.

My mother's health improved a little but her doctors thought that the journey to Calais would be too tiring for her and bring on a recurrence of her malady so it was decided that she should come no farther. Gaston was the only member of my family who would go with me until I left French soil.

Our waiting in Amiens had therefore been unnecessary for my mother rose from her sick bed and accompanied the party through the town and then took her leave of us.

She embraced me with what seemed like real affection on parting. She told me that her thoughts would always be with me and she would follow my progress with the utmost attention. She entreated me to be a good wife and she trusted I would bear many children. I must always remember that I was royal – the daughter of a King and Queen of France. I must never forget the country of my birth, and there were no matters as important as my faith and my royalty. I was going to a heretic land. God had selected me as he had St Paul and St Peter. I was to carry on with my duty and never cease until my husband and the whole of England were saved for the Truth.

It seemed a daunting task, but I promised that I would do what I could and would always remember my faith, my loyalty and my country.

As she embraced me she thrust a letter into my hands.

That night I read the letter. It was long and it stressed her love for me. She reminded me that I had lost my earthly father and only had God for my father now. I must never forget what I owed Him. He had given me to a great King and had sent me to England where He would require my services, and this would mean that through what I did there I could attain eternal salvation.

'Remember that you are a daughter of the Church by baptism and that it is indeed the first and highest rank which you have or ever will have, since it is this which will give you your entrance into Heaven. . . . Be, after the example of St Louis from whom you are descended, firm and zealous for religion, which you have been taught and for which your royal and holy ancestor exposed his life. Never listen to or suffer to be said in your presence aught in contradiction to your belief in God. . . .'

I read and reread that letter. I knew what was expected of me. I was going to a strange country. I was going to a husband whom I must strive to bring to the true Faith. I had a great responsibility.

As I read the letter I swore to God and to myself that I would do everything in my power to bring the true Faith to England.

The next night news was brought to us that there was plague at Calais and it would be dangerous for us to go there, so we must divert our course to Boulogne.

Before we could set out next morning, the Duke of Buckingham came to me in a state of great urgency.

'Your Majesty,' he said, 'I have this morning received communications from King Charles. It will be necessary for me to
return to Amiens that I may present these papers to the Queen
Mother.'

I was very well aware that he had received no papers, and I did
in fact confirm this later when I discovered there had been no
messenger from England. But Anne had stayed behind in
Amiens with my mother and for that reason he wanted to go back
to see her before he left for England.

'You must admit,' said Mamie, 'that our Duke is no laggard
when it comes to love.'

I was angry at the delay. It seemed that our journey was ill-
fated. First there was my brother's ill health, then my mother's,
and after that, plague at Calais, and now Buckingham was
darting off to suit his whims.

It was too much to be endured.

I abused Buckingham in no quiet voice and it was some time
before I would listen to Mamie's pleas to calm myself.

Then I began to wonder whether I was in any great hurry to
leave my native land, and the enormity of what was happening to
me was brought home to me. I felt there was a vague menace in
the air. I was going into a strange land among strangers.

So when Buckingham did return I was not so very eager to
resume our journey, for every day . . . every hour that passed
carried me farther away from the life I had known.

At length we came to Boulogne. The ship was waiting for us
and as I stepped aboard there was a discharge of ordnance to
mark the significance of the occasion. Mamie was close beside
me. She smiled at me reassuringly.

I was on deck watching the coastline of my country slowly
disappear from view and I felt afraid and very vulnerable on that
seething grey sea. The ship lurched and Mamie persuaded me to
go below.

The uncomfortable journey seemed to go on interminably, but
I think I was too emotionally disturbed to notice the discomforts
as some of the others did.

In due course we came close to land. I went on deck and had
my first glimpse of the white cliffs.

My new life had begun.

Discord in the Royal Apartments

It was seven o'clock on that Sunday evening when I set foot on English soil. An assembly of gentlemen was waiting to receive me and an artificial bridge had been set up so that I could disembark easily. This, I was told, had been ordered by the King who was at that time at Canterbury, which was not very far from Dover, and there he was eagerly awaiting news of my arrival.

I wondered then why he was not at Dover and would have impulsively asked this if I had not had to speak through an interpreter, for I felt more than a little annoyed that he had not been there to greet me.

I was informed that a message would be sent to the King immediately to tell him of my coming and he should be with me in less than an hour.

I replied – somewhat imperiously, Mamie said afterwards – that I was too tired to receive anyone that evening. The journey had been exhausting and I needed food and rest.

I was told that it should be as I wished and we proceeded at once to the castle where it had been arranged that I should spend the night.

The castle was near the coast and I hated it from the moment I saw it. It was very gloomy, quite unlike the Louvre, Chenonceaux, Chambord . . . those castles to which I was accustomed, and as my footsteps rang out on the bare boards I noticed how shabby everything was.

I said that I would retire to my apartments without delay for more than anything I needed rest. Perhaps some food could be brought for my lady of honour and myself. I made it clear that I wished to see no one until the morning.

At least they seemed eager to comply with my wishes and I was immediately conducted to my apartment. I gasped with horror when I saw it. There were tapestries on the walls but they were dingy and dusty. Mamie went to the bed and felt it. It was hard and lumpy. I had never seen such a bed in any of our French castles or palaces. And this was the room they had prepared for the Queen of England!

'Never mind,' said Mamie. 'Don't get angry. You can change everything later. But just for tonight accept it.'

'Don't they want me here?'

'Of course they want you! You have to remember that they do not live in the style that we do. They are barbarians compared with us.'

'What of men like the Duke of Buckingham and the Earl of Holland? They are as elegant as any Frenchman.'

'Perhaps it is just their castles which are different. But never mind about that now. We need rest. Everything will look better in the morning.'

'I don't think this place will ever look better. It will be worse when the sunlight picks out the horrors and shows them to us more clearly.'

But as usual she soothed me. We ate a little together and then she helped me to bed.

Tired as I was it was not easy to sleep. All the excitement I had felt through the wedding and festivities had disappeared and in its place was a growing apprehension.

But Mamie was right. I did feel better in the daylight, for even though it showed up the threadbare state of the bedcurtains, it lit up those dark corners and eliminated the shadows which had been so disturbing on the previous night. Breakfast was brought to the apartment and Mamie and I were eating it when a messenger came into the room.

He bowed respectfully and said: 'Pardon the intrusion, Your Majesty, but the King has arrived from Canterbury and he wishes you to know that he is waiting to see you.'

I stood up. I would see him without delay. This was the moment for which I had been waiting ever since I had seen the portrait of him and knew I was to be his wife.

Mamie was looking at me anxiously, warning me not to be over-impulsive. I smiled at her. 'He is my husband,' I reminded her, 'and I am naturally all eagerness to meet him.'

She tidied my hair and smoothed my gown. 'You look enchanting,' she whispered and kissed me.

Then I descended the stairs to the hall.

I was aware of a figure standing there and I went forward swiftly and was about to kneel and say what I had been taught I must say on our first meeting, that I had come to His Majesty's country to be commanded by him . . . but the words would not come, my voice broke with emotion and I felt the tears gushing to my eyes, while he caught me up in his arms.

He was very tender. He took his kerchief and wiped my eyes; then he kissed my forehead and my tear-stained cheeks . . . not once but several times.

'Why,' he said softly in French, for I had no English, 'I must kiss you until you cease to weep. You are not with enemies and strangers, you must know. It is God's will that you and I are here and does He not tell you to leave your kindred and cling to your husband?'

I nodded in agreement.

'Well then,' he said gently. 'All is well. As for myself . . . I will not be so much a master to you as a servant to cherish you and make you happy.'

It seemed to me that no husband could have used kinder words and I began to feel better.

'Now we will sit down and talk together,' he said. 'You shall get to know me and you will realize that this marriage of ours is not a matter for sorrow but for joy.'

He took my hand and led me to a window seat where we sat side by side.

I was able to take a glance at him. He was of medium height and I was relieved that he was not very tall as that would have accentuated my low stature. He was not as handsome as the picture in the miniature, but he was pleasant looking. There was, however, a certain melancholy aspect about him which had not been apparent in the miniature and which alarmed me faintly.

It might have been that I was a trifle disappointed in his looks but his kindness was comforting. He clearly did not seem disappointed in my looks, for I caught a glimpse of admiration in his eyes, and as others thought I was pretty I guessed he did too.

It occurred to me then that my portrait might have under-rated my attractions, for Mamie had often said that my vivacity was a very large part of my charm. I think a little liveliness might have improved him. I definitely had the impression in that first half hour that he was inclined to be morose.

He told me that we should leave for Canterbury later in the day and stay the night there. He had been there when he had heard of my arrival and had set out immediately, accomplishing the journey in half an hour, which was something of a record and showed his eagerness to be with his bride.

'You must present me to your attendants who have come with you,' he said. 'And I will present your English ones to you.'

'I daresay I shall make mistakes,' I replied. 'Matters are conducted differently here from the way they are in France, and I do not even know the language.'

'You will quickly learn,' he reassured me.

'If I make mistakes you must tell me.'

He smiled at me very gravely and tenderly. I wished he had joked a little though, brought some lightness into the conversation; but of course that was not his nature. I thought then, they could not have found a partner for me more different from myself.

He took my hand and I stood up. I came up to his shoulder and I saw by the way he looked at me that he suspected I was wearing high heels to give me height. He must have heard exaggerated reports of my low stature.

I said at once: 'My heels are flat.' I raised my skirts and held out a foot to confirm this. 'I stand on my own feet and have no help through art to make me taller. This high I am . . . neither taller nor lower.'

He took my hand and kissed it.

'You are beautiful,' he said. 'I think ours will be a happy marriage.'

I wondered even then. There was so much I did not know about England and I had already been amazed – as had my attendants – that they could have housed their Queen even for one night in that shabby old castle. And Charles my husband? He lacked the gaiety of Englishmen like the Duke of Buckingham and the Earl of Holland; there was something very serious indeed about him which I had already detected. Perhaps I should have rejoiced in that. I was not sure.

I presented my attendants to him and he in turn introduced those whom he had chosen to attend me. These meetings passed

off comfortably and it was not until the carriage arrived to take us
to Canterbury that the trouble arose.

I was walking with Charles, and Mamie was a pace or so
behind, for I had told her to keep close and not lose sight of me.

'I want to see you there all the time,' I had said, 'that is until I
get used to these people.'

'Don't worry,' she had replied. 'I will be there.'

The King's coach was waiting and he took my hand and helped
me in. I sat down and Mamie got in beside me. The King stared at
her as though thunderstruck.

'Madame,' he said, 'pray leave the royal coach at once.'

Mamie turned pale while I looked on disbelievingly. At home
the chief lady of honour always rode with my mother and the
chief gentleman with the King.

She rose uncertainly but I cried out: 'She shall ride with me.'

'There is no place for her in my coach,' said the King.

Mamie gave me an appealing glance and prepared to step out
of the coach, but I caught her skirt and would not let her go. I
never could control my temper and it was rising now. It seemed
desperately important to me that Mamie should ride in the coach.
Charles must learn what she meant to me, and I would not have
her insulted in this way.

Poor Mamie! For once she did not know what to do. The King
was glaring at her, ordering her to go, while I held her skirts
firmly in my hands and ordered her to stay.

I looked steadily at my husband and there must have been
defiance in my eyes – more than that, hatred. He looked back at
me . . . coldly, but a little bewildered I noticed.

I said coolly: 'If my chief lady of honour does not ride in the
coach then I will not either.'

'She shall travel with the rest of the attendants,' said the King.

'She is my special friend and she has always ridden with me in
my carriage and she shall do so now and if she does not I shall
stay in this dirty old castle until I can return to my country.'

It was wild nonsense really. As if I could return! As if *that*
would be allowed! I was irrevocably married to this cold-eyed
man and in that moment I hated him. But I was never very logical
in my rages. Mamie had pointed that out to me many times.

The King was white with anger. And this was the first day of
our meeting! I knew that it did not augur well for the future.

There was deep silence all about us. I saw the Earl of Holland looking on in disbelief while in the face of the Duke of Buckingham there was the flicker of a smile. I had an idea that he was enjoying looking on at this – my first conflict with my husband.

I glared at the King. Mamie said afterwards that I looked like a wild-cat and she thought I was going to fly at him. I knew my eyes were blazing and I spat out my words so fast that many of the English had no idea what I was saying, which was perhaps just as well.

I suppose I was a little hysterical. I was like that when one of my rages took possession of me, and I knew that there was more to this than appeared on the surface. It was because I was so frightened that I let my anger get the better of me.

Charles had stepped out of the carriage. I thought he was going to drag Mamie out so I clung to her skirts. She looked at me entreatingly and muttered under her breath: 'Let me go. We must stop this scene. . . .'

But I would not let her go. I felt the hot and angry tears in my eyes and willed them not to fall. I was trembling but determined. If Mamie left the carriage, I told her fiercely, I should go too.

Several of the King's ministers had come to him. They seemed to surround him and there was a great deal of whispering going on. The incident could not have lasted more than a few minutes but it seemed much longer.

Then those about the King parted and Charles stepped into the carriage. For a few seconds I waited in trepidation for what would happen next. He seated himself next to me and signed for Mamie to take the seat opposite, which she did. Then the horses began to move forward.

For a few seconds I felt exultant. I had won. And then a mood of foreboding settled on me while I saw the King's glance sweep over Mamie. There was an implacable hatred in his face.

On the way to Canterbury we came to a place called Barham Downs. There pavilions had been set up and a banquet awaited us, and among those who greeted us were several English women whom the King presented to me as the ladies of my household.

I greeted them somewhat regally because I had brought the ladies of my household with me and I could not see that I should need more than I already had. But at least I was experienced enough to know that this was not the time to raise the question. We had had enough for one day in the upset over Mamie and the carriage. So I smiled and played the gracious Queen and my husband's expression grew a little less frigid. I was hungry and I did full justice to the food which had been prepared and I did feel it was rather pleasant to be in the open fields and watch the pennants fluttering in the light breeze and thinking that all this had been set up in this green field in honour of me.

My spirits continued to rise as the ancient town of Canterbury came into sight, for the approaches to the city were beautiful with the entire scene dominated by the cathedral's magnificent tower.

It was dusk when we arrived and a splendid feast awaited us. The King now seemed to have recovered his good humour and he smiled and talked to me at table, insisting on carving the meat for me himself, which was a great honour.

Father Sancy, my confessor, was watching me, and I knew this was because as it was a fast day I should not be eating meat – but I was hungry and I felt rebellious against authority no matter from what quarter it came. Moreover I was a little triumphant after my victory in the carriage, and while I ate heartily of the meat, which seemed to please the King, I avoided the eyes of my confessor. I would be ready with my excuses when I received his reprimand – as I surely would – and I would explain to him that as I had come to live in this country I must respect its customs. I hoped my confessor had not heard of the incident in the carriage.

After we had feasted the King said there would be a small personal ceremony of marriage. We *were* married it was true, but only by proxy and he wished to be present at his own ceremony. It would be quiet and quick . . . but nevertheless a ceremony of marriage.

So this was performed in the great hall of the city and everyone could be satisfied that we had taken our vows to each other personally.

I was appalled by the state of my apartments and the bed was certainly no better than the one I had slept in on the previous night. How strange that was, for this was my marriage bed which I was to share with the King. Were the English savages? How should I ever grow accustomed to living in such conditions?

Mamie helped me undress and dismissed the rest of the women so that we could be alone. I could see she was still shaken by the incident in the coach.

'It was wrong,' she said. 'You should not have insisted.'

'I do insist and I shall go on insisting that you ride in the carriage with me as you did in France.'

'We are not in France now,' she reminded me. 'When you live in a country you must conform to that country's customs . . . particularly if you are its Queen.'

'I shall conform to none . . . but my own. I will tell you what is wrong with these people. They are heretics . . . and that means they are little better than savages.'

'Be careful,' said Mamie.

'Am I the Queen or am I not?'

'You are the King's consort, which makes you a Queen, but your title comes through him.'

'You talk as though you are on their side.'

'I am always on your side. You know that well enough.'

Then we fell into each other's arms and hugged each other.

She was very serious. 'You know that tonight you will share the King's bed,' she reminded me. 'You know what is expected of you?'

I nodded.

I saw the worry in her eyes. 'You know you have to love your husband,' she said.

'I am not sure that I am going to do that. This afternoon in the coach I hated him.'

'Oh, my little Queen, I can see trouble for you if you do not control your rages.'

'My rage worked well today did it not? You rode in the carriage because I insisted.'

'I think it would have been better if I had quietly alighted and murmured apologies about not understanding the English customs. The King would have understood and that would have been an end to the matter.'

'The matter ended in triumph for me.'

'Let us hope that we have seen the end of it.'

'What is wrong with you? Why are you different today? You would have laughed in the old days.'

'These are not the old days. Try to remember that we are in a new country . . . and remember, too, that from now on it is our country.'

'I shall change it.'

'You talk like a child.'

I narrowed my eyes. 'Do I? My mother and the Pope himself have told me that I must change it. Are they children?'

'Oh take care, dear child, take care.'

I could not shake her out of her gravity, which was so unusual with her. I should have been quite angry with her if I hadn't known that the change in her was due to her concern for me.

But she could not rob me of my triumph over the carriage incident. I had won. There was no denying that. I did realize though that my own mother would have taken a very different view of my tantrums. I should have been lectured, punished and denied what I had demanded if that incident had taken place in France.

Now I had the night ahead to think of.

How different this from the royal *coucher* at the Louvre. The King was undressed by only two of his gentlemen which would have been considered very odd indeed and quite unroyal by the standards prevailing in France.

He came to me in that shabby old room and looked round it. At first I thought he was going to comment on its shabbiness – and perhaps apologize for it – but it seemed he was only making sure that we were alone.

Then he went to the door and locked it.

He looked different in his night attire – not nearly so formidable as he had in the carriage. He seemed to have forgotten all that now and in any case he had not appeared to be displeased with me but with Mamie, which struck me as very unfair.

He lay down on the bed and made me lie beside him; then he put his arms about me and began to tell me how happy he was that I was there and how my appearance pleased him and that it was our duty to have children.

I listened and waited.

I was passive in his embrace and found I was able to endure

what followed with a certain fortitude for I knew that it was part of the duties which were required of me.

I lay bewildered afterwards and wondered what people like Madame de Chevreuse, Buckingham and Holland found so exciting about it.

The King seemed rather pleased. I was tired out by all the emotions of the day and fell asleep quickly.

In the morning when I awoke the King had already left the bed and the door was unlocked. My ladies came in to help me with my toilette and Mamie looked at me questioningly.

I nodded. 'Yes. It happened.'

'And you . . . ?'

I shrugged my shoulders. 'It was no worse than I expected.'

Mamie said: 'I knew the King was kindly.'

But she continued to look uneasy and I guessed she was remembering the incident in the coach.

I burst out: 'I don't like England. I don't like the King. I want to go home.'

'Hush,' said Mamie. 'Don't let anyone hear you say that.'

Then I threw myself at her and refused to let go; she rocked me as she might a baby. I wanted to tell her how only she made it bearable here, how I was tired of being the Queen of England and wanted to go back to being merely a Princess of France.

'I want to go home!' I cried.

'Hush,' she said. 'Don't be a baby.'

We spent another night in Canterbury which was very like the first and I was glad to leave the dingy old apartments for the fresh country air. I had to admit that the landscape was very beautiful with green meadows and majestic trees. I felt better when we were riding away from Canterbury and although I did not like my husband very much, I hoped I should not have to see a great deal of him. During the days I would be with Mamie and my ladies and we could dance and sing together and share our jokes and contempt for our new country while we talked nostalgically about the one we had left. Yes, I thought I could bear that.

We came to Gravesend where we were to stay as the guests of the Countess of Lennox. She was waiting to greet us and paid great homage to the King; then she turned to me and bowed very low. She said she was greatly honoured that we should be her guests and added that she had grave news which she thought should be imparted to the King immediately.

He looked very serious and she went on: 'It is the plague, Your Majesty. It will be most unsafe for you and the Queen to travel through the streets of London.'

My husband said: 'But the people will be expecting us. They will want their processions and all the pageantry which goes with them.'

'Nevertheless that is how it is, my lord. You will hear more of this but I thought I should tell you without delay.'

How serious the King was! He never seemed to laugh spontaneously. Perhaps that was why I found it so hard to like him.

Now instead of the pleasant welcome I had been looking forward to there was great concern and people were gathering round the King deciding what should be done.

I was taken to an apartment to rest and Mamie came with me. While we were there Father Sancy came to us and said he wished to have a word with me, so Mamie retired and left me alone with my confessor, which was the last thing I wanted.

He then began reprimanding me for eating meat in Canterbury and I said what I had prepared myself to say which was that I had only been following the customs of my new country.

'Following the customs of heretics!' he thundered. 'That is a fine way to begin! What will you do? Deny the true Faith because it is the custom of savages among whom you live?'

'That is very different from eating meat, Father.'

'You have gone against the laws of Holy Church.'

'I shall not do it again, Father.'

He seemed faintly mollified. His eyes shone with zeal and as he looked round the room his expression changed to one of contempt, although the apartment was an improvement on those I had had at Dover and Canterbury.

'And now,' he went on, 'there is consternation about your ride through the streets of London. Plague, they say. Let me tell you, my lady, there is constant plague in this accursed country and there will be until these misguided people come to the Truth. It is God's way of punishing them. It was a sad day for us when we came to this land.'

'My mother did not seem to think so. Nor did the Holy Father.'

Father Sancy wagged a finger at me. 'The Holy Father gave the dispensation most reluctantly, and for a reason.' He brought his face close to mine. 'The work must begin without delay. You have been chosen for a great task, my lady, and that is to lead these people back to the true Faith.'

I tried to look solemn. I was longing for him to go. There was so much I had to say to Mamie. I cast down my eyes and folded my hands demurely together. What should I wear for my procession into London? I was asking myself.

'And,' he went on, his voice growing louder, 'you will not do it by eating meat on a fast day.'

The simplest way to be rid of him was not to argue although it was hard to resist the temptation to do so. I murmured a prayer with him and he left.

Mamie came running in.

'I have heard that we have to go to London by barge which will prevent our having to go through the plague-ridden streets,' she cried. 'And you are to wear green. The King will wear green also. I suppose it must be an emblem of spring.'

Then I dressed and we laughed as I told her about Father Sancy and I added: 'If I want to eat meat I shall eat meat. I shall be ordered by no one, Mamie, neither priest nor husband.'

'You are a wild rebellious creature,' she said, 'and,' she added, 'you always were.'

'And always will be,' I assured her.

'We shall wait and see,' said Mamie, which made us laugh because that was what she used to say to me when I was very young.

The next morning I went with my husband and our attendants onto the state barge. The river seemed to be crowded with craft of all kinds because many of the nobility who could had come to join the escort into London, and as we stepped on board there was a volley of fifteen hundred shot which was quite deafening.

I enjoyed sailing down the river. The King beside me seemed very benign though still serious. I wondered if he ever laughed out loud. It should be another of my tasks to make him do so, but that appeared to be almost as formidable as turning Protestant England into a Catholic country. I loved the big ships of the navy which the King pointed out to me with pride as we passed. I had never seen anything like them in France and as we passed them and they fired their ordnance, it was the most thrilling moment that had come to me since my arrival in England.

It was late afternoon when I saw the great Tower of London looming up before us – not beautiful as our buildings are, but formidable and very impressive. The gay flags fluttering from its towers looked rather incongruous and as our barge approached the guns fired so loudly that I almost cried out in half terror, half delight.

The King was amused. He smiled faintly, which was a good deal for him to do; the river banks were crowded with people and they were shouting 'Long live our little Queen,' which my husband translated for me and which so pleased me that I waved my hand in acknowledgement. They seemed pleased by that, and as the King still wore that rather reluctant smile I guessed I was doing what was right.

As we progressed along the river we came right into the city and here the crowds were even greater. People not only lined the river banks but had climbed on ships lying in the river and they were shouting and waving from ships' hulls and craft of all kinds. There was one event which might have been disastrous and it happened just as we were passing. One of the ships capsized suddenly. I suppose too many people had scrambled onto it. It went down into the water and I heard afterwards that there were more than a hundred people on board.

I heard screams and cries of consternation and the attention of the crowd was turned from us to the people struggling in the water. Fortunately there were plenty there to effect a rescue and everyone was eventually brought safely out of the river and all they suffered really was a terrible fright and a ducking.

Along the river we sailed until we came to our destination, which was Somerset House. The grounds ran down to the river and here we alighted and I was conducted ceremoniously into the house. It was grander than those in which I had stayed so far in England but I still found it lacking in the elegance of our French palaces. However the journey by river from Gravesend had been refreshing and the cheers of the people – who seemed to have taken a liking to me – were still ringing in my ears so I felt a little happier.

We spent the night here in a bed which I thought very odd because I had never seen the like. But I was supposed to regard it with some awe as it had once been Queen Elizabeth's and she had slept in it many times.

Queen Elizabeth was the arch heretic and I certainly did not feel the respect that they seemed to consider due to her. In fact I found the idea repulsive and I made no attempt to hide the fact. Charles ignored my hints and behaved as though I were perfectly contented.

We stayed only a few days at Somerset House, which was too near the city for us to be safe from infection, but during that time the King went to Parliament to make his opening speech. I gathered it was not a great success though he did not tell me so. He never spoke to me on serious matters. I suppose I did not encourage confidences at that time. He must have thought me a frivolous and rather stupid little girl – which I suppose I was.

It was Mamie who told me that he had asked for money from the Parliament which would mean taxing the people, and the people hated to be taxed.

'There are many things they don't like,' Mamie told me. 'They don't like Buckingham much.'

'I don't blame them,' I retorted. 'Why don't they like him? Do they know how badly he behaved with my brother's wife?'

'Oh, they wouldn't care about that. It is not a matter of morals. People in high places can do exactly as they like in that respect. The old King doted on him. . . his Steenie as he called him because he said he bore a resemblance to St Stephen. He was his favourite young man, and he had lots of young men around him. But Buckingham is too ambitious. He fancies himself as a states-man and a ruler more than he does a lap dog . . . which was what most of the handsome young men were content to be. Well, the old King has died and now they say that Buckingham is getting a hold on the new one.'

'A hold on Charles!'

'Well, he listens to him. He's his greatest friend. They went to Spain together, didn't they, when Charles was courting the Spanish Princess? And then he came to France when it was your turn.'

'So the people don't like Buckingham. Do you know, I don't think he likes me.'

'Nonsense. It's not for him to like or dislike you. You represent the alliance with France and he worked for that, didn't he?'

'Oh, I am glad the people don't like him. It shows they have some sense . . . even if they are heretics.'

Mamie laughed at me and said I should have to grow up.

The plague was getting worse so it was decided we should leave Somerset House for Hampton Court.

I was impressed by Hampton Court from the moment I saw it. This was more like a royal residence. Approaching it from the river was to see it in all its imposing glory. When I stepped ashore and crossed the splendid gardens to the entrance of the palace I felt I was indeed a Queen of a great country.

I think there were about fifteen hundred rooms in the palace which had been built by Cardinal Wolsey at the height of his glory and taken from him by King Henry the Eighth who could not bear that a subject should live more grandly than he did. The rooms were vast – each of the fireplaces was big enough to roast an ox. The furnishings were drab but I was fast discovering that the English lacked the refined tastes of the French. They seemed either drab or garish in my eyes. But they could not detract from the splendour of Hampton Court.

'This is where we shall stay for a while,' Charles told me. 'Here we shall spend our honeymoon.'

A honeymoon meant getting to know each other and as the days passed I realized that our relationship did not grow warmer as we began to know each other more intimately.

Mamie urged me to try harder to like my husband.

'I think,' she said, 'that he is ready to love you. He finds you very attractive physically.'

'I don't find *him* so.'

'But if you tried. . . .'

'Mamie, don't be silly. How can you *try* to love someone? You either do or you don't.'

'You can be understanding. Try to see what it is that you don't like and then try. . . .'

'He never laughs. He is so serious. He doesn't approve of so much that I do. And, Mamie, he doesn't like you.'

'That matter of the coach was very unfortunate . . . happening as it did right at the beginning.'

'It is over and forgotten.'

'Some things are never forgotten.'

'Well, he had better stop disliking you, for I shall not like *him* until he does.'

'Dearest, you are very wilful.'

'I am as I am . . . and I will not change for anyone.'

'You are very young. When you grow older you will learn that we all have to change sometimes . . . we have to adjust ourselves to circumstances.'

'I will not. I will be myself and any who don't like that can do as they please. I don't care.'

Mamie shrugged her shoulders; she knew it was no use trying to make me see reason when I was in a certain mood.

I was incensed when Buckingham came to me, and from that time I hated him more than ever.

It was downright impertinent and when I realized that Charles had sent him, I hated them both and determined that I would do everything I could to annoy them.

Buckingham tried to look severe. He more or less demanded an audience, which I should have refused, but I didn't out of curiosity to know why he should come to see me.

I expected him to pay compliments and treat me as though I was a pretty woman as well as a Queen. I might have relented a little if he had. He was bold; he was blatant; and I remembered the manner in which he had tried to seduce the Queen of France right under my brother's nose.

He looked at me coolly, rather as though I were a recalcitrant child, and said: 'The King is displeased.'

'For what reason?' I asked.

'Because of your conduct to him.'

'And the King tells you this?'

'I have volunteered to convey his displeasure to you.'

'That,' I said with sarcasm, 'is noble of you.'

'The King says you show no affection towards him.'

'And what concern is that of yours, my lord?'

'It is my concern because the King tells me and has asked me to speak to you on this matter.'

'So you are to plead with me to love him? Why? Are you such a clever supplicant? You were not particularly successful with my sister-in-law the Queen of France.'

Buckingham's handsome face flushed a dull plum colour. I had touched him on a vulnerable spot and I rejoiced. He looked at me steadily while the flush on his face slowly faded, leaving it rather pale.

'I have to tell you that if you do not show more affection to the King and conform more with his wishes, you will be a very unhappy woman.'

'Pray do not concern yourself, my Lord Buckingham. I can manage my own affairs.'

'It would be wise for you to show a little pleasure in the King's company. You laugh and sing with your French companions and as soon as the King arrives with his English ones you become sullen and silent.'

'Then it is for the King and his English attendants to amuse me as my own friends do.'

'It is for you, Madam, to please the King. We are all his subjects . . . even you . . . and it would be wise for you to remember that.'

'My Lord Buckingham, I no longer have need of your presence.'

He bowed and for a moment our eyes met and I knew in that moment that he hated me as much as I hated him.

Mamie was very upset when I told her what had happened. She chided me a little for the way in which I had received him.

'I will not pretend,' I said fiercely.

She shook her head and answered: 'Dearest, you will have to curb your temper. You must, you know; it could lead you into difficulties.'

'Again you seem to be on his side.'

'Never . . . never. But you are wrong, my love. You must learn to be diplomatic.'

'I hate them all. Heretics! Savages!'

Mamie looked very distraught. 'This will not help at all,' she said.

A few days later Buckingham came to see me again. I was on the point of refusing to see him but Mamie was with me when he was announced and she advised me against a direct refusal. 'Try to be calm,' she said. 'Listen to what he has to say and reply to it with tact and calm.'

'I shall grant him nothing.'

'Perhaps not, but do it as a Queen would, not as a rebellious schoolgirl.'

Buckingham came in looking elegant and handsome. It is a pity

I cannot like him, I thought. He dresses with such taste that he looks almost like a Frenchman.

'Your Majesty!' He bowed low and kissed my hand. I could feel the anger surging up in me and I guessed my eyes were beginning to blaze as they did at such moments. 'May I say,' he went on, 'that you are looking even more beautiful than ever. The air at Hampton suits you.'

'You are good to say so,' I replied, so far quite calm.

'I come from His Majesty.'

'Oh? Is he so far away that he cannot come himself?' My temper was beginning to rise. I must remember Mamie's warning and try to keep calm.

'He has given this commission to me,' he replied suavely, 'and I have a special request to make.'

I thought: What insolence! You to make a special request to me . . . after our last meeting. But I said nothing and he went on: 'His Majesty thinks that now you have become his wife and Queen of England you should have Englishwomen in your bedchamber.'

'I am very satisfactorily served at the time,' I replied.

'I am sure of that, but His Majesty is hoping that you will soon master the English language and adopt some of our English ways. Therefore he thinks that if certain ladies came into your bedchamber they would be of service to you . . . if you would graciously allow them to.'

'Oh? And whom does he suggest?'

'He has been most gracious to me and declares I have done him great service. As you know I was the main instrument in arranging this most desirable marriage. His Majesty cannot thank me enough for bringing him such a beautiful bride, and I hope that you too, Your Majesty, feel a little gratitude towards me.'

I was seething with rage and I knew I could not contain it much longer. He did not give me time to speak but went on: 'The King has honoured me by agreeing that my wife, my sister and my niece should occupy these coveted posts.'

I stared at him disbelievingly. He would put his women about me. For what purpose? Their aggrandisement certainly . . . but to spy on me!

I burst out: 'My lord Buckingham, I already have three ladies of the bedchamber. I do not need more.'

'They are Frenchwomen,' he said, 'and the King would like your ladies to be English.'

'You may tell the King that I am perfectly satisfied with what I already have and I intend to remain so.'

He bowed and left me.

Seething with rage I sought out Mamie and told her what had happened. She was greatly distressed. She saw farther than I did. She did not want to worry me but I did make her tell me that she feared she, among the others, might be sent back to France. It was the custom when a Princess married into a foreign country that the attendants who accompanied her went back to their own country after a few days or weeks at the most.

'This is different,' I cried passionately. 'This was the arrangement. I am not to be surrounded by heretics. It was agreed that my own people should stay with me.'

Mamie comforted me and assured me that I had nothing to fear and that I had done right in refusing to accept the Englishwomen into my bedchamber.

I felt very relieved when the Bishop of Mende, who had come with me among my clergy, called on me with Father Sancy and told me that he had had to make my position very clear to the King.

'It was decided,' said the Bishop, 'that you should have English ladies to wait on you in your bedchamber. I have explained that this is quite out of the question.'

I clasped my hands together in delight, which I tried to make appear as religious fervour.

'We cannot have heretics living so close to you,' went on the Bishop.

'They might attempt to corrupt you,' added Father Sancy.

'I would never allow that,' I assured him.

'Nevertheless we cannot afford to run risks,' said the Bishop. 'I have made it clear to the King that my masters in France would take a very grave view of having these Huguenots in your bedchamber.'

'Thank you, my lord,' I said, 'I am grateful for your care.'

'You must never forget your duty to the Church,' said my confessor.

And I assured them both that I would not forget. I would keep about me my own French attendants who were good Catholics. I would fight with all my might against the heretics.

'Let us kneel and pray that you will be successful in that which God has sent you to England to bring about,' said Father Sancy.

The Bishop was less fanatical, but he was determined – even as Father Sancy was – that I should keep the Protestants out.

I was very cool with the King in our bedchamber at Hampton on the night following the visit of the Bishop and Father Sancy. He knew why, of course, and he was very anxious to placate me. I think he enjoyed those intimacies of the bedchamber far more than I did, and I thought it was perverse of him to show a little rancour because I could not share the same pleasure as he did. The fact was that I should have preferred to go home and live as I had before my marriage. True, to be a Queen was gratifying, but I sometimes felt it was not worth all that it entailed.

The King stroked my hair and said it was beautiful. He loved my flashing dark eyes and my clear complexion, even my short stature. I was feminine, he said, all that a woman should be . . . save in one thing. I did not love my husband enough.

I was silent and he sighed deeply. He said: 'It is only because I wish you to learn to speak English . . . and to love this country that I want you to have English ladies about you.'

'I would not love it the more for that,' I said. 'I can accept life here because my friends are with me.'

'But I would be your friend,' he said, 'the very best friend you have. I am your husband.'

'I would not lose those who have come with me from France for anything.'

He sighed. He did realize that it was never any use trying to convince me. He believed now that I was the most illogical, unreasoning young woman imaginable, a creature of whims and fancies, lacking completely in control of my feelings.

I know I was the main cause of all the unhappiness of those years. But I could not see it then.

So we retired to bed for our nightly ritual, which I longed to have done with so that I could sleep.

The discord between us continued and it seemed impossible to find an end to it. I knew there was a great deal of comment about the way I and my French friends behaved. We were allowed to celebrate Mass because that was part of the agreement between our two countries and my religious entourage made sure that this was carried out. But it was accepted with resentment. Mamie said the English could never forget that Mary Tudor had burned Protestants in Smithfield and at that time they had made up their minds that they would never be ruled by Catholics again. Then some of their sailors had become prisoners of the Inquisition and brought back tales of torture. The country had turned its back on Catholicism and forgotten, said Mamie, that the Protestants had not always been so kind to the Catholics among them. The English, she decided, were not an intensely religious nation. They were said to be tolerant, but their tolerance was in fact indifference. But although they might not object to Catholics on religious grounds, they were determined not to have another monarch like Mary Tudor, who was fiercely Catholic, having been brought up by her Catholic mother, Katherine of Aragon.

'It is well,' said Mamie, 'to understand the people with whom you have to live. Sum them up. Don't be afraid of them but don't underrate them.'

I don't know whether she was right but that was her assessment of them. However, I was allowed to celebrate Mass in the royal palaces with my attendants and we took advantage of this – perhaps a little blatantly. I was too careless then to see that we must inevitably be working towards a climax.

Mamie tried to explain to me what was happening, but I am afraid I found the subject rather boring and only half listened. I knew that she said something about the King's finding it difficult to fall in with the terms of our marriage treaty without offending his own people and I should really try to be more understanding towards him. He was naturally preoccupied having state matters to think of and my little tantrums must be trying to him. Moreover he could not get French help to fight Spain, and the hope of doing so was one of the reasons why the marriage had been so pleasing to him. It was all very wearying and I shrugged it aside. I did listen a little more intently when she told me that Catholic services were banned in England – except in my household.

'He had better not try to stop me and my servants worshipping God,' I cried.

'He would not. That would be going against the marriage treaty.'

'Well, let us talk of something more interesting.'

She sighed and shook her head over me. Then I rushed to her and kissed her and she was laughing at me.

When the King dissolved Parliament he looked more stern than ever and said that he was going to the New Forest to hunt for a while. He thought I might not wish to go with him and he was right in that. Perhaps, he said, I would like to stay at Tichfield, which was the estate of the Earl of Southampton.

I was delighted to be relieved of his company and was very merry surrounded by my French attendants, riding with Mamie beside me to Tichfield; but I was a little put out on reaching the house to find that the Countess of Denbigh was there. I was prepared to loathe anyone connected with the Duke of Buckingham and she was his sister. Moreover she was one of those women whom he had tried to force me to accept into my bedchamber.

In the solitude of my apartment, Mamie and I discussed her. Mamie thought she was a very strong minded woman and advised me to be careful in my dealings with her.

'Don't show that you dislike her. Don't forget that although you may dislike the Duke of Buckingham, he is the most powerful man in the country under the King, and it is unwise to offend him too much.'

But when had I ever been wise? I always listened to Mamie's advice but I only took it when I wanted to.

'What is this Buckingham family?' I cried. 'They were nothing before little Steenie attracted King James – and in a manner that is a disgrace to morality.'

'Hush,' said Mamie.

I snapped my fingers at her. 'Don't tell me to hush. Remember who I am.'

'Oh,' said Mamie, 'on our high horse now, are we? Shall I bow low to Your Majesty and walk out on all fours?'

She could always make me laugh and that was why I loved her so much.

I went on: 'It shows they were nothing . . . otherwise she would never have married William Feilding. Who was he, pray, before the earldom was bestowed on him? A commoner who had the good fortune to marry Susan Villiers. He would not have been allowed to unless he had done so before her brother caught the King's eye with his pretty face and made the family fortunes.'

'My word, you have probed into the family history.'

'Well, I happen to be interested in these odious connections of Buckingham's, and don't forget they tried to force Susan Villiers into my bedchamber.'

'The Countess of Denbigh now.'

'A title bestowed by the good graces of her brother who wants to see all his family in influential places. Oh, he has to be watched, that one.'

'And you will do the watching?'

I said: 'You are laughing at me again. I forbid it.'

'Then I will hide my laughter and present always a serious countenance to Your Majesty.'

'That is what I could not bear. There is too much solemnity around me already.'

I will admit, when looking back, that I behaved in an unseemly fashion towards the Countess of Denbigh; but then she was hardly within her rights in her conduct towards me.

She professed to be very religious and it was quite clear that she deplored the fact that Mass was celebrated at Tichfield. I will not try to pretend that I did not arrange for our services to take place as ostentatiously as I could, and those about me – perhaps with the exception of Mamie – did all they could to encourage me.

It was Mamie who told me that the Countess of Denbigh had decided that she would arrange a Protestant service to take place in the great hall at Tichfield. All the household should assemble and take part – with, of course, the exception of mine.

I was rather pleased because courtesy would demand that as the Queen was in the house her permission would have to be asked.

I discussed it with Mamie.

'I shall refuse it,' I said.

'You cannot,' replied Mamie, shocked.

'I can and I will.'

'It would be a grave mistake. Listen, my dearest, you are a fervent Catholic, but you are in a country where the Protestant religion is maintained. You must graciously give your consent and while the service is going on remain in your apartments. There is nothing else to be done.'

'Why does she arrange this while I am here?'

'Perhaps to show that while the country has a Catholic Queen, it is staunchly Protestant.'

'Then I shall refuse.'

'Please do not. It would be folly. They would hold it against you. It would get to the King's ears . . . worse still, to those of his ministers. It would not be tolerated to forbid these people to worship in the accepted religion of the country.'

I pressed my lips firmly together. In my heart I knew that she was right, but I could not stop myself rehearsing what I would say to Susan Villiers when she came to ask my permission.

Mamie was not with me when one of my attendants came rushing into my apartments.

'My lady,' cried my attendant breathlessly, 'what do you think? There is a service going on in the great hall. The whole household . . . the Protestant household. . . is gathered there.'

I was aghast.

So, she had not bothered to ask my permission. This was a double insult. First to arrange the service while I was under this roof, then to carry it out without asking my permission.

What could I do? I was not going to ask Mamie this time because I knew she would say 'Nothing.' But I was enraged and I wanted it to be known.

I had an idea. I would not go down and demand that it be stopped, which was my first reaction. I would disrupt it in such a manner as I could not be called to task for.

I gathered together a group of my attendants and told them we were going to take out the dogs. We all loved our little dogs and most of the ladies had several. We put them on their leads and I led my party down to the hall where the assembled company was kneeling in prayer. I walked across the hall to the door, my attendants following me. The dogs yapped and barked and ran about; we laughed at their antics and chatted animatedly, behaving as though we could not see the people at prayer.

At length we came out into the courtyard, laughing together. But I did not intend that it should end there. I sent about six of the ladies back to bring a kerchief for me. They went, taking their dogs with them, and I stood at the door exulting in the noise they made.

When they returned, I cried in a loud voice, 'The air is a little cold. I think I will not walk today.' Then we all trooped back. Someone was preaching but his voice was drowned in the commotion we made.

Of course everyone was shocked by what had happened – Mamie as much as anyone.

They were all talking about it. I said that I should have been consulted and that to conduct such a service without my permission was a breach of good manners; but I think that most people thought that her fault in not asking my permission was slight compared with the way in which I and my attendants had acted.

Deep shock was expressed about my behaviour. Mamie was the first to tell me that I should never have behaved as I did and that it would be remembered and held against me. Perhaps the Countess had been remiss but what I had done amounted to an insult to the Protestant religion.

I said I did not care and would do it again, which made Mamie despair.

When the King returned from his hunting trip he said nothing about the incident but I felt sure he had heard of it. There was a certain determination added to his usual sternness, and I wondered whether he was planning something.

In many ways he was delighted with me. I believe he could have been passionately in love with me then; but I was so unsatisfactory to him in many ways and a man of his nature could never quite forget that.

I did not understand this then. It is only now that I do when I have so much time – too much time – for reflection. There was consternation between the Courts of France and England. Nothing was going as anyone had wanted it to. There was so much conflict that Mamie feared my husband and my brother might be on the brink of war with each other. My brother – or I expect it was Richelieu – sent the Sieur de Blainville to try to bring some accord between the two countries. The King did not like him very much and that made it difficult for any understanding to be reached. Blainville came to see me and told me I should try to understand the English, to learn their language, to mingle with them at Court and not keep myself isolated with my French household.

Buckingham was out of the country, which always made me feel happier. He was trying to persuade Richelieu to join him against the Spaniards, so he said. I wondered whether he was still hankering after my sister-in-law Queen Anne and whether his little jaunt was to try to win her favour. After that incident in the gardens when she had had to scream for help, I believed Buckingham was capable of anything.

The Duchesse de Chevreuse provided a little bit of liveliness to the scene when she gave birth to a child. Whose? I wondered, and so did many more.

She was quite blatant about it and the Duc de Chevreuse acted as though the child were his. He must have been used to her little ways and that they should sometimes produce consequences should not be a matter for surprise.

Then Buckingham returned, apparently somewhat deflated. His plans had gone awry. I guessed they would. He could hardly win favour in France after his disgraceful conduct with the Queen. Moreover I think he was not the man to succeed at anything but winning the doting affection of men like King James and the friendship of young inexperienced men like King Charles. I wished that Charles was not so devoted to him. I believed they discussed me and my relationship with my husband and I began to suspect that Buckingham sowed seeds of discord in my husband's mind. Not that Buckingham would dare openly attack me. But he must be a master of the subtle suggestion, and I had noticed that when he was absent there seemed to be less conflict between me and Charles.

When we were alone in our bedchamber Charles would be quite affectionate; he would even smile faintly and express his satisfaction with my person and forget for a while how unsatisfactory I was in other ways, so when I wanted to make appointments in my household I decided that the best time to approach him was during one of those bedtime tête-à-têtes. I wanted to assure the position of some of my attendants and I could only do this by appointing them to vacant posts.

I had taken a great deal of trouble to draw up a list, and I had been careful to add some English names to it. In fact I had rather cleverly – I thought – intermingled them skilfully which had the effect of diminishing the number of French I had included.

I was in bed and Charles had just joined me. He had turned to me and laid his arm about me when I said: 'I have a paper here which I want you to look at.'

'A paper?' he said in astonishment. 'Now?'

'It is just a small list of those I wish to be officers in my retinue.'

'Well, I will look at it in the morning. But you know that according to the agreement with your brother which we made at the time of our marriage, it is my right to name such people.'

'Oh, you will agree to these,' I said lightly. 'There are a number of English names there as well as French.'

He raised himself on his elbow and looked at me and although I could not see him very clearly in the dim light, I knew that he had assumed that stern and suspicious demeanour.

'There will be no French in your retinue,' he said coldly. 'It would be quite impossible for them to serve in that capacity.'

'Why not?'

'Because it is my will that they should not.'

'But,' I retorted angrily, 'it is *my* will that they should. My mother wishes these people to be admitted into my retinue.'

'It is no affair of your mother's.'

'And none of mine?' I asked defiantly.

'None of yours,' he said. 'If it is not my will then it cannot be yours.'

I was so angry. If I could have done so I would have risen from the bed and made my preparations to return to France. We sat up in bed glaring at each other.

I cried: 'Then take back your lands. Take them all . . . lands . . . castles . . . everything you have bestowed on me. If I have no power to act in them as I wish, I have no desire to possess them.'

He said slowly but very distinctly: 'You must remember to whom you speak. I am your King. You are my Queen but also a subject. You should take heed of the fate of other Queens of England.'

I could scarcely believe my ears. Was he reminding me of the ill-fated Anne Boleyn and Catherine Howard? Could it be that Charles, whom I had always thought of as gentle and kindly-meaning, was telling me that if I did not behave as he wished I might lose my head.

I felt enraged and insulted. I began to weep – not quietly but stormily. I said I was utterly miserable and longed to be back in France. I was nothing here. I was insulted and maltreated. I was given a household but I had no power in it. I wanted to go home. While I was saying all this he was trying to placate me.

'Listen to me,' he said.

'I want to hear no more,' I cried. 'The more I hear the more miserable I become. Why do you use me so? Am I not the daughter of a great King? My brother is King of France. If my family but knew!'

He said: 'Your family know full well that you are being treated here in accordance with your deserts. Your brother has sent Blainville here to try to reason with *you*.'

'I have been unused to such treatment,' I wailed. 'I hate it here. I want to go home. I will write to my brother. . . .'

'Much good that will do you.'

'To my mother. . . . She will understand.'

He was silent for a while and I grew tired of talking to what seemed like no one. I slid down and buried my face in the pillow.

There was a long silence. Then he sighed and lay down too.

After a while he said: 'I will say this and that is an end to the matter: You cannot fill posts in your retinue with your French servants. These posts must be filled by English people. You have become the Queen of England and the sooner you realize it, the better for you and all concerned.'

With that he pretended to sleep and I ceased to cry.

Later he turned to me and was very tender.

But I knew I had lost the battle.

The next climax which arose was due to the coronation. Charles of course had only become King just before our marriage and in accordance with custom his coronation should take place soon after he came to the throne. His had been delayed because of the plague but with the beginning of the next year London seemed safe again and plans went ahead with great speed, for a coronation has a special significance. It is only when a King has been anointed and crowned that the people feel he is truly King.

So Charles was of course eager to be crowned.

I was the Queen and I should be crowned with him, but I could see all sorts of difficulties, for how could I – a Catholic – be crowned in a Protestant ceremony.

I discussed the matter with my French attendants and of course with Father Sancy. He was adamant. I most certainly must not be crowned in a Protestant church and indeed I should not even *attend* the coronation.

'Then I shall not be crowned Queen,' I pointed out.

'Only when you receive the crown in the true Faith,' he said.

Charles was bewildered at first when he heard my views on the matter; then he was very angry.

'Do you mean to say you refuse to be crowned?'

'In a Protestant church, yes.'

'You are mad,' he said. 'Do you value your crown so little?'

'I value my faith more,' I replied dramatically.

'You must be the first Queen who has refused to be crowned,' he said. 'Do you realize that it will be said you have no firm hold on it?'

'What would God say if I allowed myself to take part in such a mockery?'

That was when he became really angry. 'Be silent,' he cried. 'Don't dare talk so in my presence.'

He was really rather frightening then. He went away and left me. I think he was afraid he might do me some harm.

It was an extraordinary state of affairs and everyone was talking about it. The Queen would not have a coronation! The English thought I was mad; and they were annoyed with me, too, looking upon my attitude as some insult to them; but my own attendants applauded me. Even Mamie did not condemn the action, but she did say she thought it was unwise.

As for the Comte de Blainville, he was astounded, although Catholic as he was he should have understood. It meant, of course, that if I did not go he could not either. He said he would have risked the small strain to his conscience, which was meant I supposed to be a mild reproof to me. But he did add that as I was not to be crowned he could hardly be there.

Charles tried once or twice to reason with me but I refused to listen.

'The people may well take this as an insult to them and their Church. It will not make you very popular with them.'

'I care nothing for their regard,' I said.

'Then you are even more foolish than I thought,' was his terse reply.

On another occasion he tried to persuade me at least to be present in the Abbey. He would have a latticed box made where I could sit unseen.

'No,' I cried vehemently. 'It would be wrong for me to *be* in such a place.'

He spoke to me no more of the matter, but I knew that he was very displeased and that the people in the streets discussed it and said some very unflattering things about me.

However I refused to be dismayed. In those days I had the gift of persuading myself that what I did was always right. Coronation Day was the second of February, which was Candlemas Day, one of the festivals of our Church, so while the coronation was in progress, we celebrated that; but I have to admit that afterwards I could not resist watching the procession from a window in Whitehall Palace.

The King was very cool to me and I was beginning to feel a little uneasy because, although I was in fact Queen of England, I had not been crowned and I did not see how I ever could be until that day when I brought the whole country to the true Faith.

It was about a week after the coronation when the second Parliament of Charles's reign was about to be opened and that meant a grand procession. Father Sancy said I might watch it from one of the windows of Whitehall Palace, but Buckingham in his interfering way suggested that I should see it better from his family's house and his mother would be very happy if I joined her and the ladies of the Buckingham household.

I was very annoyed about this and wanted to refuse but I was feeling a little nervous because of all the fuss over the coronation.

Charles said he would escort me to the Buckingham residence and I was waiting for him to come, inwardly fuming because I had agreed to go to those I hated so much.

When it started to rain I saw through this a way out and when Charles came I touched my headdress, which was very elaborate, and looked melancholy.

He asked what was wrong and I said: 'The rain will ruin this.'

He gave one of those faint smiles of his and I knew that he was thinking I was rather an adorable child in spite of all my naughtiness and he touched my shoulder gently and said: 'Very well, remain here and watch the procession from Whitehall.'

I was delighted and settled down to do so, but very soon the Sieur de Blainville arrived. He looked very disturbed.

'Is it true, my lady,' he asked, 'that you have refused to go to the Buckingham house to see the procession as arranged?'

'It is raining.'

'It has stopped.'

'Well, it *was* raining and I told the King it would spoil my headdress.'

'That will not be acceptable to Buckingham.'

'The King accepted it. He did not want me to spoil my headdress.'

'You must leave here at once,' he said. 'I will conduct you there. Do you realize that the situation between our two countries is very uneasy. The King your brother, your mother, the Cardinal . . . they are all seeking friendship with your husband. You must forgive my saying so, my lady, but your conduct does not help to bring about what we want.'

He looked so serious and still a little worried about my action over the coronation that I said I would go with him at once.

So he immediately conducted me to the Buckingham house.

It is strange that when one does not mean to annoy one can do so more deeply than when one does. I had no idea that there could be such a storm over such a trivial matter. But of course it was Buckingham who made the mischief. When he saw that I was not with the King – so I heard from those present who had witnessed the scene – the Duke expressed great concern. He would know the real reason for my refusal to leave Whitehall Palace and that the rain had little to do with it. He was heard to tell the King that he could not hope to make much impression on Parliament if he allowed his own wife to flout him.

Charles was rather angry then. He took a great deal of notice of Buckingham and the Duke was on such familiar terms with him that he never hesitated to give him a hint of criticism if he wanted to. The result was that Charles sent a messenger back to Whitehall to say that I was to leave at once, but by the time the messenger arrived I had already left with the Sieur de Blainville.

I knew what Buckingham's comment was. He would point out that although I had refused the King's request, I left immediately when commanded to do so by my fellow countryman.

In those days Charles was unsure of himself. He was very shy and always afraid of losing his dignity. Looking back I see it all so clearly now. Buckingham had been his father's favourite and had made himself Charles's mentor, so he always listened to him and took great heed of what he said. Now, because of Buckingham's suggestions, Charles sent a message to me telling me I was to return to Whitehall Palace for if I could not come when he was there to escort me I should not remain there.

I was so thoughtless. It never occurred to me to try to understand the situation. I sent the messenger back to say that I preferred to remain where I was now, having made the journey in the company of the Sieur de Blainville.

There was no doubt of the sternness of the command which was brought back to me. I was to return to Whitehall without more ado.

I did realize then that this was blowing up into a storm and I thought it advisable to obey immediately, so back to Whitehall I went and with my attendants watched the procession from there as I had originally planned to do.

That was not the end of the matter.

I did not see the King for the rest of the day and that night he did not come to our bedchamber. In the morning there was a note from him stating that he was most distressed by my behaviour and did not want to see me again until I begged his forgiveness for my conduct.

I was astounded. 'What have I done?' I demanded of Mamie. She understood how the incident had been misconstrued. It was much ado about nothing, she said. I could easily explain my innocence to the King, tell him that I really had been concerned about my headdress and when the Sieur de Blainville had explained to me that I would be offending the Buckinghams I had taken his advice and gone with him.

'But it is all so silly,' I cried, stamping my foot in irritation. 'What a fuss . . . and all about nothing. What did it matter *how* I went to the Buckinghams. I went, did I not? It was not that I wanted to, I can assure you.'

'There is so much formality to be observed in your position.'

'And wherever the Buckinghams are, there is trouble. Have you noticed that?'

'I have. But surely you can explain exactly how it happened. The King will believe you. Go to him and tell him.'

'Why shouldn't he come to me?'

'He is the King and your husband.'

'I don't intend to be his slave. He may be the son of a King, but I am the daughter of one . . . and my father was greater than his. . . .'

'Hush, child. You talk too wildly. You must remember where you are. Remember your position. Oh, my dearest, sometimes you frighten me.'

'*I* will not be frightened by Buckingham, who is trying to make my husband hate me. Why, Mamie, why?'

'I think the Duke of Buckingham held complete sway over the King's father and now seeks to be in the same position with regard to your husband. I think he sees how the King's affection for you is growing and seeks to undermine it, lest you should have more influence on the King than he does.'

'The King's affection for me! My influence on him! You are laughing at me, Mamie. What affection has he for me? What influence have I on him?'

'Both could grow. I am sure of that. The King is ready to love you. It is for you to cherish that love. Now go to him and explain what happened and I am sure he will forgive you.'

'But there is nothing to forgive, Mamie. Why should I grovel to him. Let him come and ask *my* pardon.'

'Kings do not ask pardon.'

'Nor do Queens.'

Mamie sighed. She knew my obstinacy.

A few days passed and still the King made no move to see me. I was surprised to find that I was somewhat piqued and that I missed him a little. I was impatient always and impulsive, and I hated long waiting and silences. So in due course I asked if he would see me.

The answer came back immediately. He would be most pleased to receive me.

When I stood before him I saw that his eyes shone with a certain pleasure. I knew that he was getting ready to forgive me when I told him I had done wrong, but I had done no wrong and I was not going to say so. All I wanted to do was end the waiting. I hated going to my apartment at night and not knowing whether he was going to join me. I did begin to wonder whether I wanted him to. All I knew was that I did not greatly enjoy those lonely nights of uncertainty.

I faced him boldly. I said: 'I do not know what I have done to merit your displeasure. I had no intention of doing so. But if I have offended you I would ask you to forget it.'

I think he was as eager for reconciliation as I was, for he

smiled that faint smile and embraced me.

'The incident is over and done with,' he said.

It was not, however, the end for poor Blainville. He was first of all not permitted to come to Court and as this was an impossible situation for an ambassador to find himself in he was recalled to France. I was very sorry for him. It had come about through no fault of his and I knew that he would be accused of failing in his duties when he returned home.

The Maréchal de Bassompierre was sent to England in his place. He had been a very old and faithful friend of my father and was in fact the man who had been betrothed to Charlotte de Montmorency and had given her up when my father had wanted to make her his mistress. He had served France well and I soon realized that I should get frank speaking from him. He made it clear that my behaviour was not what it should be and that I would have to improve.

It was a trying time. In spite of all my protests, three English-women had been made ladies of my bedchamber though none of my French servants had been dismissed. The English ladies were the Duchess of Buckingham and the Countesses of Denbigh and Carlisle.

Mamie felt it was ominous and I became aware of how worried she was.

I was less so, still confident of getting my own way. I was very sullen with the three new ladies in waiting for the first week or so and refused to speak to them except when it was absolutely necessary, but gradually I began to take notice of them for they were, I discovered, three unusual ladies.

Buckingham's wife seemed to be quite interested in the Catholic Faith and began to ask me questions about it. She was by no means sceptical and I found that I quite enjoyed talking to her; I often wondered how she came to marry her odious husband but marriages were arranged for us poor females and we had to make the best of what came our way. Her sister-in-law the Countess of Denbigh also questioned me about the Faith, and they both listened attentively and were really interested in what I had to tell them. They were very deferential too and in spite of the fact that one was the wife of Buckingham and one his sister, I quite liked them. Best of the three though, I liked Lucy Hay, the Countess of Carlisle. She was a very interesting and beautiful woman. She was about ten years older than I and came from the Percy family, her father being the Earl of Northumberland. She had made a very romantic marriage after falling in love with James Hay who became the Earl of Carlisle. Her family had objected to the marriage and it would never have taken place but for the fact that her father had become a prisoner in the Tower of London and the Earl of Carlisle brought about his release, making it a condition that he marry Lucy. I liked her because she was outstandingly beautiful as well as being witty and amusing.

It was suddenly borne home to me that I could like some of the English and as long as none of the friends I had brought with me from France was sent away, I could welcome these three interesting ladies into my household.

In spite of the fact that I was growing quite fond of Buckingham's wife and sister I hated him more than ever. I was convinced that he made the King dissatisfied with me and I became even more sure of this when Mamie came to me in some distress and told me he had talked to her.

'Of what?' I demanded.

'Of you and the King.'

'How dare he!'

'He would dare anything. The King can see no wrong in him. The fact is that Buckingham tells me the King is not at all satisfied with you.'

'You mean he has told Buckingham to inform *you* of this?' I could feel my temper rising.

'Now you must calm yourself. He says that you disappoint the King in the bedchamber.'

I felt myself go hot with shame and anger.

'How dare he!'

'He says it is what the King has confided in him. He says you seem affable enough during the day but at night you become distinctly cold, and that does not please the King.'

'It is for the King to *make* me affectionate towards him. I shall tell him he will not do so through his ambassador Buckingham.'

'I pray you be calm. Let us think of this clearly. How . . . how is it with you and the King?'

I burst out: 'I should have thought that was a matter between the King and me . . . and us two only.'

'It is. It is. But you see the King has spoken to Buckingham.'

'Mamie,' I said, 'do you really think the King has spoken to Buckingham . . . or is it one of the Duke's fabrications?'

She was thoughtful. Then she said: 'If you tell me that all is well between you and the King . . . at night. . . .'

'As far as I know. I submit . . . though I do not like it very much.'

'Perhaps that is not enough.'

'But to tell Buckingham. . . .'

'If he did,' put in Mamie.

'Mamie, I know that the King and I will never be happy together while Buckingham is here. I am certain that he is going to do everything he can to drive us apart.'

'And if there were no Buckingham . . . do you think that you could grow to love the King?'

'I don't know. Life seemed so much happier when Buckingham was not here.'

'You are not dissatisfied with your new bedchamber ladies?'

'No. I like them very much. Particularly Lucy.'

'We must not allow Buckingham to influence the King.'

'How shall we stop him?'

'I don't know but we can pray for a miracle.'

I was deeply disturbed that the King had spoken of our most intimate relationship with the Duke. But had he? I could not be really sure of this and for once I did not jump to conclusions. But I was more and more wary of Buckingham and I was beginning to believe that but for him we might have avoided quite a number of the storms which had blown up and were threatening to wreck our marriage.

That last affair was, I was sure, a result of his interference.

His determination to harm me was becoming even more obvious. One day he dared ask for a private audience with me. Reluctantly I gave it and immediately wished I had not. He was an extremely handsome man – indeed he owed his rise to power to his personal appearance – and his confidence gave him an air of royalty. I was sure he thought himself of far greater importance than anyone at Court – even the King himself.

He quickly threw off the formalities and began to talk to me very intimately in a manner which infuriated me more and more every second.

'I know, my dear lady, that the relationship between you and the King is not quite what it should be. Oh, you are beautiful, there is no doubt of that . . . and you are regal being the daughter of a king, but you are young . . . so very young. . . .'

'I grow older every day, sir,' I told him with some asperity, 'and my vision grows clearer.'

He laughed rather heartily.

'Dearest lady, you are enchanting. I know where the complaint lies.'

'Complaint, sir. Of what complaint do you speak?'

'You are so fresh, so young, so innocent. Naturally, I tell the King you need to be guided in the ways of love.'

I was too astonished to speak.

'Love!' he said. 'Ah, one needs to be skilled in the art to discover its full delights. Perhaps the King is more practised in the realms of state than in the bedchamber. Perhaps. . . .'

He had moved nearer to me and there was no mistaking the gleam in his eyes. Was this, I wondered, how he had approached my sister-in-law? What was he suggesting? That I learn how to be what he called satisfactory with Charles through Buckingham?

It was monstrous. What would Charles think of this subject of his if I told him what Buckingham had suggested to me . . . well not so much suggested as implied.

'My Lord Buckingham,' I cried shrilly, 'stand away from me. Your conduct is atrocious. I wonder what the King will say when I tell him what you have suggested to me.'

He stood back, his eyebrows raised, his face a mask of bewilderment. 'My lady, I do not understand you. Suggested? What do you think I have suggested?'

'Your remarks about matters which are completely between the King and myself are offensive.'

'Forgive me . . . I just thought a little word – That was all that was in my mind. I swear it. What could you have imagined? You must realize that I have no idea why you should be so offended.'

The man was a monster, a snake in the grass and I must beware of his venom.

'I merely wished to talk to you about your attitude to the faith which prevails in this country. I merely wanted to advise

you. The matter of the Countess of Denbigh's service at Tichfield. . . .'

'That is long ago. The Countess bears no rancour and has now
become my friend.'

'I am happy about that as it brings me to another matter which I
know gives the King a great deal of concern. He wants you to
send your French attendants back to France.'

'That is something I shall never do.'

'You would find many English ladies who would be happy to
replace them.'

'I am very happy as we are. Thank you for your concern. But it
is my affair as to whom I shall choose to serve me.'

'I trust that you speak a little English now that you have three
English ladies of the bedchamber.'

'I do, but there again I do not see that it is any great concern of
yours.'

'I speak only for your own good. My great wish is to please you.'

'Then,' I said firmly, 'I will tell you how you may give me the
greatest pleasure. It is very simple. All you have to do is go.'

With that he went, leaving me very uneasy.

I should have realized that we were working towards a climax,
but my trouble in those days was that I never looked beyond the
immediate moment. If I scored a little victory I thought I had won
the war – though why there should be a war between husband
and wife I cannot now see.

It was June and we were at Whitehall. The afternoon was warm
and beautiful – just the day for taking a walk in the park near the
palace. Father Sancy walked with me and he was admonishing
me for some petty demeanour. I was not listening to him but
thinking how beautiful the trees were and what a lovely day it
was. Mamie was walking on the other side of me when we
strayed away from the park. We came to the gallows at Tyburn,
which had always filled me with horror because so many people
had died miserably there – some I knew for their faith. It was not
long ago when those good Catholics who had set out to blow up
the Houses of Parliament had died most brutally. All they had
wished to do was establish the Catholic Faith in this heretic land,
which was what I wanted to do.

I mentioned this. Mamie frowned. She hated me to speak in this way. She was a good Catholic, of course, but she was more ready to respect the beliefs of others than I was. Father Sancy grew rather fierce talking of the people who had died for their faith at Tyburn and suggested that we approach and say a short prayer for their souls.

So I agreed and we did so.

I suppose nothing a Queen does can go unnoticed. Of course I was seen and as I appeared to have enemies everywhere, the incident was embellished and distorted out of all proportion to what had actually taken place. Stories were circulated about the Court and the city. I heard that I had done penance at Tyburn; I had walked barefoot carrying a candle. I had set up an altar there; I had said Mass; I had prayed to the Virgin and the saints for the souls of those I called Martyrs and whom the English called criminals.

'Lies!' I cried. 'Lies . . . it is all lies.'

But it was strange how many people were ready to believe it.

The King questioned me about it. I told him what had actually happened.

'Unfortunate,' he said. 'Most unfortunate. Why did you have to walk to such a place?'

'I don't know,' I cried. 'We just arrived there.'

I could see that he did not believe me.

He took me by the shoulders and shook me gently. 'You must try to understand,' he said with mild exasperation.

I said: 'I won't go near the place again. It's horrible. I hate it. I feel as though I hear the cries of all those who suffered there.'

'They suffered there because they were criminals,' he said tersely.

'Not all,' I cried. 'Not all. Some suffered for their faith.'

'It would be considered quite amusing for a Catholic to complain about the wrongs done to others for the simple reason that they are of a different faith from their persecutors.'

I was silent then. I was only trying to explain what had actually happened at Tyburn.

He muttered: 'It is that priest of yours. He is nothing more than a spy. He shall be sent away. Your entire retinue encourages you to behave as you do.'

Then he left me. He was really very angry but I thought it was such a shame that he should be prepared to listen to the stories about me and seem to believe those who circulated them rather than me, his own wife.

I was very angry and hurt. To cheer me my friends said that we should have a little entertainment in my apartments at Whitehall and so they brought in their music and we tried some new dances, becoming very merry.

I suppose we made a fair amount of noise. I know we were all laughing rather loudly and I was dancing with one of the gentlemen of my household when the door opened suddenly and the King stood on the threshold.

Everything stopped and the silence was so intense that it made me want to scream out for them to start the music again. I looked at him. I was holding my partner's hand, for that was what the dance demanded, and I could see that the King thought my conduct most indecorous.

He did not speak immediately but stood still looking at us. Then he walked over to me. Everyone watched because he seemed to walk very slowly. He took me by the hand and said 'Come.' That was all. Then he led me to his apartment, which was next to mine, and when we were there he locked the door.

I looked at him questioningly.

He said: 'I have something to say to you. I have been meaning to tell you for some little time that those who came with you from France will now be returning there.'

I stared at him in astonishment. I stammered: 'What? When. . . ?'

He answered: 'Immediately. It is all arranged. I am sure the trouble between us comes from their influence. The sooner they are back in their own land the better for us all.'

'No!' I cried.

'But yes,' he answered, and added soothingly: 'You will see that it is the best thing.'

'I will not allow it,' I said fiercely.

'Now,' he went on in the same soothing manner, 'you must not be so foolish.'

I moved towards the door. 'It is locked,' he said. 'I have the key.'

'Then open the door. I want to go to them. I want to tell them what you are preparing for them. It was agreed at the marriage settlement that they should stay with me.'

'The French have not always adhered to the terms of the marriage settlement, and I am weary of these people who do nothing but cause trouble. Your confessor is all the time stirring up strife. It was he who took you to Tyburn and advised you to act as you did. He is going back to France at once . . . and the whole pack with him.'

'No,' I said faintly, for a terrible fear was gripping me and I was thinking of all my dear ones but most of all my beloved Mamie.

'Let me go to them,' I pleaded.

'You will not see them again,' he replied firmly.

I stared at him aghast, and he went on: 'They are leaving Whitehall today. Even at this moment the carriages are waiting to take them.'

'To . . . take them where?'

'Where they can be housed until arrangements are made to ship them back to France.'

To ship them to France! He talked of them as though they were bales of wool . . . my beloved friends . . . the people who made life here tolerable for me.

'I will not let them go,' I cried.

'My dear wife,' he said, 'try to be reasonable. It is better that they go. It is better that you and I learn to love each other so that no others – save the children we shall have – can be of the same importance to us.'

'I cannot believe this. You are doing it to tease me.'

He shook his head. 'It is true. They must go. There will never be peace between us two while they remain. Come with me.'

He took me to the window. Carriages were drawn up there and I saw that my friends were being directed into them.

'No. No.' I began to cry. I wrenched myself away from him because I had seen Mamie down there being put into a carriage.

'Mamie!' I whispered. 'Oh . . . Mamie . . .' Then I started to call her loudly, but she could not hear me. She looked desperately unhappy.

Frantically I beat on the window.

'Don't go. Don't go,' I screamed. 'Don't let them do this.'

The window pane cracked. I heard the sound of tinkling glass and there was blood on my hands.

Charles had me by the shoulders. 'Stop it,' he cried. 'Stop it.'

'I will not. I will not. I hate England. I hate you all. You are taking away from me those I love.'

I slipped out of his grasp and sat on the floor sobbing as I heard the carriages drive away.

I was alone. Charles had gone and I heard him turn the key in the lock. I sat there on the floor, my hands covering my face, more desolate than I had ever been in my life.

I don't know how long I sat there before the door opened quietly and Lucy Hay came in. She did not speak for a moment but helped me rise and putting her arm about me led me to the window seat. She smoothed back my hair as though I were a child, and when I put my head on her shoulder she held me tightly, saying nothing but somehow giving me the comfort I sorely needed.

After a while I said: 'They have gone . . . my dear, dear Mamie has been taken from me.'

She nodded.

I said: 'I hate those who have taken her from me.'

Still she did not speak though she knew I was referring to the King.

We just sat there in that room with the broken window and I told her how Mamie had been with me since I was a child and how she had taught me so much and how we had laughed together.

Finally she said: 'It happens to Queens. It is their sad fate.'

I knew then that she understood perfectly and that I could not have borne it if she had told me I must try to forget them. How could I ever forget Mamie?

She went on: 'They are being taken to Somerset House and they will stay there until arrangements are made. They are being well looked after.'

A little later she led me back to my apartments and I asked her to stay with me, which she did.

I blamed Buckingham, my arch enemy, the author of my sorrows. It was true that he was in France at this time, making trouble there, but I knew that it was he who had instilled in Charles's mind the need to rob me of my friends and that he taunted him with allowing me to have too much of my own way. Oh yes, Buckingham was the enemy.

I missed Mamie so much. I realized what wisdom she had tried to pass on to me and I bitterly regretted that I had not paid more attention.

I was turning more and more to my three ladies – oddly enough the Buckinghams – but most of all to Lucy. She was a great comfort to me during those days. She was so much wiser than I and she reminded me very much of dear Mamie. Her advice was very similar. Be calm. Think before you act . . . before you speak even.

I knew it was sound advice. I wondered if I could ever be disciplined enough to follow it.

When I saw the letter Charles had written to Buckingham I was so incensed that I almost tore it into pieces and threw it out of the window. I wished I had done so and then I should have delighted in telling Charles of my act.

I don't know how he could have been so careless, but I supposed he had thought it was safe in his own apartments. It was lying on a table just as he had written it, and slipping into the room I saw it.

'Steenie,' he had written.

'Steenie!' I said aloud scornfully. It was absurd how Charles doted on the fellow. He was as weak as his father. What was wrong with these Stuarts? Weaklings, that was what they were. Mary, the Queen of Scots, Charles's grandmother had been foolish – so much so that she had lost her head at Fotheringay.

I went on to read the letter.

'I writ to you by Ned Clarke that I thought I should have cause enough, in a short time, to put away the monsers . . .'

I ground my teeth. He meant by 'monsers', monsieurs, my French attendants.

'either by their attempting to steal away my wife or by making plots with my own subjects. For the first I cannot say whether it was intended; but I am sure it is hindered; for the other, though I have good grounds to believe it, and am still hunting after it, yet seeing daily the maliciousness of the monsers by making and fomenting discontents in my wife. I could tarry no longer in advertising to you that I mean to seek for no other grounds. . . . Advertise the Queen Mother of my intentions. . . .

'I pray you send me word with what speed you may whether ye like this course or not. I shall put nothing of this into execution until I hear from you. . . . I am resolved it shall be done and shortly. So longing to see you, I rest

'Your loving and constant friend

'Charles R.

I was furious. They were talking about my friends, my happiness. And he would do nothing until my Lord Buckingham gave his permission! Oh yes, Buckingham was the evil spirit who had ruined my happiness. I hated him.

It soon became clear that Buckingham approved of the measure Charles was taking against me, for it was not long before all my dear friends left for France.

Lucy took the trouble to send someone along the river to Somerset House that I might know how my friends left.

There was a little trouble, she told me. When all the barges were there to take them away, the people crowded into the streets and along the river to watch them go. At first my dear friends declared they would not leave for they had not been properly discharged and were here on the terms of the marriage treaty. The King had to send a strong body of yeomen with heralds and trumpeters and they were told that His Majesty's orders were that they were to leave without more ado. Mamie was very upset. She wept and explained that she had sworn never to leave me.

Dear Mamie. I knew she would do that.

'One of the mob threw a stone at her,' Lucy said.

'At Mamie!' I cried in horror.

'It was all right. She was not hurt. It just knocked her cap off and the man who had thrown it was killed on the spot. One of the soldiers drew his sword and ran it through the man's body. Then, weeping, Mamie allowed herself to be put into the barge.'

So that was the end. They had left me.

I could not eat. I could not sleep. I could only think of my dear friends who were lost to me and most of all of my beloved Mamie who, I knew, would be heartbroken.

When Charles came to me I refused to speak to him. I see now how patient he was, how sorry that this had happened; but he was firmly convinced (and Buckingham had made him certain of this) that all the trouble between us came from my French retinue.

I would let him see that their dismissal had made everything more difficult between us.

He told me that all my servants had not gone yet and he was arranging for one of the nurses and Madame Vantelet to stay – also a few of my servants. It was a slight concession for none of these people was particularly close and all held minor posts, so this did little to alleviate my grief.

'I want to see my confessor,' I cried.

I knew that Father Sancy had either gone or was going. He would have a fine story to tell them when he returned to France.

'I will send Father Philip to you,' said Charles.

I brightened a little. I was fond of Father Philip, who was much less stern than Father Sancy, and I would be pleased to see him.

He came and talked to me and we prayed together; he said that there were many crosses to bear in this world and I had just been presented with one of them. I must carry it bravely and keep my eyes on the goal, which was to spread the truth wherever I was and always remain steadfast in following the true Faith.

I felt much better and later Charles told me that Father Philip might stay.

I was pleased to hear that, but I did not tell Charles so. I felt in no mood to give him any satisfaction.

One of the hardest things to bear was that François de Bassompierre was not entirely on my side. I had expected condolences from him when in desperation the King sent for him to try to reason with me.

'Your Majesty,' he said, 'I must talk to you most frankly. I know you will allow me – as a loyal subject of your father and one whom he regarded as a close friend – to say exactly what is in my mind.'

My spirits sank. My experience told me that when people declared they were going to speak frankly something unpleasant was certain to follow.

'I have seen you in the presence of the King,' he went on, 'and it appears to me that His Majesty has tried to do everything within his power to make you happy.'

'Such as depriving me of my friends,' I cried petulantly.

'It is the custom when a princess comes to a new country for those who accompanied her on the journey to return in due course to their native land.'

'Why? Why shouldn't anyone . . . most of all a Queen . . . keep her friends about her if she wishes to.'

'Because, Majesty, they do not always understand the customs of the new country and it is the duty of the princess to adopt those customs as she has become a member of that country.'

'I am French. I shall never be anything else.'

He sighed. 'That I fear is at the root of the trouble.'

'How can you ask me to become one of these people? They are heretics.'

'Adequate arrangements have been made for you to worship as you wish, and I see that the King has kept his word in seeing that these are carried out.'

'And taken away my confessor!'

'I did not think you cared greatly for Father Sancy and Father Philip is left to you.'

I was silent. It was true that I greatly preferred Father Philip to Father Sancy.

'Oh,' I cried. 'Can't you see! I have been robbed of those I loved most.'

'You are thinking of your governess. She understands. She is sad, but she is not lost to you. You can write to each other and no doubt she will pay a visit to these shores at some time and you may come to France. Then you will have an opportunity of meeting.'

I felt exasperated. What compensations were letters and the occasional visit for the hours of confidences and fun which Mamie and I had shared?

Bassompierre went on to lecture me. He could see that the trouble between the King and myself was largely due to my attitude. If I could only be reasonable . . . try to adjust myself . . . much progress could be made. The King was fond of me. He wanted to be more fond. He would do a great deal to make me happy, but my demands were childish and he was the King on whom state duties weighed heavily. I was not helping him nor myself by my conduct. I was self-willed, said Bassompierre. My father would not have been pleased with me if he were here today. I was impulsive; I spoke before I thought what I was saying; I must try to curb my temper.

I scowled at him and he went on: 'It is not merely yourself you have to consider. Do you realize that your actions are causing strife between France and England?'

'They do not need me to bring strife between them. It has been there for centuries.'

'There was friendship. The marriage was meant to make that firm, and it should have done so, had you behaved in a manner which your great father would have expected you to. Instead you have made this petty war betwen your faction and that of the King with the result that they are all dismissed . . . banished . . . because they have been fomenting strife betwen you and the King.'

'You think I and my friends are to blame. You should be on my side. I thought you were French and would stand by me.'

'I am French and I will stand by you but there is much you must do for yourself. You must change your attitude towards the King.'

'Shouldn't he change his towards me?'

Bassompierre sighed. 'He is willing to do much for you.'

'Will he send back my friends?'

'You know you ask for the impossible.'

'I never thought you would turn against me.'

He was on his knees, taking my hand and kissing it. He was for me, he declared. He would do anything for me. That was why with great temerity he was telling me exactly what be believed without subterfuge, and he hoped I would see it in the way it was meant and forgive him if he had offended.

He was so handsome, and contrite in a way while adhering to his principles, that I smiled and said: 'Get up, François. I know that you do what you do and say for my good. But if only you knew how tired I am of having things done for my good.'

He smiled. I was the dear, adorable child once more.

I was sure he thought that now we had passed through the emotional preliminaries he could talk seriously to me. This he began to do. The situation between England and France was becoming dangerous. The English were very unpopular in France and the return of my attendants had made them more so. Some of them who had served me were circulating rumours about the way in which I was treated in England and my countrymen were becoming incensed.

'If the Duke of Buckingham set foot in France now he would be torn to pieces by the mob.'

'A befitting end for the monster,' I commented.

'And imagine the effect that would have on the King. Why, it could result in war.'

I was silent.

'You see, my dear lady, many eyes are on you and this marriage. Your mother . . . your brother . . . they look to you to strengthen the bonds of friendship between the two countries. They will be very sad to hear the stories which your attendants are circulating.'

'It is well that they should know.'

'But you have nothing of which to complain. You have been treated royally. The King has shown you every consideration.'

'By taking away from me those I loved best!'

He was exasperated. 'I have explained, my lady, that it is the custom for attendants to return home after a certain period. You cannot say that you – or they – have been ill treated here. Now let me explain what is happening in France. In the villages and the towns they are talking about the ills which have befallen their Princess. They speak as though you have been confined to prison and kept on bread and water.'

'I wouldn't mind that if I could have Mamie with me.'

'Do try to understand. Let me explain to you that one girl, obviously deranged, has been to a convent in Limoges and asked for shelter there. She called herself the Princesse Henriette de Bourbon and told some garbled story about having escaped from England and cruel King Charles because she was persecuted there in an effort to make her give up her Faith. I can tell you this: Thousands of people are flocking to Limoges to see this girl. They believe her and are crying vengeance on King Charles of England.'

'Surely it is easy to prove she is a fraud.'

'To any who have knowledge of Courts, of course, but these are simple people and she is succeeding in deluding them. The King, your brother, is extremely angry. He has other matters with which to occupy himself. The Huguenots are causing a great deal of trouble.'

'Tell me more of the girl. I should like to see her. Is she like me?'

'She passes herself off well, I hear. She has a certain dignity and seems to know something of the English Court. Your brother has made a declaration that the girl is an impostor and that you are living amicably with your husband in England where you are given every dignity due to a Queen.'

I was silent.

He went on: 'She has been proved in a public trial to be a fraud. She has done a penance through the streets carrying a lighted taper and is now in prison. But that does not mean that certain people do not continue to believe her.' He bent towards me. 'Please, Your Majesty, will you try to do your duty here. Do you see how easily great trouble could arise from your actions. I am sure you would not wish to be responsible for a war and to know that innocent blood was being shed because of your wilful actions.'

He did succeed in making me realize how important some trivial actions of mine might be. I said I would remember what he had told me and he went away a little happier than he had been on his arrival.

After my talk with François de Bassompierre I did try to be a little more affable to Charles and I must admit that he was only too ready to meet me in this. We became friends again and without Mamie to confide in and Father Sancy to point out the iniquities of heretics we did seem to be happier together.

He was very preoccupied at this time with affairs of state. He was more serious than ever and wanted so much to rule the country well. I heard him say that he and Steenie could manage very well without a parliament. It was Kings who had been chosen by God to rule not men who set themselves up – although they declared they had been elected by their fellow men – to say what should and should not be done.

Looking back now I can see quite clearly the danger signals even at that time beginning to show. I was not very interested in politics, but I did know that there was a great deal of trouble in France and that somehow the English were not exactly aloof from it.

Cardinal Richelieu had more or less taken over the reins of government, and it seemed that my brother – who had never been a very forceful character – was glad for him to do this. But my mother, who was a born intrigante, had become the centre of an opposing faction. The Cardinal was a very strong man but even he had his difficulties when he was surrounded by those who would be ready to stab him in the back.

I thought a great deal about Buckingham, whom I hated violently for I really believed he was the cause of the unhappiness I had endured since I came to this country.

He was very unpopular I was glad to note. I always said he owed his rise to power to his good looks and certainly not to his performance in state matters. He would have been impeached if Charles had not saved him. He had failed in an expedition to Cadiz. Why he should have imagined himself as a military commander I could not say. He had no talent for command. He could hardly be impeached for failure in war, but accusations of other crimes were brought against him. Charles saved him by dissolving Parliament. What did he want a parliament for? he would say. He could govern on his own.

Buckingham loved the applause of the crowd and wanted to regain his popularity so he began making a great show of his sympathy for the Huguenots who at that time were being a nuisance to my brother. In fact they were more than merely vociferous and the country was becoming weakened by civil war.

Buckingham wanted to send help to the Huguenot citizens of Rochelle who were being blockaded by my brother; this naturally meant a declaration of war between France and England.

I was most distressed. What a terrible position for a Queen to find herself in: her husband at war with her brother! I thought constantly of my dear friends who had been torn away from me and although I was generally able to shut my mind to what I thought of as stupid politics, it was hardly possible to do so at this time.

Charles and I were becoming more friendly, and he even talked a little about what was on his mind. He was always against the Parliament. What right had these men to tell a King what he should do? He was constantly asking that question.

'I would go without a parliament altogether,' he said, 'but I have to get them to grant me money. How can we carry on the country's affairs without money?'

He believed that he and his beloved Steenie could manage very well without those dreary men who were always putting obstacles in the way.

He tried raising money without the aid of Parliament by making every one of his subjects pay a tax. If they refused they were imprisoned. He raised an army and the men were billeted in private houses whether the owners wanted them or not. Fortunately they blamed this on Buckingham. How they hated that man! I would laugh inwardly every time I saw a sign of this. Charles, however, continued to love him. It used to make me so angry when I heard his voice soften as he said his name.

In spite of all his efforts Charles found it necessary to call Parliament, which immediately made him surrender his right to billet soldiers in private houses and to exact loans without the consent of Parliament.

How he raged against them! But he needed their help if he was going to take part in the siege of Rochelle, and he was forced to accept their terms.

I was relieved when the siege of Rochelle was over and ended in triumph for the French, partly because in my heart I liked to see my own countrymen triumphant and because it was another failure for my old enemy Buckingham. I was so delighted when I heard him reviled. There were satires and pasquinades written about him and stuck on buildings all over the country.

To try to make the people like him again and to show how he upheld the Protestant Faith he started to plan a new expedition. This time it was to relieve the people of Rochelle.

He came to see Charles, and I don't think he was very pleased to realize how much better we were getting on. He was delighted, of course, that I had lost my friends; and I wondered what fresh unpleasantness he could plot against me when he was free from his present project, for at that time he was concerned with little else but his expedition to Rochelle and he was going down to Portsmouth to make sure that all the provisions and ammunition they would need were on board.

Charles came to me after he had left.

'Steenie is in a strange mood,' he said. 'I have never seen him gloomy before. He is usually so sure of success.'

'His lack of success has probably made him doubt his powers after all. In which case it would be a good thing, for it is always well to see oneself as one really is rather than how one would wish to be.'

Charles was a little hurt as always when I criticized his beloved Steenie, but he refused to be drawn into an argument and ceased to talk of Buckingham and became my loving husband.

It was not long after that when it happened.

The King was prostrate with grief and I was very sorry for him because I knew what it meant to lose someone one loved perhaps as deeply as one had ever loved anyone. Had I not lost my own beloved Mamie?

It was ironical that the King who had robbed me of my dearest companion should now find that fate had robbed him of his.

William Laud brought the news from Portsmouth. Laud was a priest and a great favourite of both Charles and Buckingham. My husband had shown him great favour and perhaps because Buckingham had thought so highly of him, he had made him a Privy Councillor and promised him the Bishopric of London. He was already Bishop of Bath and Wells. He had grown very friendly with Buckingham because Buckingham's mother had shown signs of becoming too interested in the Catholic Faith and Charles had sent Laud to be her priest and bring her back to Protestantism. This Laud had tried to do, and while he was under Buckingham's roof had formed a great friendship with the Duke, and as the King liked to share everything with his Steenie, Laud was his friend too.

So it was Laud who came with the news.

There was tension throughout Whitehall. I had never seen the King look as he did then. His face was quite devoid of colour and his eyes stared ahead disbelievingly as though pleading with someone – the Almighty, I suppose – to tell him that it was not true.

But it was true.

'He had a presentiment that death was close to him,' Laud told us. 'He called me to him the night before. He was very serious and Your Majesty knows that was not like him. He begged me, Your Majesty, to commend him to you and request you take care of his wife and family.'

'Oh, Steenie,' murmured the King, 'as if I would fail you!'

'I said to him,' went on Laud, "Why do you say this? You have never before suggested that you are going to die. I have never seen you, my Lord, but when you are full of high hopes and good spirits." He answered me, "Some adventure may kill me. Others have been killed before me." I said to him, "Is it an assassin you fear?" And he nodded. I suggested that he wear a shirt of mail under his clothes, but he laughed the idea to scorn. "That would not protect me against the fury of the mob," he said. So he would take no precautions.'

'Oh, Steenie,' moaned the King.

I wanted to know how it had happened, every detail. The King covered his face with his hands while I asked the questions. Laud whispered to me that the King could not bear to hear more.

I could very well bear to hear more. I could listen and exult so I insisted that he proceed.

'He was staying at the house of Captain Mason in the High Street,' said Laud. 'It was convenient for the supervision of the loading. His Duchess was staying at the house with him before he sailed. He had come down to breakfast and partaken heartily of it. Then he went into the hall and paused for a moment to exchange a word or two with Sir Thomas Tryer who had come to see him. Suddenly a man stepped forward. He cried out: "God have mercy on thy soul!" and brandishing a knife he thrust it into the Duke's left breast.'

The King moaned softly and I went to him and took his hand. He pressed mine warmly.

'The Duke himself withdrew the knife,' went on Laud. 'He was bleeding profusely and there was blood spattered everywhere. My Lord Duke took two steps as though to go after the man. He cried, "Villain!" and then fell to the floor. The Duchess came running into the hall. Poor lady, she is three months with child. She knelt beside him, but he was dying and I could see there was nothing we could do. I gave him what comfort I could and it was then that he again begged me to commend him to you and ask you to look after his family.'

The King was still too overwrought to speak.

I said: 'Have they caught the assassin?'

'Yes, a certain John Felton – a discharged officer who thought he had a grievance, and when the House of Commons showed their disapproval of the Duke he believed he was doing his country a service.'

He was, I thought. Oh good John Felton!

But I had learned my lessons. I said nothing; and then I devoted my time to attempting to comfort the King.

How strange it was that the man who had done so much to drive a wedge between us in life, in death should be the means of bringing us together.

I understood Charles's grief so much and because for once I could see through someone else's eyes, I could console him, because his was the greater pain. Steenie had gone for ever but I could still write to Mamie and I hoped to see her one day.

He talked to me a great deal about Steenie and I had to control my impulses to say something derogatory about him, and then after a while I saw how comforting it was for him to talk about this beloved friend whose faults he could not and never would see.

Life for him had lost its savour and it seemed that I was the one who could make up for that. I took a great pleasure in this and he could hardly bear to be away from me. I felt tender towards him. I sensed a certain weakness in him and instead of being critical of it, it endeared him to me.

I treated him as though he were my child instead of my husband and he was grateful for that. Charles was not a man who enjoyed exerting his will. He was serious in his intentions to do right; he wanted to be a good ruler and a good husband. He had not enjoyed sending away my attendants but he had done so because he had thought it was the best for us all.

I began to understand so much and each day I looked forward to our talks, and at night, in the privacy of our bedchamber, I think we truly became lovers.

I began to wonder whether there had been two reasons why we had had such a stormy beginning to our married life. One was undoubtedly Buckingham and the other . . . could it really have been my attendants? Sancy had led me into some difficult situations culminating in the visit to Tyburn; my ladies had always reminded me that I was a Frenchwoman among the English, and a Catholic in an alien land.

Of course Mamie had done her best to help me, but she was apart from the rest.

A few weeks passed while Charles mourned Buckingham deeply, but I knew his sorrow was passing because he was finding great pleasure and the deepest satisfaction in the new relationship which was springing up between us.

Then I discovered that I was with child.

I was very excited at the prospect of having a baby, and Charles was delighted.

'It must be a boy,' I said. Then he smiled gently at me and told me I must not be disappointed if our first child was a girl. We would get boys in due course, he was sure.

I talked about the child practically all the time with my women. One of them said she was sure it would be a boy by the way I was carrying it.

'How I should like to know for sure,' I said.

One of them whispered to me: 'Why not consult Eleanor Davys.'

It was the first time I had heard the woman's name and I had no idea then that she would be the cause of frictions between Charles and me.

I talked over the matter with those three who had become my special friends among the English ladies of the bedchamber: Susan Feilding, Countess of Denbigh, Katherine, Buckingham's widow, and my favourite of the three, Lucy Hay, Countess of Carlisle. Poor Katherine was very sad at this time; she could not get over the shock of losing her husband. It was strange to me that anyone could love that man, yet she had apparently done so – as had my own husband. She told me how she would never forget coming down the stairs and seeing him lying there in the hall with his blood spattering the walls. I could quite understand why she had nightmares nowadays. We did our best to cheer her and somehow that brought us all closer together.

'Why not call in Eleanor Davys?' said Susan. I think she looked upon it as a diversion for me as well as for Katherine.

Lucy said that Eleanor Davys had foretold her first husband's death. 'She said he would die in three days,' she added, 'and he did.'

We were all awestruck.

'She would know then whether I was carrying a boy or a girl,' I said.

'Why not wait and see,' suggested Katherine. 'Wouldn't it be nice to surprise yourself?'

'I should like to know now,' I said. 'Moreover I should like to put this wise woman to the test.'

'Let us bring her in then,' suggested Lucy.

'Who is she?' asked Katherine.

'She is the wife of Sir John Davys, the King's Attorney General,' Susan told us.

'Her second husband,' I added, 'since she foretold the death of her first husband. I wonder if she has told Sir John how long he has to live.'

We were all laughing together and even Katherine managed to raise a smile.

However it was arranged that Lady Davys should be brought to me and she was only too delighted to come. In the meantime I had found out certain facts about her. She was the daughter of the Earl of Castlehaven and was quite renowned for her prophecies. If the letters of her name – Eleanor Davys – were arranged differently and her first name spelt with two lls as it often was and her surname Davie instead of Davys (which one could say was used occasionally) the result would be 'Reveal O Daniel'. This seemed very significant.

We all became very excited thinking of the revelations to come and when the lady was presented I was greatly impressed by her. She was a big woman, dark-haired with enormous luminous eyes – just the sort, I said to Lucy afterwards, which a seer ought to have.

She was not in the least overawed by me. I supposed as a prophetess a Queen did not seem so very important in her eyes.

She told us that she had a mission; she was in touch with powers. She could not explain them; she merely knew that she had been selected by some great force to be able to look at that which was not revealed to ordinary people.

I made her sit down and I told her that I had heard of her miraculous powers and there was a question I wanted to ask her. She folded her arms and looked at me steadily while I asked about the child I was to bear. There was a breathless silence round the table while we all waited for her words. She did not hurry. She sat back for a while and closed her eyes. When she opened them she gazed steadily at me and said: 'You will have a son.'

There was a gasp of delight round the table.

'And,' I cried, 'shall I be happy?'

She said, speaking very slowly: 'You will be happy for a while.'

'Only for a while? How long?'

'For sixteen years,' she replied.

'And then what will happen?'

She closed her eyes and at that moment the door opened and the King came in.

Although I was so much fonder of him now I was irritated by the interruption, particularly as he assumed one of his most serious looks. I thought then what fun it would have been if he had joined us and listened with us and giggled and enjoyed the excitement of prophecy. But that was not Charles's way.

He stood by the table and my ladies all rose and curtsied.

He was looking straight at our soothsayer and he said almost accusingly: 'You are Lady Davys.'

'That is so, Your Majesty,' she answered with pride, and I must admit showing very little deference to the King.

'You are the lady who foretold her husband's death.'

'Yes, Sire. I did that. I have the powers. . . .'

'I can scarcely believe that he welcomed the news,' said Charles coldly. 'Indeed it might well have done much to hasten his end.' He turned to me and offered me his arm.

There was nothing I could do but rise and leave with him, though I was fuming with irritation at having that interesting session cut short.

When we were outside the door he said: 'I do not wish you to consult that woman.'

'Why not?' I cried. 'She is clever. She told me that I would have a son and be happy.'

He was a little uplifted but persisted in his condemnation of her. 'She probably hastened her husband's death.'

'How could she? He did not die of poison. He just died . . . as she said he would.'

'It is dabbling in the black arts.'

I was afraid that he was going to forbid me to see her and I knew that if he did my temper would flare up and I should disobey him. It was a pity. We had been getting on so happily until now.

Perhaps he was thinking the same for he said no more. But there was an outcome. Left alone with the ladies, Eleanor Davys talked a little more and what she said was not nearly as pleasant as that which she had told me. When I returned to my women I noticed that they looked very grave.

I said: 'Did Lady Davys stay long after I left?'

'A little while,' Lucy replied, not looking at me.

'I was so annoyed to be taken away like that. I felt quite angry with the King.'

'He certainly did not like her,' said Susan.

'Did he forbid you to see her?' asked Katherine.

'He did not. And I would forbid him to forbid me. I will not be told, You must not do this and you must not do that.'

'Yet it would be awkward for her, I suppose,' suggested Susan, 'for he could forbid her to come to Court, and of course there is her husband to be considered.'

'Do you think Lady Davys is a woman to be told by her husband what to do?'

'No,' said Susan. 'She would probably tell him he had three days to live if he offended her.'

'That isn't fair,' I protested. 'I think her prophecies are true ones. She promised me a son.'

There was a strange and ominous silence round the table which immediately aroused my suspicions.

'What's the matter?' I cried. 'Why are you looking like that?'

They remained silent and I went to Lucy and shook her. 'Tell me,' I said. 'You know something. What is it?'

Lucy looked appealingly at Susan and Katherine shook her head.

'No,' I cried stamping my foot. 'You had better tell me what is wrong. Is it something Lady Davys said . . . eh? Was it about me?'

'She er . . . ' began Katherine. 'She . . . er . . . said nothing of importance.'

'And that is why you look as though the heavens are about to fall in? Come on . . . I command you . . . all of you . . . tell me.'

Susan lifted her shoulders and after a few seconds of silence Lucy nodded and said resignedly: 'Well, it is just talk, you know. It doesn't mean anything.'

'What?' I cried. 'What?'

'It is better to tell the Queen,' said Lucy. 'If it should come true . . . and I do not believe for a moment that it will . . . it is better for her to know.'

'Know what?' I screamed, my patience at an end; and now a certain fear was creeping into my mind.

'I think she made it up because she was angry about the King's interruption,' said Susan.

'If you don't tell me soon I'll have you all arrested for . . . conspiracy,' I shouted.

Lucy said quietly: 'She told us that you would indeed have a boy.'

'Well, go on. That's what she told me. There is nothing new in that.'

'But that he would be born, christened and buried all in one day.'

I stared at them in horror. 'It can't be true.'

'Of course it can't,' soothed Lucy. 'It is just that she was angry. She was so annoyed that the King came in and showed he did not approve of her.'

I stared ahead of me. I was seeing a little body wrapped in a shroud.

Susan said: 'Don't tell the King what she said or that we told you.'

I shook my head. 'It is such nonsense,' I cried. 'She is a mad woman.'

'That is what so many people say,' said Lucy quickly. 'Your son will be a beautiful child. How could he be otherwise? You and the King are both handsome.'

'My son!' I murmured. 'There will be a son.'

I had so firmly believed her when she said I was to have a son but if the first prophecy was correct, why should the second not be?

Now I began to be haunted by fears.

I don't know whether that prophecy preyed on my mind but whenever I thought of my baby, instead of seeing a laughing lively child I saw a little white one in a coffin. I could not eat much and at night my dreams were disturbed. The King was very anxious about me.

'Perhaps,' he said, 'you are too young to have a child.'

Too young! I was eighteen and would be nineteen in November. That was not so young to have a child. I did not tell the King about the prophecy. He would have been very angry with Lady Davys and I am sure he would have made some complaint to her husband. I tried to disbelieve her. After all, how could she possibly know? It had been a coincidence about her first husband. Perhaps he had been very ill and she, as his wife, knew exactly how ill.

The King was most attentive to me. In fact I think he was far more interested in me and my baby than he was in state affairs and was bitterly resentful when they took him away from us.

I hoped that we should have many children. I could see us in the years ahead with them all around us – beautiful children, the boys looking like Charles and the girls like me. They would certainly be a handsome family.

We were at Somerset House. We had arrived on a Monday and I had arranged for a Te Deum to be sung in the chapel there. While I was in the chapel I began to feel very unwell. It could not be the child yet, because it was not due for another month.

I was very glad to get out of the chapel and to my chamber. I told Susan and Lucy that I was not feeling well and that I thought I should retire to bed.

'You are certain to feel tired,' they said. 'You are getting close to your confinement.'

'Oh, it is a month away,' I reminded them.

But during the night I began to feel pain. I shouted and very soon people were crowding round my bed. I was in agony and I knew that my child was about to be born.

I cannot remember much of that night. I think it was rather fortunate for me that during much of it I was unconscious. In the evening of the next day my child was born . . . prematurely. It was weak, not having reached its full time and I heard afterwards how Charles and my confessor argued together over its baptism which had to take place immediately as it was ominously clear that speed was necessary. My confessor said that as I was to have charge of my children's religious upbringing until they were thirteen, the baby should be baptized according to the rites of the Church of Rome. Charles retorted that this was a Prince of Wales and the people of England would never allow a child who was destined to become King of England to be baptized as a Catholic.

The King, of course, had to be obeyed, and the little boy was baptized according to the Church of England and named Charles James.

Scarcely had those rites been performed when he died.

I remember waking from my sleep of exhaustion to find the King at my bedside.

'Charles,' I whispered.

He knelt by the bed and taking my hand kissed it.

'We have a son?' I asked.

He was silent for a second and then he said: 'We had a son.'

I felt the desolation sweep over me; the waiting months, the discomfort . . . the dreams . . . they had all come to nothing.

'We are young yet,' said the King. 'You must not despair.'

'I so wanted this child.'

'We both did.'

'Did he live at all?'

'For two hours. He was baptized and we christened him Charles James.'

'Poor little Charles James! Are you very sad, Charles?'

'I tell myself that I have you and you are going to be well soon. You are young and healthy and the doctors tell me that in spite of your ordeal you will soon be well again. That is the most important news for me.'

That was my first real experience of Charles in misfortune. He was always able to bear disappointments nobly and with few complaints. These qualities were to stand him in good stead later.

I soon recovered, though I learned that I had been very near to death. There had been one point where they could have saved the child at a cost to my life and the doctors had actually asked the King whom they should consider first . . . me or the child. I was told that he had answered immediately and vehemently: 'Let the child die but save the Queen.'

Perhaps I started to love him then. There was something so good about him; and if there was a vulnerability, a certain weakness, that only endeared him to me the more. Young, frivolous and impetuous as I was, there was a certain maternal feeling in my emotions regarding him. Perhaps it was born at that time.

As I lay in bed I remembered the prophecy. What had she said? I should have a son and he would be born, baptized and die all in a day.

The prophecy had come true.

It is amazing how news like that is circulated. Everywhere people were talking about Lady Davy's prophecy. She was indeed a seer. The King was very angry, particularly when it was suggested that the prophecy had so upset me that it was due to it that I had given birth prematurely.

It was nonsense. I was sure that Lady Davys really had the powers of prophecy.

Charles wanted her to be dismissed from Court.

'You can't do that,' I said. 'You are being like a petulant King who punishes the messengers for the message.'

He did see that. 'But I want no more of these prophecies. They are evil.'

'She promises good things sometimes.'

'First her husband. Then our child.'

'It was ordained that they should die. She just had preknowledge of it.'

'I want her out of the way.'

'You would never get a woman like that out of the way. You could burn her at the stake for a witch but she would curse you or prophesy something evil on the very scaffold.'

Charles was a little superstitious. I think that was why he was so angry.

He did not dismiss her from Court, but he did send for her husband Sir John Davys and asked him to put an end to his wife's prophecies. But Sir John explained to the King that his wife was a forceful woman and could not be forbidden to do anything. 'She believes she has a mission, Your Majesty. She says she will fulfil it no matter what humiliations and punishments the ignorant press upon her.'

Charles was a very understanding man. He knew what Sir John meant and he thought he was very brave to have married Eleanor Davys after what had happened to her first husband. Sir John, however, did burn some of her papers for she had been a collector of ancient manuscripts.

I was against this and argued with Charles about it. I said that if anything was going wrong it was better to know about it. I was sure that having heard the prophecy about my son I was more able to face the bitter disappointment because it was not entirely a surprise to me.

We argued and came near to quarrelling as we used to in the old days, but I remembered his tenderness towards me at the bedside and he thought of all I had gone through so we did not actually use harsh words against each other.

He looked at me pleadingly and said: 'It would please me if you did not see this woman again.'

I hesitated. I wanted to say: But it pleases me to see her. I want to know. I don't want to live in ignorance.

But we both compromised.

He said he was sending Mr Kirke – one of the gentlemen of the bedchamber – with a message to Lady Davys. He was to tell her that the Queen did not wish to see her again.

'It would be more truthful to say the King does not wish the Queen to see her again,' I said with a flash of my old temper.

He kissed me lightly on the forehead.

'My dearest,' he said, 'everything I ever do is with your good in mind.'

I knew that was true and I relented. I took an opportunity of waylaying Mr Kirke before he left with the message. One of the attendants brought him to my chamber.

I said to him: 'Mr Kirke, you are going with a message to Lady Davys?'

'That is so, Your Majesty,' he replied.

'When you hand it to her give her the Queen's compliments and ask her if my next child will be a boy and will he live.'

Mr Kirke bowed and went off.

I could scarcely wait for his return.

I set someone to wait at the gates for him and when he arrived back to bring him straight to me. When he came he was smiling happily so I knew that it was good news.

I said: 'Did you ask Lady Davys my question?'

He replied that he had done so. 'She said, my lady, that your next child would be a lusty son who will live, and that you will have a happy life for sixteen years.'

'Sixteen years! How strange! But a son, you said . . . a son who will live.'

'Those were her words, my lady.'

'Thank you, Mr Kirke,' I said.

And he went away to the King to report that he had carried out his mission.

Sixteen years, I thought. That would take us up to 1644 or thereabouts. Sixteen years . . . that was a long way into the future; and in the meantime I was to have my son and my happy years.

I went to the King. Mr Kirke had left him and I was sure he thought the matter was satisfactorily settled.

I embraced him and said: 'Our next son will be lusty and live.'

He looked at me in astonishment.

'You are with child?' he asked.

'Not yet. But Lady Davys says that my next son will live and be strong.'

I saw the joy in his face. He held me close to him and I laughed exultantly.

It was illogical of him. He was not supposed to believe in prophecy.

But he believed in this one though.

I said: 'It is not such a bad thing to believe in prophecies when they are good. It is only when they are bad that one does not want to know.'

Then he laughed and we were very happy. We were both thinking about the strong and lusty sons we would have.

The Happiest of Queens

It was nearly two years later before the promised boy was born. They had been two happy years, with the affection between my husband and myself growing with every passing week. It seemed so strange that out of those stormy beginnings this deep and glowing love had come. Charles seemed to have grown more handsome than when I first saw him. He smiled now more frequently. He had completely forgotten his obsession with Buckingham and I had been quite content with the letters Mamie and I exchanged. She was married now and had become Madame St George. Her husband was of the noble house of Clermont-Amboise so it was a very worthy match. I knew she was happy and had found consolation for our parting and I was glad of that. She had become governess to my brother Gaston's daughter, who was known as Mademoiselle de Montpensier, and I believe she was quite a handful. Mamie wrote often of her enduring love for me and assured me that she would never forget those happy years when as Mademoiselle de Montglat she had been my governess and friend. But we both realized now that it was no use grieving and my letters, I know, were just as much a joy to her as hers were to me.

I was happy. I had learned to speak English now, and although I should never be exactly fluent in the language I could converse adequately. It pleased Charles so much and I was always happy pleasing him.

We rarely ever quarrelled nowadays. Occasionally my temper would burst out and he would shake his finger at me but there would always be a smile and I would cry out: 'Oh, you can't expect me to change all at once. My temper has been with me from the cradle. I doubt it will ever leave me altogether.'

He said that he really liked me the way I was, which was very comforting and true lovers' talk.

The only trouble between us was, of course, my religion. I often thought that if I could convert Charles to the Catholic Faith and with him the whole of England, I should be completely happy.

But that was asking too much, and even I was wise enough to realize that I had a great deal.

And now . . . my child was to be born.

I kept reminding Charles of Lady Davys' prophecy and although he pretended to be sceptical, because it was a happy one, he was not really so.

I knew I had a great many enemies in the country. Some people even refused to rejoice at the prospect of an heir to the throne. They called me an idolatress – some even had the temerity to shout after me when I rode out. It was rather disconcerting; but I had always known that it might be necessary to suffer for the Faith. But there were plenty of people to rejoice in the birth and there were prayers all the time for my safe delivery and that the child should be a boy.

Well, we were not disappointed, for on the morning of May the twenty-ninth in that year 1630 I was brought to bed in the Palace of St James's and within a comparatively short time my son made his appearance. This time he was strong, lusty and clearly healthy – just as Lady Davys had said he would be.

I shall never forget the moment when they laid him in my arms. He was the ugliest child I ever saw. He was big and very dark and looked much older than one day.

'Why,' I said, 'he is a little monster.'

Charles came in and looked at him. He said: 'He is a perfect child. The doctors say he is in excellent health.'

'He is so dark . . . almost like a blackamoor.'

'Babies get lighter as they grow.'

'But,' I said, 'you are handsome. I am not considered ill-looking. Why should we get the ugliest baby in the world?'

But we were not really concerned with his ugliness. He had arrived and he was by no means sickly. Doubtless he would grow prettier with age.

The King was most excited. He held the baby and marvelled at him. 'Perfect in every way,' he kept saying. Everything which ought to be there was there; he made his presence felt with lusty yells and showed from the first his determination to survive.

We were all delighted with him; better a strong ugly child than a frail pretty one.

On the very morning of the child's birth Charles rode to St Paul's Cathedral to give thanks for the birth of his son and heir. The people cheered wildly; they liked him far better than they did me.

According to the custom my baby was baptized within a few days of his birth. I knew there would be some controversy about this because of the difference in the King's religion and mine. I had been promised that I should supervise the religious upbringing of my children until their thirteenth year and that meant of course that I could educate them as Catholics.

However, I did see that the ceremony could not take place in my private chapel because it was fitted as a Catholic sanctuary. The King said firmly that the baby must be baptized in the chapel of St James's and I was too tired and too happy to argue.

The Bishop of London, William Laud, conducted the service with the help of the Bishop of Norwich and the sponsors were my brother, the King of France, and my mother; they could not, of course, be present, and the Duchess of Richmond and the Marquis of Hamilton were their proxies.

My baby went through the ceremony without too much protest and was christened Charles.

The next thing we had to concern ourselves with was his wet nurse. She must be from Wales, Charles told me, for it was a tradition that the first words the Prince of Wales spoke must be in the Welsh language. After that he could speak his own tongue.

How I enjoyed those days. Sometimes I try to live them again through my memories. It was such a joy to have a child and a devoted husband. Charles could scarcely tear himself away from us. He tried to please me in every way and I was very happy to accept his attention and feel proud of myself because I had given my husband and the country this ugly boy.

Young Charles grew apace but his looks did not improve. His wet nurse said he was the liveliest and hungriest child she had ever known and was going to be tall; he was already big for his age. He was so forward and was more like a three months' child than one of a few weeks. I used to look at him in his cradle and he would return my gaze steadily. His nose was too big for a baby, I thought; but his lively eyes were darting here, there and everywhere.

'You are going to be a remarkable man,' I said to him; and he looked at me so intelligently that I could delude myself into thinking that he understood.

I had to write and tell Mamie all about him. She had a child of her own so she would fully understand the pleasures of motherhood. Writing to her was like talking to her and our letters had been a great solace to me since she left.

'Mamie,' I wrote,

'The husband of my baby's nurse is going to France and I am writing this letter believing that you will be very glad to ask him news of my son. . . . He is so ugly that I am ashamed of him, but his size and fatness supply the want of beauty. I wish you could see the gentleman, for he has no ordinary mien; he is so serious in all that he does, that I cannot help deeming him far wiser than I am myself. . . .

'I assure you that if I do not write to you as often as I might it is not because I have left off loving you but because – I must confess it – I am very idle. Also I am ashamed to admit that I am on the increase again; nevertheless I am not yet certain.

'Adieu. The man must have this letter.

'Your affectionate friend,

'Henriette Marie R.'

Yes, I was indeed pregnant again. I was not displeased about this as my wise little Charles had made me long for another child.

The King was delighted too. It was well for us to have several children, for although little Charles already looked as though he would be able to give a good account of himself, with plagues and other troubles one could never be sure.

Kings and Queens should have large families. Well, it seemed as if, now I had started, I might live up to what was expected of me.

Being a mother and a contented wife did not change my nature. I still loved to dance and although being pregnant did restrict me in many ways I did enjoy entertainments, ballets and banquets. I was very fond of dwarfs. The little people fascinated me and I was delighted when the two I possessed decided to marry. I declared we should have a celebration for them, which we did, and I took great pleasure in arranging the wedding. I had a masque written

for it, a musical entertainment. Our great poet Edmund Waller
wrote lyrics for it which were set to music. I sang some of the
songs but not those, naturally, which were written in praise of
my beauty. There were many of those sung at Court and I was
vain enough to enjoy them.

How the dwarfs amused us as they tumbled about the room
and when they danced on the table, I thought I should laugh so
much that it would be bad for the child I was carrying.

Charles and I made a short journey soon after that and were
entertained at the house of the old Countess of Buckingham. It
was amazing how, since the death of the Duke, I had become
quite fond of his family.

This was an occasion I shall always remember. I was seated
beside the King in the place of honour and dinner proceeded in
the usual manner with the musicians playing all the time, for the
Countess knew how much I enjoyed music.

During a short pause in the playing a great pie was carried in
and placed in the centre of the table. All eyes were on it as slowly
the pastry began to crack from within, until there was a great hole
in it and it was scattered over the table. Then out of the enormous
dish there stepped a man. He was eighteen inches high, beautifully dressed in miniature garments and with a face which was
quite handsome. He advanced along the table taking mincing
steps between the dishes. When he came to me he bowed low
and said in a very pleasant voice that he trusted I liked him well
enough to appoint him my devoted servant.

Everyone was laughing and clapping. Even the King was
smiling benignly. I think they were all aware of what was going to
happen. For me, of course, it was to be a surprise.

I begged the little man to come and stand beside me. He did
so, delicately brushing scraps of pastry from his elegant coat. I
said I should be delighted to take him into my service for I liked
well his looks and, as he would have heard, two of my little
people had married. Oh, they were still in my service but married
people were apt to be more devoted to each other than those they
served.

He nodded knowingly and said he would dedicate himself
completely to his Queen.

I kept him by me and thanked the Countess for giving me so
much pleasure.

My little man told me his name was Geoffrey Hudson and that it had long been his ambition to serve me.

So he came into my service. He was extremely intelligent and capable of performing all sorts of errands for he was quite a little statesman; and I became very fond of him and was so pleased that he had come to serve me.

That November, a year and five months after the birth of my swarthy gentleman, I produced a daughter. We decided to call her Mary and like her brother she was baptized in St James's Chapel by Bishop Laud.

A few weeks after her birth my daughter became very ill, and Charles and I spent an anxious time during the days which followed. I had been so happy to have a pretty baby and now reproached myself that I had ever complained about my son's lack of good looks. Healthy children were what we wanted, beauty could take second place.

The Countess of Roxburgh had been chosen as little Mary's governess and Mrs Bennet was her nurse; the child had the usual dry nurse, watchers, rockers, a gentleman usher, two grooms of the backstairs as well as a seamstress and a laundress and other menial servants which were the requisites of a royal infant. I greatly feared during those first days of her life that she was not going to need them.

Prayers were said in my private chapel but not all over the country because we did not want the people to know that we feared for the baby's life.

But in a week or two Mrs Bennet came to me beaming with delight. 'My lady Princess is demanding nourishment, Your Majesty. It is a good sign. She is coming through this.'

And she did.

Charles and I were so happy then. We went to the nurseries and he held young Charles, and I my frail little Mary, and Charles said with that faint stammer which was there when he was over-emotional or very shy that he would be the happiest man in Christendom if this little girl lived and I continued to love him.

Dr Mayerne, the Court physician, was soon declaring in his rather sombre way that Mary would live, and I expressed my overwhelming gratitude to him, and Charles did so more quietly but none the less sincerely.

It was not long after when, one night, as Charles was disrobed in our bedchamber that I noticed some spots on his chest. I was not alarmed at the time, but in the morning I remembered and looking at them again I saw that they had multiplied and were spreading up to his neck.

Dr Mayerne was sent for and diagnosed small pox, which threw us into a panic. He told me to remove myself at once while he looked at everyone in the palace to make sure none was suffering from the dreaded disease.

'But,' I said, 'it is my place to look after my husband.'

Dr Mayerne gave me one of his withering looks. I often laughed with Lucy about him for he was no respecter of persons and always treated me as though I were not only a child but a somewhat stupid one. Strangely enough he was French, having been born at Mayerne near Geneva of Protestant parents, and his real name was Sir Theodore Turquet de Mayerne. Ever since he had practised he had been a pioneer and had invented several cures, and he considered his work more important than anything else on Earth and did not care whom he offended in practising it. Charles's father, King James, had thought so highly of him that he had made him Court physician and Mayerne had looked after Charles ever since he was a boy.

'Anyone who goes into the sick chamber is liable to risk his or her life,' he said.

'He is my husband,' I replied, 'and I shall allow no one else to look after him.'

'You are too fond of drama,' he told me. 'This is not to be confused with play-acting.'

'I assure you I do not think of it as play-acting,' I cried indignantly. 'I am deeply concerned for my husband and I shall be with him in case he needs me.'

Mayerne shook his head but I did see a gleam of something in his eyes which I could not exactly construe. It might have been a faint glimmer of approval.

Charles did not feel very ill, which was unusual in such cases, and tried to persuade me to leave him, but I stood firmly and refused.

He said: 'You are a stubborn woman.'

'I am . . . where I love, and I can tell you, Charles Stuart, that no one is going to tear me from this room while you need me.'

He was deeply moved and turned away so that I might not see the tears in his eyes. All the same, he kept urging me to go.

I would not and I was the only one who nursed him through those days. Fortunately it was only a mild attack that he suffered; we spent the time playing games together, and but for my anxiety about him I could have been completely contented for within a few weeks he was well again. I suffered nothing, although all through his illness I had been in his bedchamber and had even slept in the same bed.

Mayerne said it was a miracle and implied that I did not deserve such good fortune since I was capable of such folly. But I think he admired me, although he considered me foolish. As for Charles, he loved me more than ever. He said he was the luckiest of men and no matter what happened to him in the future everything would be worthwhile because life had brought me to him. For a man who was not inclined to talk extravagantly that was saying a good deal and I told Lucy that I was happier than I had ever been in my life.

Alas, there was one of whom I was fond who was less fortunate. Poor Lucy retired to her rooms in great distress. The dreaded plague had struck her and for a woman like her, one of the beauties of the Court, it was the greatest blow which could befall a woman, for even if she survived, the chances of her being disfigured far outdistanced those of her immunity.

Lucy was not only one of the beauties of the Court, she was chief of them all. Edmund Waller and the poets said I was, but I think some of the beauty attributed to me was homage to royalty. To be honest, I had never been classically beautiful; my nose was too large, so was my mouth; of course I did have magnificent dark eyes and because of my nature, which so many thought frivolous, they sparkled with more vitality than most people's. My features were rarely ever in repose long enough for people to notice the length of my nose; so I gave the impression of charm, which may have been mistaken for beauty. But Lucy Hay was beautiful by any standards. Poets wrote verses to her; and she was lively and intelligent and liked to dabble in politics, she was rightly considered to be the most attractive woman at Court.

The thought of all that beauty being dimmed by the aftermath

of the small pox cast a shadow over the Court. I was delighted
when I heard that she was recovering, but she refused to admit
anyone to her chamber; and only her closest attendants were
allowed to see her, so I feared the worst.

For some time she would not emerge from her bedchamber and
we all waited in trepidation for her to appear. Some of the poets
were disconsolate. I believe they thought they had lost their main
source of inspiration.

Then she sent word to me that that night she intended to join
the company in the great hall for the evening's entertainment. I
was planning some special celebration to give thanks for
Charles's recovery. I was not sure whether Lucy's was going to be
a cause for rejoicing or not.

I remember that occasion so well. I was wearing a dress of
white satin with a large collar trimmed with points. It is strange
that when I remember certain occasions I see my clothes clearly. I
suppose it is because in those days I paid great attention to them.
I had a slight curvature of the spine which had to be disguised by
clever dressmaking. I hated anyone to know of this and often had
large collars made which hung over my dresses like shawls.
Because my dresses were like that it became one of the highest
fashions. This was a charming dress and I remember it in detail
because it was one of my favourites and that was such an outstanding evening. I often wonder whether it is good to remember
so clearly. Such memories come back and back again and I can
project myself into those times and relive them. Whether it is a
clever thing to do I cannot say. Sometimes the sorrow such
recollections bring is greater than the joy.

There was a hushed silence when Lucy appeared. She was
magnificently dressed and she had a superb figure, and that was
certainly unaltered except perhaps she was a little thinner, which
only made her look more elegant.

She was masked and we feared the worst. The mask was black
velvet and it covered the whole of her face; through the slits, her
eyes glittered. She walked up to Charles and me and bowed low.

I put my arms about her. I knew it was indecorous but I
couldn't help it. I was so distressed. My beautiful Lucy, the
shining light of our Court and forced to wear a mask!

I fancied I sensed despair in her. I tried words of comfort. I kept
saying: 'Lucy . . . *dear* Lucy' again and again.

Then she stepped back and said in a voice which everyone could hear because there was such silence: 'Your Majesties, have I your permission to unmask?'

'Only if you wish, Lucy,' I said.

She replied: 'I do. It is well for all to see.'

Then dramatically she threw off the mask. There was a gasp. Lucy was revealed, her skin dazzling pink and white, completely unmarred.

There was a rustling throughout the room and then everyone was rushing up to look at her and congratulate her.

That scene was typical of Lucy Hay.

I said that we must celebrate the King's recovery – and Lucy's – and the manner in which we should do so would be by having a play or a masque performed. I wanted one written specially for the occasion so I summoned a writer whose work we liked. This was Ben Jonson, an ageing man but one who had a light touch, and I had engaged him on several occasions to write a masque for me; and the best of our designers of scenery could work with him; this was an architect called Inigo Jones. Before I came to England the banqueting hall in Whitehall Palace had been destroyed by fire, and it was Inigo Jones who had designed the new one. He was the only son of a cloth-maker but he had done very well and there was evidence of the fine quality of his work throughout the capital. Unfortunately he and Ben Jonson did not like each other and were constantly quarrelling. Jonson had once said that if he wanted to name a villain in one of his plays he thought it would be a good idea to call him Inigo. I should have known better than to engage the two of them to work on the same production. It was not long before they were refusing to work with each other because Jonson had put his own name before that of Inigo Jones on the title page of the work.

I was so angry with them both that I dismissed them and called in Walter Montague to start all over again and give us a play we could act, which had dancing and singing in it. Wat Montague was the son of the Earl of Manchester and had lived a great deal abroad in France and Italy, and although some people said he had not the wit and panache of Ben Jonson he had a good idea of the sort of entertainment I wanted.

Consequently he produced a masque called *The Shepherd's Paradise,* which all my attendants declared was a masterpiece.

Many were going to perform in it and of course there was a part – the main one – for me. I was glad to have a big part but I did flinch when I saw the amount of words I should have to learn. I almost wished that I had retained Ben Jonson who for all his quarrelsome ways was able to say a great deal in a little space.

However we laughed over it and heard each other's words and there was a great deal of talk of the play we were going to perform both in and outside the Court.

We had an enormous audience because people were allowed to come in from the streets if they could get in. It was not always easy and the Lord Chamberlain had made several rules which kept out certain people. But it was natural, I said, that the people should want to see their Queen perform in a play so I asked the Lord Chamberlain not to be too harsh.

The play went on for eight hours; and there was singing and dancing, which I liked, and in spite of the fact that many people had to sit cross-legged on the floor and quite a number of us forgot our lines and had to be audibly prompted, it was a success and I liked to see the people laughing and having a good time. It would make them like us, I said to Charles afterwards.

Then we heard of the odious Mr Prynne.

He took this very time to publish a book which he called *The Histriomastrix;* it was over a thousand pages in length. It was a diatribe against immorality, for William Prynne was a Puritan of the worst kind, which I hated so much and grew to hate so much more than any other type of man. Play-acting was unlawful, he wrote. It was an incentive to Immorality. Plays had been condemned by the Scriptures and he was condemning them now.

The book was brought to Court and we all pored over it.

Saint Paul had forbidden women to *speak* in churches. He 'Dares any Christian woman to be so more than whorishly impudent as to act or speak publicly on the stage (perchance in man's apparel and cut hair) in the presence of sundry men and women.'

He went on to rant about women actors who were nothing more than strumpets. As for dancing that was worse still. It should be a criminal offence, and those who performed should be thrust into prison and do penance for their wickedness.

We might have laughed at such fanaticism but he did quote the Bible and the writings of many illustrious Christians; and we all knew that the attack was directed against me because I had acted, I had sung, and more than anything I loved the dance.

When the King read it he was very angry – not because he considered it important but because it was an insult to me. He thought the author should be brought before him and made to apologize. I think that would have satisfied the King, but Dr Laud, who had become Archbishop of Canterbury, saw something significant in this attack.

He believed it was directed not only against the Court but was a criticism of the vestments of the clergy and ceremonies of the Church.

'Prynne is a dangerous man,' said Archbishop Laud.

As a result Prynne was arrested and stood trial in the Star Chamber. He was sentenced to prison and fined; his degree was taken from him and he was to stand in the pillory and have his ears lopped off.

Charles thought it was a harsh sentence for writing a book but the Archbishop was stern in his condemnation. 'Men such as this could ruin the Church and all it stands for,' he said. 'There are too many Puritans in the land and inflammatory literature such as this could increase their number. Let them see what happens to anyone who dares criticize the Queen.'

That silenced Charles but I could not sleep for some nights – the least upset gave me insomnia – and I kept seeing that man in my mind's eye standing in the pillory with his ears dripping blood.

Of course he was an unpleasant creature. He was miserable old spoilsport and he wanted to make us all like him. But his ears. . . .

Charles knew that I was worried about him, and Charles was too, for he was a just man. On the other hand Prynne had attacked royalty, for there was no doubt that the Court was his target, and Charles said that he was going against the Lord's anointed – although, of course, I had never been anointed owing to my firm adherence to my own Faith.

Charles said he would order that pen and paper be taken to Prynne in prison. 'That will comfort him,' he said.

'And enable him to write more words directed against us?'

'Poor fellow! He has suffered,' was all Charles said; and I

agreed with him that he must let Prynne have pens and paper. He would have learned his lesson and not write any more against us I was sure.

Soon after Lucy had appeared to the company so dramatically without her mask a rather unusual contretemps sprang up between some of the notable men of the Court. I was particularly interested because it concerned a letter of mine and one of my favourite friends was involved.

This was Henry Jermyn who had always seemed to me a most amusing gentleman and we had found a great deal to talk about when we met for, although he was quite humble in station, he had most excellent manners and I felt at home with him perhaps because he had spent a great deal of time in Paris, where he had been sent on an embassy. He was able to give me news of my family and to talk knowledgeably about the life I remembered so well from my girlhood.

Henry was very tall, inclined to be somewhat on the heavy side; he was as fair as I was dark, with a lazy look which I found diverting. Some years before he had been appointed to the post of Vice Chamberlain and before that he had represented Liverpool in Parliament.

He was an inveterate gambler and as different from Charles as one man could be from another. Everything Charles did must be right in his own eyes. I sensed at once that Henry would not have the same regard for duty but liked to do what was most comfortable to him and which did not demand too much effort. As I was equally lazy and pleasure-loving there was an immediate bond between us. He was the sort who slipped in and out of trouble with easy grace, usually relying on his charm to extricate him from anything which interfered too much with an easy life.

There had been a little trouble on the tennis courts of Whitehall when he accused one of the men of attacking him with tennis balls. Henry had become really violent for like many people who are not easily aroused, when he was he seemed to make up for his periods of quietness.

That was a small matter compared with two other scrapes which followed closely on each other and resulted in a term of imprisonment and then banishment.

The first incident rose through the new French ambassador, the Marquis de Fontenay-Mareuil, to whom I had taken an instant dislike as soon as he arrived to replace my dear Marquis de Châteauneuf, who had been in England for some three years. There was at Court at this time a very charming young man, the Chevalier de Jars, who had come into conflict with the devious Cardinal de Richelieu and been exiled. He had come to me and as I knew that Richelieu and my mother were now enemies, naturally I made the Chevalier welcome. He was young, handsome and charming; he danced beautifully and played tennis so well that Charles – who was an excellent player – enjoyed a game with him. I was glad to see my compatriot fitting in so well at Court.

There was one man whom I greatly disliked and that was Richard Weston, Earl of Portland, who was the Lord Treasurer. Now when I try to reason out why I disliked him so much, I suppose it was because Charles thought so highly of him and I could never forget Buckingham and what a hold he had had over the King, and I think I was always afraid that someone else would rise up and manoeuvre himself into a similar position. Moreover, Weston was always refusing to give me money and at times made me feel like a pauper. When I complained of this to Charles, he gave me his slow smile and said it was Weston's duty to look after the exchequer and make sure there was always enough money for the country's needs. I said that was all very well but need he be so parsimonious? In any case there was enough money for the country's needs so why be so miserly about my little request.

Charles said that was female logic and kissed me.

However, I was not to be put off so easily and I talked to my friends like Lord Holland and the Chevalier de Jars about it.

The Marquis de Fontenay-Mareuil was aware that I confided in the Chevalier de Jars, and men such as he always imagine that conspiracies are being hatched. One day the Chevalier came to me in great distress. He told me that his chambers had been ransacked and his papers taken away.

I took him to Charles at once, who looked very grave and asked him who he thought was responsible for this action.

'I feel sure it is someone who wishes to do me harm,' said the Chevalier.

I said: 'We must find this thief, Charles, and he must be punished.'

Charles said the best thing to do was summon the French ambassador. This he did and I begged to be present at the interview because I thought that it might be necessary to defend my dear friend, the Chevalier.

I was right. Not that there was much I could do; and the effect of this was a near quarrel between Charles and myself.

Fontenay-Mareuil was very haughty. He admitted at once that it was on his orders that de Jars' chambers had been ransacked and his papers removed.

'This is stealing,' I cried out.

'Your Majesty,' replied the ambassador, turning to me and bowing, 'I am in the service of his Gracious Majesty, King Louis, and it is on his orders that I investigate the actions of the Chevalier de Jars.'

Charles nodded, seeing the truth of this.

'I have therefore removed the Chevalier's papers,' went on Fontenay-Mareuil, 'and in view of the fact that he is now without them, it will be necessary for him to return to France.'

'For what reason?' I demanded.

'That, Your Majesty, will need to be discovered.'

He then asked Charles if anything more was required of him.

When he had gone I turned to my husband. 'You are not going to let him tell lies about the Chevalier. He is a friend of mine.'

Charles spoke tenderly. 'Oh, I know he dances very well and is a merry companion, but if he is working against his King he must answer for his actions.'

'But he is *my* friend.'

'He is first the subject of the King of France.'

'Does this mean he will be sent back to France?'

'He cannot stay here if he has no papers.'

'Why not?'

'Because they have been removed by the ambassador and I have no doubt that in a few days we shall hear from your brother that the Chevalier is to return to France.'

I begged and pleaded, but Charles said that much as he wanted to give me all I desired he could not interfere with matters of state, particularly between a King and a subject of another country.

'It is *my* country,' I cried.

But he reminded me that I was now English.

I felt my temper rising, but Charles looked so distressed, and I did not want to do anything to spoil our happy life together so I curbed my irritation and made up my mind that I would be wiser to be silent as long as I did everything I could to help my dear friend.

But there was little I could do, for within a week or so the Chevalier received orders from my brother to return to France. I was very worried about him for I was certain that the odious Fontenay-Mareuil would have told tales about him.

I was right for as soon as the Chevalier set foot in Paris he was arrested and sent to prison.

After that there was a series of arrests. Châteauneuf was sent to Angoulême and kept there; even the frivolous Duchesse de Chevreuse, who I believe had numbered Châteauneuf among her admirers, was sent into retirement. Not that she endured it long for in due course we heard that she had captivated her guards and with their help, dressed as a man, she escaped into Spain.

But that was later. Meanwhile I had to think of my dear Chevalier de Jars.

This was where the trouble started for I wrote to my brother, begging him to release the Chevalier and assuring him that the young man had never been anything but a good friend to France. Unfortunately Weston's son, Jerome, was acting as a courier and had been sent to Paris with important papers to be delivered to Louis and on his way back to England with further communications he happened to spend the night at an inn where the courier taking letters to Paris was staying. They fell into conversation and Jerome, who took his duties very seriously and, as the son of his father, was well aware of plots against him, thought he was within his rights to examine the letters which were being taken to France.

Thus it was that he came across the one which I had written to my brother and another written by Lord Holland. These were private letters and the custom was to send them separately; and the fact that they were in the diplomatic bag raised the officious Jerome Weston's suspicions. He took the letters and brought them back to England to present to the King.

It was not difficult to imagine my fury when I heard what had happened. Charles did his best to restrain me, but this time he did find it impossible.

'It is an insult,' I cried. 'How dare this . . . upstart treat me like this? Am I the Queen or am I not?'

Charles tried to calm me. 'He was doing what he thought was his duty.'

'His duty . . . to insult me!'

'It was not intended to be an insult. Private letters should not be put into the diplomatic bag. Don't you see that if someone wanted to make mischief how easily it could be done. There has to be a close watch on this. All young Weston was doing was his duty.'

'Lord Holland is furious,' I cried. 'He will do that young man an injury.'

'He will be foolish if he does for that would be an offence whereas Jerome Weston has committed none.'

I was exasperated and left him. I dared not trust myself to stay longer for I should have started to abuse Charles himself very soon.

I went to my own apartments. Lucy was there with Eleanor Villiers, a niece of Buckingham, who had joined the ladies of my bedchamber some little time before.

I told them what had happened and they both expressed their astonishment that young Jerome Weston could have behaved so; that comforted me a little.

It was Eleanor Villiers who brought the news to me. She seemed very upset.

'Henry Jermyn has been arrested,' she said.

'Henry Jermyn! But why?'

'Holland challenged young Jerome Weston to a duel because he said he had insulted you and himself. Henry delivered the challenge and that is an offence.'

'What of Holland?'

'He is also arrested.'

I said: 'I will see the King at once.'

I found Charles with some of his ministers and they were already discussing the matter which had sprung up between Holland and the Westons involving Henry Jermyn.

'I must see you at once,' I said, glancing haughtily at the ministers, and adding: 'Alone.'

I could see that they thought Charles a most uxorious husband for he immediately told them he would see them later.

They left and I burst out: 'I have just heard that Henry Jermyn has been arrested and Lord Holland with him.'

'That is so,' said the King.

'But why?'

'For disobeying the law. They know duelling is forbidden and any connected with it are guilty of breaking that law.'

I said 'Holland has challenged young Weston. But why Henry Jermyn. . . .'

'I will not allow the laws to be broken.'

'He is my friend.'

'My dearest, even your friends are not friends of the crown if they break the laws.'

'This is a plot.'

'I think,' said Charles, 'that there is a plot and it is directed against my Treasurer. The young man did right to intercept the letters. He suspects that some people are working against his father and I am of the opinion that he may be right. He was acting within his duties in searching the diplomatic bags. You must understand that, my loved one. We cannot have plots within our midst and we must be ever watchful of those who foment them.'

'Do you mean that Holland and Jermyn will be punished?'

'They must answer to the law. There have been murmurings against the Treasurer, who is a good and honest man. He is careful with our money and that is what we need.'

'So you are determined to be on his side!'

'My dear, I am on the side of right.'

I could see that no amount of pleading could change him. He was the most obstinate man alive and while he thought he was doing what was right he would continue to do it.

He explained to me that it was offensive that a member of his council – as Holland was – should send a challenge to a man in the King's service who was merely carrying out his duties.

Of course neither offence was very great and all that happened was that Holland was confined for a while to his house in Kensington and Henry Jermyn was sent away from the Court for a short time to stay in a private house.

It was typical of both men that they should make the most of their captivity. Holland gave parties and it was said that he attracted all the most amusing people from Court to visit him. I heard that his parties were the most exciting thing that was happening. The Court certainly seemed a little dull without those two. I particularly missed Henry Jermyn. I did not realize how much he had amused me until I had lost his company.

Charles had become more friendly than ever with the Earl of Portland since the incident and with his son – the little spy, I called him. They were both high in Charles's favour.

I said to Charles, rather bitterly: 'It is clear that you will never listen to my desires. You punish my friends and cherish my enemies.'

'You rule my heart,' said Charles, who could be very senti- mental at times, 'but, my dearest love, because God made me King I have to rule this kingdom. Those whom you think are your friends are not truly so for if they work against me and my ministers they cannot be mine, and you and I are as one, and therefore what is evil for me is evil for you also.'

I was so happy with Charles and the babies that I did not really want anything changed; but I did think a great deal about Holland and Henry Jermyn, and after a few weeks, because I missed them so much, Charles said they could return to Court. So they came back and I was delighted. But Charles was cool to them both and his trust in the Earl of Portland seemed not to have decreased.

Charles said that Holland was unreliable and I should not become too friendly with him. I reminded him that he had arranged our marriage and I added: 'He will always have a special place in my regard because he did that.'

Charles was touched and very soon these two gentlemen were as much in evidence as ever, though I did believe they saw how useless it was to try to shift the King's trust in his Treasurer.

It was soon after that that the second trouble arose.

I noticed that Eleanor Villiers had been looking a little strained lately and it gradually dawned on me that she was in a certain condition which I myself had been in more than once so I was very much aware of the signs.

I called her to me one day, making sure that we were alone and I said: 'Eleanor, are you feeling quite well?'

She looked startled and then blushed a fiery red, so I knew I had not been mistaken.

'Who?' I asked.

She would not say at first and I thought I could not press her . . . just yet.

'How soon?' I asked.

'Five months,' she replied.

'Well, Eleanor,' I went on, 'it is a good thing I know. Your marriage will have to take place without delay.'

She was silent and I feared the worst.

'He is married?' I asked.

She shook her head.

'Then that is good. There must be no delay. Why did you wait so long?'

'He does not want to marry.'

'Does not want to marry! But he will have to keep his promise.'

'He made no promise.'

'You mean that you . . . a lady of the Court . . . without a promise of marriage. . . .'

'Yes, Your Majesty.'

I said angrily: 'Who is this man?'

And then she told me. 'Henry Jermyn.'

'Oh, the rogue,' I cried. 'Leave this to me. The King will be most put out. You know what a high standard of morality he sets upon the Court. I will speak to Jermyn at once. Go and leave this to me.'

I sent for Henry. He looked as jaunty as ever – not in the least like a man who was heading for trouble. He took my hand and kissed it.

I said: 'I have just been talking to Eleanor Villiers.'

Even then he did not look in the least disturbed.

I went on: 'She had some distressing news to tell me. I think you must know what it is.'

He put his head on one side in an amusing way he had and regarded me with earnestness. I said severely: 'It is no use assuming innocence. You know what you have been doing. You have got the poor girl with child.'

'Most careless,' he said.

'I agree with that. There is nothing you can do but marry her.'

'That I cannot do.'

'What do you mean? You cannot marry her! You are a bachelor, are you not?'

'A very impoverished one.'

'I cannot see that that should prevent your marriage.'

'Alas, the lady is also impoverished and now that her uncle is dead and blessings have ceased to flow on the family, she is as poor as I am and such poverty should always be a bar to marriage.'

'You are a wicked man,' I said.

'Who sometimes amuses Your Majesty. If I can do that I must be content.'

'The King will hear of it and be most displeased.'

'I regret that.'

'He may well order you to marry the lady.'

'I do not think the King would step outside his rights.'

'No. He always does what is right. Well, Henry, there will be trouble over this. She is after all a lady of the Court and a member of the Buckingham family at that.'

'I know,' he said mournfully.

'You *should* marry her.'

'It would not be a good marriage for either of us. She is a charming girl . . . but penniless, and I am a rogue as you say and not worthy of her.'

In spite of his light manner I could see that his mind was made up.

The King was most distressed. 'I will not have this immorality in my Court,' he said.

'You cannot make them marry though. Do you think Eleanor Villiers would want to marry a man who did not want to marry her?'

'As there is to be a child, yes.'

'But I do see Henry's point. If he marries her he will have no chance of retrieving his fortunes.'

'If he doesn't what chance has she of making a happy marriage?'

I looked at him helplessly and thought again how fortunate I was in my happy marriage.

I flung my arms round him and told him so. He smiled quietly and indulgently at my demonstrative behaviour, which was so unlike his own; he patted me and said that he would consider the matter and decide what should be done.

The King saw both Eleanor Villiers and Henry separately.

He was determined then that Henry should marry Eleanor. He said he must have promised marriage before she agreed to intimacy with him but Eleanor, who was a very honest girl, said there had been no talk of marriage.

The King was horrified, but she said; 'I loved him too much.'

Charles was touched and that made him all the more angry

with Henry. He said that as there had been no promise of marriage he could not insist on it, but he would not for one moment give his approval to what Henry Jermyn had done. He did not demand that there should be a marriage but he said that Henry would not be welcome at Court until there was one.

That meant banishment. Henry went abroad and once more I was deprived of his company.

In the meantime I had become pregnant again. I often thought that Buckingham must have laid a spell on me because during the time of his ascendancy over Charles, I remained barren; and no sooner was he dead than I became as fertile as any woman in England.

When I told Charles that I was expecting another child he was overjoyed.

'We must go to Scotland soon,' he said, 'for you will not be able to travel when your pregnancy is advanced.'

'Scotland!' I cried in dismay. I had never liked what I heard about the place. It was cold and the people were dour, so said my informants. I thought some of them in our own Court were solemn enough so I did not relish going among those who were more so.

'It is time I was crowned there,' said Charles. 'The people expect it.'

I was immediately apprehensive. I had refused to be crowned with the King in England. How could I possibly be in Scotland? I was in a very difficult position as my French advisers had pointed out. For a Queen not to be crowned was to place herself in a position which could be dangerous. On the other hand, how could I, a fervent Catholic, bow to the doctrines and customs of the Protestant Church?

'I cannot do it,' I said. 'I should hate myself if I did. It would be wrong. I cannot deny my Faith.'

Charles tried to explain patiently that there was no question of denying my Faith. All I had to do was stand beside him and be crowned. But I knew there was that in the coronation ceremony which obligated the sovereign to swear to live in the Reformed Faith. I knew what that meant. It was flouting the Holy Church, and I could not do it.

In the old days there would have been a quarrel. There was none now.

Charles looked at me sadly and tenderly; he said that he understood the depth of my feelings and would do nothing to distress me.

So he went to Scotland without me and I stayed at home to await the birth of my next child.

When I look back in the light of hindsight, and perhaps because I have become wiser than I was, I think perhaps the first seeds of disaster were sown during that visit to Scotland. I now understand the character of my husband as I never did then. Then I loved him for his concern for me, his devotion and the knowledge that he was one of the few faithful husbands at Court and because he made me feel cherished and beautiful. Now I can love him for his many sterling qualities and at the same time for the weaknesses which would destroy him.

I thought then – and I think now – that Charles was one of the most noble and virtuous men ever to sit on the throne of England; he was a good man, but to be a good man is not necessarily to be a good King; some of the greatest Kings who ever lived have been far from good in their private lives. I see now that the two lives are different and one cannot be judged against the other. We do not judge a man but a King. As a man Charles was noble and good; as a King he was often blind, often foolish, unable to see beyond his own vision, which was misted over by the firm belief that Kings are chosen by God and rule by the Divine Right.

I can see all this now; but I could not see it then. In fact I did not give much thought to it. If I had been asked I should have said that of course we should go on living as we were, raising our children, and in due course my eldest son would take the crown. There were outcries about taxes and Charles said the exchequer was in a sorry state but that had often happened before and as it never made any difference to my way of life, I ignored it.

Now I look back at Charles and try to see him as he was – a smallish man, fastidious and very reserved; he took a long time to make friends, but when he did he became devoted to them, as I had seen through Buckingham and, once he had really grown to love, with me. He was the sort of man whose friendship was to be completely trusted. He was very steadfast in his opinions, and if he liked or disliked a person it was hard to shake either his trust or his suspicion. He loved art in any form and once told me how he would have enjoyed being able to paint, write verses, or compose music; he lacked the talent of performance yet that did not mean he was not a good judge and he did a great deal to encourage painters, musicians and writers at our Court.

'I want a cultivated Court,' he once said to me.

I enjoyed these things, too, so that was an added bond between us.

Dear Charles! He could not make friends easily and he never really understood the people whom he was so anxious to govern well. Later I read a great deal about Queen Elizabeth. This was when I was trying to understand what had gone wrong. I remembered those pilgrimages she made through the country – getting to know the people, always pleasing the people; she had been much more careful in her treatment of them than she was of her intimate friends. Oh, she was a clever woman – a great Queen and a great ruler . . . but she lacked the noble personal character of my Charles.

He would become less aloof in the hunting field. He loved horses and understood them far better than he did people. Perhaps that was why he liked to be with them and avoided human contact – except with those few whom he loved.

He was so constantly reading the book his father had written called *Basilicon Doron* that he must have known it off by heart for it was not very long. It was a kind of guide book for kings and had been intended for Charles's elder brother, who had died leaving Charles to bear the burden. The theme of this book was that a King had received his crown from God. Charles never forgot that and he always believed firmly in the divine right of anointed Kings to govern their people.

I realize that I was in a great measure responsible for the people's dissatisfaction – but perhaps I should say my religion was. There were, it was true, many Roman Catholics in England, but the country as a whole was solidly behind the Reformed Church. And here was I, the Queen – a Catholic.

Charles did everything he could to make things easy for me. He never tried to make me give up my Faith and I had my chapel, which was as Catholic as anything I had in France. But the people did not like it. He had introduced certain ceremonials into the Church of which the people did not approve and Charles, believing that he had Divine guidance in this, had directed the clergy to keep silent on the matter. There was trouble with the people they called Arminians, who were followers of a Dutchman, Jacobus Arminius. He had published a book which opposed some of the teachings of Calvin, and the Commons had wanted the Arminian theory to be suppressed and were annoyed with the King's attitude. This was disastrous for him because he needed their support over the tonnage and poundage matters which could provide funds for the Treasury.

I paid very little attention – I wish now that I had paid more. I might have seen the storm clouds gathering and done something to protect ourselves from them.

Charles had dismissed that Parliament and not called another. For eleven years he had ruled without a parliament. How blind we were not to realize what forces we were building up against ourselves.

Meanwhile the King went to Scotland. There he angered the Scots by being crowned by five bishops all ceremoniously dressed in white rochets and sleeves and copes of gold and shoes of blue silk of which the Scots did not approve; moreover the communion table was arranged after the manner of an altar with a tapestry set up behind it on which the crucifix was put up.

This was bringing something which the Scots called near-idolatry into their Church and they did not like it. Moreover they strongly resented it and there was a very dangerous moment during the Parliament which Charles was forced to call in Edinburgh after his coronation, when the matter of imposing apparel on churchmen was raised.

The majority of members voted against it, but Charles, who was certain he could manage very well – in fact much better without Parliament, instructed the clerk of the court to announce that the matter had been carried in the affirmative.

Charles then said that the decision must be right since the clerk had made it, and since it was a capital offence to falsify the records were some members going to accuse the clerk? None was prepared to put the clerk into such a dangerous situation, for how could they know what would be proved against him; but the Scottish nobles were not the kind of men to allow this to pass. There were objectors and the chief of these was John Elphinstone, Lord Balmerino, who was consequently arrested and put into Edinburgh Castle. Charles had returned to England before he was tried. It was imperative that Elphinstone should be found guilty and, when he was, the people gathered in the streets of Edinburgh, threatening to kill the judge and jurors, swearing vengeance on all those who had connived against their hero Elphinstone. He had to be reprieved but was made a prisoner in his castle at Balmerino and finally he was freed.

I mention this because I think it was one of the pointers to the King's eventual fate and was the beginning of Scotland's disenchantment with him.

The King returned from Scotland in time for the birth of our next child. There was great joy on that October day for we had another boy. We called him James after Charles's father and a pretty boy he was – so different from his brother. Poor Charles, his looks did not greatly improve, but he was certainly bright and clever enough to demand attention. Beside him James and Mary looked beautiful, but a little frail.

When the King pointed this out I replied: 'All children look frail beside our dark gentleman. He is already twice as big as other children of his age. Don't worry about the others because they lack his undoubted strength. They have the consolation of being beautiful.'

The arrival of a new baby was certain to arouse the controversy of religion. If Charles had not been a King who took his duties so seriously I was sure I could have made a Catholic of him by this time. But of course the English were a stubbornly Protestant people. I had always maintained that they were not deeply religious. They were Christians; they worshipped God, but they were a lazy people and they did not greatly care to bestir themselves until some issue was presented to them which they considered worth fighting for. How formidable they could be when this happened I did not learn until later. At this time I saw only their lazy indifference. Another thing which I had not seen was that there was a Puritan element beginning to arise in direct defiance of the beautiful church ceremonies and the gracious way of living which I flattered myself I had introduced with the help of Charles, who was such a great lover of art and all its beauties.

The trouble started with the baby. A boy was more important

than a girl and, as he was a possible King, next in line to the dark gentleman, he must be baptized by the King's Protestant chaplain. James was christened and created Duke of York and Albany. I was very proud of him because he was a good and beautiful baby, but I did feel that as he was mine I should not give way to the Protestants on every point, so I engaged a wet nurse knowing that she was a Catholic – in fact choosing her for that reason. It was soon being whispered about the Court that the nurse would inject the baby with idolatry and Charles's advisers warned him that the nurse must either be converted to Protestantism or go.

Charles came to me in some distress. He told me about the complaints and said that if the woman would only make certain statements she would be allowed to remain.

I protested. 'She is a good nurse. The baby has taken to her. I might not be able to find another as good.'

But Charles was adamant as he could be on some occasions, and I could see that in a matter like this my wiles would avail me nothing.

He sent for the nurse and gently explained to her that she had done her work well and that the Queen was highly satisfied with her as a nurse but she must remember that the baby could in some circumstances become the King of England and the English thought he should not have a Catholic nurse. All she need do was take an oath to the effect that the power of the Pope to depose princes was impious, heretical and damnable.

'Take this oath,' said the King, 'and all will be well.'

The nurse started to scream in horror: 'Deny the Pope. Deny the Holy Father his rights. Never . . . never . . . never. . . .'

The King said: 'Then you will leave this palace at once.'

I was very distressed and although the King tried to comfort me I refused to listen to him. I said that every woman in the country could choose the nurse for her own child but a Queen, a daughter of Henri IV, was denied that right.

The King went on trying to comfort me, making allowances for my state, I know; but I was really distressed, not only because of the nurse, but because I had believed till then that I was making some headway and that Catholics were treated much more leniently in England than they had been before my arrival. I had strong hopes that I was beginning to make the King see the rightness of the Catholic Faith and I had thought how wonderful it would be if I could convert him, and, through him, the nation. I should go down in history as another St Augustine or Bertha of early England. And now I could not even have a Catholic wet nurse for my baby!

I refused to eat and I lay sullenly in my bed and was so despairing that I became really ill. The King sent for doctors who could not put a name to my malady. 'The Queen is depressed and so upset that she has lost her vitality and her interest in life,' said the doctors.

Charles was beside himself with anxiety. He really did love me, and I hated to worry him; but I was upset for I did see in this dismissal of the nurse the hopelessness of my dreams.

As I lay there, one day Charles came to the room and with him was the Catholic nurse.

'She is to come back,' he said simply. 'I have given permission. I will silence the gossipers. I hope that pleases you.'

I just held out my arms and we clung together. I was so happy – not only to have the nurse back but because of this further sign of his love for me.

I was better within a day.

There was another little trouble a few days later. The King's Protestant chaplain came to me and explained to me what great good I could do the King and the country by renouncing the Catholic Faith and embracing Protestantism.

What a proposition to make to an ardent Catholic! *I* denounced him and his Faith vehemently but he persisted; he went on his knees and prayed. This angered me. As if *I* did not know the meaning of prayer!

I cried out: 'It is you who are mistaken. You will burn in hell. God will never forgive you for renouncing the true Faith.'

I became hysterical and ill again.

The King came and soothed me. I must be calmer, he said. He knew how strongly I felt about my religion and he had done everything he could to make life easy for me. He had relaxed the laws against Catholics and that was making the people displeased. A great deal of our unpopularity was due to that. I must know that he would do everything he could to please me.

'Anything?' I asked.

'You know that I would.'

'Then there is one thing I want more than anything in the

world. Dear husband, I want you to stand beside me in worship.'
He sighed and said: 'Ah, little one, I would that could be.'

I was confident then that one day Charles would see the light. I
threw off my lethargy, my fury against those who had taken the
nurse – but I had her back, had I not? – and I determined to fight
as never before for the conversion of my husband to the true
Faith.

There were many people to report what was happening in
England and I realized that the general opinion abroad was that I
had a great influence on the King and was bringing him round to
my Catholic point of view. I think there was some truth in this
and perhaps it was the reason why I was becoming more and
more unpopular in England. I ignored this in my heedless way,
believing with Charles that Kings were the Lord's anointed and
the common people at length must realize that they had no right
to do anything but accept this. However, there were high hopes
in Rome because I was regarded as the Pope's good ambassa-
dress.

Baby James was just over a year old when Gregorio Panzani
came to London. He had been sent by the Pope to visit England in
particular to talk to me. I was greatly flattered and I really did feel
that in spite of a few steps backward I was making some progress.

Father Philip presented Panzani to me as soon as he arrived in
England and Panzani was most gracious.

'The Holy Father himself thanks you for what you have done
and what you are doing for the Faith in this misguided land. You
have been as a mother to these ungrateful people. Can you, do
you believe, bring them to true understanding?'

I was filled with emotion.

'I cannot tell you how much I esteem the good opinion of His
Holiness,' I answered. 'Tell him to rest assured that I will do
everything within my power to please him and God.'

'His Holiness is aware of this but will be overjoyed that you
have confirmed it.'

My impetuosity took charge. I was so pleased that my efforts
were recognized and I wanted to get the ultimate credit, so I said
confidentially: 'I firmly believe that before long I shall have converted the King to the Faith. He is a saintly man; he appreciates

what is holy. Yes, I am convinced that ere long I shall bring about his conversion.'

'That,' replied Panzani, 'is the best possible news I could have heard and exceeds my expectations.' He went on to say that he greatly desired a meeting with the King and I told him I would arrange it without delay.

When Charles heard that Gregorio Panzani was in England and had actually visited me informally he was greatly disturbed. He looked at me with that tender exasperation which I knew so well and said: 'This could be dangerous. What will be said if the people hear that you are secretly receiving messengers from the Pope?'

'If you receive him his visit will not be secret,' I said logically.

But Charles merely shook his head at me.

I then said that I had promised Panzani should meet the King, so Charles could not humiliate me by not receiving him.

Charles demurred. He was far more worried about the people who surrounded him, and many of them were his enemies, than I realized then.

At length he said that a meeting should take place, but it would have to be in secret . . . not official.

I was delighted. That would do very well, I cried and embraced him and told him I was the happiest and luckiest of women to have such a husband.

A meeting was arranged and Panzani and Charles met without any fuss. I was not present at their meeting but I knew it was an amicable one.

It was impossible to keep the arrival of Panzani a complete secret. Several members of the Court knew he was in England; however, realizing the King wished that the visit should not be considered an official one, they kept quiet.

But these matters cannot long be kept secret. There is certain to be someone who cannot resist talking too much, and one day when Charles and I were together playing some parlour game a guard came in to tell us that there was a man outside who was begging an audience with the King on a matter, he said, of grave importance.

'He does not look in the least dangerous,' said the guard, 'and he carries no weapons.'

'Then bring him to me,' said the King.

The man was brought in. He proved to be one of that sect which was becoming more and more prominent in England during the last year or so: a Puritan. He was very plainly dressed and his hair was cut in an odd fashion which made his head look round.

I was convulsed with amusement when the man said in a very confidential whisper: 'Your Majesty, I thought you should know that a dangerous man has arrived secretly in England.'

The King said: 'A dangerous man! Who is this?'

'Your Majesty, it is one of the Pope's men. I have information that his name is Panzani. I decided it was something you should know at once.'

Although I could scarcely keep a straight face, the King managed to.

'Thank you for warning me,' he said.

And our round-headed Puritan went on his way convinced that he had done his duty.

How I laughed about that afterwards – but not with the King. He admired the man for coming to tell him that he thought he was in danger.

'I could see that he thought the manner in which we live somewhat sinful,' I commented. 'I saw his eyes roaming round the tapestries and some of the furnishings. I think he thought they were symbols of the Devil.'

'Poor fellow,' said Charles. 'It must be a sad thing to be blind to beauty.'

I laughed over the incident with Panzani. He was a very sophisticated gentleman, and pious as he was, could still compliment me on my gowns and scents. Father Philip was very pleased with me and he told Panzani that he reckoned in three years or so the King would become a Catholic and then it would only be a short time before the country followed. When this happy state of affairs occurred the religious world would have to be grateful most of all to the Queen of England.

They were intoxicating words, and foolishly I believed them. How was I to know that it would be a very different story and that I should play quite a big part in bringing about not triumph but disaster?

But it really did seem as though we were going to succeed because, although Panzani did not come until December, the following March Richard Weston, Earl of Portland, the Treasurer who had been at the heart of the trouble over my letter, died and in his final moments he sent for a Catholic priest to administer the last rites.

Then there was Wat Montague, the poet who had written *The Shepherd's Paradise*, which had caused Prynne the loss of his ears. Wat had been abroad and recently returned to England announcing that he had seen the light and become a Catholic. He was proposing to go to Rome and join the Fathers of the Oratory.

Ah yes, I thought, we were indeed making progress.

Then I discovered I was pregnant again.

While I was awaiting the birth of my child, my new chapel in Somerset House was completed. What a joyous day that was when it was consecrated. It was so beautiful with a wonderfully painted dome in which archangels, cherubim and seraphim appeared to be floating above our heads; and it was my happy task to draw the curtains and reveal all this beauty.

I was so moved when Mass was celebrated that there were tears in my eyes. It seemed to me the ultimate triumph that I had made this corner in a land alien to the Truth. Soon, I promised myself, there should be chapels everywhere – not so grand as this, of course, because this was a royal chapel, but places where Catholics could go freely to worship. I would not rest until I had turned the heresy of England to true belief.

Charles could not be there to worship with me, of course, but as a connoisseur of art and beauty he came to admire the work, and his eyes glistened with appreciation.

Panzani congratulated me in private. 'But,' he said, 'this is not enough. What we need is conversions . . . of men in high places.'

I was a little cast down for I thought I had done very well. He comforted me and said that the Holy Father was delighted with my efforts. I had done more than he had thought possible at the time of my marriage, but there was a great deal to be done yet and we must not be complacent.

To tell the truth I was not feeling any great desire to do anything but rest, for my baby was shortly due to arrive, and however frequently one gives birth – and in my case it seemed to be an event which began again as soon as one was ended – one does every time have to face an ordeal.

It was a cold December day when Elizabeth was born. I had spent an exhausting day in labour and as night was falling – at ten o'clock to be precise – my daughter made her appearance.

However irksome the waiting has been, it always seems worthwhile at that moment when the little one is there and one's inconvenience is over . . . for the time being. I loved the child at once and I was rather glad that it was a girl. The only one who gave me cause for anxiety was Mary, who seemed to be delicate and had given us one or two frights. My eldest, Charles, flourished, although he did not grow any less unprepossessing. Perhaps that is the wrong word, but he was definitely lacking in beauty, though it did seem that he had a great deal of charm to make up for that. I had never seen a child win people to his side as Charles did. James, for all his innocent beauty, could not compete, and I could not be anything but surprised and delighted by my still rather swarthy eldest. He said the most amusing things and he was so serious contemplating the world with those large dark eyes and clearly finding it diverting.

I sometimes wished that I could go right away to Oatlands with the children and Charles and live like a simple noblewoman. Should I really want that for long? I was not sure. My frivolous nature did enjoy the masques and balls and all the beautiful clothes and jewels that seemed part of them. I was by nature an intriguant, I suppose. I loved to be in the thick of adventure. I had so enjoyed Panzani's visit and that enjoyment had been greater because of the secret understanding between us which I knew would be against the wishes of those serious puritanical people who were springing up everywhere.

A new baby was an additional expense. She was put into the care of the Countess of Roxburgh, who was already looking after her elder sister Mary; but she had to have her suite of attendants befitting a royal child – her dresser, her watchers, her nurses, her rockers and quite a number of minor servants. Moreover, Charles's nephews – the sons of his sister Elizabeth – came to visit us and that meant lavish entertainments. Charles Louis, the elder, was a little dull, but Rupert was a very attractive young man of about seventeen. Charles took a great fancy to him and he to Charles. It was fun to have the young men at Court and there was one entertainment which stands out in my memory. Lady Hatton gave a wonderful show at her place in Ely Court, and the masques, plays and balls and firework displays lasted for a whole month. Lady Hatton closed her entertainment with a ball for the citizens of London. It was not for people of the Court, she said.

It was Henry Jermyn who suggested that we go incognito and I thought it was an excellent idea.

'But how?' I asked.

'We shall have to dress as citizens,' said Henry. 'I'll be a merchant. Your Majesty can be a shop-keeper's wife.'

What fun we had! I instructed one of the seamstresses to make me a suitable gown and a bonnet which hid my face to a certain extent because it was just possible that someone might recognize me. I sent for my lace woman who kept a shop somewhere in the city and let her into the secret. She promised to take us in with her.

It was so amusing dancing with the citizens and interesting to listen to their talk although a little disconcerting that there were some who had harsh things to say about the way in which Catholics were getting a footing in the country. There were even one or two comments against me, but I didn't take them very seriously. They only seemed to add to the fun as I was intent on enjoying the evening and Henry Jermyn was so amusing posing as a merchant and Lord Holland – always good for adventure – was excellent company.

Charles was at this time in good spirits, for to celebrate the birth of the new baby, Louis and Rupert had brought with them presents from Charles's sister Elizabeth and the Palatine her husband, and these happened to be four paintings of great beauty and nothing could have pleased the King more. He was delighted to add the two Tintorettos and Titians to his collection, and I often found him gloating over them. The Arab horses – snow white in colour – which had accompanied the paintings, Charles had presented to me.

'I am sure you will enjoy them more than I would,' he said fondly. 'And I have my pictures.'

It was hardly likely that with a new addition to the family making us the proud parents of four healthy children and all the merrymaking we were going to worry ourselves about the depleted state of the exchequer.

It was certainly not in my nature to do so.

I was a little saddened to hear that Lady Eleanor Davys, who had prophesied that my first child would be born, christened and buried on the same day, had become a widow. She had prophesied Sir John's death, which she had said would take place within three days of her prophecy and it did. It was reported that when she had looked sombre and worn something dark in mourning for him, he had said: 'Don't weep while I am alive and I will give you leave to laugh when I am dead.'

There was a great deal of talk about her and her prophecies at the time of Sir John's death. I should have liked to consult her again, but I knew that Charles would not be pleased if I did and I was so happy in this wonderful relationship which was growing between us and which was becoming stronger every day, that I did my best not to upset him now.

Only recently Lady Eleanor had been committed to the Gate House Prison and fined three thousand pounds. I don't know exactly what she did but she had been accused of some crime through her writings. She did not care about this but continued to write. Whether she was in league with the Devil I cannot say, but she sincerely believed in her prophecies and that it was her duty to make them.

A new Papal agent had arrived in England. This was George Conn. He was a Scotsman of great charm and good looks who had been sent to the Scots' College in Paris and Rome and gone on to complete his education afterwards at Bologna, where he had become a Dominican friar.

His mission, I learned later, was to mingle with the people of the Court and persuade them – with the utmost subtlety of course – to embrace the faith of Rome. Panzani had been too ambitious. He had planned to convert the whole country. The new idea, which came with George Conn, was to convert the important people of the Court; and this was what George was setting out to do.

Having travelled a great deal he was possessed of a sophistication which made people forget he was a priest. Charles enjoyed his company very much indeed – almost as much as I did; and he was very soon popular at Court. He had some rooms in the house he had acquired made into what he called the Pope's Chapel, and Catholics from all over the neighbourhood went there to worship. George Conn told me that the Pope was delighted with what I was doing in England and as a symbol of his approval sent me a beautiful gold cross studded with exquisite gems. I wore it proudly and told my friends that I regarded it as my most precious possession.

One day George Conn showed me a beautiful picture of St Catherine which he said he was going to have framed for me. I loved it on the spot and asked if I might see to the framing myself. I then decided that I would not have it framed after all but have it attached to my bed curtains so that the first thing I saw on opening my eyes was the beautiful serene face of St Catherine.

George Conn was very pleased with me but he pointed out that as there was a great deal of work to be done we must not be complacent. I was so delighted that Charles enjoyed talking to George almost as much as I did.

Once Charles said: 'I think I am a Catholic at heart.' And George and I exchanged glances of triumph for I at last believed victory was in sight. I suppose George was too wise to think so.

But there was no protest when one of the preachers said in a sermon which he gave for the King and the Court that the people who had brought about the English schism were like tailors who cut out garments and find themselves unable to piece them together and become so bemused that they do not know what they are doing.

I began to feel very proud of myself for there I was, a happy wife and mother, and upon my shoulders had descended the great task of leading the country of my adoption back to salvation. I was seeing myself at that time as one of the great figures of history. I should be remembered as that Bertha of whom some people were fond of reminding me.

There were set-backs of course. I was sure Charles wanted to become a Catholic. There was nothing of the Puritan in him, but he had at his coronation vowed to uphold the Reformed Faith as all anointed sovereigns must do and which was one of the reasons why I had refused to be crowned with him.

I had made a habit of taking my son Charles to Mass. It had, after all, been one of the clauses of the marriage settlement that I was to have charge of the children's religious education until they were thirteen. Charles was only six years old but he was very interested and asked a great many pertinent questions as he did about everything, and he happened to mention something of this when he was with his father.

Charles was taken aback. 'Surely,' he cried, 'you did not take the boy to Mass?'

'But, of course, he must go to Mass,' I said. 'He is six years old. I want. . . .'

Charles laid his hands on my shoulders and looked at me with that half-exasperated, half-tender look which I seemed to inspire so often.

'My dearest,' he said, 'you cannot take the Prince of Wales to Mass.'

'But why not?'

'Because, my love, he will one day be King of this country. He will take his oath, as I have, to adhere to the Reformed Faith.'

'But I am to have charge of his education until he is thirteen.'

'You must not take him to Mass.'

'And if I insist?'

'I hope you will not, my dearest, because if you do I shall have to forbid you and you know how it grieves me to forbid you anything.'

So of course I had to obey, but in my heart I knew that Charles leaned towards the Faith and, if he had not been the King who had sworn to adhere to the Reformed Faith, I am sure he would have admitted it.

It was only later that I realized that all these small incidents were like a smouldering pile in which the smoke is only seen in occasional escaping wisps. But the fire is there waiting to break out. I could not see it then though. I was foolish and frivolous, congratulating myself on the work I was doing.

Quite a number of the ladies of the Court were becoming involved with religion. George Conn was so persuasive and he never talked religion openly, only in the most subtle manner. I had the greatest admiration for him.

Lucy Hay professed interest, but I thought in my heart that she did so lightly. In fact she had a fondness for George Conn's company. Quite a lot of the women were like that. They flirted with the ideas as they did with the men, while they had no intention of becoming involved in anything seriously.

It was different with Lady Newport. She became very involved and I think she had always been a little inclined towards Catholicism, for her sister was a Catholic. George Conn had made a special effort with her and so had Wat Montague, an old favourite of mine who had now returned to England with Sir Toby Matthew, a much travelled and zealous Catholic. We all believed that a little persuasion would bring her to the decision she was longing to make.

Lady Newport's husband, who was Master of the Ordnance and a stern Protestant, had forbidden his wife to dabble in idolatry, as he called it; but Anne Newport was a persistent woman and she was growing more and more certain that the true Faith was that of the Catholic Church. Her conversion was delayed, for oddly enough she had become greatly influenced by her glover who, humble though he was, was something of a preacher and a Protestant belonging to that sect of Puritans which had become more and more prominent since such efforts to bring back the Catholic Faith had been made in the country.

She said to me: 'I know he is humble and merely a glove-maker but he has a power . . . a way with words which can only be inspired.'

I replied: 'Bring him along and let George Conn talk to him. We'll see how his inspiration stands up to that.'

Lucy, with the rest of my ladies and friends like Wat Montague and Toby Matthews, was always excited when I proposed something unconventional, and in due course we all assembled and summoned the glover, George having already consented to talk to him.

When I saw the glover I disliked him on sight simply because here was another of those Puritans in plain black garments and that ridiculous haircut which made their heads look round.

George Conn looked elegant and handsome and so worldly that I was sure he confirmed all the glover's suspicions about idolatrous Catholic priests. The result was as we all predicted. The poor man had a certain eloquence, it was true, but to watch him in verbal conflict with George was like watching two combatants fighting with a spade and a sword. George's rapier thrusts were soon getting home and the poor glover was growing more and more bewildered.

At length he cried: 'Pray give me leave to retire. I must think . . . think . . . You bemuse me. I am mazed. . . .'

George smiled and laid his hand on the poor man's shoulder. 'Go in peace, my friend,' he said. 'Go and ponder what I have said. You will find yourself confronted by the truth at every turn.

Never forget that when you leave the tanglewood of ignorance, I shall be the first to welcome you to the paths of truth.'

I had rarely seen a man so bewildered. He left us in a daze and we all clustered round George and congratulated him.

'You were so clever,' I said. 'Poor man! It was most unfair of me to set you against him.'

'It was right for you to do so, Your Majesty,' replied George. 'Another of your good deeds.'

'You were so clearly the victor,' added Lucy.

'The truth will always prevail,' answered George.

That interview was to have startling results. A few days later the glover went mad. He could not reconcile himself to either form of religion and, as religion was the centre of his life, he was lost in a maze of beliefs and disbeliefs. We were all very sad to hear of his tragedy, for he was a worthy man and a most excellent glove-maker.

But the event which caused the greatest stir was the conversion of Lady Newport. She came to me in great uncertainty one day.

'Madam,' she said, 'I need your help. I have been talking to my sister and I am now convinced which is the true Faith. I want to be reconciled to the Church of Rome. I want to make my confession and proclaim my beliefs, but how can I do this? If my husband discovers what I am about to do, he will shut me away, send me out of the country . . . do anything to prevent my conversion.'

Intrigue ever fascinated me and I was delighted to help her, for bringing people to the true Faith was my great purpose. I was longing for everyone to know that we had a convert in Lady Newport because I guessed that would bring quite a number who were wavering to make a decision.

So I consulted George Conn.

He came up with an idea. 'Let it be a secret until it is actually done,' he said. 'Otherwise there may be powerful people who will do everything within their power to prevent it. Let her visit one of your Capuchin friars at that time when she would normally be returning from some entertainment perhaps.'

Anne Newport thought it was a good idea and she said that she could go to a performance at Drury Lane and on her way home call at Somerset House and see the friar there.

So that was what we arranged. Lady Newport went to the theatre and on the way home visited the chapel and made her confession to the Capuchin friar; and then she was reconciled to the Catholic Church.

Another convert! I congratulated myself that I was winning my war against heretics. I was, however, unprepared for the storm which the conversion of Lady Newport brought about. The fact that his wife had become a Catholic enraged the Earl of Newport. He was a clever man, which was not surprising considering that his mother was Penelope Rich, the daughter of Lettice Knollys, Countess of Leicester. Even now people talked about that forceful woman. The fact that Penelope's son was illegitimate – his parentage was shared with Charles Blount, Earl of Devonshire – had not stopped his inheritance or impeded his advancement. Not only had he been made Master of the Ordnance for life, but he had made considerable profits out of the office and he was not the sort of man to stand quietly by while his wife defied him on a matter which he considered of great importance.

He went himself to see Charles. He ranted and raged and was clearly distressed. Charles expressed deep sympathy. Newport, of course, dared not say anything to Charles about me, but his implications were that I and my little coterie were infiltrating mischievously and undermining the accepted Faith of the country. He blamed several of my close associates, naming Wat Montague and Sir Toby Matthews.

'Your Majesty,' he begged, 'I pray you send Montague and Matthews out of the country. I am sure that they and some of their friends are at the root of this disaster.'

Charles was very sorry for Newport's distress but he knew that I would be rejoicing in my convert. However, he did not think it was good for such a fierce Catholic as Montague to remain at Court in view of growing resentment, but he did nothing for he knew how upset I would be if Montague were sent away.

Very soon a bigger issue grew out of the matter. When he found the King reluctant to act, Newport went to Archbishop Laud to complain that he feared the King was too much influenced by his wife to take any action which might not be in accordance with her wishes.

This was the beginning of the antagonism between myself and Archbishop Laud. There had been times when I had had hopes of Laud for he was a man who loved the ceremonies of the Church. I had mentioned to George Conn that if the Pope would give him a

Cardinal's hat he might become our man. I am not sure now whether I was right about that, but in any case he did not get his red biretta. On the other hand he said that he 'laboured nothing more than that the external public worship of God –too much slighted in most parts of the kingdom – might be preserved and that with as much decency and uniformity as might be, being still of the opinion that unity cannot long continue in the Church when uniformity is shut out.' This implied that he loved all the ceremonies of the Church and it was natural that I should think he was leaning strongly towards us. Had he not amended the Prayer Book and imposed it on Scotland in place of the liturgy which had been prepared by the Scots bishops?

The son of a Reading clothier, Laud was indeed a clever man to have climbed so far; such are always the most difficult to bend to one's wishes. I have always recognized that they are possessed of a very special cleverness to have risen up and overcome their handicaps and one must in assessing them – particularly as an enemy – have a special respect for them.

There was another point: many people suspected that his attitude to the ceremonies of the Church meant that he was a secret Catholic and as he was aware – far more than I was – of the growing resentment in the country, he was eager to prove himself staunchly Protestant. He therefore complained at a meeting of the Council that since the coming of the Papal agents, Panzani and Conn, there had been many conversions to Catholicism and there was too much favour shown to Catholics and he thought that both Walter Montague and Toby Matthews should be prosecuted.

When I heard this I was enraged, and from then on the Archbishop was my enemy. Poor Charles was in a dreadful dilemma. He could quite understand Lord Newport's fury; he saw the Archbishop's point; but he was very eager not to upset me.

I realized then – and I think so did many others – how important I was becoming in the country. I had had such success with the Pope's agents; I had done so much to make life easier for our Catholic subjects that I was beginning to be thought of not so much as the frivolous pleasure-loving Queen as the power behind the throne. My husband listened to me because he loved me so much and hated to disappoint me so that I was almost in the position of being his most favoured and influential minister.

I heard that Laud had said to Thomas Wentworth, whom the King greatly favoured and who had just returned from his duties in Ireland: 'I have a very hard task and God, I beseech Him, to make me very good corn, for I am between two great factions very like corn between two mill stones.'

I was made fully aware of the importance of this by George, who came to me in great haste to tell me what was happening at the Council.

'I think we have gone a little too far too quickly,' he said. 'Laud has suggested to the Council that the Catholic chapels should be closed down, including yours of Somerset House, and the counsellors have agreed with enthusiasm that this should be so.'

'I will never allow that,' I cried.

'I beg of you be careful,' begged Conn. 'Do not ruin the good work we have done so far.'

'Nothing can ruin that,' I assured him. 'We have saved souls and that is our endeavour. Do not take this threat too seriously. I know Charles. He would never agree to a step which he knows would make me very unhappy.'

When Charles came to me he was really distressed. 'Laud wants all the Catholic chapels to be closed down,' he said.

'What!' I cried. 'That man is a monster. Let him go back to his father's clothier's shop.'

'He is the Archbishop of Canterbury,' he reminded me gently.

'But he loves the ceremonies of the Church. He hates these miserable Puritans as much as I do.'

'He supports the Protestant Church, my love.'

'I will not allow him to shut my chapels. Charles, you will not allow this. You have promised me. . . . Oh, Charles, promise me now. Not my chapel. . . !'

He soothed me and swore that my chapel should not be closed, although he added: 'There is no alternative for the others. They will have to be closed wherever they have sprung up.'

The controversy went on for a long time and it did show how thoroughly the people disliked the Archbishop. It has always amazed me to see how the common people dislike to see one of their own rise to great heights. One would have thought they would be delighted. But no. His humble birth was continually flung at Laud, more so by the common people than by the nobles. It was said that he was at heart a Catholic and ought to admit it. At

least, they said, the Catholics like myself and George Conn made
no secret of their idolatrous beliefs.

Poor Charles, he did not know which way to act. He was
advised that he could not ignore the growing feelings against the
Catholics, and on the other hand, how could he hurt me?

In the end he compromised. He agreed that there should be a
proclamation threatening Catholics in the country; but at the
same time he had so weakened the laws against them that they
did not amount to very much. He tried to do what he had to do
without offending either protagonist.

I laughed and told him he was very clever. He was serious
though and seemed to be looking into the future with very
melancholy eyes.

Dear Charles! He was only vaguely aware of the dangers which
were springing up around him – but he was not quite so blind as I
was.

There was sad news from my mother. She was in great
distress. It seemed that she had quarrelled irrevocably with
Richelieu, and that he governed France. He had made it clear to
her that she was not wanted there; in fact he had actually sent her
into exile.

I worried a great deal about her. It was dreadful that she, who
had always been such an imposing figure during my childhood,
should now be reduced to this.

'Who is this Richelieu?' I cried to Charles. 'Merely a priest – a
Cardinal it is true – and yet he has set himself up as the ruler of
France, and he has decided that there is no place there for my
mother.'

The King said something very strange then. It was almost like a
prophecy, but he did not know that, and I certainly did not. 'Yes,'
he said slowly, 'it is strange. And what is happening here? I often
think there are some who would like to do the same to me.'

I laughed disbelievingly, but he went on seriously: 'There is
trouble brewing, my dearest. Scotland. . . .'

'That awful country,' I cried impatiently. 'Haven't the Scots
always been troublesome?'

He agreed with that. Then he went on: 'There is something
about these Puritans. I can understand the situation when there

is a desire to supplant one king by another who it might be thought has a greater claim to the throne. But these people seem to have set themselves against kings and all that Kingship means. They seem as though they want to abolish that rule and set up their own.'

I continued to laugh and Charles managed to smile. It was such an incongruous idea. There had always been kings; and who were these people who went about looking like black crows with their ridiculous haircuts?

If only we could have looked into the future then, perhaps we could have done something to prevent the holocaust. I think we might well have. When I look back I see the way we came was strewn with warnings which we ignored.

But for the time there was the problem of my mother.

Charles knew it would be a mistake to give her refuge in England, but he also knew that it was what I wanted. I could not bear the thought of her going about Europe like a beggar pleading for sanctuary. I wondered how my brother could allow her to be treated so, but I supposed he was under the thumb of that hateful old Richelieu. At least he gave her a pension but he was adamant about her leaving France. To be turned away from one's home must be horribly humiliating, particularly when one had in the past been its ruler.

She was now in Holland and one of Charles's agents there had sent a message to tell him that be believed she had plans for coming to England.

'The people would not like it,' said Charles, and he looked at me sadly. It was a great sorrow to him that the people had turned against me. I think he would rather have heard them cheer me than himself. He rarely ever did. I was not only a foreigner, I was a Catholic and that was enough to turn a great many people in England against me. 'And,' went on Charles, 'you know the state of the exchequer. We can hardly afford to entertain your mother in the manner she would expect.'

'Poor dear lady,' I said. 'I daresay she would be pleased to receive any warm welcome from someone who cared about her.'

Charles was very depressed and I knew this was because he had sent a messenger to Holland to tell his agents to do everything to dissuade my mother from coming to England.

She must have known that she was unwanted but, being my

mother, that did not deter her. I was her daughter; she imagined that I was rich and powerful. I was after all the Queen of England. Perhaps she did not know that there were certain difficulties in the country now, but even if she did she would sweep those aside. I knew her well. She was the sort of woman who made circumstances fit her needs.

I wondered how she felt about the new baby at the Court of France. There had been great excitement there for months because Anne of Austria, after twenty-three years of infertility, had given birth to a boy.

However I knew that the King was probably right in not inviting her to England but on the other hand I did feel that I had failed her. I decided I would try to persuade Charles to let her come if only for a brief visit. But that would mean that if she liked it here her visit would not be a brief one.

This was the state of affairs when we heard that my mother had actually set sail from Holland and was making her way to the English coast. Moreover she was bringing with her one hundred and sixty attendants and servants, six coaches and seventy horses, which was a clear indication that she expected to be received in a manner worthy of a Queen.

Charles was nonplussed. 'But I have not invited her,' he cried in despair. 'I have not given her permission to come here. . . .'

I knew that he was thinking of what it was going to cost to house my mother and I hated to see the furrows in his brow, but what could I do? I went to him and slipped my arm through his while I looked up at him pleadingly. 'I could never be happy if we turned her away,' I said. 'She is my mother. . . .'

He tried to explain to me the cost and the attitude of the people – but eventually I won. The fact that I was pregnant again made him very anxious not to upset me. He promised that he would go himself in state to meet her to show everyone that she came as an honoured guest. I should prepare rooms for her and have three thousand pounds to spend on any alteration or new furniture which I deemed necessary. She was my mother and for that reason, naturally he must welcome her.

I hugged him and told him he was the most wonderful husband in the world and my mother would be so happy to see what a perfect marriage I had made.

He was as good as his word and set out for Chelmsford and I

went to St James's, where the children had their apartments, and chose fifty rooms for my mother.

My baby was due in four months' time and I was feeling heavy and tired but exhilarated by the thought of seeing my mother. I had told the children that she was coming and the elder ones were very interested. Charles was now aged eight and different from the others, with his black hair cut into a fringe which almost covered his black brows, under which his flashing dark eyes were the most lively I ever saw in a child of his age. Mary, only a year younger, was beautiful and so was James; Elizabeth was three and Anne only a baby. She had been born in March of the previous year and within a few months I had become pregnant again. And I was not thirty yet! I often wondered how many children I would have. I was happy to be the wife of an ardent and loving husband and to have produced a growing family but frequent childbearing was often taxing and I certainly did not feel well at this time.

However, I tried to forget my own discomforts and prepare for my mother. Riders came in breathlessly to tell me that she had had a good reception in London, that people had hung out banners in the streets and that the Lord Mayor in all the splendour of his office had greeted her. I was immensely relieved because one could never be sure of the people of London and, with all those horrid Puritans about, they might have decided to become hostile. But they did love pageantry and it may have been that they found that more entertaining than a stupid riot. But I liked to think they did homage to my mother as a woman who had once been Regent of France and was still mother of their Queen.

I heard the sound of trumpets which meant that the cavalcade was approaching St James's. Young Charles was right beside me and the others came toddling up. I hurried into the courtyard. I could not think of ceremony at such a moment.

I ran to my mother's coach, the children at my heels, and I tried to pull open the door. One of the coachmen opened it for me and as my mother stepped out, I was so overcome with emotion that I dropped to my knees and begged her to give me her blessing.

With great joy I took her into the palace and showed her the apartments I had had made ready for her. I was rather shocked by her appearance. It was, after all, a long time since I had seen her. I had been the fortunate one. I had learned to love my husband and had made for myself a family life so felicitous that I could not believe many people were so blessed. Poor Queen Marie! She was sixty-five years old and her life during the last years had been very uncomfortable. She had never been beautiful and events, with the aid of time, had ravaged such looks as she had had. But I was quick to realize that the indomitable spirit had remained intact, and so had the determination to manage the lives of all those about her.

She talked incessantly. She was poor . . . yes *poor*! She, the Queen of France, now lived in abject poverty. She had her jewels . . . oh yes, she had been clever enough to bring those with her and it had occurred to her that she might have to sell some of them.

'I will buy them, dear Mother,' I cried. 'That will give you some money and you will know the jewels are safe.'

She patted my arm. She said I was a good girl and as I was rich she would be glad to accept the money for the jewels and know that they were safe in the family.

I said: 'I am not really rich, my lady. There is always trouble about money. There is never enough. Charles is always wanting money and unable to get it except by unpopular taxation.'

'The perpetual cry of Kings!' replied my mother. 'Of course there is money, dear child. There always is in a country. It is a matter of knowing how to extract it. You shall have the jewels. I may not be here long, you know, to burden you.'

'Burden us!' I cried. 'Dear Mother, how can you talk like that?'

'I did not mean I am going to die,' she replied. 'I know you are pleased that I have come to be with you. It was far too long that we were apart, Henriette chérie. I will stay with you and help you. But I may be called back to France.'

'Do you think the Cardinal. . . .'

'The Cardinal!' She spat out the words. 'He is plagued by a terrible cough. He can't keep warm. I hear he sits by the fire drinking that sickly strawberry syrup which is the only thing which gives his throat some relief. He crouches over the fire because he cannot keep warm. How long do you think he can last like that?'

'You really think he is desperately ill?'

'I *know*, my child. You don't think I have been idle. I know what is going on. One advantage of being in exile is that one can send out one's spies and no one can be absolutely sure who they are. There are always advantages in life, child.'

'I cannot understand my brother's turning you away.'

'Oh, he is a weakling, Louis. He always was. He is guided by his wife and the Cardinal. He is nothing . . . a puppet . . . a cypher.'

'And the baby?'

She nodded, smiling. 'A healthy boy. Another Louis.' She came close to me. 'No, I shall not be here with you long, dear child. A breathing space, that's all I need. My astrologers have told me that Louis cannot last more than a year or so. He is a sick man. He was never strong. And then when he is dead . . . can a baby rule? Little Louis XIV will be still in his nursery. Then it is for me to return and take over the reins as I did when your father died.'

'And this is the prophecy?'

'It is and I have had the best astrologers in Europe. Their verdict is always the same. So it would be advisable for your Charles to make me happy here. I could be of great importance to him later on.'

I was overawed. It all seemed so plausible and I had seen the evidence of astrologers and soothsayers. I should never forget Eleanor Davys and her prophecy about the first baby I had had.

My mother's presence at Court did mean that I must spend a great deal of time with her, which gave me less time for my husband. She loved the children and was most impressed by Charles. She even liked his looks and said he had inherited them from some of my father's ancestors – The Brigands of Navarre she called them.

'He has a look of your father,' she said. '*Mon Dieu*, how he reminds me! Quick, lively, eyes everywhere. Let us hope they do not linger on every woman in the vicinity as your father's did. I had to shut *my* eyes to his infidelities and I did so without complaint . . . for the sake of the crown. You, my dear Henriette, have no such trouble with your husband. He seems a mild man . . . but devoted to you. There seems to be nothing but pregnancies for you. I know what that means. Your father always took time off from his lights of love to fill the royal nurseries. How different you are with your Charles. You are a very fortunate woman, Henriette.'

I told her I realized that and if only Charles would stop worrying about the troubles of the country and those wretched Protestants – and worse still Puritans – I could be completely happy.

'It appears there is always trouble for rulers, but you have done
well and I believe even the Holy Father is pleased with you.'

'How is Madame St George? Have you heard?'

'I haven't seen her since I left France, of course. I think she is
happy with that little tyrant. Gaston dotes on his daughter. It is a
pity he could not get a son. Little Mademoiselle de Montpensier is
very rich, for Gaston's wife, as you know, left everything to her
when she died. It is a pity it did not go to Gaston. It is a mistake, in
my opinion, for young people to inherit large fortunes.'

'She will find it easy to get a husband.'

'My dear child, they are waiting to pounce. Gaston will have to
be careful. I should be there to make sure no mistakes are made.
Well, perhaps soon . . . according to the prophets. . . .'

I was a little sad at the thought of Louis' dying. After all, he was
my brother and although I had seen very little of him and I did
think of him more as the King of France than a relation, the bond
was still there. My mother was so sure that he was going to die
and I couldn't help feeling a little horrified that she seemed to be
looking forward to the event.

Power! I thought. How people crave for it! I didn't think I did.
What I really wanted was to be with my husband and family in a
peaceful country where there were no troubles – but of course
that must be a country which had turned to the Catholic Faith.

My mother was saying: 'I could have returned to Florence.'

'Oh, my dear lady, that would have been wonderful,' I replied.
'You could have gone back to your family.'

'Oh yes. The Medicis would have welcomed me. They have a
strong family feeling. It would have been strange to be in
Florence again, to stroll along the Arno and to live in the old
palace. But think how I should have gone back. A Queen yes, but
one who had been turned out of her adopted country by her own
son and a Cardinal. No, I could not do that.' For a moment the
mask of optimism slipped from her face and I glimpsed a rather
fearful old woman. Fleetingly I wondered how much she really
believed in those prophecies. She added slowly: 'I could not go
back to Florence . . . a failure.' Then the mask was back again.
'One day, I shall be very busy. If I have to return to France – I am

sure the message will come before long – then I shall be fully engaged with affairs in Paris.'

While she was waiting for all that, she concerned herself with affairs in England.

The children were very interested in her and I was delighted to see how well they got on. She wanted to take charge of the nurseries. Charles, oddly enough for such a precocious child, had always taken a wooden toy to bed with him. He had had it when he was about two years old, had formed an attachment to it and his nurses told me that he would not go to sleep without it.

'Nonsense,' said my mother. 'Of course he must give it up. It is not becoming in a Prince of Wales to need toys to go to bed with.'

She talked to Charles very seriously and somehow made him see that it was childish and not worthy of a future King.

When that argument was put to him he allowed them to take the toy away. He was very interested in the fact that the would one day be King and was already talking now and then of what he would do, and it was only this which made him relinquish his toy.

He was a shrewd, often devious little boy. We were amused by the incident of the physic, but at the same time it did show that he had a clever, if crafty, nature. The fact was that he had refused to take some physic which his Governor, Lord Newcastle, thought he needed and Newcastle had complained to me, so I wrote to Charles telling him that I had heard he had refused to take his physic and if he persisted I should have to come and make him take it as it was for his health's sake. I added that I had told Lord Newcastle to let me know whether or not he had taken his medicine and I hoped he was not going to disappoint me.

Lord Newcastle visited me next day with a note which he said the Prince had sent him.

'My Lord,' Charles had written in his still childish script and on ruled lines to keep the writing straight, 'I would not take too much physic for it doth always make me worse and I think it will do the like for you. I ride every day and am ready to follow any other direction from you. Charles P.'

I could not help laughing and was so impressed by the wit of my son that I told Lord Newcastle that we would not impose the physic for a day or so and if the boy was well enough without it he deserved to escape.

How could I help being proud of such a boy? And I was sure that even my mother could not succeed in getting the better of him.

My mother was complaining now that Mary ate too much at breakfast and must expect to be sick if in addition to manchets of bread and beef and mutton she took chicken as well. Also she drank too much ale.

It was true that when her rather large meals were curtailed Mary did seem better.

My mother was not popular. People thought she was too extravagant and that too much money was being spent on her entourage and entertainment. It was true that she expected to live like a Queen – but then she was a Queen.

The weather had changed as soon as she arrived, and the southern half of the country was engulfed in storms and gales which caused a great deal of damage. The people, always super-stitious, said it was a sign and meant that the Queen Mother was going to be a menace to the country. It was very upsetting and I was afraid my mother would hear these rumours. But if she did, she brushed them aside. I had forgotten her capacity to accept only what she wanted to happen.

Whenever the weather was bad during my mother's stay in England, the Thames watermen would shout to each other that this was more of the weather the Queen Mother had brought to England, as though she used some malicious influence in the heavens to make us uncomfortable.

As a Queen she looked upon luxury as her natural right and maintaining her household was a drain on the exchequer. She did not, however, see why the people of England should not pay for it. They did, and complained bitterly about her in the streets and now and then I overheard unflattering comments. It was said that she was a trouble-bringer and there was never tranquillity when she was nearby. There was grumbling about the people of England being taxed to pay for her "shaggrags" – by which I presume they meant her household.

Charles grew worried and told me he had sent a message to King Louis urging him to invite his mother back to France. 'It is the best way,' he said. 'She pines for the old life in Paris. I know that she has entered into intrigues in the past, but I feel sure she would promise not to if you would only have her back.'

Charles explained to me that, apart from the expense of keeping her in England, her presence was an irritation to the people and that was something he wanted to avoid because he was growing more and more uneasy about the state of the country.

I hated to see him worried so I made no protest, but Louis wrote back to the effect that however much his mother promised not to meddle she would be unable to prevent herself doing so because she was a meddler by nature; and he would not give her permission to return to France. He was sorry for his brother-in-law but he must be as firm as Louis himself was and explain to Queen Marie that her presence was no longer wanted in England.

But how could Charles do that! She was after all my mother and in spite of those traits of hers which I had to admit were there, I loved her. Charles could never do anything to hurt me if he could help it, so she remained.

It was true that she meddled. One day she said to me: 'I was not idle in Holland. All the time I concerned myself with your good and that of the children. I sounded them on the possibility of a match between the Prince of Orange and one of your girls.'

'The Prince of Orange!' I cried. 'He is of no great importance.'

'I didn't mean for Mary, of course. Perhaps Elizabeth.'

'She is three years old!'

'My dear daughter, we have to think of the alliances of our children when they are in their cradles. I will discuss the matter with the King.'

'No, my lady,' I said firmly. 'I will discuss it with the King.'

'Oh,' she said, a little huffily, 'you two seem to talk nothing but lovers' talk. State matters have their place too, remember.'

'They will be the state matters of England,' I retorted coolly, and wondered if I was becoming as hard towards her as Louis was. We must show her that she could not interfere in English affairs any more than she could in French. Hadn't she learned her lesson? Surely being turned out of her home must have made her realize something. But no doubt she blamed Louis and Anne . . . and the Cardinal of course, for turning away one who could have been – as she would see it – a great help to them.

At the first opportunity I told Charles what she had suggested.

'The Prince of Orange!' he said. 'Oh, he is too petty a prince to mate with a princess of England.'

'So thought I,' I replied. 'But my mother talked of it when she was in Holland and she tells me that the Prince of Orange would be very happy with the match.'

'I have no doubt he would. No. Not even for one of our younger daughters would he be good enough.'

There was one other point which seemed to have escaped them all and of which I was very much aware: the Prince of Orange was a Protestant. When my children married I wanted to make sure that they married Catholics.

I was getting bigger but still able to walk a little in the gardens. I loved those of St James's with the deer park and the terraces. I enjoyed walking there with Charles and the children. Charles was always so tender and affectionate and everyone marvelled at his care of me . . . especially when I was in the condition I was at this time.

Charles and I would sit on one of the seats and the children would run about making a great deal of noise with all the dogs yapping round them; and the ladies and gentlemen made such a charming sight walking on the paths round the palace.

Happy days they were, when Charles looked so handsome and was so different from the rather shy young man whom I had first met. I rarely heard him stammer now; he didn't when he was at peace and happy; and he certainly was with his family. He liked to hear little domestic details. He answered young Charles's questions gravely and gave his attention to James when he accused Mary of taking his share of the custard tart they had had for dinner. I was sure he would have been happier being just with us than coping with his ministers.

Why couldn't everyone stop complaining? I asked myself. Why could they not enjoy life as we did walking in the gardens of St James's.

Winter came in fiercely. 'Queen Mother weather,' said the boatmen.

It was at the end of a bitter January that my baby was born. It was a little girl and she was hastily baptized and christened Catherine, for she died a few hours after her birth.

The Human Sacrifice

After the death of Catherine I think happiness was over for me, although perhaps I did enjoy snatches of pleasure when I was able to convince myself that all was well; and even when I was most apprehensive I could not have conceived the magnitude of the horror which was waiting to spring on me, crushing my joy for ever and making me wait each day for the release which only death could bring.

Where did it start? It is difficult to say. Scotland – I sometimes think – that land of trouble which I hate, with all the squabbling over a prayerbook. But who am I to talk? Who was more sternly religious than I? Had I not from the moment I had set foot in England worked to bring the country back to Rome from which it had been so ruthlessly torn by that monster Henry VIII, simply because he wished for a new wife? But the succeeding monarchs had had their chance and had done nothing. I see now that the Protestant Faith suited the English – not the Puritan branch, which was as intense as our Catholic – but the easy going, not too demanding Church of England.

Was it religion? Perhaps to some extent. Then if it were, I was indeed to blame.

But no. That was not the real reason. I was not the only one.

I suppose Archbishop Laud with his rigid insistence on the ceremonies of the Church, the correct vestments of the clergy, all the ceremonies which were akin to the Church of Rome, had done much to bring about the Puritan strain, and consequently to result in what was tantamount to a new party composed of solemn men who thought it was a sin even to laugh; as for dancing and singing, to take pleasure in those meant to them to be on the road to hell. Laud was anxious not to be called a Catholic, but he resembled one in many ways, and he had become the most unpopular man in the country.

Charles respected him very much and Charles was always loyal in his friendships, but I think the man he preferred above all was Thomas Wentworth. Charles admired him enormously for he had often in the past proved himself to be an honest man. He had recently returned from Ireland, where he had done well by promoting the growth of flax, opening up trade with Spain and abolishing piracy in St George's Channel. His aim had been to make the Irish as prosperous as the English and dependent on England while they realized that it was in their interest to be loyal to the English.

Wentworth's conduct of affairs had led Charles to believe that it was men like him whom he wanted at home and he sent for him. Soon after his arrival in England, Thomas Wentworth was created Earl of Strafford.

That year came in on a rather melancholy note. I knew that Charles was very worried although he was cheered by Strafford who, he confided to me, was one of the ablest men he had ever come across and loyal too. For that reason I tried to like the man, and I found I could when I rid myself of a certain jealousy for he was a most elegant, gallant and courtly gentleman.

I was beginning to see myself a little more clearly than I had before. I had had time for reflection during my pregnancies and to my dismay (although I did not let Charles know this yet) I was pregnant again. The experience with Catherine had been so distressing that I had hoped for a little respite. To suffer the discomforts of nine months only to find there is no result, or that it is snatched away from you almost before you have received it, is a devastating experience for a woman. The point was that I realized I had been jealous of Charles's appreciation of Strafford. Buckingham had a great deal to answer for; I suppose that during my happy life with Charles I was always looking out for some clever man who might try to snatch him from me . . . not that anyone could do that now but they could diminish the regard he had for me and that was something I could not bear.

But it was not so with Strafford and when I overcame my initial dislike, I was grateful to him for the comfort he brought to Charles; and then I found I liked him for himself. There was someone else in my household who liked him very much. That was Lucy Hay. Lucy was ten years older than I which made her bordering on forty, but no one would have believed it to look at her except that the years of experience – and I suspected very great experience – had made her more fascinating than ever; in spite of being no longer young she was still the most attractive woman at Court.

Katherine Villiers and Susan Feilding attended services at Somerset House and were coming out into the open and declaring their conversion to the Catholic Faith, which endeared them to me. But fond as I was of them both, it was Lucy whom I liked best to be with. She was so amusing and bright, and was always in the midst of some intrigue which sometimes she would talk about and at others be so secretive that she fascinated me more than ever.

It was no secret that she had become Strafford's very good friend. They were a magnificent pair – the cleverest man and woman at Court, I guessed. I wondered what they talked of in their intimate moments.

I impressed on Charles that it was no use letting people know how anxious we were about everything. We should make life seem as normal as possible, and to celebrate the coming of the New Year I arranged a masque and a comedy in which I was going to take the most important part.

Charles thought it was a good idea and we had an amusing time discussing the play and the part I would take – and, of course, my costume. Lewis Richard, who was Master of the King's Music, composed the songs and we ordered Inigo Jones to make the scenery and design the costumes so that we could make sure to have a dazzling spectacle.

That masque stands out vividly in my memory. I suppose it was because it was the last one I played in at Whitehall. It was a brave attempt and Charles, no less than I, determined to make it memorable. I really did enjoy prancing about the stage dressed as an Amazon in silvery armour and a helmet which sported a magnificent feather.

The winter was harsh and the New Year came in grimly. I was feeling ill because of my condition and my spirits suffered through memories of Catherine's birth and death.

Strafford called at Whitehall one day and when he left Charles was very depressed. He came to me as he always did to tell me the news for, bless him, he always behaved as though I had a grasp of state matters, which was far from the truth, although I must say that I did try my best to understand.

'Strafford wants to call a parliament,' he said, 'because we must have money to prosecute the war against the Scots and that is the only way to set about getting it.'

I frowned. I hated both parliaments and wars against the Scots. One was hard enough to bear but the two of them together were intolerable. Wars took Charles away from me and that was tragic for us both; parliaments made laws and they were nearly always aimed at the Catholics, which meant myself.

'Need it be called?' I asked. 'Parliaments always mean trouble.'

Charles agreed that they did. There had always been conflict between him and them because he could never see why a King should not be an absolute ruler since he had inherited the crown through birth and was therefore God's chosen ruler. No, certainly Charles had no wish to call a parliament. But he needed money to carry on the war and a parliament would have to find a means of raising it.

'I wish they would let us live in peace,' I said.

'I could not agree with you more,' replied the King. 'But I suppose Strafford is right. He usually is.'

'So you will call this parliament?'

'I have no alternative.'

'Well then, call it, and let us hope it does not last long.'

As a matter of fact it did not. It lasted only three weeks and it was that one which was called the Short Parliament. Charles was uneasy. There were three men he mentioned to me. One was John Pym, a strict Presbyterian, who was evidently a man of great powers and was becoming the leader of that party in the Commons which was opposed to the King; then there was John Hampden, who had endured a spell in prison for refusing to pay what he called the forced loan – an act which had made his name known throughout the country and turned many a man to his favour; and the other – a man whose name I had not heard before but which was to become engraved on my mind for ever – was a connection of Hampden's for I believe Hampden's mother was his aunt; he came from Huntingdon and was the member for Cambridge. His name was Oliver Cromwell.

These were the men whom Charles feared. They were not in favour of imposing a tax to raise money for war on Scotland and they carried the House with them. Charles was in desperation.

At first I was delighted that the Parliament was so short-lived;

but it seemed there was little to rejoice about. Then Strafford came forward with a suggestion. Because of the good work he had done in Ireland he had been made Lord Lieutenant of that country and he said he could raise an army there and bring it over to fight for the King.

That was where the mischief started. I do not know even now who our enemies were. Perhaps there were so many of them that it was impossible for me to know them all. I believe that Richelieu was at the heart of many of the conspiracies against us. As a ruler of the French it was to his advantage to see a weak England; he did not want to see the English helping friends abroad who were the enemies of France. It was devious politics – far too involved for me, and I had not then learned the art of unravelling these mysteries. I saw life in bright light and dark shadow . . . with little shading between. For me there were the good and the bad and there was no wrong in the good, no right in the bad. I am afraid my emotions not my mind guided my thoughts.

Charles was a saint; I was his devoted wife; and any who were against us were villains. It was as simplified as that.

If we had our enemies abroad, heaven knew we had enough living close.

Strafford was firm beside the King and there were many who agreed that he was the most able statesman in the land. For that reason there were many more waiting to destroy him.

They seized their opportunity. Soon after the dissolution of the Short Parliament rumour was sweeping through the country like wildfire. Strafford was going to bring over an army of Irishmen on a pretext of fighting the Scots but actually to subdue the English.

London was in an uproar. Charles came riding with all speed to Whitehall where I was, for being six months with child, and somewhat melancholy, not only worried about the country's affairs, but still brooding on the death of little Catherine, I was spending a great deal of time resting.

Charles told me of his fears. 'They are against Strafford,' he said. 'And if they are against him it is because they are against me.'

'You are the King,' I reminded him.

'That is so,' he answered, and looking at me fondly he asked about my health and said he wanted to go over to St James's on the next day to see the children.

We spent a pleasant evening until one of the guards came in
with a board he had found attached to the gates of the palace. On
it was written: 'Whitehall to Let'.

There was a sinister implication in the message which made
Charles turn pale.

He said: 'I think you should leave for the country while you are
still able to travel.'

'I wanted the child to be born in Whitehall.'

'No,' said Charles gently. 'It would be better to go to the
country.'

While we were talking a letter was brought to him.

'Who sent it?' he demanded of the guard.

'One of the serving men said it was passed to him by one of the
guards at the gate who did not recognize the man who handed it
to him.'

I looked over Charles's shoulder and read: 'Chase the Pope and
the Devil from St James's, the lodging of the Queen Mother.'

Charles and I looked at each other for some seconds without
speaking. Then I said: 'What does it mean?'

'Our enemies have done this,' said Charles.

'It is a threat . . . to my mother.'

'Someone is raising the people against us,' said the King.

'I must go to St James's without delay,' I cried. 'They are unsafe
there.'

'We will go together,' said Charles.

We rode to the palace and were relieved that we met no hostile
crowds on the way. I think we were prepared for anything.

When we arrived at St James's it was to be greeted by my
distraught mother. She looked wild-eyed. 'I have not been fed,'
she cried. 'How could I be? They have been sending notes calling
us idolaters. They should be hanged, all of them. Charles, what
are you thinking of to allow such conduct from your subjects!'

I silenced her, bidding her remember that she spoke to the
King, but Charles just smiled and said: 'There are times, Madam,
when a king . . . or even a queen . . . is not powerful enough to
stop the cruelty of enemies. They must first be found and then
condemned.'

She turned away. I guessed she was wishing herself far from
here and I could not help thinking that there was a little good in
all evil for if this decided my mother that she could not live in

troubled England that was not entirely to be deplored. This sounds heartless. I loved my mother. I wanted to see her happy and comfortable, but I did realize that she was causing friction here; she was interfering with the way in which the children were brought up and I knew she was in secret teaching them to become Catholics. I had turned a blind eye to this but recent events had taught me to be a little more watchful; and I could guess at the fury which would be unleashed if it were thought that the Prince of Wales and his brother and sisters were being brought up outside the Church of England.

The children were concerned, particularly Charles, who was very solemn. Lady Roxburgh told us that he had had several nightmares and she thought he had something on his mind. She had asked what troubled him and he would not answer though he did not deny that there was something.

Charles and I were determined to find out what was worrying him and I said that I did not think he could possibly be aware of the depressing state of affairs outside St James's; but it seemed he was.

Charles called the boy to him and my son stood before his father, his dark eyes alert, his expression attentive.

'What is wrong?' asked the King. 'You know you can tell me or your mother anything. Come. Don't be afraid.'

'I am not afraid,' said Charles.

'Then what is worrying you?'

'How many kingdoms did my grandfather leave you?' He did not wait for the answer but supplied it himself. 'Four,' he went on. 'There are troubles in the country. I know of them. I listen to the people talking. They think I am too young to understand and that is an advantage because they do not lower their voices or choose their words. Yes, I am anxious because although you, my father, were left four kingdoms, I greatly fear that I, your son, may find myself without one.'

I broke in and cried: 'What a wicked thing to say to your father!'

Young Charles regarded me from under that black fringe and said: 'You asked for the truth, Mam. I but gave it. If you do not wish to hear the truth it is best not to ask for it.'

The King put his hand on the boy's head and said: 'You do well, my son, to speak what is in your mind on these matters. I am having trouble. That is true. I have enemies who send out rumours. People listen to them and learn half truths. Have no fear. I shall fight for this kingdom, so that when the time comes it shall be yours.'

I was too overcome to speak, for when my son talked of what he would inherit I could only see the figure of my beloved husband lying dead before me and that was more than I could bear at that moment.

Charles saw this and understood. He said: 'I shall take your mother to her bedchamber. She is not well.'

'She is pregnant,' said young Charles. 'I hope it is a little girl. I would prefer a sister.'

'Now you go back to the nursery,' commanded the King. 'I can assure you that I know how to defend my kingdom and when the time comes it shall be handed . . . intact . . . to you.'

'Thank you, sir,' said young Charles gravely.

When we were alone the King said: 'He is a bright boy. One to be proud of.'

'I liked not his words.'

'Sweet wife, do not blame the boy for looking to his inheritance. I would rather he did. He would be ready to fight for his rights, though I pray he will never have to. Oh God, how I pray for that! And now, my love, all this unpleasantness is bad for you. Will you promise me that you will make preparations to leave London at once?'

'I promise,' I told him, 'and I have already decided where.'

'Where is that?'

'Oatlands. I like it and it is pleasant to be close to the river.'

'Could not be better,' said Charles. 'Soon then . . . you will leave for Oatlands.'

I was very fond of Oatlands, perhaps because it was just far enough from London to make access to the capital a not too strenuous journey and in addition had the charm of the river. Moreover Charles had granted me the estate for my life and I felt it was therefore my very own. I was always excited when I passed through the beautiful arched gateway designed by Inigo Jones, who had also built the silkworm room which had been planned by my predecessor, Anne of Denmark, Charles's mother. There were two quadrangles and three enclosures with the garden beyond; and the principal quadrangle had a battlemented gateway with angle turrets and bay windows. Everything about Oatlands pleased me. It was not large, as palaces go, but there was royal dignity about it. Oh yes, I was very fond of Oatlands.

I should have been serene during those last months of pregnancy, but I could not think so much of the coming child as of Charles. I fancied he had anxieties which he did not always impart to me – not because of a lack of trust or because he thought such matters would be beyond my understanding, but because he feared to worry me. Perhaps, though, I worried more being in the dark.

I was not the sort of person who could sit and wait. I was completely without patience and always felt better when I was taking some action, and I was apt to take it without due thought simply because I was eager to do something.

It was while I was waiting for the birth of my child that I wrote to the Pope. It was a daring thing to do, but I remembered how pleased he had been with me and what Panzani and Conn had said about his appreciation of my efforts to bring people to the Faith. I had my beautiful cross which I wore constantly to remind me.

Sadly poor George Conn had died. He had had to leave England because the winters were too damp for him, but he did not live long when he returned to Italy. I now had Count Rosetti in his place and was quite fond of him, but he could not be such a friend as George had been.

However, greatly daring and not telling Charles for I was sure he would have forbidden it, I wrote to his Holiness telling him that the Puritans of England were trying to destroy my husband, who desperately needed funds to fight against them. Would the Pope come to our aid?

When I had despatched the messenger, I felt better. I was sure the Pope would do something for us. After all, he had been so pleased with me.

The weather had grown hot and I was dreading my confinement. I was haunted by memories of the last and I wished fervently that Mamie could have been with me. There were times when I missed her sorely. I should have loved to have her wise comments on the situation now. Of course there was Lucy. Lucy was amusing, vital but different from Mamie. She lacked that motherliness which I had always sensed in Mamie and which had been such a comfort to me. There would never be another Mamie. She had three little children of her own now and had not been very well of late. I longed to tell her of our trouble but even I realized that it would be dangerous to write letters about such secret matters.

Every day now I looked for a messenger from the Pope. I imagined myself telling Charles what I had been able to achieve. How delighted he would be with his clever little wife!

In the meantime there was the baby and the time for its arrival was getting nearer and nearer.

It happened on the eighth day of the month. The birth was easy and the child healthy. This time it was a boy, and I was so delighted when they put him into my arms. The ordeal which I had been dreading was over and there seemed to be no fears about this one.

'I do declare,' I said to Lucy, 'I never felt so well after having given birth to a child.'

'It's a good sign,' Lucy told me. 'The boys always come more easily than the girls.'

I forgot everything else in the next few days and just lay in my bed. Charles came to see me and the boy and we were very happy for a while. I had only one regret. I had no good news from the Pope to give him.

Never mind, I told myself, it will come and it will be a further reason for rejoicing.

Then he had to leave for the Border because the Scots were at their mischief again.

It was about a week after he had left when the messenger came from the Pope. Eagerly I read what he had written and I have rarely been so disappointed in my life. The Holy Father would be willing to help and could send as many as eight thousand men. He would do so as soon as the King of England embraced the Catholic Faith. Until then the Holy Father regretted that he would be unable to do anything to help.

My disappointment was so bitter, I just buried my head in the pillows and wept.

After that I suffered such a tragedy that I forgot all my anxieties about everything else.

My little Anne fell ill. She had always been the delicate one and had been troubled by a cough from her birth, but after the arrival of my son, whom we christened Henry, she seemed to grow worse.

I was with her night and day towards the end and I prayed constantly that her life might be spared to me. She was three years old and although I had lost Catherine this was not the same. Catherine had died within a few hours of her birth. She had scarcely lived at all and was just a baby to me; but Anne . . . she was my child . . . my little daughter . . . for three years I had loved and cared for her and now . . . she was dying.

She was too good for this world, I thought. I shall never forget those last moments at her bedside and in spite of everything that memory is one of the most tragic of my life. I can see her lovely little face, the gravity of it, the knowledge in the beautiful eyes that death was close.

'I cannot say my long prayer,' she said, meaning the Lord's Prayer, 'so I must say my short one.' She paused awhile to collect her breath. It was pitiful to watch her. 'Lighten mine eyes, oh Lord,' she prayed, 'lest I sleep the sleep of death.'

Then she closed her eyes and that was the end.

I flung myself down by her bed and gave myself up to bitter tears. Charles came to me and we sat together in silence for a long time. Then he took my hand and reminded me of the beautiful healthy family we had.

'We are singularly blessed,' he said, 'not only in our children but most of all in each other.'

Then we clung together almost as though some premonition had come to us that we might not always be together and we must cherish what time was left to us.

After a while we talked of Anne, and Charles said he wanted to know the cause of her death, so he ordered that there should be a post-mortem. He feared that death might have been due to some accident – perhaps a fall about which we had not been told. Our old friend, Sir Theodore Mayerne, presided over the examination which revealed that Anne had died of a suffocating catarrh with an inflammatory disposition of the lungs, accompanied by continual fever, difficulty in breathing and a constant cough.

The doctors said that she could not have lived long no matter what had been done for her.

This satisfied us in a way because we knew that we had not
failed her.

We laid her to rest in Henry VII's Chapel in Westminster Abbey
and the memory of the sweet child lingered with us to sadden our
days.

So grief-stricken had I been by the death of our little daughter
that I had temporarily forgotten the troubles which were springing up all around us.

The Scots were giving us trouble as usual and Charles said that
as he had no money there was nothing to be done but call another
parliament. I was against it. When had parliaments ever done us
any good? I assured Charles he could govern better without a
parliament.

At least I was right about that, for no sooner was the Parliament
installed – led by the odious Pym – than it acted in such a
dastardly way that even I would not have thought it capable of.

I might have seen that those men were determined to destroy
the King, and they were beginning to do this by robbing him of
his most able supporters. They were accusing Strafford of
criminal acts against the State. This was such arrant nonsense
that it made me laugh them to scorn at first; but I was wrong.
They were wily, powerful men, and they were well aware of what
they were doing.

Poor Charles was beside himself with anxiety.

'They are accusing him of treason,' he cried. 'Pym is instituting
an enquiry into Strafford's conduct in Ireland.'

'But that could only be to his credit!' I cried.

'They will say he was planning to bring over an Irish army to
England to fight against the English.'

'That's nonsense!'

'Of course it is nonsense but they are determined to bring him
down. Don't you see, they are in truth striking against *me*?'

I put my arms about him and kissed him tenderly. I assured
him that we would overcome our enemies and save Strafford
from their venom.

'We will prove them wrong,' I declared. 'We will teach a lesson
to those wicked men who are trying to work against their King.'

'My little love,' he said, 'what should I do without you?'

I often thought of that and the irony of it. I know now that he would have done so much better without me. Who knows, he might even have been saved!

Impetuous, unworldly, without even the smallest understanding of the situation, I plunged in to save him. How much better it would have been for him if I had left him to his own devices! Dear Charles, he was the best man and husband in the world. But as a King – and I must be truthful now – he was weak. He was obsessed by the desire to do right and this gave his unscrupulous enemies power over him. Moreover be believed that whatever he did *was* right because he was King. But because of this determination to choose the right course he vacillated, not taking action when he should and then hastily plunging in and doing what was unwise.

I blush now to think of the months that followed. I had always been foolish; now I added recklessness to my folly. I loved Charles so dearly, so intensely. I was not a sensual woman; my love for him was protective, almost maternal. In different circumstances I could have been a happy and contented mother, but a Queen does not have the same opportunities of being with her children as other women have. They are kept from her by a guard of nurses, governesses, rockers, servants of all sorts. Tradition placed them there and there they must be. I thought of Charles as one of my children, particularly during those days when, deprived of Strafford and fearful for him, he seemed so bewildered. I could have been perfectly happy living somewhere like Oatlands, walking with the children and Charles, listening to their chatter, watching over their meals. But that was not for me.

Now I saw my Charles in distress and I was going to do everything in my power to take the burden from him.

I tried to placate those stern men of the Parliament – those sombrely clad gentlemen, many of them with the plain round hair style which I so hated. I wrote several letters addressed to the Parliament. I apologized for my chapel at Somerset House. I told them I would be very careful only to act as was necessary. I knew that the Pope's envoy Rosetti was not approved by some of them and if it was their wish I would have him removed. If there was anything they wished me to do I should be glad to listen to it. I was grovelling and that was against my nature; and my humiliation was increased because they ignored me.

Father Philip came to me.

'Why will not the Holy Father help me?' I demanded. 'A great deal of this trouble has come about because I worked so zealously for the Holy Church.'

'You know the Holy Father's price. Charles must embrace the Catholic Faith. Let him do that and he can be assured of the Holy Father's help.'

'If he became a Catholic the Puritans would immediately depose him,' I reminded him.

Poor Father Philip! What could he say? As for me, I was beginning to see how dangerous everything was becoming. I was certain now that we must show the people that we were not fanatical Catholics, that we were quite ready to accept their allegiance to the Protestant Faith and it seemed to me that the best way of doing this was to make approaches to the Prince of Orange.

Recently he had wanted our daughter Elizabeth for his son. Although Elizabeth was a second daughter we had thought the match demeaning. The Prince of Orange was of small consequence in the world and we were the ruling family of a great country.

I said to Charles: 'They are Protestant and many have said that I was against the match because I wanted Catholic alliances for my daughters.'

'Which you did, dear heart,' replied Charles.

'Of course I did. But the Prince of Orange is very eager.' I laid my hand on his arm. 'Let us do this. Let us show the people how ready we are for a Protestant alliance. Let us give Mary – our eldest – to the son of the Prince of Orange.'

He stared at me in disbelief. Then I saw the realization of what this would mean dawn in his eyes.

Charles was a man who needed someone to rely on – Buckingham, Strafford . . . men like that. Buckingham had been despatched by the assassin's dagger and it could well be that Strafford might go by the executioner's axe. I was left to him. I might not be clever and shrewd and have little knowledge of affairs but I was more staunchly loyal to him than anyone in the world could be.

He clung to me and that made me all the more determined to do everything I could however much others might disapprove. I would do anything . . . just anything for him.

When Archbishop Laud was arrested, Father Philip and Rosetti came to me and talked very seriously about the Puritans in Parliament.

'The time has come for the King to declare his conversion to the Catholic Faith,' they said. 'Now is the moment. The Parliament is ready to rise against the King. If the King would announce his conversion, the might of the Pope would be behind him and the Parliament with its Puritans would be quickly subdued.'

'The King will never do it. He has sworn to govern the country in the Reformed Faith.'

'A man can change such an oath if he has the might of an army behind him. How many of his subjects would be ready to follow him?'

'Not so many as would be against him.'

'Let him say then that he wants liberty of conscience to think and worship as he pleases.'

'He will never do it. I will speak to him but even I could not persuade him to that.'

'They have Strafford. They have Laud. Who next?' asked Rosetti.

'I do not know,' I cried in despair.

They would be horrified when they heard of the proposed marriage with the House of Orange. But the people were not, although it did not have the impact I had hoped for.

Strafford and Laud were still in the Tower.

Of course the Prince of Orange accepted with alacrity and there was a lull in our unpopularity because of the coming marriage.

Mary's wedding should have been a wonderful occasion but it was not. Our first daughter to marry – and her husband a petty Prince! But that was not really why we were depressed.

The trial of Strafford had begun and in our hearts we knew that it was really a quarrel between the Throne and the Commons. It was King against Parliament. Charles was wretchedly unhappy. He had always been loyal to his friends and he had loved Strafford who, he knew, had been condemned not for his betrayal of his country but for his loyalty to his King.

Charles had written to him. I had been beside him as he wrote and mingled my tears and prayers with his.

'The misfortune which has fallen upon you,' wrote Charles, 'being such that I must lay by the thought of employing you hereafter in my affairs, yet I cannot satisfy myself in honour or conscience without assuring you now in the midst of your troubles, that upon the word of a King you shall not suffer in life, honour or fortune.'

We were both happier when he wrote that, for those wicked men who accused him would do their best to bring him to the scaffold, but it would be the King who would have to sign the death warrant so Strafford could not go to the block unless the King agreed to his death. 'And that,' declared Charles, 'is something I will never do.'

They had set up a great tribunal in Westminster Hall and the peers and Lord Chancellor on the Woolsack were there with the judges – and also the Commons. How I hated them in their black clothes. Cruel Roundheads, I called them.

I watched, with the King, behind a trellis. I had said that the two elder children should go with us – so Charles and Mary came. I shall never forget the intent look on the face of my serious son. Young Charles was determined to learn how to be a king. Mary was a little apprehensive. I supposed she was thinking of the young bridegroom who would soon be coming to claim his bride.

We sat there throughout the day, and at night returned to Whitehall Palace. We grew more and more depressed as the days passed. I had to do something for I could not endure inactivity.

I wrote again to the Pope. I begged him to let me have five hundred crowns for I believed that if I had this money I could bribe the members of Parliament. It was a wild idea and as soon as I had done it I regretted it and saw the folly of it. But watching those horrible Roundheads in the hall with the cruelty on their stern pale faces and knowing that they were doing their best to hound dear Strafford to his death made me desperate and I was sure that they were such villains that they would be open to bribes.

That was not the height of my stupidity. I knew that Lucy was rather interested in their Puritan doctrines. It was laughable. Lucy a Puritan! Her main preoccupation was with her gowns and her complexion. But Lucy was like that. She favoured contrasts, and oddly enough she had become quite friendly with the odious Pym.

I guessed that she was worried about the Earl of Strafford and she must be believing that Pym might help to get him released. How clever of her! Pym carried great weight in the Commons. He was their leader, and of course the best way to serve Strafford was to be friendly with men like Pym, to try to make them understand that in no way could he be called a traitor.

I told Lucy that I too would like to meet some of the Parliamentarians that I might talk to them and attempt to make them see reason.

She said it would have to be in secret.

'Could you bring them to Whitehall?' I asked.

'Well, you know I am talking to Pym quite a lot nowadays.'

'Yes, I know. You are so clever, Lucy. What could you arrange for me?'

Lucy loved intrigue. She said we could use one of the rooms in the palace. One of the ladies was away for a time so why should we not use hers? Lucy would see whom she could bring to the palace.

So there I was creeping through the corridors of Whitehall after dark, lighted by the taper I carried, meeting those men whom Lucy arranged should talk to me. They were astonished; they were overawed although they held their stupid uncurled heads high; they were respectful; they listened; but they did not commit themselves to help Strafford, which was what I wanted them to do.

I did not tell Charles what I was doing. It was unconventional and he liked to do things by order. But after a while I began to see that the operation was useless and told Lucy so. She agreed with me.

So the Strafford trial went on and, listening to it every day behind the trellis, I was certain that those men down there were going to insist on his destruction, no matter what the verdict.

But we held the trump card, I told Charles. He had promised Strafford that he would never sign the death warrant and they could not kill him without the King's authority.

That thought sustained us during those days.

Towards the end of the month our bridegroom arrived with some pomp, escorted by a fleet of twenty vessels in charge of the famous Dutch Admiral van Tromp. Charles despatched the Earl of Lindsay to welcome him in his name when they arrived at

Gravesend and in due course the Prince rode into London in the carriage Charles had sent for him. As the Prince came close to the Tower one hundred pieces of ordnance were discharged as a welcome, and it was about five o'clock in the evening when they arrived at Whitehall. Charles was worried because of the strange mood of the people, who were overexcited by the trial of Strafford and taking sides with the Parliament against the King.

It would have been disastrous if they should riot and attack our visitors, so he had ordered the guards to be out in full force – which looked like a guard of honour but which was really one of protection.

I liked the look of the young Prince. He was fifteen years old – Mary was only ten – and quite good looking. Moreover it was obvious that he was pleased by the match and it was only natural that he should be. He had the sad state of affairs in England to thank for it; it would never have been made in happier circumstances.

Mary was at Somerset House so she was not present at our first meeting and the Prince immediately asked our leave to visit her there. Charles said that the permission was readily granted and he felt sure that the Prince would want to pay his respects to the Queen Mother at St James's before making the journey to Somerset House.

The Prince bowed and said that he would first call on the Queen Mother although I knew he was all impatience to see Mary; but as Charles said to me, he thought we should be there when they met and while William was visiting St James's we could go privately and with all speed to Somerset House, which we did; and I was so pleased to see the first meeting between the young couple.

It lifted my spirits for they liked each other on sight and I knew from experience how terrifying it can be to be sent to a bridegroom whom one has never seen.

I said to Charles: 'I have one prayer to make at this moment and that is that Mary may find almost as great a happiness with her husband as I have had with mine. . . . I would say, as great, but my dearest, there can be only one most perfect husband in the world and I have already taken him.'

Charles smiled in that rather embarrassed way he had when face to face with my extravagant words and deeds, but he was greatly moved and he did say that his prayer would be worded in exactly the same way except that he would substitute wife for husband.

Whitehall chapel was prepared for the ceremony and the bridegroom appeared looking very handsome in red velvet, adorned by a collar of Vandyke point lace. Mary looked beautiful. She was somewhat simply dressed in a gown of silver tissue and her jewellery was all pearl. Her hair was tied with silver ribbons so that she gave an impression of absolute purity. I myself had chosen her dress and I was glad that I had insisted on such simplicity for I thought that, standing beside her red-velvet-clad bridegroom, she looked elegant, while the poor boy looked over dressed, *nouveau riche* . . . and to tell the truth a little crude.

I did not participate in the ceremony. How could I since it was Protestant? I sat with my mother and my daughter Elizabeth in a curtained-off gallery from which we could watch the scene below without taking part in it.

The Bishop of Ely performed the ceremony. Our Archbishop, I was reminded with a pang of fear, was a prisoner in the Tower. The King gave his daughter away and the Prince put the ring on her finger.

Then the entire company proceeded to the great chamber where the banquet was to take place. It was an impressive scene with the magnificent tapestries on which was depicted the defeat of the Spanish Armada lining the walls. How different England had been then! I reflected ruefully. How the brave men rallied to their Queen and fought for their country. And my Charles is such a *good* man. Queen Elizabeth was not always a good woman. How was it that she had bound men to her when my beloved Charles lacked the power to do so?

There followed the farcical ceremony of putting the bride and groom to bed. There was to be no consummation as Mary was too young and she would not go with her bridegroom when he left for home, but stay a little longer with her family.

My little girl was undressed, put in a night robe and lay down in the beautiful state bed adorned with blue velvet which was in my chamber. Then the Prince of Orange came in. He looked very pleasant in a robe of blue and green satin lined with silver. He was put into the bed where he kissed Mary and the two children lay there together, one at each end of the bed with a considerable distance between them. They stayed there for fifteen minutes then Prince William kissed Mary and left the bed.

The ceremony was completed. My daughter was married to the Prince of Orange.

Now we must return to the dismal way of life which we had temporarily left to celebrate the marriage.

During those dark days which followed the wedding I was constantly looking for some ray of hope. I thought I had found it when George Goring came to me with what seemed like a splendid idea.

I liked George Goring. He was the son of the Earl of Norwich and was exceptionally handsome and charming. His looks led him into temptation, however, and he was somewhat profligate and because he was so extravagant he had had to go and live frugally abroad for some time. But he had good friends – among them the Earl of Strafford – and a place was found for him in the Army where he had the rank of colonel with the command of twenty-two companies. He was shot in the leg in battle, which had resulted in his being a little lame.

When he asked for an audience I was delighted to grant it and even more delighted when he laid his plans before me.

'The trial is going against Strafford,' he said, 'and the Parliament is striking at the King through the Earl.'

I replied that I feared this was so.

'Well, Your Majesty,' said the dashing man who was about the same age as I was, 'are we going to sit back and let them lead us by the nose?'

'It is the last thing I want to do.'

'Well, we must act,' said Goring. 'The Army should be in London and the first thing to do would be to seize the Tower.'

My eyes gleamed and I clapped my hands. Action at last. Positive action. It was what I had craved for.

He talked excitedly about how he would achieve the desired effect. He would want to be made Lieutenant General of the Army. That would be essential.

I agreed that this should be.

'Madam,' he said, 'I came to you because I know what weight your word carries with the King. I knew I could be sure of your understanding and sympathy. Will you put this plan to the King?'

I said that most certainly I would and I could scarcely wait to see Charles.

When I did see him I was so excited that I began by telling him that we were going to defeat our enemies because we had the Army on our side and I would prove this to him.

He looked rather abstracted. Then he said: 'First I will tell you my news.'

'Yes, yes,' I said impatiently. 'What is it? Be quick for you will be so excited by *my* news.'

'I want to tell you of a plot which involves the Army.'

At first I thought he was talking about the same one and that George Goring must have gone to him after all. But that was not so. It seemed that there was another plot which involved four Members of Parliament – all officers of the Army – who were disturbed by the course events were taking.

'They tell me,' said Charles excitedly, 'that the Army does not like the Parliamentarians and is eager to rise against them.'

'This is wonderful,' I cried. 'Who are these men?'

'They are all in Parliament and that is significant. You know them: Henry Percy, Henry Wilmot, William Ashburton and Hugh Pollard.'

'And George Goring. . . ?'

The King looked surprised and I could contain myself no longer. 'George Goring has been to see me. He has a wonderful idea for seizing the Tower and bringing down troops from the North to take London.'

'George Goring . . . ' murmured the King. Then he turned to me, his eyes alight with hope. 'So there are two separate plots afoot. This shows well the feelings of our friends. Oh, my love, at last I see some light in the sky.'

I hugged him fiercely; then I was serious and so was he, I could see that we both had the same idea. There must not be two plots. The conspirators must join up and work together. Taking the Tower was an excellent idea; the four noble gentlemen must be informed of it.

'We shall link up the two parties,' I cried excitedly.

'With the greatest care,' replied Charles. 'You know we are

closely watched. It would not do for us to be seen with either party yet.'

'We need a go-between,' I said, my eyes sparkling.

'Someone whom we can trust. Who is the most loyal supporter we have. Jermyn, I think.'

I was very fond of Henry Jermyn. The slanders which have been uttered regarding my relationship with him are utterly false, but that does not mean I did not have a great regard for him. To be involved in these plots was dangerous and, for someone who was outside both of them and would have the delicate task of linking them up, it could be doubly dangerous.

'Not Jermyn,' I said firmly. 'He is too close to us. Any unusual movement on his part would be immediately noticed.'

'We must have someone we can trust.'

'I know, but I don't think it would be wise for Henry Jermyn to do this.'

'I think it would be most unwise to trust anyone else to do it.'

'Jermyn is *not* the man.'

'Jermyn *is* the man.'

In the past there would have been a stormy scene but we did not have those now; we were both too emotionally involved with danger and each other for quarrels. I did not want Henry Jermyn to involve himself in danger. I relied on him a good deal and he had been a great comfort to me. He was such a merry man and Charles was so sober. Of course my feelings towards Jermyn were those of a Queen to a dear friend and were quite different from my relationship with Charles.

At last I agreed that Henry Jermyn should meet both sets of conspirators and persuade them to work together. Henry willingly undertook the task but after a while he came to me and I could see that he was a little worried.

'Goring is a very ambitious man,' he said, 'and you know the King is really more in favour of the Percy and Wilmot plan to get the country to declare for the King against the Parliament. Wilmot confessed to me that he thought the capture of the Tower would prove too difficult and if it failed the entire enterprise would fail with it. Goring is not very pleased. He is set on being in command. Wilmot however wants that role for himself.'

'Oh, these petty quarrels,' I cried. 'They should forget about them at such a time.'

I thought they had, for Goring gave way to Wilmot and went to Portsmouth to make preparations as we had decided.

It was Lucy who broke the news to me. She was very well informed of what was going on and I talked to her a great deal, although Charles had warned me not to mention the Army Plot to anyone . . . simply not anyone . . . and I had obeyed him in this.

I knew by her face as soon as I saw her that something dramatic had happened. I cried: 'What is it? What is it?'

'There has been a plot,' she told me. 'The Army is involved. They planned to take the Tower and march on London.'

I felt my heart beating wildly as the colour drained from my face. 'A . . . a plot?' I stammered.

'Yes . . . against the Parliament. Wilmot is one involved, with Percy.'

'No!' I cried.

'This will decide the case against Strafford.'

'Why Strafford? He has nothing to do with it.'

'He is against the Parliament and for the King.'

'I . . . I don't understand.'

'John Pym spoke in the House about it. He has all the details and a list of the conspirators.'

I thought: Can we never succeed? Then I thought of Henry Jermyn whom I had allowed to become involved. They would be called traitors . . . all of them and I knew what sort of death awaited traitors. I was sick with fear and worry and while we were talking a guard come to the door of the apartment.

'Your Majesty,' he said with his usual respect, 'I have orders that no one shall leave the palace.'

'Does that include the Queen?' I asked ironically.

'My orders were no one, Madam.'

'Young man,' I said. 'I am the daughter of Henri Quatre, the great King of France. He never fled in danger nor am I about to.'

The guard looked ashamed and murmured that he must obey his superior officers.

'I do not blame you,' I told him. 'It is your masters who will have to pay for this.'

There was one thought in my head. I must get a message to Henry Jermyn. He must get away quickly as, of course, must all the conspirators.

I smuggled a message out to him and was relieved when I

heard that he had already left London and was on his way to Portsmouth to warn Goring of what had happened. They would have no alternative but to leave the country and from Portsmouth they would have a good opportunity of doing so.

Meanwhile I remained at Whitehall but I did see that it was dangerous for me to stay there. The best plan would be for me to leave secretly and to make my way to Portsmouth. If I could get there and across to France I could see my brother and perhaps raise money and gather an army to fight for Charles.

I think I might have got away for the guards had now been withdrawn. I had gathered together my jewels and a few things and arranged for the coach to be ready, but just as I was about to leave, the French ambassador arrived at the palace. He regarded me with some dismay when he saw that I was on the verge of departure.

'Your Majesty cannot leave now,' he cried. 'That would be disastrous.'

'How can I stay here? The people are murmuring against me. It is not safe for me . . . my mother or my children.'

'Nevertheless to go now would be the worst thing possible. Do you know what is happening?'

I covered my face with my hands. 'I only know that everything we do results in failure. I have to get away. I have to find money and men. I must save the King.'

'Your Majesty, the Army Plot was betrayed to the Parliament by George Goring.'

'George Goring! No! Never!'

'That is so. He wanted to be in command and there was conflict with Wilmot on this issue – so to take his revenge he informed against the plotters.'

'I cannot believe it.'

'Whether Your Majesty does or not it is true,' he said. 'The conspirators have escaped to France. I will say this for Goring. He let Jermyn go . . . Jermyn came to warn him that the plot was betrayed and, not knowing who the traitor was, urged Goring to get away quickly. Goring could have arrested Jermyn on the spot but apparently he had enough decency to desist from that.'

'And Jermyn?' I asked anxiously.

'Is safely on his way to Rome.'

'I thank God for that.'

'And, Madam, do you know what is being said about you and Jermyn?'

'I know people will tell any lies about me.'

'They are saying that he is your lover. If you fled now and joined him and the others what is now speculation would be taken as certainty.'

'Oh, the wickedness of it!' I cried. 'How dare they!'

'They would dare much,' said stern Montreuil, 'and I beg you to give them no more cause to do so. Some of your ladies have been questioned and they speak of nocturnal visits to meet men of the Parliament.'

'It was to persuade them to help the Earl of Strafford.'

'The actions of a Queen who made midnight assignations with various men could be misconstrued.'

'I never heard such nonsense. I am the King's loyal wife and subject.'

'We know, Madam, and those close to you have no doubt of it. But a queen must not only be beyond reproach but be seen to be, and your behaviour has scarcely been restrained.'

'This is no time for restraint. It is time for action. Oh, why is everyone against me!'

'That is untrue. As your brother's ambassador I am here to serve you and I can do that best by giving you the truth.'

He had gained his point. I knew that I must stay for a while yet.

That very day news came. The revelation of the Army Plot had decided them. Strafford was found guilty – among other charges – of attempting to bring an army over from Ireland to fight the English.

He was sentenced to death.

I know that Charles has been blamed for what happened next and I know too that he had no alternative but to do it.

What terrible days they were! They marked the beginning of the débâcle.

The King came to Whitehall. He was strained and more unhappy than I had ever seen him. His thoughts were all for Strafford. He had loved that man, and I had been fond of him too. Neither of us could bear to contemplate what would happen to him.

'He must not die,' Charles said again and again. 'I have promised him that he shall not die.'

'You are the King,' I reminded him. 'You will refuse to sign the
death warrant and they cannot kill him without that. You are still
the King, remember, though these miserable Puritans try to
pretend otherwise.'

'No,' said Charles firmly, 'I shall not sign the death warrant.'

London was afire with the desire to see Strafford's head
severed from his body. Why did the common people love such
sights? Was it because those whom they had envied might now
be envying them since, in spite of lack of wealth and standing,
they at least had life. Perhaps. But in any case the mob was
howling for Strafford's blood.

There were rumours coming from every direction. Some said
the French fleet had seized the Channel Islands. That made them
curse me . . . and my mother. Poor Mother, what a choice she
had made when she insisted on coming to England!

The night that followed was one of the most terrifying of my
life. The shouts and screams of the mob can reduce even the most
brave to fear; it is the sound of those who are like baying animals
intent on destroying their prey; there is no reasoning; there is
nothing but the desire to inflict pain and torture on those whom
they have decided to attack.

The wicked scandals about me, the accusations against that
good man, the King, the demand for Strafford's blood, when all
he had done was be a loyal statesman – all these were excuses
those blood-crazed men and women had fed to themselves. If
they had had any power to think and paused awhile to do so they
must have seen them as false. But the very thin layer of civiliz-
ation had been broken apart and they had emerged like animals
in a jungle hunt. They were worse. Animals hunt for food; they
hunted just for the lust of revenge on those who had enjoyed
what they thought of as the luxuries of life. How I hated them!
The feeble-minded, unwashed, envious bloodthirsty dregs of the
human race.

They were clamouring at the gates of Whitehall. I could
vaguely hear the shouts of 'Justice! Execution.' Justice! What
justice was there for a good man like Strafford? Execution? Yes.
They wanted blood. Strafford was to appease them first. They
were like hungry wolves following a sleigh. Throw out Strafford

so that we can feed on him. That will satisfy us . . . for a time.

Catholics were crowding into my chapel to pray, for they saw this as something more than the mob's fury against Strafford. My name was bandied about too freely for their peace of mind. Some of them collected their valuables and were making efforts to get to the coast.

I sent a messenger to Pym, as the leader of the Commons, asking him for protection. Lucy helped me. She professed friendship with Pym and he must have been rather flattered by the attention of such a beautiful lady of the Court. I knew of her relationship with Strafford and I was sorry for her, guessing what she would be suffering now.

Pym's answer was that I should prepare to leave the country for that was the only way I could be safe.

Charles arrived at Whitehall. The people did not hate him so much. If he would sign Strafford's death warrant doubtless they would cheer him.

He was distraught.

'What can I do?' he cried. 'Strafford has been loyal to me. He was my friend . . . my good friend. I have promised him that although it may be necessary to remove him from his post, I will never let him die.'

We clung together. He stroked my hair. 'This is a sorry state of affairs,' he murmured. 'It grieves me that I have brought you to this.'

'You brought me only happiness,' I told him. 'Always remember that.'

Then we sat together, holding hands and in a way comforting each other.

'Whatever happens,' said Charles, 'you and I have known such a happy life together as few people experience.'

It was true and it was wonderful how, even with the mob howling at the gates, we could feel a certain happiness as long as we were together.

Suddenly there was a quietness from without and Charles sent one of the guards to see what was happening. What they had to tell made me shiver with horror. Someone in the mob had said that the Queen Mother was the real culprit. Nothing had gone well since she had come to England. She even had a malevolent effect on the weather.

'To St James's!' they had cried.

I buried my face in my hands. I would have been glad if my mother had left England but she was still my mother and I loved her in a way. I could not bear the thought of her being subjected to humiliation. It was true she had meddled: she had tried to make Catholics of the children; she had urged me to take a strong line with those who had gone against me and perhaps I had been influenced by her; she had openly flouted her adherence to the Catholic Church and her contempt for that of the Protestants; she so often forgot that she was a guest in this country and she had cost Charles a great deal of money by keeping an establishment for which she could not afford to pay. Yet she was my mother.

And the younger children were with her at St James's. Only Charles was with us at Whitehall and Mary was at Somerset House.

The long night seemed as though it would never end. Charles and I sat hand in hand hardly speaking, worn out with exhaustion but unable to sleep.

In the morning several of the bishops called on Charles.

'There is nothing to be done other than sign the death warrant,' they said. 'The people have made up their minds that they want Strafford's blood.'

'I cannot do it,' Charles insisted. 'I have given my word.'

'My lord,' said one of the bishops, 'there comes a time when certain action must be taken. It is better for one man to die than thousands.'

'Thousands . . . ' echoed Charles.

'The people are in an angry mood. I fear they would attack the palace first.'

'My wife . . . my children . . . ' cried Charles.

'My lord, none of them is safe. It is Strafford's blood they want. He is a symbol. If you refuse to sign the death warrant you are going against Parliament for they have passed the sentence. To refuse to sign it is defiance against Parliament.'

'I do defy them. I will not sign away the life of a man who has shown me nothing but friendship and loyalty.'

The Bishops were dismayed. 'We fear the consequences. They will break into the palace. The Queen. . . .' They looked at me solemnly. 'The people murmur all the time against the Queen.'

I looked at Charles and saw the frank terror in his face. It was fear for me and the children.

He said: 'Give me time . . . time . . . ' And I knew that he was wavering.

The Bishops left and Charles turned to me. 'What am I going to do?' he cried in despair. 'You are in danger. The children. . . .'

I said: 'Charles, you must not think of me. You must do what is right.'

'How could I not think of you? I would do anything . . . anything rather than that harm should come to you.'

Then we kissed tenderly and were silent for a long time. His resolution was wavering. He was going to give them what they wanted, not out of fear for himself – he was the bravest man on earth – but because he dreaded what they would do to me. I think we both remembered that queens had been beheaded before. Worse still, if I fell into the hands of the mob, they would tear me to pieces before the judges could condemn me.

Our son came to us. He was very grave for he was fully aware of what was going on. Young Charles had always been pre-cocious. He looked at his father questioningly and the King said: 'They are crying for Strafford's blood. How can I sacrifice one who has served me so loyally?'

Our son surveyed us solemnly and I thought how serious and kingly he looked – tall, commanding even at his age – he was eleven years old but already looked like a king. His dark rather saturnine looks gave him an air of authority. He was the sort of child whom none could ignore.

The King said: 'My son, you shall take a message to the House of Lords. I will appeal to their sense of justice. It will be our last attempt to save the Earl of Strafford.'

Young Charles was eager to play his part in the drama and all night the King and I sat up drafting the letter which our son would take. We were sure he could not be ignored and would attract sympathy by his very youth.

In the morning young Charles put on robes of state and took his seat in the House of Lords. There was I heard a stir of interest as he entered and I could imagine that gravity, that kingly dignity which was so impressive in one so young.

He presented the letter. If the matter had not gone so far it might have had some effect. But it was too late and our last attempt failed.

The King was deeply moved to receive a letter from Strafford himself. Strafford realized what was at stake. He could perhaps see more clearly than I or the King. He knew that this struggle was between the King and the Parliament and there was still time to save the country from civil war. The Parliament had decided on his death; if the King did not agree to accept their verdict they would rise up against him and try to destroy all that the monarchy stood for. Strafford must have seen that, and loyal subject that he was to King and country, he released the King from his promise.

Charles was deeply moved and I think that helped him to his decision. All next day the people were filling the streets. They made for Whitehall and St James's. The situation was becoming very dangerous.

I had been urging Charles not to give way but now I saw that if he did not it would be the end of us all. I thought of my mother, my children, the King himself . . . and my commonsense told me that Strafford would have to go.

Charles was beside himself with grief. He had given his word to Strafford, but Strafford had released him from his promise. He believed in his heart, though, that the King would never agree to his execution.

'You have done all you could,' I reminded Charles. 'No one could have done more.'

The King nodded. 'But I gave my word. Perhaps . . . I should keep it.'

'At what cost?' I asked. 'Your children . . . me. . . .'

'Don't,' he begged. 'I could not bear life if you were harmed.'

'We must be reasonable, Charles. I was fond of Strafford. I know he was our loyal friend . . . but many lives are at stake.'

He embraced me. He was calm and cold and I knew he was thinking of me and the children.

Then he said slowly: 'There is no other way out. I must sign.'

Strafford's execution was fixed for the next day – the twelfth of May – a day I shall never forget. Charles insisted on knowing what Strafford had said when he understood that Charles had signed the death warrant.

Charles never got over it. I am sure to the last he remembered

Strafford and in his mind's eye saw the man whom he had tried to save being given the news that the King had betrayed him – for that was how Charles saw it and would not see it otherwise, however much I pointed out to him that it was not betrayal for Strafford himself had advised him to do it. But he heard that Strafford had murmured: 'Put not your trust in princes.' Poor man, he must have been overwrought. Not so much for himself but wondering about his family.

He had sent a message to Archbishop Laud, who was also lodged in the Tower, to be at his window as he passed and give him his blessing. Laud was there, and blessed him as he passed and then fell fainting to the floor as Strafford went on to the scaffold on Tower Hill.

Crowds came to see the deed, and there was a hushed silence when he raised his hand and spoke to them.

There were plenty to tell us what he had said and this was the gist of it.

'I had always believed parliaments in England to be the happy constitution of the kingdom and the nation and the best means under God to make the King and his people happy. Do not let the beginning of the people's happiness be written in letters of blood.'

There was a warning there, but the people would not see it.

He died nobly as would be expected of such a man, refusing to have his eyes bound and asking for a moment of respite to say a silent prayer, promising that when he had prayed he would lift his hand as a sign to the executioner to wield the axe.

Thus he died and so ended the troubles of his earthly life.

Ours were just beginning.

The Spy

When I went to see my mother she was in a state of panic. She had faced the fury of the people of her own country so was no stranger to unpopularity which was reaching danger point.

'I must get away,' she said. 'I must leave this country. I tell you this, Henriette. I picture those people storming the palace. They would have no respect for queens. I did not think this could happen here. I had thought you were well settled. These people are barbarians. They hate the King. They hate you. And it seems that most of all they hate me. Savages! Like uncivilized people they turn on those who are foreigners to them.'

'They turned on Strafford,' I reminded her. 'He was no foreigner. And yes, dear mother, I think you should go . . . if that is possible.'

'You should come with me, my dear.'

'And leave Charles!'

'Come with me. Perhaps we could go to France.'

'My brother would not welcome us.'

'Shame on him! His own mother and sister!'

'He is first of all King of France.'

'He has no mind of his own. Between Richelieu and that wife of his. . . . She gives herself airs now that she has produced the heir to the throne. *Mon Dieu*, she took long enough to do it.'

'Charles thinks that no hindrance would be put in the way of your going.'

'Then I shall leave as soon as possible.'

'I have thought of something. We have a new ally now in the Prince of Orange. This marriage might not have been so degrading after all. I know that Orange has little standing in Europe, but he is very rich. It may be that he will help to raise an army for us and I could bring it back to stand with the King's. And then we could make war on these Puritan Parliamentarians and let them see who is the master here . . . they or their anointed King.'

'It is a good idea. I want to leave as soon as possible. I shall never sleep peacefully in my bed until I am out of this country.'

I said that I would consult Charles. 'He would not want me to go,' I added. 'He would hate my being out of the country.'

Oh come,' said my mother impatiently, 'you talk as though he is a passionate bridegroom and you plan your honeymoon.'

'Our being together is a long honeymoon. There is no restriction that I know of as to how long they shall last.'

My mother lifted her shoulders in exasperation. She was not the sort of woman to understand love like ours.

I left her then and when I saw Charles I told him what was in my mind. He always listened to what I had to say with as much attention – no more – than he listened to his ministers.

'Mary is too young for the consummation but the Prince of Orange is urging us to send her to Holland. Why should she not go? She will be safer there than here. I can take her . . . perhaps travel with my mother . . . and then I could say that I am going to the spa in Lower Lorraine because I am in poor health. Of course I should not go there, but be in Holland and perhaps try to see my brother. Who knows? If he were actually face to face with me he might not be able to refuse my pleas for help.'

On consideration Charles thought it a good idea.

'We should be separated in any case,' he said, 'as I have to go to Scotland.'

'Scotland again!'

'I plan to placate them, to give them what they want and to enlist their help against those in England who are against me.'

I clasped my hands. Any new project filled me with hope even though, had I pondered more intently, I might see that it was doomed to failure befire it began. But my nature was such that as long as I was feverishly putting some plot into action I could see nothing but success. Charles was a little like that too. Perhaps that was why we plunged into wild schemes without giving them due thought.

When Parliament heard that my mother was planning to leave they gave their wholehearted permission for her to go. No one could have said more clearly: Good riddance. They even helped her on her way by giving her a sum of money for the journey.

As to my leaving, they were very suspicious about that.
Naturally they suspected my trip to the Continent had been
arranged for a purpose other than my health. They were insulting. They gave orders that my jewels were not to be taken out of
the country and they instructed Sir Theodore Mayerne to
examine me and decide whether the waters of a foreign spa were
necessary to preserve my health.

Old Mayerne could be one of the most irritating men I knew. Of
course he was a Huguenot and not very sympathetic towards the
Catholic cause. I think he looked upon me as a wayward child. He
could not bring himself to say that my health would be endangered if I did not take the waters. I was annoyed with him when I
heard what he had reported and the verdict was that I was not to
be allowed to leave the country.

I raged at Mayerne, who surveyed me sardonically. I could not
threaten to dismiss him from the royal service. He was too
valuable for that and Charles would never have agreed. He
admired Mayerne as the best doctor in Europe and he had
often said that his frankness was symbolic of his nature. 'He
is incapable of dissembling,' said Charles, 'and those are the sort
of people we need about us, those who tell the truth for its
own sake and do not suppress it out of fear or in the hope of
favour.'

So I had to accept his judgement, knowing of course that it was
the truth. But I stormed at him. I had suffered a great deal during
the uncertainty over Strafford and I was worried every hour of
the day for our future.

'I am afraid I shall go mad,' I said to Mayerne, at which he
looked at me steadily.

'You need have no fear,' he replied, 'for you already are.'

I could not help laughing at him. What a way for a subject to
speak to his sovereign! But he did not see me as a queen. In his
opinion I was an hysterical overwrought woman who was either
imagining or pretending she suffered from ailments which would
be cured in a foreign spa.

So with Charles in Scotland and my mother on the way to
Antwerp, I went to Oatlands. There I would work out how I
could get Mary to Holland and accompany her; and even if I were
not allowed to leave the country it would be better for Mary to go.
She would be much safer in Holland.

I was trying to find a little peace while I waited for Charles to return. If he could please the Scots, if he could get them on his side, who knew, we might put an end to this miserable Parliament. Parliaments had always caused trouble. I agreed with Charles that a king had been chosen by Divine Right to rule and surely that should be enough without parliaments interfering. They always caused trouble. Why could they not leave us in peace?

But they could not . . . even at Oatlands. Word was sent to me that the Prince of Wales was visiting me too frequently and that I was endeavouring to instruct him in the Catholic Faith.

My reply to that was that the King had chosen his governor and I was well aware that it was not the King's will that any of our children should be brought up in the Catholic Faith.

That had to satisfy them, but an extraordinary thing did happen while I was at Oatlands. One day the local magistrate came to me and asked to see me in private. I saw him at once and he told me that he had received an order from Parliament to get together all the militia of the district and bring them to Oatlands by midnight. They would be met by a company of cavalry officers and would be told what was expected of them.

'I came to Your Majesty,' said the magistrate, 'because I feared that it was a plot against you and I would have you know that it is my desire to serve Your Majesty with my life.'

I was always deeply moved by such expressions of loyalty and I thanked the magistrate warmly. I told him that there might well be a plot to capture me or my children . . . all of us perhaps. 'I have many enemies, my friend,' I said. 'They are those grim-faced men who think they are holier than God Himself. We have many of them in Parliament, I fear, and they plan to do me a mischief. I thank you for your warning. Now I shall be ready.'

And I was ready. The day passed quickly and I was exhilarated in spite of everything, because immediate action was demanded. I saw that everyone in the house was armed. Then we waited for nightfall and the assault.

It did not come.

I wondered why because I was sure of the integrity of the magistrate and he swore he had received the instructions he had explained.

I could only think that whoever had planned it had got wind of the loyalty of the magistrate and his men and did not want to meet opposition.

But the incident did make me feel that I ought to make plans to get away; and if they would not sanction my departure I must leave secretly.

Plotting, discarding plans, discussing the matter endlessly with Lucy who, I felt, was the only one I could really trust, planning for the horses I should need on the road to Portsmouth . . . all this made time pass quickly.

I decided I would leave Oatlands for Hampton Court for word had come to me that Charles was on his way home. At Hampton I could meet some of the most influential men in the country and I hoped to persuade them to stand with the King.

It was wonderful when Charles arrived at Hampton. We clung together for a long time as though we would never let each other go. The children were there too and they had their share of affection. But for Charles I was the one who meant most to him and so it was with him in my affections.

We talked and talked. The trip to Scotland had not been a success but that did not seem to matter as long as we were together again.

Quite a number of people came to Hampton to welcome the King and it was like old times and, ever ready to hope, I told myself all was going to be well again.

We were going to make a triumphant return to Whitehall. Some of our friends told us that there would be a civic welcome for us. The people were delighted because my mother had gone and that was a great source of irritation removed; the Papal envoy had left; the King had returned from Scotland without that army of Scotsmen which it was feared he might bring with him.

'Our troubles are over,' said the hopeful ones; and of course I was ready to believe them.

And then this unfortunate thing happened. We were all standing at a window looking out – the King, the children, myself and one or two of our friends – when a gypsy came up and asked for money. She had a basket on her arm; she was bent and deformed and such a strange sight that some of our party began to laugh at her.

There was a general titter. I did not like it because I never laughed at people's deformities. I had my dwarfs, it was true, but

I always treated them with the respect due to normal human beings. It was not their stunted growth which appealed to me but that I saw a certain beauty in them and they were such good servants. *I* was not one who laughed at the gypsy.

She looked up at us and her face was malevolent, evil. I drew back for I saw that her eyes were fixed on the King and myself as well as our children.

She took out a hand mirror from her basket and handed it to the King.

'I don't want it,' he said.

'Look into it,' she commanded, 'and see what you can see.'

The King looked at it and I who was close, looked too. I gave a little shriek. The King had turned pale. Others crowded round and looked into the mirror but they could only see their own faces and that was all I could see now, but just for a few seconds I had seen something else . . . and so had the King.

The mirror had shown us the King's head . . . without his body.

I was almost fainting. The King had put an arm about me and I heard the cackle of the gypsy.

'Did you like what you saw, my lord, my lady? You should give me money. You should always treat the gypsies well or they might show you what it is better for you not to see.'

'Give the woman money,' said the King.

It was thrown down to her. She picked it up and put it in her basket. She took the mirror which had been given back to her. She said: 'In that room in which you stand another will be sleeping. He has a dog with him. That dog will die . . . and when he dies the kingdom will come back to the King.'

With that she hobbled away leaving the company twittering with excitement and myself almost fainting in my husband's arms.

He said I needed to rest and he took me to our apartment in the palace.

'It was terrible,' I gasped.

'It was an illusion,' he replied. 'How could something which was not there be seen in the mirror?'

'We both saw it,' I reminded him.

'It could not have been so,' he replied.

Then he tried to comfort me with the good news that the people of London were giving us a welcome.

'They have changed towards us,' he said. 'Those who were shrieking outside the palace are now going to receive us with affection.'

'Can we trust those who change so quickly?'

'They had what they wanted. Strafford dead . . . and your mother gone. They will love us again, you will see.'

'I do not trust such fickle love,' I said.

Then he held me fast and thanked God that we were together again.

The weather was cold but there was a new warmth in my heart as we rode side by side into Moorgate where the Mayor and aldermen were waiting to greet us. We were presented with two richly caparisoned horses and a golden coach. The Mayor told us that the horses were for the King and the Prince of Wales and the coach for me and the younger children.

Charles was so delighted that he knighted the Mayor and the Recorder on the spot and when this pleasant ceremony was over, the merchants of the city crowded round to kiss the King's hand.

My two Charleses mounted the horses which had been presented to them and with the children I stepped into the coach and we drove down to the Guildhall.

I had not been so happy for a long time as I was when I rode through those streets under the fluttering banners and the strips of cloth of gold which they had put up to welcome us.

My husband and son looked so noble on their magnificent horses. I wondered how any could turn against them for the sake of those ugly roundheaded creatures with their black clothes and miserable faces.

There was a sumptuous banquet for us at the Guildhall and the city dignitaries had brought out the gold plate which they only did on the most important occasions.

What a welcome! It showed the mood of the people. We had only had to sacrifice Strafford – which I knew still worried Charles – and get rid of my mother, who had been one of the main causes of our unpopularity. It was a pity that she had ever come. Well, she had gone now. She would be in Antwerp. I hoped she was not making trouble there.

All was going to be well. We must be strong. We must stand

firm. I would talk to Charles about that. Dear good man that he was, he was too lenient, too ready to believe the best of everyone.

At last we arrived at Whitehall, tired but jubilant.

All was going to be well in the end.

I talked to Charles that night when we were alone. He had ideas. He was going to dismiss the guards which the Parliament had set up in Westminster to look after the Houses of Parliament.

'Their guards will go,' he said. 'Mine will be there. I know you think I give way too easily, but I have not been idle. There are men loyal to me in the kingdom and they have their own trained bands. They shall guard the Houses of Parliament.'

I clasped my hands in pleasure. 'That is excellent,' I said.

'Of course,' went on Charles, 'they won't like it. Men like Pym will have their suspicions.'

'Let them,' I cried. 'We'll make sure that our guards are loyal.'

'I wish that I could arrest certain members of the Parliament. They should be impeached for their disloyalty to the crown.'

'Why not?' I asked excitedly.

'I am unsure,' he answered.

'Which would you arrest? Pym for sure, I would say.'

'Certainly Pym; Hampden is another. Then there are Holles, Strode, Haselrig. . . . They are the ones I most distrust. If we could be rid of them we might make some headway in Parliament.'

'You must arrest them.'

'I will think of it.'

'Soon,' I whispered.

Then he lifted me in his arms and said it was time we went to bed.

I could not sleep much. I was thinking of the wonderful reception which the city of London had given us. It was often said that if London was with you, the whole country would be.

It was changing. Perhaps the panic had been unnecessary and we had feared too much, become too nervous, let ourselves be led by fear.

I must keep Charles to his resolution. He would achieve much if he could take those men by surprise. If he could ride into the House of Commons with guards to arrest them, they could be put

into prison before they realized what was happening; and once
they were there it should not be difficult to make the people see
that they were a menace to peace.

He must do it. He must.

I knew he would waver. He was always tormented by his fear
that he might not be doing what was right. This was right . . .
absolutely right. What had they done to dear good noble
Strafford? Murder. Judicial murder if they liked, but murder
nevertheless. They should all go to the block for that alone.

I could scarcely wait for morning.

Charles was thoughtful. He was pondering on the enormity of
what he proposed to do. It was coming into the open, he said. So
far, although it had been in people's minds, no one had mentioned yet that such divided opinion in the country was heading
towards civil war. That was a prospect which should make
anyone who wished the country well pause and think.

Now Charles was pausing and thinking.

I urged him; I persuaded him; I hinted that to let such an
opportunity pass was cowardice as well as folly. If he did not
grasp this chance and use it to advantage he could not blame
anyone but himself if he had to fight for his kingdom.

He looked at me with horror and I cried out: 'Yes, I keep my
eyes and ears open. I keep myself alert . . . for you. I cannot stand
by and see you lose your kingdom. Dearest Charles, you must act
. . . now. This is the time. Let this go and you may not have
another opportunity.'

At last he made his decision. He knew that he would not be
able to face me if he did not make the attempt.

He was ready. He was going to do it. I embraced him feverishly. 'I am so proud of you, my King,' I said. 'Everything is going
to change now. This is the turning point.'

He whispered to me. 'I will go now. If one hour passes without
your receiving ill news of me, you will see me when I return
master of my kingdom.'

I bade him farewell. 'My heart goes with you,' I said.

'I will be back,' he told me. 'Give me one hour.'

I don't think I have ever known an hour take so long to pass. I
could not stop myself glancing at my watch every few minutes.
Lucy was sitting with me. 'You are restless this morning,
Madam,' she said.

'No . . . no . . . Lucy. Not restless.'

'Well, I declare this is the third time you have looked to see the time . . . and all in the last five minutes.'

'Oh . . . you are mistaken,' I said and she smiled and spoke of other things.

When I remember that morning, I am so ashamed. I curse my folly, my stupidity . . . my blindness. Why could I not see what was right under my nose? The burden of guilt becomes intolerable when I look back.

At last the hour was over. Now! I thought. It is done. At this moment those men are under arrest. Everyone is going to see that the King is indeed the King. He will brook no interference from a set of miserable sly-faced scheming Puritans.

I jumped up. I could contain myself no longer. Lucy was beside me. 'Something ails you, I know. It has been worrying you this last hour.'

'I am not worried . . . not any more,' I cried. 'It is time for rejoicing. I have every reason to hope that the King is now master of his realm. Pym and his confederates will have been arrested by now.'

Lucy stared at me. 'Is that so?' she said. 'Has the King gone to the House of Commons to arrest them?'

'He has indeed.'

'Then there is every reason to congratulate the King. I am going to bring a little wine so that we can drink a toast to him.'

'Do that, Lucy,' I said.

She ran out of the room. I was astonished that she did not return. But I was too excited to bother very much. I went to the window and stood there waiting.

I waited for a long time.

The King eventually returned . . . dejected. Then I heard the terrible news.

The arrests had not taken place. Pym and his friends had been warned of what was about to happen and had fled, so that when the King with his guards entered the House of Commons, they had already left.

Charles was desolate. It seemed that fate was against us. Who could have warned them? There had been so few of us who knew what was planned.

'There is a spy close to us,' I said.

'I fear so,' replied the King. He went on to tell me that he had been delayed when he was about to enter the House of Commons. 'You know what it is like when I go to the Parliament. They are lying in wait for me. They all have some grievance, some petition to present. I must stay and listen to them. They are my subjects. I did not worry about the loss of time because I thought that only you and I shared the secret. So I was late going into the House. I believe they had left but a few minutes before.'

'But how . . . why . . . ?'

'Someone knew and warned them.'

'But who could?'

He looked at me sadly. 'You did not mention the matter?'

'Only to Lucy . . . and that after the hour had passed.'

'But Lucy Carlisle has become Pym's mistress.'

'Oh . . . *mon Dieu.*' I felt sick with horror. 'Lucy? Not Lucy. She is friendly with Pym. She finds out what she can from those devious Parliamentarians so that she can tell us, help us. . . .'

'It may be,' said Charles sombrely, 'that she talks to you and passes on to them what they want to know.'

'You can't mean that Lucy. . . .'

'I was told that a messenger went to Pym. He came from her.'

'I will send for her immediately.'

I did so, but Lucy was not in the palace.

'What did you tell her?' asked the King.

'Nothing . . . until the hour was up. Then I asked her to rejoice with me because you were master of your realm for you had gone to arrest those trouble-makers and the deed was now done.'

'Within an hour! It must have been a good half an hour later before I was able to get into the House. Time enough for her to warn Pym . . . which she did.'

I covered my face with my hands.

'Oh Charles,' I cried, 'I have destroyed your plan! I, who would give my life for you, have destroyed you.'

But he wouldn't hear of it. He tried to comfort me. He told me it was unimportant. All that mattered was that I loved him. We would forget this disaster.

'But it was *my* fault. You may forgive me but I shall never forgive myself.'

He rocked me in his arms as though I were a baby and I

marvelled at this love for me and that he should care so deeply for one whose folly had dealt him such a blow.

What could I do to convince him of my love for him, to show my gratitude for his forgiveness of my folly? What could I ever do to show him how much I loved him?

I longed for an opportunity to die for his sake. But such opportunities do not come.

We did not at first realize how disastrously we – or rather I – had mismanaged that affair. The King's intention was now known and our little flush of popularity was over. It seemed that everyone was turning against us. No, that was not true. There were some faithful friends. Lord Digby for one suggested taking a company of his cavaliers and pursuing Pym and the rest, and when he had found them putting them under restraint. Perhaps that would have been the best thing to do. However, the King forbade it.

At least we were now shown who were our true friends. I was bewildered and quite stunned by Lucy's perfidy though when I looked back over the last years I can see that a wiser person than I might have guessed. Her friendship with Pym should have told me. How could I have been such a fool as to imagine that she was feigning that interest in him and his affairs for the sake of me! What hurt me more than Lucy's unfaithfulness was the fact that I had been the one to foil Charles's plans. Sometimes it seems to me that no one could have worked more indefatigably against him than I who loved him and would have died for him.

But as I said we sorted out the good friends from the false. Men like the Earl of Holland and the Earl of Essex made excuses to retire from Court and in my newly found wisdom I knew what that meant.

We became really alarmed when the mobs started to roam the streets. They carried placards on which was written the one word: Liberty. I did not know what they meant by that. Did they think they would have greater liberty under the stern Parliamentarians' Puritan rule than they did under that of the King?

My mother was gone; the Pope's envoy was gone. What did they want of us now?

Charles was afraid for me because it was against me that the might of their venom was turned. He thought it better for us to leave Whitehall and we prepared to go.

It was a terrible journey. We sat there in the gilded coach which had so recently carried us through cheering crowds and as we went, faces looked in at us . . . frightening faces, hating, leering, threatening . . . I knew not what.

How glad I was to leave Westminster behind and come to the green fields surrounding Hampton but the mansion itself, although always beautiful and a place I had especially loved, now held memories of a wild-eyed gypsy holding a mirror to our eyes.

When we entered it seemed dark and unwelcoming. No one came out to attend to the carriage. Our guards helped us to alight and the air struck cold as we entered. There were no fires to greet us and no apartments had been made ready.

All through the night the King and I, with our three children Charles, Mary and James, shivered in one room.

'At least,' I said to Charles, 'we are all together.'

'We cannot stay here,' he replied. 'Tomorrow we will leave for Windsor.'

This we did and what a comfort it was to see the beautiful castle, which looked so strong and royal that there seemed a special significance in it at this time. I was so glad to escape from the cold unwelcoming ambience of Hampton, which I felt I could never really like again whatever happened.

'We must be prepared,' said the King. 'Pym and his friends know that I would have impeached them. They will do every-thing they can to raise the country against me. It is going to be a matter of deciding between the King and the Parliament. I put my faith in my loyal subjects.'

'There are countless numbers of them,' said Denbigh. 'We will call them together. They will all understand the menace of the Puritans.'

I said: 'We must raise money and I am the best one to do that. I am sure that I could persuade my brother to help us if I could only see him.'

They looked at me expectantly and I was thinking: If only I could do something really wonderful! If only I could make up for this terrible thing I have done. I was sure that they all blamed me for the position in which we now found ourselves. The arrest of those ringleaders would have stemmed the tide against us.

Charles was the only one who tried to pretend that it was not so very important.

I was desperate to show him what I would do for him.

It seemed to be a good idea. Help was desperately needed. The Pope's conditions were too harsh. In exchange for helping Charles to keep his throne the Holy Father was demanding that he act in such a manner as could not end in anything but his losing it. The people of England would never accept a Catholic king. I knew that now. Our friends did not forget for one moment that I was the sister of the King of France and, although they did not expect altruism from Louis, they knew that he would not want to see a monarch deposed. There was a possibility, therefore, that he would give aid, and who better to plead for it than his sister?

I rather pinned my hopes on the Prince of Orange. He was so delighted to have secured our Princess that he might be willing to give money or arms. I warmed to the project. I would go to Holland on the pretext that I was taking my daughter to her husband.

'The Parliament did not agree to your leaving the country before,' Denbigh pointed out.

'I will leave this time with their permission or without it and I will take valuables with me so that I can barter for what we need.'

The King looked at me with pride. He said: 'I shall have to go to Hull, so we should be separated in any case. At Hull there is the store of ammunition which is in readiness for attacking the Scots. If I can secure that I shall be ready to face my enemies if need be.'

This then was to be our plan. The King would go to Hull so that if necessary he would have the means to fight. In the meantime with or without Parliament's permission I would take my daughter to Holland.

'We should first wait for permission,' said Charles, eager to keep everything peaceful for as long as he could, and to our amazement no objection was raised to my leaving the country with my daughter.

I said we must go with all haste in case they changed their minds and tried to stop us and everyone agreed that this should be so.

Charles conducted us to the coast. First we stayed in Canterbury, where the cold of the February winds was more bearable than the coldness in my heart. I was to leave Charles and as ever when he said goodbye to me I asked myself when we should meet again.

I tried to smile. I told him that the project was going to be successful and in time our troubles would pass away. There would be no black-clad grim-faced Puritans to spoil our happiness.

'It is going to be so hard without you,' said Charles. 'When you are with me nothing else seems of any great importance.'

'I know,' I answered. 'So it is with me. But all is going to come right in the end. Sometimes I feel that happiness like ours has to be fought for . . . paid for. My love, I am going to bring back such aid for your cause that we shall beat those rebels into the ground.'

'My fierce little general,' he said, 'don't stay away too long.'

'Not for a moment longer than I can help,' I assured him, 'and our reunion will be the sweeter for our having been parted for this little while.'

I wished we could have lingered in Canterbury beneath the shadow of the great cathedral but we had to pass on with all speed, for who knew when our enemies might change their minds and try to stop my departure?

The next day we left for Dover. It was a brave sight to see the Dutch ships in the harbour – a squadron of fifteen commanded by Admiral van Tromp.

I said to Charles: 'How eager they are to have their little Princess. I am sure they will want to help her father and mother.'

A surprise awaited us, for with the fleet had come Prince Rupert, who had visited us earlier with his brother, Charles Louis. We had been amused at the time of Mary's wedding because Charles Louis had refused to come. He had been sulking because Mary was marrying the Prince of Orange instead of him. Rupert, however, had been there and this bright handsome young man seemed to be really fond of us.

He greeted us with affection and said that he had heard there was trouble in England and that he would put himself at the disposal of his uncle to fight those miserable Puritans.

Charles thanked him and said there was no question of war and he thought that all sensible people realized that that was the last thing that would do anyone good. He was thankful to say it had not come to that and he fervently hoped it never would.

Rupert was clearly disappointed and as he did not wish to stay in England if there was no fighting to be done, he said he would go back to Holland with us and protect me and my daughter.

Charles replied that he would indeed be grateful to his dear nephew if he would do that.

'The Queen is my most precious jewel,' he said. 'Care for her and you serve me in the way for which I am most grateful.'

So it was agreed that Rupert should return with us.

The last farewell! I shall never forget it. It is one of those memories which stay with me for ever.

To draw attention from his real purpose, which was to go to Hull where the stacks of ammunition were being held, Charles was dressed in hunting clothes. He had let it be known that after saying goodbye to me he was going north on a hunting expedition.

He kissed first our daughter, then he turned to me and held me in his arms. He kissed me again and again. Then he released me only to catch me up in his arms once more.

'How am I going to live without you?' he demanded.

'In the same way as I must perforce live without you.'

'Oh, my dearest, don't go. Never leave me.'

'I will come back with riches . . . with what we need to fight our enemies. Then, my dearest love, we shall be together and live happily for as long as our lives shall last.'

More kisses. More embraces. We could not bring ourselves to release each other.

But I must go and at last I reluctantly tore myself away. He stood watching me as I went aboard. I stood on deck, he on the shore, and we looked longingly at each other until the ship began to move slowly away.

Then he galloped along the cliff, his hat in his hand waving . . . waving. . .

I could not see him clearly for the tears in my eyes, but I went on waving until he was out of sight.

She–Majesty–Generalissima

I hated the sea. When I was sailing it always seemed to put on its most malevolent aspect, and we were only a little way off the English coast when the storms arose. These journeys always seemed endless, but at least the stormy weather took my mind off my parting with Charles. I was in a state of anxiety most of the time, not so much from fear of drowning as that the ships carrying my plate and valuables would be lost.

My fears were not without foundation, for when Helvoetsluys was in sight one of the ships went down in the rough sea. I was grieved to see that it was the one which contained the equipment to fit up a chapel for me in the apartments which would be given to me during my stay.

That seemed a bad omen.

I had very few friends with me. Among them were Lord Arundel and Lord Goring – the father of George who had betrayed the Army Plot but who had returned to us so contrite that Charles had forgiven him, saying that he would be the more eager to serve us because of his lapse from fidelity and would want to make up for the trouble he had caused us. I had my confessor Father Philip and Father Cyprien Gamache; and among the few ladies Susan, the Countess of Denbigh and the Duchess of Richmond – and a few of my French attendants.

How wonderful it was to be on dry land. I was immensely relieved when, with Mary beside me, I stepped ashore at Hounslerdike. The eager young bridegroom was waiting for us there and the welcoming cannon thundered out as he escorted us to the coaches which would take us to the Hague.

There was no doubt of the respect in which the Prince of Orange held us. I had not been mistaken in his delight at the marriage; I did not want ceremony though. I wanted to make my transactions quickly, to build up an army and take it back to Charles.

I was met by Charles's sister, Elizabeth of Bohemia, who was very beautiful although she took little pains with her appearance and now seemed somewhat ravaged by the tragedies which had befallen her. There could not have been two people more unlike. She made me aware of how she despised that attention I gave to my appearance and the clothes I wore (something which was born in me and which I had never cultivated), my smallness, my femininity; perhaps she knew that my folly had not helped her brother's cause. She had never forgotten that she was an English Princess and was angry because of what was happening in England. She could not have been more deeply concerned about that than I was, and the fact that she was inclined to blame me was something I found hard to bear at that time.

Rupert was kind and respectful; he exuded the desire for adventure and was determined to obey the wishes of the King and look after me. Charles Louis was still sulking and did not appear.

I thought that if only Charles had been with me and all was well at home, what a happy occasion this could have been.

March had set in, cold and blustery, and during the journeyings and triumphal entry into the capital I was growing more and more impatient. But the Prince of Orange was determined to honour us. How I could have laughed with Charles at the gauche behaviour of these Dutch. They lacked the manners of the English Court and I remembered that I had found those far less gracious than the ones I had grown accustomed to in my girlhood. The Burgomasters kept their hats on in my presence which at home would have been considered an insult, and at first I thought this might have been intended because some of those simply clad, unsmiling men bore a certain resemblance to our own Roundheads. But it proved to be just ignorance. I thought when the mistake was explained to me I would break into hysterical laughter for one of them kissed the hand of my dwarf, Geoffrey Hudson, thinking he was one of my sons.

How indignant my sons would have been at that!

I used to cry at night longing for Charles. The only consolation I could find was in writing to him; and as I did so my eyes would brim over with tears which dropped onto the paper making great blots.

'The marks of love,' I told him they were. They would prove to him how I wept for him.

It was a great day when I received a letter from him. It contained little news of the progress of affairs, but it assured me – his dear heart – that his days were dark without me and that he was entirely mine.

The weeks flew past. So much time was spent in ceremonies and I realized that I should have come quietly for there were few opportunities of conducting the business which I longed to complete.

By the time we left the Hague for Rotterdam, May had come. I chafed against the delay. Charles was writing regularly and his letters constantly expressed his devotion, but they were no substitute for his presence. We had worked out a little code before I left and it gave me a delicious sense of intimacy as I opened his letters and read. I lived for those letters and the day when I would return to him.

In the midst of this, one of the daughters of the Prince of Orange died and the ceremonies were brought to an abrupt end. We returned to the Hague and the Prince of Orange joined his army. He insisted that we inspect his troops, which was all for our honour, of course, but I could get no answer to the real question: How much help could I wring from them? Or perhaps, could I get any help at all?

At length it was intimated to me that while the Prince of Orange was ready to mediate between the King and the Parliament it would be unwise to supply arms for Charles to fight his own subjects. The people of Holland were sternly Protestant and not unlike our own Roundheads. He could not go against the wishes of his people.

Then I must try to barter with the jewellery and plate which I had brought with me. There followed for me a period which was something like a dream. I became a kind of saleswoman, a pedlar displaying my wares and trying to bargain with people the like of whom I had never known before.

It was a disheartening business. Most of the people who came to see me were Jewish and had a keen eye for business. They admired the jewels. Who could fail to do so? They were the priceless heirlooms of England.

They were beautiful, one merchant told me and his eyes glistened as he touched them reverently. 'But, my lady, these jewels are not yours to sell. They are the property of the Crown.'

I was angry. 'My husband gave them to me so I cannot see how they are not mine,' I retorted.

'If we bought them they could be demanded back as goods sold when the seller had no right to sell.'

'That's nonsense,' I cried.

'It is how it would be,' insisted the merchant. 'And who would want to buy a crown like this? Who would wear it but a monarch?'

'You could break it up. The rubies are priceless.'

'Break up such a beautiful thing, my lady! You are asking me to break my heart.'

So they argued and the real reason was that if they bought those jewels they could be demanded back and a court of law would doubtless say they had no right to them. It was understandable from their viewpoint.

They were interested, though, in some of the smaller items. I knew I should not get a very high price for them but supposed anything was better than nothing.

My journey was not being a success and I was beginning to wonder what Charles was doing without me there to guide him. I know that sounds conceited and nonsensical too, considering the mistakes I had made, but much as I loved Charles I could not be blind to his weaknesses, and most of all the easy way in which he gave in when pressed. He needed me there to make him stand firm against his enemies.

It was a great blow to learn that Hull had declared against him and that when he had sent out little James to occupy the city in his name, the gates had been shut against him. Hull! That city where was stored the ammunition intended for the Scots!

'It is disaster all the time,' I said to the Countess of Denbigh. 'We are the most unlucky people on Earth.'

A messenger came – not from Charles this time, but from someone on behalf of my mother. She was living in abject poverty in a small house in Cologne. Her attendants had all deserted her because for a long time she had been unable to pay their wages, and she had been forced to break up the furniture to burn in the grate because she suffered so much from the cold. She had little longer to live and she wanted to see me before she died.

I prepared to leave at once but was told that the visit would be frowned on by Holland for there was a strong republican feeling here and they did not like queens. While I was hesitating another message came. My mother was dead.

Desolation hit me then. My mother – the wife of the great Henri IV, the Regent who had once ruled France, to die as a pauper! How could my brother have allowed that?

What was happening to everyone and everything around us? I could not believe that the world had grown into such a cruel place. There was another death which saddened me even more than that of my mother. It was years since I had parted from Mamie and during that time Charles had become of such import- ance in my life that my affection for him was greater than anything I could ever feel for another person. But I had loved Mamie dearly and always would. She had been the dearest companion of my childhood. And now she was dead.

I was stunned when I heard the news following so closely on the death of my mother.

Mamie was too young to die. Her life must have been very different after she had left me. Marriage . . . children . . . had she been happy? She had given me the impression that she had been but how could I be sure? And she had had little children. Dear Mamie, how she must have loved them and they her! She had become governess to Mademoiselle de Montpensier, who must have been a trying charge, and yet she was at Mamie's bedside when she died and Mamie had commended her children to her for her last thoughts had been for them. She had remembered me too.

I wept bitterly. I should have been there. Dear Mamie, I thought. I hoped she had been as happy in her marriage as I had . . . but that was impossible for there was no man on Earth like Charles. Mamie had been so pleased that I had found happinesss in marriage.

'Dearest Mamie,' I murmured. 'Rest in peace and may God bless you.'

In the midst of my mourning for my mother and my dearest friend, there was one piece of good news. Messengers arrived from George Digby, Earl of Bristol, and Henry Jermyn. They wanted to join me but first wished to know if they would be welcome. I sent off at once to say I should be delighted to receive them.

'There is so much I could do with the help of trusted friends,' I wrote.

So they joined me and in spite of everything my spirits were lifted a little. I often thought how happy I could have been if Charles were with me and this was a state visit. With the Prince of Orange and his father away from the Court on military manoeuvres there were not the same entertainments. Mary seemed to pine for her husband, which pleased me because I longed for my children to enjoy the happiness I had found in marriage – or should have done if our miserable enemies had allowed me to. Alas, there were not many men in the world like Charles.

Henry Jermyn did a great deal to cheer me. Digby did what he could but he was too fond of the sound of his own voice and was constantly declaiming about the wrongs of the Parliament and such matters which did not make him very popular. Henry Jermyn was different. He was merry and charming and somehow made me feel that everything was not as hopeless as it had seemed before his arrival.

The Princess of Orange gave birth to a daughter and I was asked to hold the child at the font and as a compliment to the new member of the family the child was to be given the name of Mary. But I held firmly to my convictions which could not allow me to be present at a Protestant church ceremony, so Mary took my place.

There were some – perhaps Henry Jermyn among them but he was too discreet to mention the matter – who thought that I should not have risked offending the Prince and Princess of Orange by refusing to take part in the ceremony, but nothing on Earth would induce me to go against my principles.

With the coming of Henry and Digby luck changed a little. I discovered that, though I could not sell the royal jewels, I could pawn them, for there were some merchants who were ready to advance large sums of money on the understanding that if the jewels were not redeemed by the payment of this money with interest they could legitimately claim them.

I was never one to think far ahead. I needed the money at that time and I needed it desperately and here was a chance of getting it. Ammunition, an army, ships . . . they were far more important to me than jewels.

Moreover the Prince of Orange who had publicly said he could not aid me, was less rigid in private. He was very proud of his connection with the royal family of England and did not want to see it become of less importance. Unobtrusively ships were beginning to slip across the North Sea and were lying at anchor in the river Humber. I was really becoming rather pleased with my mission after all. It had taken longer than I had anticipated and I had not done it in quite the manner which I had believed it would be done, but what did it matter as long as the mission was accomplished.

With what joy I wrote to Charles to tell him of my success, but whatever news we had for each other was always overshadowed by our declarations of love. I asked tenderly after his health and told him he must not worry. *I* was working with him. He was going to be surprised at what I was able to do. We should soon have those miserable Roundheads skulking away, hiding themselves in the country. I was longing to be in England, I told him. 'Holland does not suit me. The air must be different from that of our land which you love because it is yours, and I for the same reason. I have pains in my eyes and my sight seems sometimes not so good. I think perhaps I have shed too many tears and they need the balm of seeing you since that is the only pleasure which remains in this world, for without you I would not wish to remain in it one hour.'

Rupert came to me one day at the end of August. He was wildly excited.

He said: 'The King has set up his standard at Nottingham. I shall go and fight beside him. This is war.'

So it had come. I had known it would for some time, but to hear it was actually so was a great shock to me. I had to get back. I could not remain away any longer.

I began my preparations to return.

It was sad saying goodbye to Mary. The poor child wept bitterly.

'But you understand, my love,' I reminded her, 'that I must get back to your father. I am leaving you with your kind new family and I believe you are already in love with your Prince and he certainly is with you. In happier days you will come to our Court and we shall come to yours. I shall enjoy wandering through those lovely gardens of the Hague Palace. The ornamental walls and the statues and fountains are very fine and the lovely stately hall is almost as large as our own at Westminster. You will soon be with us, dearest child, so don't fret. Pray for us. Your father is the best man in the world and we are all so lucky to belong to him. Never forget that.'

Poor child, she was so young! It was too much to expect that she could hide her grief.

I hated the sea. It has never been kind to me. Sometimes I thought there was some malevolent force which was determined to make me as uncomfortable as possible whenever I set out on it. I had my dear old dog Mitte with me. She was always such a comfort and I would not be parted from her; I dreaded the day when death would take her from me for she was very old. I loved all my dogs and had always been surrounded by them, but Charles had given me Mitte and she had been with me so long. So I talked to her and she nestled against me and I whispered to her that we should soon be home.

The *Princess Royal* was a fine old English ship and we set sail from Scheveningen with eleven ships all full of stores and the ammunition which I had been able to buy. I must say I was feeling rather proud of myself and I prayed fervently that I should reach England without mishap. As the great Admiral van Tromp accompanied us, I was confident that we had a good chance of doing this.

I might have known that there would be no easy voyage for me. It was not in my destiny to have that good fortune. No sooner were we a few miles from the coast than the wind arose. What discomfort! There we were in our horrid little beds, tied down to prevent our being thrown out by the violent pitching and tossing.

That journey was a nightmare but oddly enough I seemed able to endure it better than my companions. Perhaps I had suffered so often at sea that I was prepared for it; perhaps I was so fearful of the future and of what would happen to Charles and his kingdom that a storm at sea seemed of less consequence to me. Moreover I was not so ill as some of the others and found that if I could escape from my bed and stagger onto deck, the fresh air revived me. Everyone thought this was highly dangerous but I insisted. My ladies who felt they must accompany me wailed out their wretchedness.

'We are all going to be drowned,' they cried.

'No,' I answered. 'Comfort yourselves. Queens of England are never drowned.'

I was so elated at the thought of going home and by the transactions I had been able to make that I could not be downhearted. They all marvelled at my high spirits and I couldn't help laughing to see my attendants attempting to observe the etiquette of the Court and serve me in an appropriate manner though the mischievous winds tossed them about and some of them were obliged to approach me on all fours.

We had several priests on board. They lost a little of their dignity for they thought they could not possibly survive, and I could not altogether restrain my mirth to see their fear. They were usually so tutorial and I had resented being told even by priests that I was sinful and that I must make this or that reparation. So I could not help but be amused to see *them* in terror of sudden death when they might not have time to make their last confessions and so die without the forgiveness of their sins.

Some of them shouted to the heavens, detailing what sins they had committed, so it could not be anything but funny to hear these men who had set themselves up as our pastors admitting to such sins as fornication and dishonesty, revealing that they ⊥ who had set themselves on such high pedestals the better to instruct us in *our* duty – had the same acquisitive and prurient tastes as so many.

After we had tossed on that wicked sea for nine days we sighted land. Alas, it proved to be Scheveningen from where we had started out.

As we came into port my daughter, with the Prince of Orange and Prince William, was there to greet us for news had reached the Hague at we were being driven back to Scheveningen.

I stumbled on deck, not realizing what a pitiful spectacle I must have presented – pale-faced, tousle-haired, my garments, which I had been unable to change for nine days, stained and malodorous.

The gallant Prince drove his carriage into the sea so that I could be lifted into it and not have to face the eyes of the curious crowd which had assembled on the shore.

Our terrifying trip was over and had merely brought us back to the place where we had started, minus two ships; but most people thought we were lucky to have lost only two.

The first thing I did when I was bathed and changed was sit down and write to Charles.

'God be praised that He has spared me to serve you. I confess I never expected to see you again. My life is not a thing I fear to lose except for your sake. Adieu, dear heart.'

I was determined to stay only long enough to recover from the ordeal so that we could be refreshed and ready to start again.

We landed at Burlington Bay in Bridlington. It was bitterly cold for the snow lay on the ground, but I did not care. I had landed safely and I had a squadron of ships containing the treasures we needed. I was exultant. Soon I should be with Charles.

It was a quiet spot but I noticed a little thatched cottage close to the shore and this appeared to be the nearest habitation and the only one from which I could watch the unloading of the stores so I said that was where we would stay.

I sent some of the men to arrange this and very shortly I was in the cottage eating food which had been prepared for me. Now that I had arrived I realized how exhausted I was. During the first disastrous stage of our voyage I had hardly slept at all and now that I was becoming easier in my mind there was nothing I needed so much as sleep. And I think this applied even more to my attendants, who had suffered far greater from the ravages of the sea than I had.

We could not begin to unload until I heard from Lord Newcastle, who was in charge of the area and who, I knew, was a staunch supporter of the King. I needed his help in the operation, for we should have to get the arms and ammunition to the King's forces as soon as possible. So the wisest thing to do was to rest.

I went into the little room which had been made ready for me and I stood for a moment looking out of the tiny window at the fog which was settling on the sea and my eyes strayed to the snowy-roofed houses of the town. Where was Charles? I wondered. I should soon know. I could imagine his delight when he heard that I had landed safely in the country.

Then I lay down on the bed and was soon fast asleep.

I was awakened by the sound of a shot and as I sat up in bed I heard voices and running footsteps as the door of my room was flung open. Someone came and stood close to the bed.

'Henry!' I cried for in the dim light I could recognize Henry Jermyn.

'You must get up at once,' he told me. 'We have to get out of this cottage. Four ships belonging to the Parliament have come into the bay. They know you are in the cottage and are opening fire.'

He seized a robe and wrapped it round me.

'Hurry!' he commanded, forgetting in his agitation that he was speaking to the Queen.

I allowed myself to be wrapped up and hustled into the open, where my ladies and other attendants were impatiently waiting.

'We must get away from the shore,' said Henry; and even as he spoke the cannon balls were firing on the village and one hit the roof of the cottage I had just vacated. 'Hurry,' went on Henry. 'We must take cover.'

Then suddenly I remembered that Mitte was still sleeping on my bed. I stopped short and cried: 'Mitte. She is back there in the cottage.'

'We cannot think of a dog now, Your Majesty.'

'You may not,' I retorted, 'but I do.' And breaking away from them I ran back into the cottage.

Although a cannon ball had hit the roof it had not destroyed the place and Mitte was curled up and sleeping soundly through all the commotion. She was a dear old creature and quite infirm nowadays but I always remembered her as the mischievous puppy she had been when Charles gave her to me. I snatched her up and ran out of the house to where my party was anxiously waiting for me.

Henry would have taken the dog from me but I would not let her go.

The shots were coming faster and one came so near that when it buried itself in the ground the soil came up and was spattered over our clothes and faces. I was hurried through the village to the ditch which surrounded it and Henry made us all lie in this so that the shots could whistle over our heads and where, apart from a direct hit, we could be safe.

I crouched there with Mitte in my arms and my thoughts were for the ammunition I had brought to England. It would be unendurable if after all my endeavours it were to fall into the hands of the enemy.

After about two hours spent most uncomfortably in the dirty ditch, the firing ceased. Some of the men went out to see what had happened and came back with the news that van Tromp had sent word to the Parliamentarians that if they did not cease their bombardment – neutral though his country was – he would open fire on them.

I was delighted of course but a little annoyed with van Tromp for waiting so long before making his declaration.

'He took his time,' I commented drily.

How relieved I was to see our attackers had retired! They must have realized that they could not have made much of a show against van Tromp and his mighty squadrons.

Henry Jermyn convinced me that I could no longer stay in the cottage, even though the damage from two cannon balls had been slight.

'Boynton Hall is but three miles from here,' he explained. 'It is the only mansion in these parts. Three miles is not such a great distance and you could come to the coast and from there each day watch the unloading of stores.'

'Boynton Hall? To whom does it belong?'

Henry grimaced. I always told him that his mischievous humour would be his undoing – but I liked it all the same.

'I am delighted to tell Your Majesty that it is the home of Sir Walter Strickland,' he said.

I raised my eyebrows and then we were both laughing. Strickland had been the envoy to the Hague at the time I was trying to raise money and arms, and as he was a firm supporter of the Parliament he had done everything possible to frustrate me.

And it was to his estates that Henry was suggesting we go!

'He is far from home serving his masters,' said Henry slyly. 'As Your Majesty well knows, when sovereigns travel through the realm it is the delight of all loyal subjects to place their houses at the royal disposal. It is an honour none would want to forgo. You are not going to deny Lady Strickland that pleasure?'

I ceased to hesitate. I must be near the coast and I could not stay in the cottage. I must maintain my royalty as best I could if only to remind myself that I was still the Queen.

'Very well,' I said. 'Let it be Boynton Hall.'

What would have happened if Sir Walter had been there I cannot imagine, but the ladies of the household were thrown into a flutter of excitement on my arrival at their gates.

Henry went on ahead and explained to them that I had come

and would stay for a few days. He added that he knew that they were aware of the honour done to Boynton Hall.

Lady Strickland was presented to me and she fell to her knees. Custom dies hard and I was sure she and the ladies of the household were more pleased to receive the Queen than they would have been to have some miserable old Roundhead come to stay with them; and after the first hesitation Lady Strickland set her servants working in the kitchens and had the best apartment prepared for me. She even brought out the beautiful family silver plate which they used only for their important guests.

The next day men came from the Earl of Newcastle to unload the ships and work got under way. There were no more threats and the operation was carried out successfully. It was widely known that I was in the country and I could imagine Charles's impatience. I knew that he would come to me as soon as was humanly possible.

In the meantime, to my fury, I received a letter from General Fairfax, one of the leaders of the Parliamentary cause.

'Madam,' he wrote,

'The Parliament has commanded me to serve the King and Your Majesty in securing the peace of the northern parts of the country. My highest ambition and humblest suit is that Your Majesty would be pleased to admit me and the forces with me to guard Your Majesty; wherein I and this army shall all of us more willingly sacrifice our lives than suffer danger to invade the trust imposed. I am, Madam,

'Your must humble servant Fairfax.'

When I read that letter I was overcome with rage. Did the man think I was a fool? And what would he do when he came to guard me? Imprison me most likely. 'No, Master Fairfax,' I said, 'I am not as easily caught as that. If you came near me I should immediately have you arrested so that you could no longer harm the King.'

I was longing to get away with the armaments and to march to join the King. What a moment that would be when we met!

I had by this time brought the stores ashore but the difficulty of transporting them worried me a great deal. Ten days passed and still I could not find waggons in which to carry all that I had brought. I should have to get help and there was no more news from Lord Newcastle. I thought then that if I marched to York with the army I had managed to accumulate I could take some of tho stuff with me and leave the rest at Bridlington with men to guard it until we could get it removed.

There was a letter from Charles.

'Dear Heart, Although ever since last Sunday I had happy hopes of thy landing, yet I had not certain news before yesterday. I hope thou expects not welcome in words, but when I shall be wanting in any other way according to my wit and power of expressing my love for thee, then let all honest men have doubt and eschew me as monster. And yet when I shall have done my part I shall come short of what thou deservest of me. I am making all haste to send my nephew Rupert to clear the passage between this and York. . . . My first and chiefest care shall be to secure thee and hasten our meeting. So longing to hear from thee I continue eternally thine. . . .'

I wept over his letter and then prepared to make my way to York. I had been able to acquire two hundred and fifty baggage waggons and these I loaded with ammunition, arms and valuables. I had now several thousand horse and foot, for many of the King's loyal subjects had joined me.

Just as I was about to leave Henry said to me: 'What excellent silver they have at Boynton Hall. It would be a pity if that were sold for the benefit of our enemies.'

'What are you suggesting?' I cried. 'That we take the silver?'

'Borrow it. Promise payment when the King is safe on his throne. It is rather amusing. Sir Walter Strickland's silver . . . going to help the King.'

The more I thought of it the more I liked it. I hated Sir Walter. He had made things very difficult for me in Holland, but his wife was a pleasant creature and I am sure that but for her husband she would have been entirely with us.

I sent for her and said: 'You live very comfortably here, my lady. Do you think it right that while the King and I must take what lodgings we can get it is fitting for Parliamentarians to live in such style?'

The poor woman blustered and did not know what to say, so I went on quickly: 'I am, therefore, taking your plate. It is very pleasant and tolerably valuable. The King needs all the support he can get and I am sure you will think it goes in a worthy cause . . . whatever your villain of a husband should believe. I was never one to blame a wife for her husband's misdeeds . . . so we are taking your plate. We are not stealing it . . . just holding it until all is well. When the trouble is over we will redeem the plate and it shall be given back to you. In the meantime I will give you a pledge . . . as is always done in such transactions. You shall have this magnificent portrait of me as a pledge for your plate and a memento of my visit to Boynton Hall.'

So we left taking the plate with us and leaving the portrait with Lady Boynton.

As we travelled westward we met a crowd in the midst of which was a very disconsolate man seated on his horse with manacles on his wrists and his legs tied under the horse's belly. The crowd was shouting abuse at him and I stopped and asked who he was.

'It is Captain Batten, the commander of the squadron which sailed into the bay, and he is the man who did his best to murder you,' I was told.

'I am glad to say that he did not meet with success,' I answered.

'Thank God for that, Your Majesty,' said Henry who was riding beside me.

'Thank you too and all my loyal friends,' I replied with emotion. 'What will happen to this Captain Batten?'

'He was captured by our royalist friends who are incensed that he did his best to kill you. They'll hang him . . . or worse. It will be the end for him.'

'But I have already pardoned him. He was, I suppose, doing what he thought to be his duty. Moreover he did not kill me. Therefore he shall not die by my wish.'

The crowds who had gathered to see me watched with interest and I told them that I bore no ill will towards Captain Batten. 'I have pardoned him,' I said. 'He shall not die for he did not succeed in killing me.'

When Captain Batten heard that he had been pardoned at my command he came to see me. The guards did not want to let him come near me, but I fancied I knew a little more of human nature than they did.

I said: 'He is a brave man. He will not hate me since I have just saved his life.'

And I was right. He threw himself at my feet. He told me that he would never forget my merciful act and his great desire now was to serve me.

I smiled at him. He had a good honest handsome face.

'Very well,' I said. 'Let us see. You are in command of a squadron. Perhaps you can persuade others to follow your example and turn faithful subjects to the King.'

'I shall endeavour to do so,' he said, and added: 'With all my heart.'

He kept his word and I doubt whether the King or I had a more loyal supporter after that than Captain Batten.

When I arrived at York people flocked to my banner and it was heartwarming to see them. I was very happy when William Cavendish, the Earl of Newcastle, arrived. I had always been fond of him. He was loyal, gallant and handsome and so eager to fight for our cause that he was inclined to be a little reckless. Charles was always wary of such impetuosity but I was inclined to favour it. William gave me confidence and I knew he had his Whitecoats all over the North. It was true that they were not trained soldiers but they were his tenantry and they regarded him as their lord for he was a generous one and I heard that they liked their uniforms made of undyed wool – hence the name of Whitecoats.

Then there was James Graham, Earl of Montrose, the romantic Scotsman who had suddenly become our friend. He also was very handsome and, although not tall, of a marvellously stately bearing which distinguished him in a crowd. I took a great liking to him in spite of the fact that he had at one time helped the cause of the Covenanters and had commanded their troops. He had been anti-royalist then and defeated those in Scotland who had risen in favour of Charles at both Stonehaven and the Bridge of Dee. But when the Covenanters had refused to make him their supreme commander, he had abandoned them and declared his support for the royalist cause.

I spent a great deal of time discussing the future plan of action with him and William. Henry Jermyn was always present at our conferences and I enjoyed them so much because I found all three men charming as individuals – I had always been rather fond of handsome men – and they were all vital and ambitious and hated indecision, which I fear was a fault in my beloved Charles.

Montrose wanted to go to Scotland and raise an army for the King and said that it should be done before the Parliamentarians got a grip on the country. William had engaged in several skirmishes with Parliamentary forces; as for Henry he was always anxious for action. I felt that if it were left to us we should soon have some decisive movement.

Charles, however, was against what we were doing. He wrote reprovingly, reminding me that only three years ago Montrose had been an enemy. Charles did not trust what he called turn-coats. I might have pointed out the case of Captain Batten and reminded him that when an enemy turned, through gratitude he very often became a loyal servant. It was no use trying to change Charles's opinions. Although he could never make up his mind quickly, when he did he could not be moved from his standpoint. He would not trust Montrose and sadly I had to explain to the Earl that the King declined his offer.

This made a certain coolness between myself and Charles – nothing much of course; but I could not help being a trifle piqued after all I had suffered and done, and I suppose he was anxious – as he had so often been – about my impetuosity.

Nothing could weaken our love and we were both very contrite when that little storm had blown over and our letters were more loving than ever. We longed to be together and chafed at the delay. From York I made a few little skirmishes and not without some success. I enjoyed riding at the head of my tropps, often with Montrose, Cavendish or Henry beside me.

The Parliamentarians pretended to be sceptical of my endeavours but I believed they were beginning to regard me with some concern. I called myself She–Majesty–Generalissima. I rather liked the term and what it implied and encouraged my friends to use it.

My spirits lifted when I heard people singing one of the songs written by a royalist. My attendants also hummed it as they went about their work.

It was the words I liked:

God save the King, the Queen, the Prince also
With all loyal subjects both high and both low

The Roundheads can pray for themselves, ye know
                                    Which nobody can deny.
Plague take Pym and all his peers
Huzza for Prince Rupert and his Cavaliers
When they come here those hounds will have fears
                                    Which nobody can deny.

I was astounded one day when news came from France of my brother's death. He had always been a weakling, but I had not realized that he was near death. Coming so soon after my mother's end it shocked me a great deal. I know I had not seen him for many years and that he had been far from helpful to me in my need; but death is so final. And he was after all my brother and King of France.

Anne had become Regent as little Louis XIV was too young to rule and I did not think she would be a very good friend to me. She was very much guided by Mazarin, who had been a close associate of Richelieu; so France had once more passed into the hands of a Regent and a wily churchman.

But I had too many troubles of my own to ponder much on the fate of my native land. I should have to wait for events to show me what would happen there and in the meantime those of England were such as to demand all my attention.

My mood changed from day to day. If I was exhilarated over one success, I could be sure that my joy would not last.

Catholic priests were being persecuted in Puritan strongholds and my heart bled for them. Then the Parliament decided to try me for high treason. They did not even give me the title of Queen. I remembered then how Charles had pointed out to me the folly of refusing to be crowned. But did it matter to me? 'Let them find me guilty if they want to,' I cried. And they did. I did not care. I was working for my King; and there were days when I was certain of victory just as on others I was sunk deep in despair.

In one of these moods I wrote to Charles: 'Being patient is killing me, and were it not for love of you, I would with the greatest truth, rather put myself in a convent than live in this way.'

I think the enemy were a little afraid of me which showed they viewed with misgiving the success I had had. They attempted to drive a wedge between me and Charles and they could not do this in any other way than by slandering me in my private life, so they attacked my moral character. But Charles knew and I knew that the love between us was too strong to be hurt by these calumnies. He did not belive them for one instant when they said I was more fond of William Cavendish than a virtuous wife had a right to be. They had long accused me of being Henry Jermyn's mistress. I could shrug all that aside. I hoped Charles could.

Then they began to sneer at my title. They changed it to 'Mary, by the help of Holland, Generalissima.' They always referred to me as Queen Mary – as many people did. I think they found the name Henriette too foreign although it was people in England who had changed it to Henrietta.

But I was certainly in high spiits when at last we reached Stratford-on-Avon and were there entertained by a sprightly and witty lady in a pleasant house called New Place. This lady was the granddaughter of the playwright William Shakespeare and she had many an amusing anecdote to relate of her illustrious grand-father.

But the great excitement was meeting Rupert there. He had grown considerably since I had last seen him and was handsome, vital and seeming to enjoy the conflict. I shall never forget how disappointed he had been when we met at Dover and he learned that the war had not started. He talked excitedly and gave me the impression that victory was in sight. Best of all, Charles was on the way and very close now. We were to ride to Oxford to meet him.

In the Vale of Kineton the meeting took place. I cannot describe my feelings as I saw him coming towards me. Charles, my beloved husand, and beside him my two sons, Charles and James. I was too moved to speak as we came close and so was he. I saw the tremor of his lips and the tears in his eyes.

Then he dismounted and came to my horse and taking my hand kissed it with fervour. He lifted his eyes to mine and all his love for me was there for me to see – as I knew mine was for him.

The joy of our reunion was almost like a pain, so intense was it and I wondered how we had lived without each other all this time. It was only because I was working for him, waiting for this reunion that I had been able to endure the separation.

Now here we were . . . together.

I greeted my sons. How they had grown! Charles still looked

swarthy and incredibly wise. James was handsome but somehow very much in Charles's shadow.

I was so happy and I thought then that it was only because of the wretchedness I had endured that I could feel this great joy now.

We rode side by side back to Oxford and all the time we were talking not of war, not of the parlous state of the country, but of how we had missed each other every hour of the day and night, how we had lived only for this reunion.

I sometimes tell myself that those few months I spent in Oxford were the happiest of my life. It was so wonderful to be with Charles and to marvel at the intelligence of my sons. Young Charles at thirteen seemed quite a man of affairs. How quickly he grasped the situation and although he assumed a somewhat lazy attitude I knew he missed nothing. I noticed that his greatest interest was aroused by pretty girls. I mentioned this to the King, who laughed and said that Charles was but a boy.

The King told me that he had arranged our meeting in the Vale of Kineton because it was close to Edgehill, where he had fought a victorious battle against the Parliamentarian forces. The enemy might say it was scarcely a victory but the Parliamentarian forces' losses were far greater than those of the royalists and that was the real test. But whatever the enemy said, the advantage was with Charles, who had been able to take Banbury and march on to Oxford without resistance. That old traitor Essex had gone to Warwick. It was particularly depressing when members of the nobility ranged themselves against us. What was Essex doing on the side of the enemy? One could forgive men like Pym more easily.

My lodgings were at Merton College, in which was a beautiful window overlooking the Great Quadrangle. I had many of my attendants in a suite close to the Fellows' Gardens and they were very happy there. I remember still the old mulberry tree which had been planted by James I. I often think I should to see that once again.

The weather was warm and sunny for most of the time – or so it seems looking back. I loved to sit in my rooms with my dear little dogs all about me. Mitte had survived her adventures and was

more demanding than ever and although some of my attendants
said she was ugly and bad tempered I pretended not to hear – I
only remembered the days when she had been an adorable puppy.

Many people came to see me. I was still the Generalissima.
Nobody could sneer at my efforts now. Hadn't I been to Holland
and brought back that which we needed more than anything? I
had ridden at the head of my troops. The Parliament had thought
it worth while to impeach me. I was a force to be reckoned with.

Some said that the King listened too much to me. They even
likened me to the ivy which clings to the oak and in time destroys
the tree. That was something I was to remember in the years to
come.

But now the days were made for pleasure. We all believed that
we were going to succeed. We were going to march back to
London, take up our residence in Whitehall and fight our
enemies. Charles and I used to walk arm in arm though the
cloisters and sometimes our sons were with us. We talked and
talked of what we would do, and everything seemed set fair.

There were of course minor irritations and some which upset
me a good deal. I could not bear to hear of the break-up of my
chapel, which it had given me such pleasure to erect. The mob of
savages had forced their way in and destroyed the place. Rubens'
picture over the High Altar had been spoiled; and the seat in
which I had been wont to sit had been treated with special
violence to indicate hatred of me. But what shocked me most was
the thought of those ruffians breaking off the heads of Christ and
St Francis from their statues and playing ball with them.

There was other sad news too. Edmund Waller, who used to
write such beautiful verses for me in the old happy days, plotted
in London to destroy the Parliamentarians and bring back the
King. It was discovered and Waller was now in prison. Worse
still, one of my faithful servants, Master Tomkins, who was
concerned in the plot, had been hanged outside his own front
door in Holborn.

But as Charles said, we must not brood on these matters. We
must look ahead to victory and when that was achieved we
would remember our friends.

'If they have not died in the meantime,' I added.

'We will not forget the families of those who have served us,'
answered Charles.

Oxford became a very elegant place during our stay there. People came from all over the country to be at Court and almost every house in the town had to take in lodgers to accommodate all who wished to be there. The finest ladies and gentlemen were grateful for the smallest rooms in tiny houses. The citizens of Oxford were delighted for we were bringing prosperity to the town. The colleges were loyal and determined to help us. The belltower of Magdalen was loaded with ammunition to fire down should we be attacked. We strengthened the walls, and even the professors came out of their colleges to help dig ditches.

Rupert was there with his brother Prince Maurice and at night they used to go out to see if they could find any of the enemy to fight. The Puritans hated Rupert. They called him Robert the Devil. He was a great asset to our cause for he could not have been more enthusiastic and determined on success if he had been fighting for his own country.

Autumn was on the way and that beautiful summer was nearly over. It was to live in my memory as the last truly happy time I was to know, and perhaps the intensity of my joy in it was the knowledge that it was fleeting. I knew I had to grasp every delightful moment and savour it . . . and this I did.

In September Henry Jermyn was created Baron Jermyn of St Edmundsbury, an honour well deserved. A less happy event was the impudence of the Earl of Holland, who had worked with the Parliament and had the impertinence to present himself to the King and expect to be treated with the old friendliness which we had shown him in the days before his defection.

This time Charles was inclined to forgive and forget, but I never could.

Henry advised me to try to accept Holland because of his importance and he pointed out to me that if such men decided they had wavered towards the wrong side and were eager to make it clear that they were back on course, that was all to the good. It should mean that the general feeling was that we were the winning side.

I could never bow to expediency in that way and I was annoyed with Charles for what I called being duped by such men. Our roles had reversed.

Holland was trying to persuade Charles to make some sort of patched-up peace with the Parliament and I was urging exactly the opposite. I wanted Charles not only to call himself King but to be King. And if he were truly so he could not be dictated to by men like Holland, who were ready to give their services to the other side if they thought it was to their advantage to do so.

I was right as it was later proved because, although Holland was with the King at the siege of Gloucester, he soon came to the conclusion that he could do better with the Parliament and left Oxford. He was one of those men who liked to hold themselves aloof from complete involvement and watch which way the conflict was going before leaping to the winning side.

I was aware of this but could not make Charles see it and, though Henry agreed with me, even he thought we could make use of Holland.

When the Earl left Oxford and took his seat in the Parliament I guessed that meant he felt the Roundheads had the greater chance of success. I had no patience with such men and, however much good they could bring when they happened to be on my side, I did not care.

I wanted only faithful friends around me. I was deeply hurt by traitors and still felt the wounds inflicted by Lucy Hay's treachery.

But as the autumn mists rose over the town I began to experience certain familiar symptoms.

I was once more pregnant.

It was the worst possible time for this to happen. I was tired and ill; the country was in a state of civil war; we had healthy children and did not need another child. However, it had happened and I should love this child when it was born – if I did not die in producing it, for to tell the truth, I felt near death, and as the months passed I became more and more indisposed. I was suffering badly from rheumatism, which was no doubt due to all my travels and sometimes sleeping in damp beds; and to add to my discomfort was this unwanted pregnancy!

Charles was deeply disturbed. He wanted me to go to Exeter, where I could stay in Bedford House and he would entreat Dr Mayerne to come to me. I wondered whether the rather perverse Sir Theodore would do that even for the King. He was old and did not want to concern himself in the country's conflicts I was sure.

But he had always loved Charles and had been his physician since Charles was a boy. He may have thought of me as a foolish woman and made no attempt to hide his opinion, but for Charles he had something like reverence and when Charles wrote to him: 'For the love of *me* go to my wife,' he could not refuse.

I also wrote: 'Help me, or all you have done in the past will be of no use.' Then realizing that this was the kind of statement which might make him refuse I added: 'If you cannot come to me in my extreme need I shall always remain grateful to you for what you have done in the past.'

The result was that Dr Mayerne came with all speed to Exeter, where in a state of considerable anxiety on account of the King, I awaited the birth of my child.

I wrote to my sister-in-law Anne of France to tell her that I was expecting a baby in June. We had never been great friends but she herself had suffered a great deal from the dominance of Cardinal Richelieu and that might have made her more gentle and sympathetic towards the suffering of others. She was now in a strong position as Regent, with Mazarin beside her to guide her, and her standing must be more firm than it had ever been. I was looking to her for help. Perhaps I could go to France if I ever recovered from this birth and there raise money and arms as I had done in Holland.

The response was immediate and I knew that I had been right in thinking that success often changed ambitious people for the better. She sent me fifty thousand pistoles, which was a good sum, and with it came everything I would need for my confinement. She wrote that she was sending Madame Perrone, her own *sage femme*, whom she could thoroughly recommend.

I was absolutely delighted at both this display of Anne's friendly feelings towards me and for the money – the greater part of which I immediately sent to Charles for his armies.

It was a hot June day when my daughter was born. She was a beautiful child from the moment of her birth and, perversely, because she was the one I had not wanted, I loved her more dearly than the others.

I called her Henriette after myself and later I decided on Anne after the Queen of France in gratitude for past favours and in hope of future ones. But for the time being she was simply Henriette.

I was very anxious about my new daughter for I feared that events were not moving as we had imagined they would during that flush of euphoria which Charles and I had experienced during our reunion.

I sent word to Charles at once with the news of our daughter's birth, telling him not to believe rumours which were being circulated to the effect that she had been born dead. She was very much alive and very beautiful and I was sure that he would only have to see her to love her.

He sent word that she was to be baptized in Exeter Cathedral according to the doctrines of the Church of England. Dear Charles, he was terrified that I would have her baptized in the Catholic Church!

He was right, of course, and I suppose Dr Mayerne was too when he implied that a great many of the troubles through which England was passing were due to my adherence to the Catholic Faith and my efforts to introduce it into the country.

I immediately complied with Charles's wishes and our little one was taken to the cathedral where a canopy of state had been hastily erected, but the ceremony was naturally conducted without the usual pomp.

Whatever was happening outside I did feel that joy which mothers feel when they have been safely delivered of an infant. If Charles could have been with us – even for a brief time – I could have forgotten what was happening in the outside world.

It was just over a week later, when I was still in bed and weak from my ordeal, when Henry Jermyn came to see me in some agitation.

He cried out unceremoniously: 'Your Majesty is in danger. Essex is mustering troops in the town. He is going to ask for its surrender or there will be a siege.'

'Then we must leave here without delay.'

'That would be unsafe. Essex's army is even now firmly entrenched about us.'

'Can he really be such a brute? Does he not know that I have not yet risen from child-bed.'

'He knows well and doubtless thinks it is a good time to force his will on you.'

'Bring me pen and paper. I will write to him asking for safe conduct. If he has any compassion at all he will give it.'

Henry obeyed and I wrote a letter to the Earl of Essex asking him to allow me to go unmolested to Bath or Bristol – a favour I greatly resented having to ask.

When his reply came back I was furious. The request was denied. I should have known better than to make it. Essex, however, stated that it was his intention to escort me to London where my presence was required to answer to Parliament for having levied war in England.

That was tantamount to a threat. I knew then that I had to get away before they captured me.

How could I travel with an infant only a few days old? I was distraught. I did not know which way to turn. I believed that the fiendish Essex had contrived this because his main object was to capture me. How I loathed and despised the man. He should have been with us. He had turned against his own upbringing and his own people. I could more readily forgive that traitor Oliver Cromwell, whose name was being mentioned more and more and who seemed to be responsible for the greater success which the Roundheads were having now. Yes, I could forgive him. He was a man of the people – but when men like Essex turned against their own, that was unforgivable.

But it was no use wasting time in expressing my fury against Essex. I had to think how I was going to escape, for escape I must. If they captured me and took me to London it would be the ultimate disaster. Charles would promise anything to free me.

I had to escape, and as I could not take my new-born daughter with me, I must, perforce, leave her behind.

I sent for Sir John Berkeley, who was the Governor of the city of Exeter and a tenant of Bedford House where I was living. I already had Lady Dalkeith with me, a woman of great integrity who, Charles and I had agreed, must be the one to look after our daughter. In this we proved right. I shall never forget what I owe to that woman.

Briefly I explained that for the King's cause I had no alternative but to escape. The Roundheads were almost at our gates and their object was to capture me and take me to London, there to accuse me of treachery to the Crown.

'This as you know would be such a blow to the King that he would do anything to save me, jeopardizing his own throne and losing it if need be. There is only one course open to me. I know you understand that.'

Sir John said he did indeed and would do anything I asked of him. Lady Dalkeith joined her loyal expressions to his and told me that she would defend my child with her life if need be.

I took her into my arms and we wept together. Sir John raised my hand to his lips and kissed it.

So fifteen days after the birth of my little Henriette I left her, desolate and heartbroken as I was, for I knew it was the only course to take.

I waited until night fell and then dressed as a servant and, with only two of my attendants and a confessor, I escaped from Bedford House.

We had arranged that others of my household who were determined to accompany us should leave the house at various times in disguises so that they should not be recognized. My faithful dwarf, Geoffrey Hudson, who had stepped out of a pie to comfort me in no small degree, had begged to be of the party and I could not refuse hime. He knew of a wood near Plymouth in which there was an old hut, and he suggested that we should make this our meeting place and all make our way to it by different routes.

When dawn came we were only three miles from Exeter and it was clearly too dangerous to walk about in daylight, for there were so many soldiers about. We found a hut. It was tumble-down and filled with straw and litter and we hastened to take refuge in this when we heard the sound of horses' hoofs. It was fortunate that we did for the horses belonged to a group of Roundhead soldiers who were on their way to join the forces who were gathering on the outskirts of Exeter.

Our dismay was great when we realized that the soldiers were coming straight to the hut and we were thankful for the litter underneath which we were able to hide ourselves.

When I heard the soldiers right outside, my heart seemed as if it would suffocate me and I had rarely been so frightened as when I heard the door creak. We all held our breath as a soldier stepped inside the hut and kicked some of the rubbish aside.

I prayed – something incoherent and silent – and on that occasion my prayers were answered for I heard the man shout: 'Nothing in here but a load of rubbish.' Then the door creaked again and the soldier was no longer inside the hut.

We waited breathlessly, listening. The man must have been leaning against the wall of the hut. He was talking to another.

He said: 'There is a reward of fifty thousand crowns for her head.'

I knew they were talking of mine.

'I'd like to be the one to carry that to London.'

'Who wouldn't? Fifty thousand crowns, eh? A goodly sum and ridding the country of the Papist whore at the same time.'

It was difficult to curb my anger. I wanted to go out to them, to denounce them for the traitors they were. Traitors, liars, defamers of virtue and my religion. I restrained myself, thinking of Charles. I would endure anything for him, discomfort, insults, pain, hardship . . . anything for Charles.

It was some time before they passed on, but we did not emerge from the hut until darkness fell; then we sped on our way. We were fortunate after that and reached our rendezvous in the woodland cabin in safety. There I was rejoined by many of my faithful friends including Geoffrey Hudson, who had brought Mitte and another of my dogs with him, for he was certain that I should be unhappy without them.

How the good friends made up for the treacherous ones!

At Pendennis Castle Henry Jermyn was waiting for me with a suitable guard and when he saw how ill I was he immediately gave orders that I was to be carried on a litter for the rest of the journey to Falmouth. How thankful I was for his thoughtfulness! And what a relief it was to see a fleet of friendly Dutch vessels in the bay.

Before I went on board I wrote to Charles explaining why I had left the child behind. It was for his sake for if I had been captured by our enemies, as I was sure I should have been had I remained in Exeter, that would have been a great blow to our cause.

'I am hazarding my life that I may not incommode your affairs. Adieu, dear Heart. If I die believe that you will lose a person who has never been other than entirely yours and who, by her affection, has deserved that you should not forget her.'

I stood on deck, exhausted almost beyond endurance, but determined to remain there until I could no longer see the land where he was . . . as desolate and unhappy by this parting as I was.

Murder in Whitehall

Once again the sea proved that it was always my enemy. No sooner had I returned to my cabin for a much needed rest than I heard cries of alarm and Henry Jermyn came dashing in looking distraught.

'Pray don't be alarmed,' he said, 'but we have sighted three ships which are obviously pursuing us.'

'Enemies?' I asked.

'I fear so,' replied Henry. 'I should stay here. We are equipped to fight them.'

'If we stop to fight we shall never escape,' I cried. 'We must be free of English waters as soon as possible.'

'If we do not fight they could take us.'

'They shall not take me,' I cried vehemently. 'I will die first. To take me would be disaster to the King's cause . . . far greater than my death would be.'

Henry was aghast. 'My dear lady,' he stammered, 'you must not talk thus. Your death would be the greatest sorrow that could befall me.'

'Personal sorrows cannot be weighed against major calamities, dear friend,' I said. 'Help me up.'

'Where are you going?'

'To see the Captain.'

I would not listen to his protests and tired as I was made my painful journey to the deck. The Captain looked amazed when he saw me; and by this time the enemy were drawing very close.

'Do not stop to return the fire,' I commanded. 'Let out all sails. Make all speed ahead.'

'My lady, these ships are determined to take us.'

'They must never do that. When you think it impossible to escape, set fire to the powder. Blow us up. I must not fall into their hands.'

When they heard me, all those who were in attendance on me and who had crowded onto the deck began to cry out in alarm. The Captain looked startled but he was a man who would obey orders. I thought Henry was going to remonstrate with me so I said: 'I shall go to my cabin and there await the outcome of this, and whether it is to be freedom or death I shall be ready.'

Then I left them and when I reached my cabin I began to have serious misgivings. It was all very well for me to die if I wished to, but what right had I to condemn others to the same fate?

'For Charles,' I said. 'If I became a prisoner that would be the end for him. They would use me to subdue him. No, I must either live to serve him or I must die in the same cause.'

Suddenly I heard shots which were almost immediately followed by cries of: 'Land!' It could not be France which was sighted. It must be the Channel Islands. So there was hope yet. If we could reach land, if the people would help me. . . . Just at that moment I heard a loud explosion and the ship seemed to leap in the air and then begin to shiver.

We are hit, I thought. All is lost.

The ship appeared to have stopped.

At any moment I was expecting the Captain to obey my orders. This must be the end.

I waited . . . and then because I could endure the suspense no longer I came out of my cabin. I saw Henry. He was on his way to me. He told me that the rigging had been hit.

'Are we sinking?' I asked.

'We are very close to the coast of Jersey and the Roundheads are moving away fast because a number of French ships have appeared and are bearing down towards us.'

'Praise be to God,' I cried. 'Once again I am saved and all with me. Oh Henry, how cruel I was. Believe me, I regretted it as soon as I gave that order.'

Henry understood me well. He knew I was near hysteria and he was always calm and somewhat jocular at such times, which was the best way to soothe me.

'Come up with me,' he said. 'See the Captain. I think he has decided to make for Dieppe.'

It was like a miracle, but my old enemy the sea had not done with me yet. Even as we were in sight of Dieppe a violent gale arose. Henry advised me to return to my cabin and this I did and as I lay listening to the tempest all about us I wondered if Fate was playing another trick on me, making me believe that I had escaped the Roundhead ships by a miracle, only to become a victim of the storm.

But after an hour or so of terror and with the knowledge that my escort had been scattered and my frail ship was battling alone, we were at length thrown up on a rocky coast.

I stared at the land before me. France! The land of my birth.

'A fine way to come visiting it,' I said to Henry.

'You will be an honoured visitor,' he assured me. 'Don't forget you are the daughter of France's greatest King.'

I could have wept with emotion. I felt so sick and ill, so anxious about what might be happening to Charles; but there was a certain lifting of my spirits because I was at last in France.

A little boat took me ashore and I stood there staring up at those rocks. I wanted to feel the soil. I wanted to bend down and kiss it but we could not stay on the narrow strip of sand. We had to climb the rocks. On hands and knees I crawled. I was bruised and my hands were bleeding; my hair hung about my face and my gown was torn. I climbed to the top of the cliffs and there before me lay the tiny Breton fishing village.

Dogs were barking; fisher folk were running out of their houses, carrying hatchets and scythes, believing us to be marauding pirates.

'Hold!' I cried. 'We are not pirates. We have not come to do you harm. I am the Queen of England, the daughter of your own great Henri IV. I need help. . . .'

They approached cautiously. But I had come to the end of my endurance. Henry Jermyn was there to catch me in his arms as I fell.

When I recovered consciousness I was lying in a small room and Henry was at my bedside. I struggled up, feeling sick and dizzy.

Henry said: 'It is all right. The people here know who you are and will do everything within their power to help you.'

'Oh Henry,' I cried weakly, 'what should I do without you.'

'No need to wonder,' he said, 'because while there is life in my body I shall be here to serve you.'

I was weeping with emotion. I felt so helpless and it seemed that fate was determined to heap one sorrow upon me after another.

'What now, Henry?' I asked.

He was thoughtful. Then he said: 'The Queen of France has shown herself to be a good friend. I think I should go to her with all speed and tell her that you are here in dire need of help. That should be the first move.'

'I shall feel very uneasy without you.'

'You will be surrounded by good friends. You don't have to fear the Roundheads here. With your permission I will leave first thing in the morning. You need doctors first, I think. You have suffered a terrible ordeal and following so close on the birth of your daughter it has put a great strain on your endurance.'

I saw that he was right and I told him that much as I regretted to lose his company for the short time I hoped it would be, he must go.

He left the next day and I was deeply moved when visitors began to arrive at the tiny thatched cottage to see me. The gentry, from miles round, rode into that little fishing village with food and clothing, horses and carriages.

I thanked them and they knelt to me, eager to pay homage to the daughter of their great King.

Very soon I was able to move on but I could only travel in short stages and it took us twelve days to reach Nantes. From there we went to Ancenis and when we arrived in that town I was greeted by the Comte d'Harcourt, who told me that Henry had been received by the Queen who was most grieved by my plight and had sent him to tell me so. With him were two physicians.

I felt so relieved to be among friends and was immediately better; but when the doctors examined me they were grave and said that I must take the Bourbon waters.

It was a great delight to see Henry again, particularly as he was overjoyed with the result of his mission. The Queen had given him ten thousand pistoles to defray the cost of the journey and a patent for a pension of thirty thousand livres.

Why had I ever thought that Anne was not my friend? What a happy day it had been when she had joined our family. Now of course she was virtually ruler of all France. This was the first good luck which had come my way for a long time.

One of the most delightful gestures of all was the Queen's understanding of my need for a personal friend, someone in whom I could confide, someone whom I could trust, someone who could be something of what Mamie had been to me in the past. She sent me Madame de Motteville and I loved her from the moment I saw her.

Her mother, a Spaniard, was a good friend of Queen Anne and had come with her to France when Anne came to marry my brother. Her father was a Gentleman of the Bedchamber. And she herself was beautiful and charming, very quietly spoken and gentle, yet shrewd and understanding. I was as grateful for my new friend as I was for the pistoles and the livres which were helping to make my life comfortable.

In Bourbon l'Archambault I began to get better. It was such a beautiful place with an atmosphere of such peace that each day I awoke to a feeling of rejuvenation. So many hideous disasters had befallen me that I could not single out any particular one to brood on. My greatest sorrow was parting with my husband; but at least I was here and he was in England and while both lived there would always be the hope of being together again.

It was a hot August. From the window of the castle I could look out on waving corn and watch the oxen pulling the carts across the fields and through the little lanes. Within the ivy-covered walls of our castle we were sheltered from the inquisitive eyes of those who were in the town to take the waters, for invalids had been coming since the time of the Romans as the waters were said to be beneficial. I certainly began to improve and with such good friends at hand as dear Henry Jermyn and Madame de Motteville, of whom I was becoming fonder every day, my health was rapidly returning.

Dear Madame de Motteville had troubles of her own. She confided in me a good deal. She was a widow now, although only twenty-three years of age. She had been married when she was eighteen to a man of eighty but her bondage had not lasted long and now she was rejoicing in freedom as, she said, only those who had lost it would understand what a pleasant state it was to be free again.

'Without the chains of affection,' I amended. 'Sometimes I

think love is a gift bestowed to bring the greatest joy and the greatest sorrow. One cannot have one without the other, for an intensity of love brings constant anxiety, particularly when one must be parted from the loved one.'

How right I was! No sooner did I begin to experience a return to health and a raising of my spirits than I had news from England.

There had been a fierce battle at Marston Moor – a defeat for the royalists, and although there had been heavy losses on both sides and over four thousand soldiers had been killed, three thousand of those were Cavaliers. My dear Lord Newcastle's own regiment of Whitecoats, who had put up such a fierce resistance, had been cut to pieces and the whole of the artillery and baggage of Charles's army had been captured with ten thousand arms.

They were gone now – my hopes of early victory. This was disaster. Charles would be desolate and I would not be there to comfort him.

The Roundheads were jubilant. They owed a great deal, it was said, to that wretched man Oliver Cromwell who had trained his men and somehow inspired them with talk of God and vengeance, making it almost a religious war.

As for their attitude towards me, it had become abusive, and they were circulating pamphlets about me.

I saw one of them which gave an account of the battle of Marston Moor, and of me was written: 'Will the waters of Bourbon cure her? There are other waters open for her to drink in the Protestant Church, the waters of repentance, the waters of the Gospel to wash her clean from Popery. Oh, that she would wash in those waters and be clean!'

I wept until I had no more tears. I felt a terrible lethargy come over me, a hopelessness. Fortune was against us.

But my moods never lasted long and my dear quiet but wise Madame de Motteville was there to talk to me calmly and give me the help I needed.

Although I was living quietly in my ivy-covered castle with its pepper-pot towers like so many I had known in my youth, storms gathered about me . . . small in comparison with the tempest which was raging in England, but they seemed violent while they lasted.

Although I had begun to feel better, the ordeals through which I had passed had affected my health. I could not see very well and

seemed to have lost the sight of one eye; my body was unnatur-
ally swollen and I developed an ulcer in my breast. When this was
lanced I felt better and my body became more its normal size.

Then my favourite Geoffrey Hudson was in trouble. He was
often teased because of his size and he certainly had a dignity
which he did not like to be assailed. I could understand it
perfectly and had always made a point of treating him as I would
any normally sized man about me. I think that was one of the
reasons why he adored me.

There was some joke about a turkey. I never quite knew what it
was. Probably they likened Geoffrey to one and this incensed
him more than anything and naturally the more angry be became
the more they liked to tease.

One day in a rage Geoffrey said he would challenge to a duel
the next man who mentioned turkeys in connection with him. I
did not hear of this until it was too late. There was a young man in
the household called Will Crofts who could not resist taking up
the challenge. Geoffrey was serious and they chose pistols as the
weapons. Crofts, treating the matter as a joke, had no intention of
aiming seriously; but to Geoffrey it was no joke and he shot
Crofts dead.

I was angry and distressed for I was fond of Crofts and particularly of Geoffrey, and alas, it was not for me to decide what
should be done. We were on French soil and subject to French
laws and the penalty for murder was death. The only one who
could override this was Cardinal Mazarin. I was not sure of his
true friendship for me and it occurred to me that I might have
favours to ask of him in the future; therefore I was loth to begin
asking for anything that was not for Charles.

But this was poor Geoffrey. He wept with me. I told him he had
been a fool and he agreed with me. He was not afraid of death, he
said, if that was the penalty. He cared very much though that I
should be without him to care for me.

I was deeply touched and decided that I must do everything I
could to save him, so I did after all beg Mazarin for leniency.

The Cardinal kept me in suspense for a long time and then
finally sent word that the dwarf could go free if he left the
country. Poor Geoffrey! Sometimes I think he would have preferred death to leaving me. I certainly had some good friends,
even if others betrayed me.

He wept bitterly and his sadness was unbearable but finally he left me. I never knew what became of him for I never saw him again.

Events moved fast after that. My brother Gaston came with his daughter to escort me to Paris. It was an emotional meeting with Gaston, whom I remembered from my nursery days. We two being closer in age than the others had been together a great deal. I did not know this young man in his extremely scented garments, his quick black eyes and tufted beard and moustaches. He looked at me with some surprise. I was sure he did not recognize me either for I must have changed a good deal from that attractive girl who had left for England all those years ago. Illness had tampered with my looks and all that remained to me of them were my large eyes, which if they did not serve me well had retained something of their former beauty. Gaston's daughter was a pert miss whom I did not like very much. She was utterly spoiled, having inherited a vast fortune through her mother which had made her the most desirable heiress in France. But they were my family and it was good to be with them – even though I returned to them a wreck of what I had been, a miserable exile and supplicant for aid. Not the happiest way to come home!

As we approached the outskirts of Paris the Queen herself with her two sons, little Louis XIV, who was six years old and his brother Philippe, the Duc d'Anjou, who was four, came to meet us.

I was deeply moved to see my little nephews; they were such beautiful children, particularly the younger; their dark eyes sparkled with excitement to see me and they regarded me with undisguised curiosity.

But it was Anne whom I wanted to see. She had changed a good deal in the sixteen years since we had last met. She had grown fat, but was still proud of those beautiful white hands and she had forgotten none of the old gestures which she had employed to show them off.

But there was such kindliness and compassion in her plump face that I wept with joy to see her and there was such warmth in her embrace as to send my hopes soaring.

'You will ride with me in the coach and the boys will accompany us,' she said.

Thus I rode into Paris seated with the Queen Mother, the little King and his brother.

We drove through streets which I remembered and now they were hung with bunting in my honour. How kind Anne was! I felt remorseful to remember that when she first came to France I might not have been so kind to her as I should have been. My mother had disliked her and coloured my attitude towards her. But that was all past. Anne did not remember – if there was anything to remember – and now she had only friendship to offer.

We went over the Pont Neuf to the Palace of the Louvre where I had been born.

'Apartments have been made ready for you here,' said Anne.

I turned to her and pressed her hand, too moved for speech.

The next day Cardinal Mazarin came to see me. The Cardinal was an extremely handsome man, and I could see at once why he had acquired such a sway over the Queen. There was something quite fascinating about him and, although I had not at first believed the rumours about the love between him and Anne, I now began to think that there might be some truth in them. Later I was to hear that some people were of the opinion that there had been a marriage between them. I could hardly accept that but it was clear that Queen Anne and Cardinal Mazarin enjoyed a very special relationship.

He was shrewd – he would have had to be that to have been selected by Richelieu as his successor – and it was strange that Richelieu, who had been Anne's enemy, should have brought to her notice the one who was to become her very close friend.

My concern was not with the intricate relationship between those whom I hoped would be my benefactors. It was to enlist their help and save my poor beleaguered Charles.

Anne, I was sure, would have promised a great deal. Mazarin was cautious; and it occurred to me that he was not altogether displeased by the way events were going in England as they meant that country could not interfere effectively in the policies of France. Anne was a good-hearted woman ruled by her emotions, but Mazarin was an astute statesman and he was going to make sure that everything worked to the advantage of France.

He was extremely kind and gentle with me; he told me how much he disliked the English Parliament and those traitors who had risen against the King, but as military help from France would be considered an act of war, he reminded me he would have to go cautiously.

I could never bear caution and in spite of the warm welcome I had been given I began to feel depressed. It was true I was able to send Charles a part of the pension Anne had given me, but that was nothing compared with what I had hoped to send in men and arms.

Eventually Mazarin put forward the suggestion that I should approach the Duke of Lorraine. The Duke was friendly with Spain and had great resources with which he proposed to help that country. Now if those resources could be directed to England, they could be of inestimable help to Charles.

'The Duke could easily be weaned from Spain,' said Mazarin. 'He likes a cause and I am sure yours would appeal to his chivalry and feeling for the nobility.'

I could not afford to lose any opportunity so I at once sent an agent to Lorraine. At the same time I put out feelers at the Court of Holland. My son Charles was growing up and would need a wife. Why should she not be the eldest daughter of the Prince of Orange? I made it clear that the Princess would need a very large dowry if she was to marry the Prince of Wales.

News from home filtered through to me. It was worrying. My old friend the Earl of Newcastle, on whose loyalty I would have staked my life, had decided that he could no longer live in a country which suited him so ill and had given up his command and gone to Holland where he proposed to settle down. I guessed that he had been heartbroken by the decimation of his Whitecoats at Marston Moor.

He was not the only Royalist who left the country. It was significant. Those men must have made up their minds that Charles had little chance of keeping his crown.

But Charles had determined to fight on. I worried constantly about him. I dreamed of him in fearful situations. Men like Fairfax, Essex and Oliver Cromwell haunted my dreams.

'Take more care of yourself,' I wrote to Charles. 'You risk yourself too much and it almost kills me when I hear of it. If not for your sake then for mine, look after yourself.'

There was a rumour that he was suing for peace. This terrified me and I wrote to him to take care of his honour and begging him to be true to the resolutions he had made. He was the King – anointed in the eyes of God. He must never forget that.

His reply put new heart into me. Nothing . . . no fear of death or misery would make him do anything unworthy of my love.

I think our love for each other was greater than it had ever been. Adversity had strengthened it. We lived only for the day when we should be together; and it was that hope which kept us both going when disaster stared us in the face.

There was a new ray of hope when the Duke of Lorraine sent word that he would let us have ten thousand men, and the Prince of Orange offered transport. I was delighted. I was getting somewhere; but just as I was about to write off to Charles and tell him the good news, the States General decided that to allow these men to pass through their territory would be considered an act of war by the Parliamentarians and they could not permit it.

How I raged and stormed! Why should it not be an act of war! Why were they afraid of those miserable Roundheads!

I knew the answer. Our enemies were gaining ground and many people believed that Charles was already defeated.

I turned to Mazarin but he, too, impressed by the Roundhead ascendancy, found that he also could not allow us to bring our men and arms through France.

Disaster on all sides! if it had not been for the hope of seeing Charles one day, I would have asked nothing more than to retire from the world, to enter a convent and there wait for death; but while he lived, I wanted to live. I must be ready if ever we should be free to be together again.

His letters comforted me. I read them again and again.

'I love thee above all earthly things,' he wrote, 'and my happiness is inseparably conjoined with thine. If thou knew the life I lead . . . even in point of conversation which in my mind is the chief joy or vexation in life, I daresay thou would pity me, for some are too wise, others too foolish, some are too busy, others too reserved. I confess thy company hath perhaps made me hard to please but not the least to be pitied by thee who are the only cure for the disease. . . .'

It was not until the end of that July that I received news of the crushing defeat at Naseby. The general view was that this was the beginning of the end but I would not allow myself to believe that. While Charles was alive and I was alive I should go on hoping and working.

Why had it happened? Why was Fate against us? I raged. I stormed. I shouted. I wept. But what was the use? It would have seemed at the start of the battle that we had a fair chance; but as usual everything went against us. Charles had chosen his position on the raised land called Dust Hill about two miles north of the village of Naseby and we had been stronger in cavalry than the enemy, but the skill of Fairfax and Oliver Cromwell decided the issue. Prince Rupert who had had some initial success and thought he had won the battle went off to attack the Parliamentary baggage and came back to the heart of the battle too late to save it. Fortunately both Charles and Rupert managed to escape. The Roundheads lost two hundred men and the Royalists one thousand, but that was not the whole sad story. Five thousand men were taken prisoner with all our guns and baggage, as well as Charles's private correspondence.

It was disaster . . . the greatest we had had.

Queen Anne very kindly offered me the *Châteaux of St Germain* for the summer and I was grateful for that, and there in the beautiful castle I brooded on what was happening at home.

There was worse to come. Rupert had surrendered Bristol to the Roundheads. Bristol . . . that loyal city! Charles said he would never forgive Rupert for giving it up. Poor Rupert! Poor Charles! How wretched they must have been! Charles, after Naseby, had lost half his army. What hope had he against Cromwell's trained men? Cromwell! That name was on every lip. How I hated him and yet there was a tinge of admiration in my venom. If only he had been for us instead of against us. He had trained men to an excellence which could compare with the regular army and at the same time he had imbued them with religious fervour. He was the greatest leader in the country and he was against us. None more fervently so. His aim was to destroy the monarchy, and after Naseby and the loss of Bristol it looked as though he were going to do it.

My anxiety was intense. Charles was more or less a fugitive and my children, with the exception of the Prince of Wales, were in the enemy's hands. They were treated as commoners, all royal rank denied them; and there was a rumour that my little Henry,

the Duke of Gloucester, was to be apprenticed to a trade. Shoe-
making was being considered.

I wept until I could not see. I thrust aside the comfort my
friends had to offer. I would not listen – even to Henry Jermyn
and Madame de Motteville.

But after a while I began to bestir myself. Everything was not
lost. Charles had gone to Scotland; he was going to see if he coud
persuade the Scots to help him against the Roundheads. They
would settle their religious differences; he would promise them
almost anything in return for their help.

It was a desperate situation but just as my spirits had sunk to
their very nadir, I was hoping again and beginning to make
plans.

My hopes were on my eldest son. He had escaped to Jersey and
I wanted him to come to France to me. He was fifteen years old
and if I could get him advantageously married it might be
possible to raise a fresh army which I could send to England. The
suggestion of a Dutch marriage had not been received with any
great enthusiasm by the Prince and Princess of Orange. This
meant that they were beginning to suspect that the Roundheads
had almost won the day and that the heir to a throne which might
not be there was not a very good match. I wanted him with me. I
did not want to be separated fom all my family. I longed for my
baby more than any of the other children; I worried about her
constantly. She was just over a year old and I wondered what
would become of her. I knew that when Exeter had fallen to the
Roundheads she had been removed to Oatlands and was still in
the care of Lady Dalkeith.

I wrote to that good and faithful woman and begged her to do
all she could to bring my daughter to me, although before, when
she had been in Exeter with her at the time of the siege, I had
abused her for not leaving the city with my child.

Many royalists had come to me in France, which was another
indication of how badly everthing was going at home. Some of
them did not like the idea of the Prince of Wales's coming to
France because they thought that I would endeavour to make a
Catholic of him and if he became one that would put an end to his
ever succeeding to the throne. I had other ideas. I wanted a good
marriage for him.

Lord Digby was one of those who was against my sending for

the Prince and I knew it was because of religion, but I managed to
persuade him of the necessity to get arms so that the King might
fight again, and finally I won their agreement, and they went off
to Jersey to tell the Prince that I wished him to come to Paris.

They were a long time gone and in due course I had a communication from Digby to the effect that the Prince was very
reluctant to leave Jersey because he had become enamoured of
the Governor's daughter. This was the first of Charles's countless
love affairs which were to be talked of all over Europe. He was
only fifteen but he was already showing the way he would go.
That he could dally in such a way when so much was at stake
angered me. I sent urgent messages to Digby, but still Charles
would not leave the Governor's daughter.

Meanwhile there was news from the King. He was going to
Scotland. I was frantic. I wrote to him asking him to command
our son to come to me at once.

While I was waiting for his arrival, which could not now be
long delayed, I turned my attention to my niece, Mademoiselle
de Montpensier or the Grande Mademoiselle as she was often
called – the richest heiress in France. She was in fact Anne-Marie-
Louise d'Orléans – a royal Princess, daughter of my brother
Gaston and therefore worthy to mate with the Prince of Wales on
account of her birth and doubly so on account of the money she
had inherited through her mother. I did not greatly care for her.
She was a haughty, arrogant creature and being fully aware of my
unfortunate position she was not going to let me forget it. She
flaunted her superiority. Her clothes were always so much richer
than those of others; she scintillated with precious jewels as
though to say, 'Look at me. The richest heiress in France! The
most desirable wife for some lucky man. He shall be of my choice
though.' She had been spoiled all her life and now it was too late
to correct that. She was very fair, which made her outstanding in
our dark-haired almost black-eyed family. Her large blue eyes
were slightly prominent and although she had not inherited our
darkness she certainly had the big nose of the family. She glowed
with health and I rather spitefully noticed that her teeth were
discoloured and spoilt her looks. She had visited me now and
then, having been prevailed on to do so by kindhearted Queen
Anne, and she would sit with me superciliously noting, I was
sure, my clothes, which if they were a little worn were more

elegant than hers. I thought her somewhat vulgar and if it had not been for her immense fortune I would not have considered her for one moment as a suitable bride for Charles.

Ah, but that fortune! I must set myself out to win it.

'You have never been to England,' I said to her. 'Oh, what pleasures you have missed.'

'There is not much pleasure to be found there now, Madame.'

'The green fields are there . . . those little rivers all sparkling in the sun. There is no country quite so beautiful. I confess I long for a glimpse of those white cliffs once more.'

'Let us hope the King is able to keep a hold onto the crown.'

'Can anyone doubt it? This is nothing . . . a rebellion of a few wicked men. Rest assured the King will recover all very shortly.'

'He has been rather long in doing so, dear aunt.'

'Victory is within his grasp.'

She was looking at me cynically. I knew she was thinking: Naseby. Bristol. The King in Scotland feebly trying to win the help of an ancient enemy. The family scattered.

'The Prince is growing up,' I said. 'He will be there to stand with his father.'

'He if fifteen, I believe. *I* am seventeen.'

'I know it well,' I said. 'But you are much of an age. I have a feeling that when he comes here you are going to be very good friends.'

'I do not greatly care for the society of young boys,' she answered slyly.

'Charles is a man. He is older than his years. Why, in Jersey. . . .'

But no. I was being impulsive again. It would be unwise to tell her of his philandering with the Governor's daughter.

She went on: 'My aunt died recently, as you know.'

'I still mourn my dear sister,' I said.

'The King of Spain will be looking for a wife, I daresay. His period of mourning will soon be over.'

The minx! I thought. She is teasing me. The King of Spain! Her aunt's widower who is now in the marriage market. And he has a crown to offer her . . . not the promise of one.

Those protuberant blue eyes were laughing at me. She was saying: I see right through you, dear Aunt Henriette. Do you imagine that I do not know how eager you are to find a rich wife for your son?

Perhaps I had meddled again. Perhaps it would have been better to let Charles do his own wooing. If the affair in Jersey was an example he would be able to do that very well indeed.

It was June when my son arrived in Paris. He could not defy his father's orders even for the sake of the Jersey charmer. He arrived a little resentful but he was soon on the look-out for fresh conquests.

I was delighted to see him and for a few moments we just clung together. He had always been a strong boy. He had grown very tall and had an air of dignity which pleased me. He looked every inch a King. He still had the swarthy looks he had been born with; his features were too big for good looks and indeed if one studied his face he was really quite ugly; but he was possessed of such charm – his smile, his voice, his manner – that in any company he would be distinguished, and his royal bearing was apparent. I was proud of him.

When he arrived the Court was at Fontainebleau and kind Queen Anne immediately sent an invitation for us to join her there.

Charles and I rode together and when we were within a few miles of the palace we were met by the Queen in her coach with little King Louis. She expressed her pleasure to see Charles, and when we alighted at the palace she gave him her arm to conduct him in while I was left to the care of the little King.

It was not long before Charles was engaged in a flirtation with his cousin La Grande Mademoiselle, as she liked to be called, but it was soon clear to me that she was only amusing herself and there could be no official ceremony until England was once more in the hands of its King.

In the meantime the King was in Scotland and I trembled for what was going on.

Life could not be all sorrow – even mine. What a wonderful day it was when Lady Dalkeith – Lady Morton now that her father-in-law had died – arrived in France with my little Henriette. I could scarcely believe this good fortune, so accustomed was I to bad.

Madame de Motteville brought me the news and I ran down to

find them there. I snatched up my baby. She did not know me, of course, for she had been only fifteen days old when I had left her and now she was two years. She could chatter a little and she looked at me gravely. I thought how beautiful she was – the most beautiful of all my children and the most beloved – and always would be.

It was a wonderful reunion. I could almost believe that my fortunes had changed. From despair I allowed myself to revel in absolute happiness . . . for a short while.

Dear Lady Morton – to whom I had not always been kind, for I am afraid I had the common fault of blaming others when misfortune struck me. Who could have been kinder, more loyal, more loving than this good woman! Henriette loved her and would not be separated from her and I welcomed her with all my heart and asked forgiveness for my unjust criticisms of the past, at which she fell on her knees and said she only wished to serve me and the Princess for the rest of her life.

Ah, I thought, if only we had more faithful servants like this dear lady!

I settled down to hear of their adventures, because the clever woman had actually escaped from Oatlands.

'The Commons had decided that the Princess Henriette should be placed with her brother and sister at St James's Palace where her retinue would be dismissed and that would have meant me,' Lady Morton told me. 'I had promised both you, Madam, and the King that I would never leave the Princess except on your orders so I decided that the only way was to escape to you.'

'Oh, my clever, clever Anne!' I cried.

'We should never have been allowed to leave,' she went on, 'so I decided on disguise. I had with me a Frenchman, Gaston, who had been in the household and he posed as a valet and it was arranged that I should travel as his wife and the Princess was to be our child – a little boy. I thought that best in case we should be suspected. I left letters behind with people whom I could trust, asking them to keep our departure secret for three days, which would give us time to get well on our way. And then we left.'

I listened intently. It was the sort of plan I would have worked out myself.

'I told the Princess that she was not a princess any more. She was a little boy and her name was Pierre, which I thought in her childish chatter sounded a little like Princess if she should let it be known who she really was. She did not like it at all, nor the ragged clothes in which we had to dress her. We had some scares along the road . . . not the least those resulting from the Princess herself, who was eager to tell everyone she met that she was not really Peter or Pierre but the Princess. I cannot tell you, Madam, what a joy it was to be on that boat.'

'I cannot tell you what joy you have brought me!' I replied.

My little daughter's coming lightened my days considerably. I had two of my children with me now: Charles and Henriette, my eldest and my youngest. It was a comfort to see how those two loved each other. Charles, whose main interest, I had to admit, was in young ladies, still had time to spare for that very small one, his own sister. He bestowed on her the pet name of Minette; as for her, her eyes would light up every time they fell on her big brother.

But naturally we could not be happy for long. How foolish Charles had been to put his hopes on the Scots. I could not believe my ears when I heard that they had sold him to the English. The price had been four hundred thousand pounds.

'Oh, the base treachery!' I cried and was mad with grief.

In my heart I knew that this was indeed the end, but I knew too that I would go on fighting as soon as I had recovered from the shock. I would always fight . . . even with death and despair staring me in the face.

Charles wrote to me: 'I am almost glad of it. I would rather be with those who have bought me so dearly than with the faithless who have sold me so basely.'

Now the Cavaliers were coming to Paris in large numbers. They came to the Louvre and as the royal family was not there and I had almost the whole of the vast palace to myself I lodged them there. Some of the French criticized me for allowing them to have Protestant services in the Louvre and I reminded them that King Charles had never denied me the liberty of worshipping in my own faith and I could at least do the same for those who came to me with the object of furthering his cause. Rupert came. He was disheartened and somewhat resentful against the King who had reviled him after the loss of Bristol and seemed to have forgotten everything he had done in his service.

I placated him. I begged him to understand the state of mind in which the King must be . . . a prisoner of his enemies in the country which he had been chosen by God to rule.

My son went to Holland in the hope of getting help, and there his sister Mary, now Princess of Orange on the death of her husband's father, welcomed him warmly. Poor Charles did not have a very happy time for almost immediately he contracted small pox and was laid low for some weeks. I suppose I must be grateful that he recovered but I did at the time find it difficult to be grateful for anything, so weighed down was I by my misfortunes. My thoughts were all with my husband – a prisoner in the hands of his enemies!

Looking back, I wonder whether there might have been a hope even then of saving his crown and his life, for some people seemed to think that he could have come to terms with Cromwell. Now it is clear that he did not understand the people with whom he had to deal. He had some idea that if he offered them peerages they would agree to set him back on the throne. He never could understand men like Cromwell. I can see the situation more clearly now. When it happened I was as blind as he was.

Charles did smuggle out a letter to me in which he stated that he was going to win them over and as soon as he gained power he would hang them all.

Cromwell was too wise a man not to realize this possibility. I had always found it hard to see the enemy's point of view, but I realized that Cromwell's intentions were not entirely to gain power for himself – although this is what he did. Some thought him a bad man, but few could deny that he was a brave one. He never spared others, nor did he himself. He was a deeply religious man. He had said he took up arms for civil and religious liberty, but most of us have come to know by now that when people talk of giving the people religious liberty they mean liberty to worship as the oppressors think fit. I am sure my dear Charles did not wish to restrict the religious liberty of his subjects. Cromwell referred to himself as 'a mean instrument to do God's people some good and God service,' but he brought great tragedy to many an English family and more to that of his King and Queen than any other.

I was delighted when my son James escaped to Holland. That was something to enliven the dreary days. He had been placed by the Parliament with his sister Elizabeth and brother Henry at St

James's, though they were allowed to visit the King at Caversham and later at Hampton Court and Zion House, where he was kept in restraint. I would sit for hours imagining those meetings and longing to be with them.

James had been playing hide and seek with his sister and brothers and during the game had managed to elude the guards and get down to the river where friends were waiting with clothes – those of a girl – and when he was dressed in them he must have been a rather attractive sight for James had always been a pretty chiild. His brother Charles would never have been able to disguise himself as a girl! They got him across the sea to Middleburg where his sister was waiting to welcome him. Charles was already there and I was sorry to hear that they were soon constantly quarrelling with each other.

I wrote to them reminding them that quarrels within the family were something we could not afford. We had enemies enough outside the family. There must be none within.

So that weary year was passing. The King a prisoner, the Parliament wondering what they would do with him. I longed to be with him. I wanted to share his fate whatever it was. If I could join him in his prison and we could spend our last days together, I would ask nothing more.

I wrote appealingly to the French ambassador, begging him to put my request before the Parliament. Let them give me permission to be with my husband. I would willingly join him in his prison. Let them do what they would with me if they would only let me be with him.

I settled down to await an answer. None came. I learned afterwards that the French ambassador had presented my letter to the Parliament and that they would not open it.

Good news at last! Charles had escaped from his gaolers. He was in the Isle of Wight and had found refuge in Carisbroke Castle.

It was about this time that war broke out in France. I was so immersed in my own affairs that I was taken by surprise when it burst upon us.

Poor Anne, she was distraught and terrified that her son would lose his crown. The war of the Fronde had started. It was really a revolt by certain factions against Mazarin to whom, in her infatuation, Anne had handed over the reins of government. Some

people objected to this and it was the same old story: dissatisfaction with the rulers and then war . . . which is no good to
anyone. The nobles were annoyed because there were too many
foreigners in high places – Italians mostly, as Mazarin naturally
favoured his own race. Taxation was oppressive and the Parliament complained that their wishes were overruled by the
arrogant Cardinal.

The people were taking up arms and the name Fronde was
bestowed on the uprising. It was scarcely a war as the name
implied for it was called after a fronde – a kind of catapult used by
the street boys of Paris to fight their mock battles with each other.

When the people put up the barricades I went to see Anne. I felt
I could be of some use to her, my experiences of discontented
subjects being great.

Anne, who had left everything to Mazarin to conduct, was less
worried than she had been.

'It is a slight disturbance,' she said.

'My dear sister,' I replied, 'the rebellion in England began as a
slight disturbance.'

I think she took notice then. She could not ignore that terrible
example across the Channel. The Court fled from Paris and took
up residence first of all in Ruel and afterwards at St Germain.
When the Court left Paris I remained in the Louvre. The in-
surgents had no quarrel with me. But now I knew what it meant
to live in abject poverty. My pension had stopped and because I
had sent the bulk of it to help Charles I had nothing left with
which to buy food and keep us warm.

My little Henriette could not understand what it was all about.
Poor child, she must have thought she had been born into a
hostile world. I wished I could have given her a happy childhood
. . . a royal childhood . . . the sort to which she was entitled. But
we were together . . . I must be thankful for that.

I don't think I have ever been so miserably uncomfortable as I
was that Christmas of 1648. I had suffered much before but now
there was bodily discomfort to add to mental torture. I had
endured illness but never before had I come near to starvation
and, far worse than suffering myself, was to see my child cold and
hungry. Her beautiful dark eyes seemed to grow larger every day.

Paris was in chaos. There was a war and to make life more
uncomfortable the Seine had burst its banks and flooded the

town. From the windows we could see the roads looking like canals whipped up by the bitter winds. That wind whistled through the windows and there was no way of keeping warm.

I could not see how we could continue in this way. My household was sadly in need of food. Even Henry Jermyn had lost his high spirits. What could we do? Where could we go? This was supposed to be our refuge.

It was a dark and gloomy morning; the rooms were full of the cold wintry daylight; outside the clouds scudded by, heavy with snow. My little Henriette was in my bed. I had gathered everything I could . . . rugs and draperie . . . to put over the bed and keep her warm. I sat in a chair beside the bed with a counterpane wrapped round me. Henriette watched me with wide eyes. I said: 'Why don't you try to sleep, my darling?'

Her answer wrung my heart with misery. 'I'm so hungry, Mam.'

What could I say to that?

'Perhaps there'll be some soup today,' she went on, her eyes brightening at the thought.

'Perhaps, my love,' I answered, knowing there was nothing in the palace with which to make soup.

At that moment Lady Morton came in carrying a piece of a wooden chest which she put on the fire.

'That's a little better, dear Anne,' I said.

'It's the end of the chest, Your Majesty. Tomorrow we shall have to find something else. This will last through the day, and it should give a good blaze.'

'Nothing seems to keep out these biting winds.'

Anne looked pale and thin, poor woman. She had come through that miraculous escape . . . to this. Was she wishing that she were back in England accepting Roundhead rule? At least she might not be cold and hungry there.

She went to the bed and felt Henriette's hand.

'It's warm,' she said.

'I keep it hidden away,' Henriette answered. 'When I put it out it freezes. Will there be soup for dinner?'

Anne hesitated. 'We shall have to see.'

It was like a miracle for there was soup for dinner after all. How strange life was! I was lifted up one moment and cast down the next. It must have been about an hour later when we had a visitor

– none other than the Cardinal de Retz, one of the leaders of the
Fronde movement. He had taken it into his head to see how I was
faring at the Louvre and when he entered the room he stared in
horror to see me huddled in my chair and my little daughter
peeping out from under the mass of rugs which I had thrown
over her.

'Your Majesty,' he cried, 'what is the meaning of this?'

He knelt beside me and kissed my hand.

I said: 'You may well ask, my lord Cardinal. We are wondering
in this place whether we are going to die of cold or starvation.'

'But this is . . . monstrous!'

He was truly shocked. I had always rather liked him. He had a
reputation for being somewhat dissolute in his youth and that
seemed to have put a certain kindliness in him, a quick sympathy
for other people's troubles which those who have lived vir-
tuously sometimes lack. In any case he was horrified.

He stammered: 'That a daughter of our great King should find
herself thus. My dear lady, I shall not waste time talking to you . I
am going to have all you need for the time being sent in. I will see
to that myself. Then I shall bring this matter up before Parliament. I am sure all noble Frenchmen will be horrified to know
that you and your daughter are in this state.'

I could have him kissed in my gratitude. He was as good as his
word. Within a few hours logs and food were being delivered
from his own house. it was wonderful to smell food cooking. We
were all very jubilant that day.

The next day he spoke of us in Parliament. A daughter and
granddaughter of our great King Henri IV starving in the Louvre
with her faithful attendants! It must be rectified at once. So
eloquently did he speak that it was; and I was granted the sum of
forty thousand livres.

It was useless now to send this to Charles, so it was spent on
bringing comfort to my long-suffering household, and I was
happy for a while to see my little daughter's eyes sparkle as she
had her soup and afterwards when she held out her hands to the
logs crackling in the fireplace.

My joy was short-lived. The New Year had come – the most
bleak and bitter of my life. I had had no letters from Charles but
news was filtering through. He had been taken from Carisbroke
Castle to Hurst Castle and from there to Windsor. From there he

was brought to St James's Palace to stand trial in Westminster Hall.

'Trial!' I cried. 'These villains will *try* the King! One day I promise you . . . one day . . . we shall see the heads of Cromwell, Essex and Fairfax on London Bridge. The indignity! What is he thinking, my dear Charles, and I am not there at his side.'

I was hysterical with grief and fear. I should never have left him. I should have stayed by his side. No matter what happened it would be better for me to be there.

My two chief comforters were Henry Jermyn and Madame de Motteville. Henry assured me that they would not dare condemn the King. 'The people will never allow it,' he said.

'Yes,' I cried, clutching at the smallest hope. 'The people always loved him. I was the one they hated. Oh, Henry, do you really think the people will stand with him? Will they rally round him . . . flout those wicked Roundheads?'

'They will indeed,' said Henry. 'You will see. Soon he will be acclaimed. He will send for you. The family will be united.'

Even if I did not entirely believe him it was good to listen to him. He was so tall, handsome and commanding that he always gave an impression of being about to set everything to rights. It was wonderful to have him with me at such a time. When I told him so, he kissed my hand and said: 'Do you think I would ever leave you?'

'If you did,' I answered, 'that would be the end of everything for me.'

Madame de Motteville, faithful as she was, could not comfort me in the same way. She was very anxious and it was all for my sake. She was so gentle and quiet, fearing the most terrible disaster and perhaps trying to prepare me to face it when it came.

February was with us. I could not understand why there was no news.

'What was the result of the trial?' I demanded. 'There must have been a result. Why don't we hear?'

Henry frowned and looked out of the window. 'It is not always easy to get news through,' he murmured.

I noticed that some members of the household avoided looking at me.

'Something has happened,' I said to Madame de Motteville: 'What is it, I wonder.'

She did not answer.

I was getting frantic. I called Henry and said: 'Henry, you know something, don't you. For God's sake tell me.'

He was silent for a few moments and then he looked at me and said: 'Be of good cheer. Yes, he was brought to trial and they condemned him.'

'Oh . . . God help me . . .'

Henry had his arm about me, supporting me.

'All will be well,' he said. 'Listen . . . listen . . .' His face was so distorted he could not speak. It seemed like minutes but it must have been less than a second. Then the words came rushing out. 'All is well. . . . He was saved . . . at the last moment. . . . They were going to behead him. He was taken from St James's to Whitehall. . . . He came out of the banqueting hall there to the scaffold. . . .'

'Henry . . . Henry . . . you are killing me. . . .'

He took a deep breath and said firmly: 'As he laid his head on the block, the people rose together. They cried, "It shall not be. Charles is our King. Down with the Parliament." '

'Henry. . . .' I was almost fainting with relief.

He said, 'All will be well. . . .' and he kept on repeating that.

I thought his behaviour and his manner of telling very strange but that was later. At that moment I could think of nothing but: He is safe. The people would not allow it. They were his faithful subjects after all.

'His subjects have a great affection for him,' I said. 'There are many who will sacrifice life and fortune for his sake. I am sure the cruelty of those who persecute him will only make those who love him the more eager to serve him.'

I talked to Madame de Motteville, to Henry, to all my attendants, of the miraculous escape the King had had.

'There will be more news soon,' I said. 'Good news. This is the turning point.'

There was no news next day. During the night I had lain in bed listening for the sounds of arrival. None came. Another day passed and another.

'It is strange,' I said, 'that there is no news.'

Tension was rising. Something very strange was going on. Even Henry seemed different. He had lost his gaiety and I fancied that Madame de Motteville was avoiding me.

I had to do something because the suspense was becoming intolerable.

I said to Henry: 'Why do we not hear? The Court will know what is happening surely? I am going to send one of the gentlemen to St Germain to find out if they have heard anything.'

'I am sure,' said Henry, 'that they would let you know immediately if they had.'

'They are concerned with their own troubles. I shall send a man at once with instructions to come back to me with all speed.'

Henry bowed and I sent a man whom I could trust to St Germain.

We had had dinner. Conversation was stilted. Nobody seemed to want to talk about what was happening in England, which was the only subject which interested me.

My confessor, Father Cyprien, had said grace when the meal was over and as he was about to leave Henry went to him, laid a hand on his shoulder and whispered something.

I cried: 'What is wrong? What are you whispering about?'

Henry looked at me, his face stricken and I saw then that Father Cyprien's hands were shaking.

'What is it? Please tell me,' I begged.

Henry came to me, his face a mask of misery. He said: 'I lied to you. It was not the truth. The people did not come to his aid.'

He led me to a chair and kneeling at my feet lifted his agonized face to mine.

'I could not tell you. I had to lie. . . . It did not happen that way. They took him out to the scaffold in Whitehall. . . . He died . . . like the brave man he was.'

I was frozen with grief. I stared ahead of me. I did not see them all round me. I saw only his dear face.

I could not move. A stifled sob broke into my consciousness. It was one of the women. Henry was looking at me, his eyes pleading for forgiveness, for the lies he had told me . . . because he loved me.

There was nothing now. He was gone, my King, my husband, my love. The murderers had taken him from me.

I could feel nothing for them. That would come later. At this moment I could do nothing . . . think of nothing but this overwhelming tragedy.

Charles was dead and I should never see that dear face again.

Despair

I do not know how long I sat there. I was unaware of time, of all those kind people around me who shared my suffering.

It was Madame de Motteville who in due course put her arms about me and helped me to my bed. I lay there and she knelt beside it. I could see the tears glistening on her cheeks. I shed none. My grief went too deep for tears. They were for ordinary tragedies, disappointments and frustrations; this was the greatest disaster that could befall me, and I longed above everything else to be lying beside him in his cold grave.

I dare not think of him . . . that beautiful head which I had so often caressed. . . . No, anything was better than thinking of that.

'Merciful death,' I prayed, 'take me. Let me be with him in death as I was in life.'

Madame de Motteville was speaking gently. 'Madame, dearest lady, you must live for your son. There is a new King of England now. God bless Charles the Second.'

She was right, of course. I saw that. I could not selfishly indulge my grief. What would he have said? He believed in the crown, the divine right of kings to rule. The King was dead. Now it was Long Live King Charles the Second. My son was nineteen years old. He was strong; he was royal.

Perhaps there was something yet to be saved.

'Madame,' said Madame de Motteville, 'you will wish to send a message to the Queen of France.'

'Yes, yes,' I answered her. 'Send someone to her, tell her of my state. Tell her that the death of the King, my husband, has made me the most unhappy woman in the world. Oh, warn her, my dear friend, warn the Queen of France. Tell her never to exasperate her people unless she is certain she has the power to subdue them. The people can become as a savage beast. My dear lost lord the King has proved that. I pray that she will be happier in France. Now I am desolate. I have lost that which meant more to me in life than anything else . . . a King, a husband and a friend.'

Madame de Motteville bowed her head and turned away because, I knew, she could no longer endure looking on my terrible grief.

I called on God to help me. I reproached Him for allowing this thing to happen. And then I repented and said that I knew it was His will and I wanted strength to bear it.

Madame de Motteville told me that she would go to Queen Anne and tell her what I had said; and as she was about to depart I called her back.

'There is one thing I wish you to say to her. Ask her this for my sake. If she does it, there will be a little lightness in the dark gloom of my life. I beg her to acknowledge my son the Prince of Wales as King of England, King Charles the Second, and my son James, the Duke of York, as his heir presumptive.'

Madame de Motteville left me and I realized that when I thought of my son I was beginning to live again.

I wanted to know all that had led up to that terrible climax in Whitehall but it was a long time before I was able to piece together the entire terrible events. Charles's later life had been strewn with misfortune. Even after the escape to Carisbroke, where he had expected to find loyalty, he had been betrayed by Colonel Hammond, the Governor of the island. It was understandable that Charles should have expected Hammond to be his friend for he was a nephew of his chaplain. What Charles did not know was that he had married a daughter of John Hampden and become an ardent partisan of Oliver Cromwell. At first Hammond had treated Charles like an honoured guest but even while he was doing this he was informing the Roundheads where Charles was, and my poor husband soon realized that he was a prisoner. How he must have despaired! But he would be calm and more serene than most men would be in his position, and while at the castle he had walked on the ramparts for exercise and played on the bowling green and spent a great deal of time reading.

I heard how he had made an attempt to escape when he

discovered the perfidy of Hammond. There was a faithful attendant called Firebrace who acted as his page and planned escape
with him. Firebrace's scheme was that he should cut through the
bars of the prison window, but Charles had thought this would
attract attention and he believed he could squeeze his body
through. He tried it with his head. They were ready. A ladder
was placed against the window for it was planned that when
Charles was on the ground below Firebrace would get him across
the main courtyard to the main wall which he could descend by
means of a rope. Men were waiting with a spare horse and close
by was a boat which was ready to carry him to France. Everything
was in order and would have succeeded but for the fact that
Charles had miscalculated and although he got his head through
the bars he was stuck between his breast and shoulders and could
move neither in nor out.

Alas, poor Charles! Sometimes I think that Heaven itself was
against him. If ever I had a chance I would find the good Firebrace
and reward him for his attempt to help the King.

After that Charles was taken to Hurst Castle, a dreadful place
which was situated on a kind of promontory off the Isle of Wight.
There could not have been a more uncomfortable place, lashed as
it was by the winds and at high tide cut off from the island. I could
picture him in that grim fortress. He must have thought of some
of his forebears who had offended their enemies and ended up in
places such as Hurst Castle where they were done to hideous
death.

Fortunately he was not long in Hurst Castle and from there was
brought first to Windsor and then on January the fifteenth to
London.

By this time Cromwell was in control and I wondered, not
without some satisfaction, how the people liked being under
the orders of the military. His soldiers took great pleasure in
breaking up many of the beautiful churches and homes which
in their narrow Puritan minds they thought were sinful. They
even desecrated Westminster Abbey. The stupid people! Now
they would learn what it was like to be ruled by men who had no
joy in them, who made harsh rules and thought it was a sin to
smile.

So they brought my Charles to trial and condemned him to
death. I do not want to recall all the horrendous details. It is too

painful even though it is so long ago. He was serene and went to his death like the brave man he was.

I cannot bear to think of the last time when he saw our two little ones, Elizabeth and Henry, who were brought from Zion House to take their last farewell of him.

I have heard it many times from different sources and each time I weep.

How could they be so cruel to two innocent children!

When my daughter Elizabeth saw her father she fell into passionate weeping. She knew what was in store for him and how different he must have looked from the handsome father she had known. He had suffered so much since they had last met. I pictured his greying hair, his resigned looks – but he would always be handsome, impeccable in dress and manner.

She could not speak to him through her weeping, and little Henry seeing his sister cry, joined in.

Charles drew them to him and embraced them. Elizabeth was only twelve but immediately afterwards she wrote down exactly what had happened. I have read it many times and each time it fills me with an infinite tender sadness.

'I am glad you have come,' he told her, 'for there is something I wish to say to you which I could not tell to another and the cruelty of it, I fear, was too great to permit me to write it. . . . But, sweetheart, you will forget what I tell thee.'

Elizabeth assured him that she would not. 'For I will write it down,' she said, 'and it will be with me for as long as I shall live.'

'Do not grieve,' he said. 'Do not torment yourself for me. It will be a glorious death which I shall die, it being for the laws of the land and for religion. I have forgiven all my enemies and I hope God will forgive them too. You must forgive them, as must your brothers and sisters. When you see your mother. . . .' And this is the part which I could never read without my tears blinding me . . . 'tell her that my thoughts have never strayed from her and my love for her will be the same until the end. Love her and be obedient to her. Do not grieve for me. I shall die and I doubt not that God will restore the throne to your brother and then you will all be happier than you would have been if I had lived.'

Then he took little Henry onto his knee. 'Sweetheart,' he said, 'now they will cut off thy father's head.'

Poor little Henry stared at his father's neck and seemed utterly dismayed and bewildered.

'Heed what I say, my child,' went on the King. 'They will cut off my head and perhaps make thee a King. But mark what I say, you must not be King as long as your brothers Charles and James live. Therefore I charge you, do not be made a King by them.'

Poor little Henry tried hard to understand. Then he drew a deep breath and said: 'I will be torn into pieces first.'

Then they prayed together and Charles commanded them always to fear God and this they promised to do.

One of the bishops came to take the children away; they were weeping bitterly. Charles watched them and when they reached the door he ran after them and snatched them up that he might embrace them once more and they clung to him as though they would never let him go.

The hour was fixed. They brought him dinner but he was in no mood to eat.

'You should eat, sire,' his Bishop Juxon warned him. 'You will faint for lack of food.'

'Yes,' agreed Charles, 'and it might be misconstrued if I did that.' Whereupon he took some wine and food.

When he had eaten he said: 'Let them come. I am ready.'

But they did not come. There was a delay. Two of the military commanders who had been chosen to superintend the murder refused to do so at the last minute. Nothing could shift their decision; they were jeered at and threatened; still they would not take charge of the grisly task. Their names were Hunks and Phayer. I would remember them, too.

There was a small grain of comfort in knowing that they had to offer one hundred pounds to one who would aid the executioner – and thirty-eight people refused.

In the end they had to threaten one of the sergeants from another regiment to do the deed, and the executioner himself had tried to hide himself and when he was found he had to be threatened, too, and offered thirty pounds to do his work. They insisted on wearing masks as they did not want to be seen as executioners of the King.

It must have been a great joy for Charles to receive from our son Charles a blank sheet of paper with his signature at the bottom. Our son had written in a separate note that he would pledge himself to carry out any terms which might be imposed on him in exchange for his father's life.

Charles kissed the paper and burned it.

I heard that he slept quietly on the night before he went out to face his murderers. Thomas Herbert who, as Groom of the Bedchamber, was sleeping in the room with him awoke shouting in his sleep and he told the King that he had been disturbed by a nightmare. He had dreamed that Archbishop Laud had come into the room and knelt before the King while they talked together.

The King knew why he was shaken. It was because Archbishop Laud was dead, having been executed four years before.

They could not sleep after that although it was only five o'clock.

When Herbert was dressing him he said he wished to be as trim on this day as he had been on the day of his marriage. They said his voice broke a little when he said that and I knew it was because he was thinking of the sorrow this day would bring to me.

He bade Herbert bring him two shirts.

'It is cold outside,' he said. 'The wind might cause me to shake on my way to the scaffold and I would have no imputation of fear, for death is not terrible to me. I am prepared, I thank God. Let the rogues come for me when they please.'

I do not want to think of that scene but I can picture it so clearly and I cannot get it out of my mind. I can see the mass of people who would not be allowed to come too close to the scaffold and were kept back by the many soldiers whom Cromwell had commanded should be there. How apprehensive he and his friends must have been!

Charles stepped out through the banqueting hall for one of the windows had been removed so that he could do this.

I often wonder what his thoughts were as he went up to the scaffold. Of me, I like to think; and yet again I did not want him to think of me then because I knew that to do so would increase his sorrow.

What does one think of when one faces death? He was a good man, a man who had tried to do his duty, and if he had failed to please his people it was through no lack of effort on his part. He had always done what he believed to be right; and I knew – and was proved right in this – that these would be seen to be unhappy days for England and those people who had fought – valiantly I must admit – for Cromwell would soon be longing for the days when people could sing and dance and be joyful; they would regret those harsh laws of the Puritans ere long. And I was glad. I hated them. I was not calm and thoughtful like Charles. They were my enemies . . . those men who had put to death a great good man and I fervently wished that they would all burn in hell.

So he came out looking beautiful as he always had and without showing a tremor of fear.

I could imagine his looks of contempt for the bewigged and masked murderers who had not the courage to do the deed in the open but must cower behind disguises.

The executioner knelt and asked forgiveness.

Charles's reply was quiet and dignified. 'I forgive no subject of mine who comes hither to shed my blood.'

When he stepped up to the scaffold there was a terrible hush in the crowd. The executioner in a quiet and respectful voice asked him to push his hair under his cap.

This he quietly did.

He said in a clear voice: 'I go from a corruptible to an incorruptible crown.' Then he took off his coat and doublet.

He asked the executioner to make sure that the block was firm. 'Now,' he said, 'I will say a short prayer in silence and when I lift my hands I shall be ready for you to strike.'

That was the end.

My Charles, King, husband, lover, friend and martyr was dead.

They told me that a groan was heard through the crowd of people and that there was a terrible sense of foreboding in Whitehall that day.

I had to shut myself away for a while. I could not bear to see my attendants, let alone hear them speak to me. There was so much to remind me.

My poor little Henriette, who was not yet five years old, was quite bewildered. She would watch me and her eyes would fill with tears.

'I am doing no good to her and none to myself,' I told Lady Morton. 'She would be better with you alone.'

Lady Morton had too much good sense to deny this and so I decided that for a while I would seek the peace and solace of my favourite Carmelite convent in the Faubourg St Jacques. I gave my daughter into the care of Lady Morton with instructions that she should look after the child's creature comforts while Father Cyprien should see to her spiritual welfare. I thought I could not do better than that and I gave myself up to meditation and prayer and lived a life of seclusion governed by bells. I needed it. I was angry with the Almighty for what seemed like indifference to my suffering and for permitting the cruel murder of my husband. I knew I should not complain; it was His will; but I railed against such treatment and I could not be reconciled until I had wrestled with myself.

I dressed in black, which I swore I would do to the end of my life. I would mourn for Charles as long as I lived. I looked very like one of the nuns of the convent in my long rustling skirts and I wore a cap with a widow's peak which came over my forehead and with a black veil cascading from the back.

When I had been a few weeks in the convent and was beginning to accept the fact that I must learn to live without Charles, Father Cyprien came to see me and gave me such a lecture that I felt like boxing the man's ears, priest though he was. Then I knew I was becoming myself once more.

'What are you doing shutting yourself away from the world?' demanded Father Cyprien. 'Have you forgotten that you have a son and that he has to regain his throne? Have you forgotten that you are the daughter of the great Henri IV? Is it fitting that you should spend your days thus in idleness when there is work to be done?'

'Have I not done enough . . . and to what avail?' I cried.

'Your father did not give up in *his* struggles. When he suffered temporary defeat he fought again and so came to greater glory.'

'Murdered,' I reminded him, 'as my husband was . . . but differently. I'd rather Charles had gone by the knife of a madman than the action of coldblooded murderers and pilferers of his throne.'

'That is more like you. Your household needs you. Have you forgotten your young daughter? She pines for you. And what of

your son? You must bring Charles to Paris. There must be no
more delay. He has a throne to fight for.'

Two days later I left the convent.

Father Cyprien was right. I should be planning. It did wonders
for me. I was alive again. I was going to live through my children.
I was blessed in them. Charles was a son a mother could be proud
of; James had come to Paris from Holland; he was good looking
and his manners were as charming as those of his brother
Charles. I had always insisted on impeccable manners. It
was strange but loving my husband as I had I was able to see
where he had failed. That aloof manner of his had alienated
people and it may have been one of the causes why so many
turned against him. Rulers must not keep themselves too much
apart from their subjects; it was not easy to keep the balance
between royalty and the necessary bonhomie needed to win
people. My father had had it to a great degree; my son Charles
had it; James less so, but it was there and he was young
yet.

Mary had been a wonderful friend to us and she and the Prince
of Orange, who were so devoted to each other, had shown us
comforting hospitality and had done everything to help us. I had
my precious Henriette with me now but the two who worried me
were little Elizabeth and Henry – both in the hands of the Roundheads. If I could only have them with me I should be greatly
relieved.

What we must do was to get Charles fighting for his throne, and
the first thing was for him to come to me here in Paris.

I wrote to him. I had been able to redeem some of my rubies
when I first came to France and was hoarding them for the day
when I would sell or pawn them to raise money for my son's army
as I used to for my husband's.

Charles must marry and his bride must be someone who could
help him regain his throne.

I was pleased when the Grande Mademoiselle called on me at
the Louvre. She was very gracious to me and condoled with me
on my loss. I tried not to give way to emotion before her for she
was not exactly a comfortable person, very different from warmhearted Queen Anne who had been so good to me when I needed
help.

I said: 'My son will be coming to me in Paris soon.'

'I was under the impression that your son was with you now, Madame,' she said.

'You are referring to my son James, the Duke of York. I meant the King.'

'Oh yes . . . of course. He will be King now . . . if he can regain his throne.'

'There is no doubt that he will do that,' I said sharply.

'I am glad to hear it.'

Her eyes were speculative. She could not deceive me, this sly Grande Mademoiselle. She had suffered two disappointments. The King of Spain had married his niece, so poor Mademoiselle was not to be Queen of Spain. The Emperor of Austria had chosen one of his cousins. Mademoiselle's nose was decidedly out of joint. It might well be that she would not be quite so supercilious now regarding her cousin Charles. It was true he had yet to regain his throne but having seen those of Spain and Austria slip out of her grasp, the ambitious creature might be feeling she could not be too selective. Moreover she must be about twenty-two years old – quite mature for a marriageable princess. She had been considering herself the most delectable marriage prospect for a very long time. Was she beginning to doubt?

'When will he be in Paris?' she was clearly trying to keep the eagerness out of her voice.

'Very soon, I promise you.'

'You mean you promise yourself, dear aunt, not me.'

Oh, she was an insolent creature! If it had not been for her money I would not have received her, let alone considered her as a daughter-in-law.

Charles did not immediately respond to my summons. First he made excuses and then he merely said he was not yet ready.

I was getting frantic and I suggested to Henry Jermyn that he approach Mademoiselle and make an offer on Charles's behalf for her hand.

Henry was a little reluctant and wondered if it were wise but I insisted. I had to keep events moving for while something was going on, it was balm to my wounds. Only while I was absorbed in some project could I forget that Charles was dead.

Henry came back in some dismay, and reported what had happened.

'I told her that when he had seen her Charles had been so

overcome by admiration that he had become speechless. Mademoiselle has a sharp tongue. She retorted: "Oh, I thought that was due to his ignorance of the French language. He did not converse at all. In my opinion the inability to converse detracts from a personality more than anything else." '

'She can be a most unpleasant creature.'

'She has always had a high opinion of herself.'

'I thought that she might have been a little more humble after the snubs she received from Spain and Austria.'

'There had been no commitments for the King of Spain or the Emperor of Austria to enter an alliance with her,' Henry reminded me.

'No, but it was an understood possibility. Go on.'

'Then she said that she would prefer to discuss the matter with Charles himself and could not commit herself to a go-between. She added that since Charles was so much in love with her he would doubtless change his religion. If he did that she would be assured of his devotion and then would begin to consider the matter.'

'The minx! She knows that if he changed his religion he would have no chance of regaining his throne.'

'Dear Madam, I fear there is nothing we can do but await the arrival of the King.'

It was summer before Charles arrived in Paris. I thought he looked very impressive with his tall figure and ugly good-natured face, his musical voice and his kingly bearing. There was a certain aloofness in his manner towards me. I realized later that it was his way of telling me that he was going to decide his own affairs for himself. My little Henriette was beside herself with joy and it gave me great pleasure to see the affection between those two. She leaped into his arms and clasped hers about his neck. She was his little Minette and he was more than an adored brother; in her eyes he was a god.

It was pleasant to watch; but I was impatient to put Mademoiselle's vast fortune to good use in restoring the crown.

I dismissed everyone so that we were alone and told him that Mademoiselle was more than ready to listen to reason.

'Of course she will try to test you and suggest that you change your religion for her sake, but you must not take that too seriously.'

'I take it very seriously,' retorted Charles. 'And the answer is that I have no intention of making it impossible for me to return to England as King.'

'I know. But laugh it off, Charles. Carry her off her feet. She is, I sense, a somewhat anxious young lady. The King of Spain and the Emperor have just chosen elsewhere in spite of her fortune.'

I had noticed a young woman in the company who had come from Holland with him. She was very handsome in a bold and brazen way. I had asked questions about her and had been given evasive answers, but in view of what I knew of Charles and his exploits in Jersey I began to have suspicions.

I felt a twinge of uneasiness when I heard that she had a baby – a child of two or three months.

'By the way, Charles,' I said, 'who is that handsome young woman who seems to have a place among your attendants?'

'You must mean Lucy,' he said.

'And who, may I ask, is Lucy?'

'You may certainly ask, Mam,' said Charles putting on a regal air, reminding me that although I was a Dowager Queen he was the King. 'Her name is Lucy Walter and she is a special friend of mine.'

'A *special* friend?'

'You heard aright, Mam. That is what I said.'

'Oh . . . and the child?'

'Mine, Mam. Mine.'

'Charles, this is. . . .'

He lifted his shoulders and smiled at me. 'He is a very amiable child.'

'Your father never behaved like this.'

'No, Mam. And I must never behave as he did.'

I felt as though he had struck me across the face. He was repentant at once for he had loved his father; but he was right, of course. Charles's behaviour had been in a great measure responsible for what had happened to him.

He said gently: 'Lucy is a pleasant girl. She is devoted to me and I to her. She is a great diversion.'

'There was the Jersey girl.'

'Also a charming creature.'

'Charles, you must be more serious.'

'I assure you, Mam, no one could be more serious than I. I have one ambition and that is to regain my throne.'

'Mademoiselle must not hear of this Lucy Walter.'

He lifted his shoulders.

'Charles, do you understand this match could be of the greatest use to you. Her fortune. . . .'

'I know her fortune is great.'

'Then Charles, you must woo her. It should not be difficult. She is the most arrogant conceited creature on Earth.'

'And this creature is to be my wife!'

'The money . . . it could make all the difference. Please go to see her. Flatter her. That will be necessary. Queen Anne has arranged that you shall met at Compiègne . . . in the *château* there. It is really rather romantic.'

'There is nothing so romantic as a large fortune,' said Charles cynically.

However he did agree to go to Compiègne.

It was a disaster – as I believe Charles intended it to be. He looked more distinguished than anyone in the company because he was so tall that he towered above them all. Queen Anne was there, as eager to help as ever and with her the young King of France. I was amused to see that Mademoiselle had dressed with particular care with her hair specially curled; and her blue prominent eyes were taking in every detail of Charles's appearance.

He was distantly polite with her and it was rather a difficult meal. Queen Anne and Mademoiselle were both eager to know how everything was going in England but in spite of this being of paramount importance to him, Charles appeared to know very little, having been so long in Holland, he explained, and having to rely on hearsay. I could see that Mademoiselle was finding him rather dull and that he was growing more and more indifferent to her opinion of him. His French was not nearly as good as his brother James's and he had to excuse himself more than once because of his paucity of the language.

When the ortolans were brought in Charles declined and took instead a piece of mutton, which deeply shocked Mademoiselle, who assumed that his tastes were crude and that he was no husband for a lady of refinement.

When the meal was over Queen Anne, always eager to help, arranged that Charles and Mademoiselle should be alone together.

What happened during that brief interview – it lasted no more than fifteen minutes – I cannot be sure, except of one thing. Charles was determined to choose his own bride and had no intention of allowing me to do it for him.

It was all very unsatisfactory. Mademoiselle was certainly very piqued; as for Charles he maintained a solemn enigmatical air and I supposed that he who knew so well how to attract women was equally well versed in the art of driving them away.

He told me afterwards that he did not pay her compliments because he could think of none that fitted; but as it appeared to be expected of him – by both the Queens of England and France – he had made a formal declaration to Mademoiselle by, as he took his leave of her, saying that Henry Jermyn spoke better French than he did and would therefore be better able to explain what he wished to say to her.

Henriette was with her brother whenever she could be. I said to her: 'You must remember he is the King. You must be very respectful to him.'

She only laughed and said he was her dear brother Charles and she was his Minette and she did not have to be the least bit respectful. He loved her dearly and told her so.

Naturally I was delighted to see the affection between them. Henriette was a dear child. I kept her close to me and supervised her education myself and with the help of Father Cyprien I was bringing her up in the Catholic Faith.

Lady Morton did not altogether approve of this and because I was so fond of her and would never forget how she had brought Henriette out of England to me, I was very anxious for her to have the benefit of the true Faith too. I confided this to Henriette. I said: 'My darling, you love Lady Morton, do you not?'

Henriette said she did indeed.

'Then,' I said, 'is it not sad that she should be left in darkness? We should try to bring her into the light with us. . . . It would give me the greatest happiness if our dear Lady Morton would cease to be a Protestant and become a Catholic. We must try to help her. Will you?'

'Oh I will, Mam,' said my little daughter fervently.

Some days later I asked how she was getting on with the conversion and she told me very seriously that she was trying very hard.

'What do you do?' I asked.

'Hug her and kiss her and I say to her, "Dear Madam, do be a Catholic. Please be a Catholic. You must be a Catholic to be saved." '

I smiled and I learned that Lady Morton was touched but it did not change her. She implied that she was aware of our little plot and she told me with a smile that she believed Father Cyprien was in fact instructing her rather than Henriette.

Henriette soon betrayed her zeal to her brother and this was the beginning of trouble.

One could never be sure what Charles was thinking. He was not a man to lose his temper – he did not take after me in that – but gave the impression of a kind of insouciance, an indifference. At times he seemed content to dally on the Continent and I wondered whether he was making any real efforts to win back his crown. But when he was determined on something he could be very stubborn. He exasperated me sometimes because it was impossible to quarrel with him. I would rather he had flared up in anger so that I could know what he was thinking.

He said to me: 'Mam, it is unwise for Minette to be brought up as a Catholic.'

'*I* think,' I retorted, 'for the sake of the child's soul it would be unwise to bring her up in any other way.'

'It was the cause of much of our troubles.'

'One often has to fight for one's Faith. The Faith is strewn with martyrs.'

'My father one of them.'

He was sorry then because any mention of the late King filled me with melancholy which persisted for days.

'He had other troubles,' he went on softly, 'God rest his soul. But, Mam, if it is known in England that Henriette is being brought up as a Catholic and I approve of this, it could jeopardize my chances of regaining the crown.'

'I cannot see that.'

'I can,' he said. 'The people will be afraid that I or James might be the same.'

'I would to God you were! Listen to me, Charles. When I married your father there was a clause in the settlement that I was to have charge of my children's religious instruction until they were thirteen years old. That was never carried out.'

'It would have meant that we should all have been Catholics, for what children learn in their early years usually settles them for life. No, Mam, Henriette should not be allowed to talk so constantly of her religion and efforts to convert Lady Morton.'

'She is but a child.'

'It would be better to take her out of the hands of Father Cyprien.'

'I will not do it,' I said firmly.

Charles sighed. He did not want to hurt me for there was a very kind side to his nature. He hated trouble and when it was there tried to avoid it by delegating someone else to take care of it. As a king he could do that. I thought it was a great fault in his nature but later I began to see that it was an asset. He did not waste his emotions on petty quarrels. He rarely lost that magnificent serenity which later was to give him the reputation of a cynic. So now he did not insist, but I knew the matter was not at an end, someone else would be set to persuade me. In fact he gave the task to Sir Edward Hyde, a man I loathed, but whom I had to admit had always been loyal to the royalist cause and he was now Charles's constant companion and adviser.

I soon despatched him with a few sharp words.

However it did make a coolness between Charles and me and it showed me clearly that my son had no intention of taking my advice.

A few weeks later the Emperor lost his young bride and I could not resist a dig at Mademoiselle.

'Perhaps I should congratulate you on the death of the Empress,' I said slyly. 'For if the affair failed formerly it is sure to succeed next time.'

She flushed hotly and replied haughtily: 'I had not given thought to the matter.'

'Some people prefer old men who must be nearly fifty with four children to a handsome King of nineteen years old. It is difficult to understand but must be accepted, I suppose. Do you see that very handsome young woman over there. My son likes her very well.'

Charles was standing by at that time and I think he was annoyed to be discussed in his presence; but I, his mother, would do as I pleased.

I went on: 'My son is too poor for you, Mademoiselle. All the same he does not want you to know of his feelings for the young lady. He is very much afraid that I should mention her to you.'

Charles bowed to me and then to Mademoiselle and walked out of the room, his face inscrutable so that I could not tell how annoyed he was. But I guessed it was very deeply. He was very cool to me afterwards though always polite.

I was angry with myself. I had been foolish to say what I had when all that mattered to me now was my children's affection and well being. But I was angry about Mademoiselle and it did seem such a good opportunity missed. And he could have charmed her had he wished to. Heaven knows he was successful enough with other women.

The French Court was still at St Germain because the Fronde troubles kept starting up and Anne felt it was unsafe to bring the young King back to the Louvre. I was still there but I had noticed a growing antagonism towards me. At first they had all been so sorry for me and remembered that I was the daughter of their beloved Henri IV; now they saw me as royal, closely connected with Queen Anne and therefore Mazarin; and I was beginning to get hostile looks, and so were members of my household.

Anne was afraid for us and sent messages asking us to come to her and the King at Saint Germain. Charles agreed with me that we ought to accept the invitation, for the mood of the Parisians was growing more and more hostile.

So one day we set out; but of course we could not leave in secret and as we passed through the palace gates an angry crowd was waiting for us. They jeered at us. It was true that I owed money to many tradesmen and they must have feared that they would never get it and that I was leaving in order to escape paying them.

I wanted to explain, but how can one talk to a crowd of menacing people.

I was the one they hated. They crowded round my coach and I had a few horrifying moments when I feared they were going to drag me out and kill me.

Few mobs can be as terrifying as a Paris mob. They seem far more fierce than the English and I feared that they might become very violent indeed.

Then just as I was certain that some ruffian was going to wrench open the door of my coach and drag me out, my son Charles appeared. He looked so tall and dignified in his black mourning garments that for a few moments he startled the crowd. Those few moments were enough. He laid his hand on the door of the coach and told the coachman to proceed slowly. He walked beside the coach as we went through the crowds, and I was amazed at the manner in which they fell back; and it was all due to that magnificent presence of his. He was unarmed; he would have been unable to defend himself with his sword against the mob; but still they recognized and respected his royalty.

I watched him through a haze of tears and I knew that one day he would be a king in very truth.

That incident moved me deeply and perhaps it did him too, for after it our relationship began to change. I felt I could not dictate to such a man; and he seemed to come to a new understanding and realize that everything I did – however misguided it might seem to him – was meant to be for his benefit and was done out of an excess of love.

After Worcester

I was glad that the relationship between Charles and myself had changed and that when he did go we parted as loving parent and devoted son.

Everything seemed to go wrong for us. We had planned that he should go to Ireland and use it as a stepping stone to England; but no sooner had we agreed that this would be the best plan than we heard that Cromwell had gone to Ireland on a punitive expedition, so that put the project out of the question.

Charles decided however that he could not remain in Paris and set out for Jersey with his retinue, which included his mistress Lucy Walter and her few months' old son whom they had named James. It was very irregular but I had come to the conclusion that I must not try to interfere too much with Charles.

At least in Jersey he could keep an eye on what was happening in England and be ready to go through Scotland, perhaps, if Ireland remained unsuitable.

Just as my hopes were beginning to rise fate struck me another blow. This one I found very hard to bear. It was a long time since I had seen my two children who were the prisoners of the Roundheads but I thought of them every day and I was constantly turning over in my mind plans to rescue them.

I worried more about Elizabeth than Henry. She was a little older and more able to appreciate sorrow, and I knew how deeply affected she had been by her father's death for I had news of her from time to time and I had written letters to members of the Parliament imploring them to send my daughter and little son to me. What harm could such children do to any cause?

But those cruel men would not release my children and I continued to fret for them.

I had just had news that Charles had landed in Scotland and that he was promised help. He had had to buy it dearly and had

agreed to the Covenant, to renounce treaties with the Irish rebels
and to uproot Popery wherever it should be found once he had
regained his kingdom. For this the Scots would rally to his cause
and provide an army with which to invade England and win his
crown for him.

I was furious when I heard that. It seemed like a betrayal of his
own family. It could only be directed against me. And there was
little Henriette too. She was a Catholic now, even as I was.

I fumed with rage and it was Henry Jermyn who reminded me
that my own father had made peace and become King of all
France because as he had said, when Paris had refused to
surrender to a Huguenot, 'Paris is worth a Mass.'

So Charles was in Scotland and there was hope. And now . . .
this fresh blow. If only I could have been with my child, if I could
have spoken with her, held her in my arms, I should not have felt
so bitter. What sort of men were these to ruin the lives of little
children?

My little Elizabeth was only fifteen. What unhappy years they
had been for her! She must have been about seven when the
troubles started – a sweet, loving child, my own little daughter
whom I had scarcely seen while she was growing up.

The Roundheads had put her and her brother in the care of the
Countess of Leicester at Penshurst. I knew Penshurst. A delightful castle set on a pleasant incline with woods, fields and hop
grounds around it. I remembered well the old banqueting hall
lighted by its five Gothic windows and I could picture my
children seated at the oak table there. The Parliament had
announced that there was no royalty now and that the children
were to be treated as those of an ordinary nobleman. They would
not have cared about that, I was sure; what would have broken
their hearts was the separation from their family. I had heard that
the Roundheads suspected the Countess of ignoring orders and
showing the children too much respect; they had even sent some
of their men to Penshurst to make sure their orders were carried
out. How I despised them for their persecution of two helpless
children!

Apparently the spies were most dissatisfied by the manner in
which the Countess treated the children, swearing that she gave
them too much deference. Dear Countess! I had always liked her
and it had given me some relief to know that the children were

put into her hands for the reports I had heard at that time filled me with dread. The talk of apprenticing Henry to a shoemaker had horrified me for I knew those wicked men were capable of doing that. There was a rumour that they were to be sent to a charity school and were to be known as Bessy and Harry Stuart.

Lady Leicester had brought in a tutor for them – a man named Richard Lovell, who had instructed her own children; but even so this brave and noble lady could not go on defying the Parliament. There were frightening rumours at that time. One was that the children were to be poisoned and I was terrified that they would disappear as long ago two little Princes had vanished in the Tower of London.

When Charles landed in Scotland the Roundheads must have been alarmed and perhaps because they thought an attempt to rescue the children might be made they removed them to Carisbroke Castle.

I wondered what my two little ones felt at being sent to the prison where their father had spent some of the last days of his life.

A week after they had arrived at Carisbroke Elizabeth and Henry were playing bowls on that green which had been made for their father when there was a heavy rain shower and the children were wet through. The next day Elizabeth was in a high fever and confined to her bed.

She must have been in a low state and very melancholy to be in her father's prison and she must have remembered that last interview with him; she had loved him so dearly and had mourned him ever since. The poor child must have wondered from day to day what her own fate would be in the hands of her father's murderers.

If only Mayerne could have been with her! But they had dismissed him and they were certainly not going to allow any member of the royal family to have the services of the renowned doctor. He was nearly eighty now but still as skilful and it might have been that he could have saved my child's life.

One of the doctors whom they were obliged to call in – Dr Bagnall – did send to Mayerne and ask his advice and the good doctor sent back medicines, but it was too late.

My dear child knew she was dying. I tried to imagine the sorrow and desolation of poor little Henry. Elizabeth gave him her pearl necklace and sent a diamond ornament to the Earl and Countess of Leicester. It was all she had to leave.

They were determined that no honour should be paid to her. She was placed in a lead coffin and taken by a borrowed coach to Newport, attended by a few of those who had served her in the past. The coffin was placed in the east part of the chancel in St Thomas's Chapel and they put a simple inscription on it

Elizabeth second daughter
of the late King Charles
Deceased September 8th M.D.C.L.

No stone was erected and the letters E.S. were engraved in the wall above the spot where the coffin had been laid.

So died my daughter, the child I had borne with such joy and loved with such devotion.

It was small wonder that I thought Heaven itself was against me.

Children are both a blessing and an anxiety. I loved mine dearly but we were often in conflict.

There was James. He was growing up very different from his brother; they were unlike in every way except in their impeccably good manners, which I had insisted be instilled in them. James was fair and Charles had those swarthy looks which must have come down from an ancestor of Navarre, so they never looked like brothers. James's temperament was difficult and it was the easiest thing in the world to quarrel with him whereas it was impossible to quarrel with Charles, who could be serene, evasive and indifferent, and when one thought he had acquiesced he would go away and do exactly what he had planned to do from the first.

I know I was not the easiest person to live with. I had been born with a desire to impose my will on others but it was meant to be for their good, though they so often could not see this.

James was restive, hating, I suppose, to be cooped up in Paris while his brother was in Scotland. I think he rather resented being the younger son and in spite of his undoubted good looks and Charles's far from handsome ones, he was always over-shadowed by his brother.

Well Charles was no longer with us in Paris and James was difficult. I sometimes think he enjoyed quarrelling and looked round for trouble. Heaven knew life was hard enough for me to bear. What were his troubles compared with mine?

Some trivial matter flared up one day and James took it seriously. He turned on me and said: 'I want to get away. I'm tired of being here. You tutor me in all things. I am old enough to think for myself.'

'You are clearly not,' I retorted. 'You talk like a foolish boy and that does not surprise me because you are one.'

In a very short time we were shouting at each other and James was behaving very badly, forgetting entirely the respect due to me, not only as his mother but as Queen of England.

I cried: 'Whatever I do, I do for you children. You are my main concern.'

Then he turned on me and said something which I found it very hard to forgive. 'Your main concern!' he said almost sneering. 'I thought your main concern was Henry Jermyn. You are more fond of him than you are of all your children put together.'

I stopped short to stare at him. Then I cried out: 'How dare you!' And I struck him hard across his face with the back of my hand.

He turned quite white and for a moment I thought he was going to return the blow. Then he turned away and strode from the room.

I was very upset. Of course I was fond of Henry Jermyn. He had been beside me, my faithful friend and helper, for many years. Moreover he was a jolly man, a handsome man who raised my spirits; and heaven knew I had need of a few like him around.

But what was James suggesting? That he was my lover!

I had never been a sensual woman. What I called 'that side of marriage' had never greatly appealed to me. It was my duty to produce children and that I had done in full measure. I had loved my husband completely and still did. But to take a lover now that he was dead . . . I could never do that. It would seem like disloyalty to him.

And yet . . . had I taken a lover? Not in the physical sense, but the truth was that I did love Henry Jermyn and if I lost him my life would be empty indeed.

I was terribly shaken and was expecting James to come to me with apologies, but he did not.

He had left Court.

It was heartbreaking that he should have gone like that before I had had a chance to talk to him. I wondered where he had gone and speculated that he had joined his brother in Scotland. But no. It turned out that he had gone to Brussels where he had been made very welcome.

This was most embarrassing. Not only had James left me after making that devastating statement but in Brussels he was on territory which belonged to Spain and Spain was at war with France.

I made up my mind that I would send him no money and as he could not exist without it he would have to return to me.

Then there was Mary. She had always been a good daughter and the marriage to William of Orange had turned out to be advantageous in the end, although at first we had all thought it was a little degrading for the daughter of the King of England to marry a mere Prince of Orange and we should never have allowed it to happen but for the fact that we had wanted to placate the Parliament by a Protestant match. Yet Holland had been our good friend and it was largely due to Mary and her husband.

I had always thought of Mary as a good daughter. She had extended help to Charles – of whom she was very fond – and her Court had provided a refuge for many of our supporters.

And now for the first time she was pregnant. I was delighted at the thought of a child and I wrote to her telling her that if it were a boy she must name him Charles after her father and brother.

There came sad news. The Prince of Orange had been struck down with small pox and within a few days of contracting the disease had died. The Dowager Princess Amelia who took a great pride in forcing her will on others and whom I had never liked, gave orders that Mary was not to be told of her husband's death until after the confinement.

The news, however, leaked out, but Mary was determined to give birth to a healthy child, and she did. I was delighted when I heard the news. 'Our little Charles,' I called the baby.

My chagrin was great when I heard that the dowager Princess had insisted that the child be named William after his father, and to my disappointment Mary agreed with her.

It was wonderful news that we had the child but his father's death was a tragedy for us all. When I heard it I said it seemed as though God wished to show me that I should detach myself from the world, by taking from me all those who would lead me to think of it. The loss of my son-in-law made me see this very clearly, for my hopes of Charles's restoration to the crown were based largely on William of Orange. And my daughter obeyed the wishes of her mother-in-law rather than those of her own mother!

Wherever I looked for comfort there was none.

The Queen of France however was very good to me. She commiserated with me over the deaths of Elizabeth and my son-in-law.

'Life is very cruel,' she said. 'One can be happy for a time and then it strikes . . . and does not always strike singly but many times as though to stress the fact that we are all at the mercy of our fate.'

I told her then how anxious I was on her behalf.

'Believe me,' I said, 'I have experience of the people. They are like savages when aroused. I shall never forget Charles standing at my coach door when I came out of the Louvre. They were all around me. I am sure it would not have taken them long to tear me to pieces.'

Anne looked a little impatient. She was easy going and I was sure she believed that Mazarin was so shrewd and clever that he could do anything. She did not like me to warn her. My criticism of Anne – and Heaven knew I should not be critical of one who had been so good to me in my need – was that she liked to pretend that what was not pleasant was not there.

After all I had suffered I saw the folly of this. One must be aware all the time. Think the worse . . . and face up to it as a possibility. If only Charles and I had done a little more of that I might not be in the position I found myself in at this time.

But because I felt it was my duty to warn her, her frowns did not stop me, and I went on to give her advice until finally she said in exasperation: 'Sister, do you wish to be the Queen of France as well as the Queen of England?'

I looked at her sadly and did not take offence at the rebuke. I merely said gently: '*I* am nothing. Do *you* be something.'

I think she saw my meaning and at that moment faced the truth and saw herself possibly in my position – a Queen without a kingdom. Perhaps she was realizing what an empty title it was when one had lost one's throne.

She was immediately sorry for her harsh tone, remembering all I had suffered and most of all the recent death of my daughter, for she was a devoted mother, living for her children, so she could understand the terrible sorrow a child's death could bring.

She put her hands over mine and said: 'Oh, my poor sister, I know your sadness and I know that sometimes you wish to leave it all and go to the Faubourg St Jacques and stay there with the nuns. Is that what you wish?'

'How well you know me! If I had a choice I would go there and pass the rest of my days in peace. But how could I do that? I have my sons . . . my little Henriette. . . .'

'I know,' said Anne. 'You could not rest there. I have been thinking of you and there is something which I believe could bring you great cheer.'

'It is difficult to think of what could do that. Only my son's restoration could make me happier and even then there would be so much sadness to look back on.'

'You are indeed the unhappy Queen, my sister. But I know you have always wished to found an order of your own.'

I looked at her in amazement and she smiled at me.

'I was thinking that to found your own convent would bring great ease to your mind and spirits. Am I right?'

'To found my own convent! Oh, what a dream! But how could I? All the money I have from the sale of my jewels must go to the battle for the throne.'

'I would help you with the convent,' said Anne.

I could not speak. I fell into her arms and hugged her.

At length I said: 'I bless that long ago day, dear sister, when they brought you to Paris to be my brother's wife.'

'You did not like me very much at first.'

'True affection is that which grows with the years,' I answered and added, 'I shall never be able to show you my gratitude or to tell you what your friendship has meant to me in my adversity.'

'It is in adversity that true friendship is seen,' she answered. 'Now let us plan. First we must find a suitable site. Do you know the country house on the hill at Chaillot?'

'I do,' I cried. 'It is a fine house. The Maréchal de Bassompierre used to live there. My father gave the house to him. It has been empty since his death.'

'That is why I thought of it. I have asked the price. It is six thousand pistoles.'

'Dear Anne, would you indeed do this?'

'Guessing that you would like it, I had already decided on it.'

I felt happier than I had for a long time and the Queen and I forgot our troubles in planning our convent. We should both use it as a retreat, and then I looked over the place with her and chose the apartments we should have when we came to the convent. The windows overlooked the Seine and the Avenue of the Cours La Reine.

I think Anne was as happy as I was planning it.

It was nearly two years since Charles had left France, and I was dreadfully worried. Rumours were coming across the Channel. Some reported that he was sick; others that he was dead. I refused to believe them. Something within me told me that Charles would survive. He had had to swear what the Scots wished him to and this he had done in order to gain their support, and for this he had been crowned at Scone but if ever he was victorious over the Parliamentarians he would be a Presbyterian King on both sides of the border.

Cromwell was marching to Scotland and soon we had news of the Royalist defeat at Dunbar and the capture of Edinburgh by the Roundheads.

Charles then marched south into England. It was a desperate move but I could see it was the only one to take in the circumstances. I hoped and prayed that there were some loyal Englishmen left in England to join him. Alas, he was disappointed in this and few came to augment the ten thousand men who constituted his army. Charles had impressed all with his bravery and his excellence in the field. He was always calm and serene and seemed not in the least perturbed by danger and disaster. It was a wonderful gift to have. I could admire it although it certainly had not come through me.

Battle took place at Worcester and when the news came to us it was the old story. Disaster for the Royalists. Success for

Cromwell. And what had happened to Charles? He had disappeared. It was then that the rumours started to come, thick and fast.

Most people thought he was dead.

My nights were haunted by evil dreams. Where was my son? What other and greater evils had Fate in store for me?

I was seated in my apartments in the Louvre sunk in the deepest despair when a man burst unceremoniously in. I stared at him, a little alarmed and then incensed by the intrusion. He was well over six feet tall, gaunt, and his hair was cut in the manner I loathed – that of the Roundheads.

He cried out: 'Mam. It is I.'

Then I flew to him, tears streaming down my face. 'It *is* you. Am I dreaming . . . ' I stammered.

'No, Mam. I am indeed here . . . and the first thing I did was to come to you.'

'Oh Charles . . . Charles my son. You are safe then. Oh thanks be to God.'

'I come to you defeated, Mam. But it will not always be thus.'

'No . . . no. Oh, Charles, I have had such fears . . . such dreams. I will send for your sister. She has been sunk in melancholy. First she must know that you are here. Then you can tell me all that happened.'

I shouted for attendants and sent them running to the Princess Henriette.

While I waited I took his hands . . . I kissed them. I pressed him to me. He smiled in his rather sardonic way, but there was tenderness in him.

My little seven-year-old daughter ran into the room and into his arms. He picked her up and danced round the room with her.

'I knew you would come. I knew you would come,' she kept chanting. 'They couldn't kill *you* . . . not even wicked old Cromwell.'

'No,' he said, 'not even wicked Old Cromwell. I am indestructible, Minette. You will see.'

'And when you have won the crown you will take me to England with you. We shall be together for ever and ever. . . .'

'When I win the crown miracles will happen.'

I loved to see them together and wished fleetingly that Charles had the same affection for me that he had for his sister. But of course she was a child and children showed only adoration. I had a duty to perform and that sometimes made one displease those whom one loved most.

He must tell us of his adventures, I said. I could not wait to hear.

'You have been away a long time,' Henriette accused him.

'The absence was forced on me. I would rather have been in Paris than in Scotland with those Presbyterians. They are a grim crowd, dear Minette. *You* would not like them. It is a sin, they consider, to laugh on a Sunday.'

'Do they save up their jokes for other days?'

'Why, bless you, jokes are sin too. Think of the things you like doing best and I'll be ready to wager that all would be a sin in the eyes of the Presbyterians.'

'Then I am glad you are back. Will it be like that in England?'

'Not while I am King. For that life is not for a gentleman of my tastes.'

He talked of his escape after Worcester and the terrible defeat his forces had suffered there. He had his faithful friends though and chief among them were Derby, Lauderdale, Wilmot and Buckingham. Yes, the son of that evil genius of my youth was one of Charles's closest associates. He was about three years older than Charles and I hoped he was not going to exert a similar influence over my son as that which his father had held over my husband. But I fancied my son was not the sort to be influenced. I was eager to hear more. Charles had escaped from Worcester – a man with a price on his head. He told us how the Earl of Derby had produced a certain gentleman – a Catholic at that – Charles Giffard, to guide him through unknown country to Whiteladies and Boscobel; how he, the King of England, had paused at an inn for food and afraid to stay there and eat it had ridden away with bread and meat in his hands.

I had never seen Charles so moved as he was when he told us of his first glimpse of Whiteladies, the farmhouse which had once been a convent. It was the place he had come to for shelter, and the two brothers who were living there – the Penderels – were staunch royalists.

'There was I,' said Charles, 'seated in this humble farmhouse surrounded by my friends, Derby, Shrewsbury, Cleveland, Wilmot and Buckingham with Giffard and the Penderels . . . planning what we should do next. The Penderels sent a message to Boscobel where more Penderels lived. You should have seen the clothes they gave me! A green jerkin and doublet of doeskin and a hat with a steeple crown. I looked like a country yokel. You would never have recognized me.'

'I think I should have recognized you anywhere,' I told him fondly.

'Wilmot had sheared my hair to this offensive cut. You know Wilmot. He made a joke of it – and a bad job, I must say. The Penderels trimmed me up afterwards, for as they wisely said, it must not look like a job that had been hastily done. I had to try to walk as a yokel would, and to talk like one. They were hard lessons, Mam.'

'I'm glad to hear it,' I told him. 'But you managed well enough I have no doubt.'

'No, indeed not. I made a poor rustic. Wilmot said his lord the King kept peering out from under my Roundhead haircut. I walked so far that my feet were bleeding and Joan Penderel, the wife of one of the brothers, washed my feet and put pads of paper between my toes where the skin was rubbed. I can tell you I was in a sorry state. Then news came that the neighbourhood was full of Roundhead soldiers . . . all bent on one thing. To find me and put me where they had put my father.'

I shivered and touched his hand gently.

'I'm sorry, Mam,' he murmured.

I nodded and he went on: 'A very good friend came to Boscobel to warn me. He was Colonel Carlis, a man I greatly trusted. He told me I was most unsafe. The soldiers were searching every house and could not fail to come to Boscobel. What could we do? He went out of the house and saw near by an enormous oak tree in full leaf. The Colonel said "That is our only hope." So he and I climbed the tree and hid ourselves among the leaves. The Penderels said we were quite invisible and unless the soldiers decided to climb the tree, they would never see us. And, Mam, there is my little miracle. From the tree we could see the soliders searching the wood and the houses . . . and they never thought to look up into the oak tree.'

So we were back where we were. He was alive and well; he had

had great adventures; and, as I had come to expect, all had ended in defeat.

He had become very cynical. I sometimes thought he had given up all hope of winning the crown and had decided to live where he could enjoy life. He liked his friends, good conversation – and women, of course. I was glad to see that he was rid of that brazen Lucy Walter, who had been blatantly unfaithful to him during his absence. I suppose two years was too long for a woman of that kind to wait. But she had the boy. What a pity that was! Charles seemed to have an affection for the child. From what I saw of the infant he was strikingly handsome.

I could not rid myself of the thought of the Grande Mademoiselle's money lying idle when it might have been equipping an army. I still hoped for the match.

She was in exile from the Court at this time because she had openly helped the Fronde. Her father, Gaston, was a supporter of them too, which was disgraceful as he was going against his own family. Always flamboyant, Mademoiselle had on one occasion gone into battle and it was significant that she had done this at the town of Orléans when the Fronde had taken it by storm.

What was she trying to be? Another Jeanne d'Arc!

She did show a certain interest in Charles. He had become something of a hero since his adventures after Worcester and I had never seen him talk as much as he did about them, for usually he was inclined to silence about his exploits. But these adventures seemed to have a fascination for him and he was ready to talk of them to any who asked him.

Mademoiselle gave a series of what she called "Assemblies". She was still not able to attend Court but she snapped her fingers at that and made sure that she invited the most interesting people and that the food she gave them was far more delicious than that served at Court.

Charles was always invited to these occasions and I really believed she was considering him as a husband. She must be getting a little anxious now. She was twenty-five, no young girl, and the Emperor had married his third wife and again declined my ambitious niece.

On one of these occasions when I was present she made a point of talking to me. I think she took a malicious delight in raising my hopes that she might take Charles as a husband.

'He has changed since his adventures,' she told me. 'He has become more mature . . . more serious . . . more mellowed shall we say? It is wonderful what hiding in an oak tree can do for a personality.'

'You too have changed, niece,' I reminded her. 'You have also become more . . . mature. After all it must have been a great adventure to play the Maid of Orléans.'

'It was . . . indeed it was. I heard that the King of England is too fond of many women to be faithful to one.'

'You speak of women . . . not of wives.'

'Do you believe then that a man who has been promiscuous in his youth will in marriage become a model husband?'

'It is possible.'

'It would be something of a miracle. Think of your father, dear aunt.'

'I often do, and he was your grandfather, remember. We should both be proud of him. He was the greatest king France has ever known.'

'I trust my little husband will be as great.'

'Your . . . little husband!'

'Well,' she looked at me maliciously, 'there is not much difference in our ages . . . eleven years and a few months. Louis is already fourteen.'

'He does not seem to be enamoured of the prospect since he banished you from Court,' I said sharply.

'Little Louis banish *me*! Oh no, that was old Mazarin and his Mamma.'

'Nevertheless I doubt. . . .'

She smiled at me sardonically and I dropped the subject for I was afraid my anger would explode.

The Frustrated Mother

Life was not all sorrow. At the end of the year I had word that Cromwell had decided to allow my son Henry to join me. I suppose this was because even Roundheads had some feeling, and the death of my daughter Elizabeth had caused a certain amount of dismay throughout the land. She had always been such a good child – a near saint – and her death had been so pathetic. Whatever the reason, Henry was given permission to leave.

Minette was delighted at the prospect of having a new brother with us. She asked countless questions, which alas I was unable to answer as my little son had been kept away from me for so long.

He arrived in Holland where his sister Mary received him and was so delighted to have him that she wanted to keep him with her. I had no intention of allowing that because I knew that she would endeavour to bring him up as a Protestant, and it was a secret resolve of mine that he should be, like his sister Henriette, Catholic.

He arrived in Paris and was so delighted to be with his own family. He immediately conceived a great admiration for Charles – whose adventures he had followed whenever he was able to – and he and Henriette worshipped him together. There was something about Charles which inspired this fervent devotion. I often wondered whether it was partly due to his height or was it his easy-going manner and superficial charm? In any case these two children adored him.

It was as though when something good happened something bad had to follow quickly. We now heard that the countries of Europe were accepting the new government of England and that Cromwell was making treaties with various countries. France was on the point of making them too, which would mean that the English government would be having a representative in Paris.

Charles said to me: 'That would be an intolerable situation as far as I am concerned. You know what would happen. I should be asked to leave.'

'You should tell them to do no such thing.'

He looked at me in exasperation. 'Dear Mam,' he said, 'if the King of France, the Regent or Mazarin ask me to leave, I have no alternative but to go. There is only one course open to me. I must leave before they ask me to.'

I suppose he was right and in any case he began making arrangements.

Henriette was beside herself with grief; so was Henry. I was sorry to see him go but I reminded myself that when he was not there I could carry out my intentions with regard to Henry's religious training.

Henry had begged Charles to take him with him. 'I am not a boy any more,' he cried. 'I am nearly fifteen. That is old enough to fight.'

Charles hesitated. He was very fond of Henry and he liked the boy's spirit. But I was against it.

'He is but a child, Charles,' I said. 'He needs to be educated and where better than in Paris? It would be a sin to take him away from his lessons at his age.'

Charles saw this in time and Henry suffered bitter disappointment.

Charles said: 'I promise you, brother, that in a few years you shall be at my side.'

And Henry had to be satisfied with that.

Before Charles left for Cologne where he had decided to stay for a while, he spoke very seriously to me. 'Henry is a Protestant,' he said. 'He is a Prince of a Protestant country. He must remain so. You must not try to make him a Catholic, Mam.'

That had been exactly my intention and he knew it.

I hesitated and Charles went on: 'If you do not give me your promise, I cannot leave him with you. I shall either take him with me or send him to my sister Mary who, as you know, was loth to part with him.'

So I promised and Charles left. But after he had gone I thought that although I had promised, to bring up my son in the true Faith would be such a good thing that it would outweigh anything that was wrong in breaking a promise.

Henry had brought with him Mr Lovell, the tutor whom the
Countess of Leicester had given him when he was at Penshurst.
The two were devoted to each other and Mr Lovell was a firm
Protestant. Charles favoured Mr Lovell because he had been such
a good tutor and had been in fact responsible in some measure for
the release of Henry. The tutor had personally gone to London
and seen several of the leading men in Cromwell's government
and because Mr Lovell was a good Protestant they listened to
him, and his advocacy and the death of Elizabeth had been
factors in their decision to release Henry.

Charles said Mr Lovell was a faithful servant, the sort wise men
grapple to them with bands of steel.

Mr Lovell would stand in my way, I knew, and I might have to
get rid of him, but I must work carefully and not let him know
what I planned.

I was feeling more alive now that I had my two youngest with
me and I could plan for them both. Henriette, the best loved of
them all, gave me cause for anxiety. She was rather thin and
delicate. I wished that she were more of a conventional beauty;
although she had great charm and a lovely skin, her back, like
mine, was not quite straight. I watched over her anxiously. I had
great plans for her, which must be kept secret. I did not see why
she should not marry her cousin Louis, in spite of the Grande
Mademoiselle's pretensions. What a glorious prospect! My little
one Queen of France. But why not? They both had the same
grandfather; she was the daughter of the King of England, and
although the French government was so cruel and misguided as
to recognize Cromwell, kings were still kings.

I was beside myself with joy when she was invited to take part
in a ballet in which the King and his brother, Anjou, would take
part. Henriette danced to perfection and I doubted there was
anyone at Court who was as light on her feet as my child.
And when she danced all that dainty elusive charm was
apparent.

What a delight it was when the curtain rose on that scene to
reveal my nephew Louis XIV, who was then about fifteen,
magnificently attired as Apollo on the throne with the Muses
around him. The piece was the wedding of Peleus and Thetis and
my little Henriette had her part to play in it. I sat watching her,
with my eyes filled with tears, sighing and regretting that her

father could not be beside me to applaud our most enchanting child.

My hopes were high. She was eminently suitable to be the bride of the young King.

I had turned my attention to Henry and was finding him rather a stubborn little boy. When I talked to him about the glories of the Catholic Church he replied: 'That may be, Mam, but it is not for me. I promised my father that I would cling to the Faith in which I was baptized and which is the Faith of my country.'

I laughed. 'Oh, you are such a dear little boy and it is good to remember your father, but if only he were here he would understand. Think what the men of that Faith did to him.'

'I promised him, Mam,' he said firmly.

Well, he was young and he would be pliable. I would achieve what I wanted in time and that would mean that two of my children were saved. In the meantime, to show his independence, Henry went off every Sunday to the Protestant service which the English residents in Paris had set up.

But if he was determined, so was I. He had a strong supporter in Mr Lovell and I was wondering more and more how I could get rid of him. To have him dismissed openly – which was what I should have liked to do – would have caused an outcry. Charles would hear of it and Charles was the King, whose word had to be obeyed, even by his mother. My children were not so ready to indulge me as their father had been.

The idea struck me that if I could send Henry away to some renowned tutor, the services of Mr Lovell would no longer be required. I thought of Walter Montague who was the Abbot of St Martin's near Pontoise and also my Grand Almoner. He was a great friend of mine and an ardent Catholic, having been converted nearly twenty years before when he had witnessed the exorcisms of the Ursuline nuns at Loudon. We had been friends ever since he had come to France at the time of my marriage, and after his conversion we had become much closer. He would understand at once what I wanted and would be as keen as I was to turn my son into a Catholic.

I sent word to Charles explaining that Henry was too fond of the society of idle boys and that I believed he should be sent to some quiet place to study. What better than to Pontoise where our good friend the Abbot could supervise his education.

I could not dismiss Mr Lovell or Charles would have been very suspicious and he would not believe that Henry had gone to Pontoise without his good tutor merely to study quietly.

It must have been disconcerting for Mr Lovell to be the only Protestant – with Henry – in a Catholic community and very soon he did not see how he could remain there. It was not difficult to suggest that he take a little trip to Italy as I believed he had always wanted to see that country.

I was relieved when he went without fuss, not knowing that he had talked to Henry, explained my motives and those of the Abbot and urged him to stand firm until he could let his brother, the King, know what was happening.

The Abbot wrote to me that he had high hopes that the conversion would be soon. He had talked to the boy of the possibilities which lay before him. As Duke of Gloucester, son of one King and brother to another, he would have special advantages. It was a great honour to wear the Cardinal's hat.

But Henry did not see it that way. 'The boy has a strong will,' wrote Montague. 'He says he cannot attempt to defeat me in argument but he knows what is right and what his brother expects of him and nothing will shake him in his determination to do his duty. He insists that his father told him to adhere to the Faith in which he was baptized and his brother, the King, wishes him to do the same. He added: "You can do what you like to me. I will cling to my Faith as I promised my father before he died." '

As the weeks passed the Abbot was growing more and more impatient and Henry more stubborn. The boy wrote to me asking for leave to return to Paris, and seeing that it was no use keeping him there, I gave my permission.

When he arrived I noticed the firm set of his lips. I could see his brother Charles in him and it was ironical to realize that they had inherited their determination to have their own way from me, not their father.

Henry was clever too and I was incensed when I heard that he had sent for Bishop Cosin to ask his advice as to how he should answer the Abbot when he was cross-examined by him. Cosin was a staunch Protestant and a real enemy of the Catholics. My husband had sent him to Paris to act as chaplain to those of my

household who belonged to the Church of England and at first he
had worked from a private house until that had proved to be
inadequate when a chapel had been fitted up to accommodate the
expanding congregation. Cosin was a man highly respected by
all. At first I had believed I could convert him. He would certainly
not have been accepted in England now because he was almost as
much opposed to the Puritans as he was to the Catholics. He loved
the rituals and ceremonies of the Church just as Archbishop Laud
had, though whereas that had been Laud's undoing, Cosin, who
had escaped to France, prospered. Nothing could have been
farther from the truth than to imagine he would turn to Catholicism. He was fundamentally against it, and because he was one of
the greatest speakers of the day, he was feared while he was
respected.

To think that my son Henry had gone to him made me anxious
and determined that something must be done at once.

I sent Henry back to Pontoise; but this time he had papers
which had been written for him by Cosin and naturally the
support of such a man increased his obstinacy.

I determined to act drastically and to send him to the Jesuit
College of Clermont. When Henry heard what was to happen he
grew white with rage. Once in a Jesuit college he would be unable
to escape. He stormed at me: 'I would rather be the prisoner of the
Roundheads at Carisbroke,' he cried. 'At least I was not bullied
then to go against my conscience.'

'You are a wicked boy,' I told him. 'You will be grateful one day
when you see the light.'

It was on the very morning when he was about to depart that
messengers arrived in haste from the King. There were letters for
me and for Henry. Charles reproached me for having forgotten
my promises not only to him but to my husband. There were
letters of rebuke for several of my friends and particularly Henry
Jermyn who, said the King, could have restrained me from my
irresponsible actions.

Worst of all was the letter to Henry.

I read it myself for Henry could not resist showing it to me. I
was incensed because Charles began by saying he was in receipt
of Henry's letter. So the boy had actually dared write to him!

' . . . it is the Queen's purpose to do all she can to change your
religion in which if you do hearken to her, you might never see

England or me again. . . . Consider well what it is to be . . . not only the cause of ruining a brother who loves you well but also your King and country. . . .

'I am informed that there is a purpose to send you to a Jesuits' College which I command you, in the same grounds, never to consent to. . . .'

What could have been more devastating to my plans!

When I read the letter I let it drop to the floor and took Henry into my arms.

'Dear child,' I said, 'my thoughts are all for you. I wanted you to push aside these temptations . . . nothing matters so much as the salvation of your soul.'

'I am determined to save it,' said the young rebel, 'by doing my duty to my King, my country and my religion – and that is the religion into which I was baptized.'

His eyes were blazing. So were mine. How could a son be so disobedient to his mother! I asked angrily.

'I am obedient to my King and my conscience,' said Henry.

Where had he learned such things? From Cosin, I supposed.

'Go to your apartments,' I said. 'I will send Abbé Montague to you. You must listen to him.'

'I am weary of listening to him. My mind is made up.'

All my calm deserted me. I saw only a disobedient son for whom I had worked and planned. Charles, James, Mary . . . they were all turning against me. And now Henry . . . aided by his brother.

I cried out in fury: 'If you do not embrace the Catholic religion I never want to see you any more.'

Henry looked at me in amazement.

'Yes,' I cried. 'Go! Get out of my sight. You are a wicked, ungrateful boy.'

Henry went and I did not see him until a few days later. I was on my way to Chaillot. I needed the peace of the place where I could contemplate this breach in the family. I could not bear it – most of all to see Henriette weeping all over the place. She had been so happy when Henry came; they were always talking about Charles's adventures and how wonderful it would be when he regained his throne. And now Henry was in disgrace. She could not understand it and I could not bear the sight of her little woebegone face. So I would go to my beloved Chaillot for a few days.

As I was about to leave the palace Henry ran out and came to me.

'Mam,' he said quietly, and I knew he was asking that we forget our grievances which I should have been so happy to do if he would only fall in with my wishes; but he was as firm as ever in that, so I turned my face away from him.

I was smiling grimly on the way to Chaillot. I would show the boy what it meant to defy me. I was the Queen of England whatever those Puritans said. I was also his mother.

I heard afterwards that he left me and went straight to the Protestant service – for it was a Sunday – but when he returned to the Palais Royal it was to find that there was no food for him and that even the sheets had been taken from his bed to indicate that there was no longer a place for him there.

It was Henriette who told me what had happened because he had come to say goodbye to her before he left. She was heart-broken.

There were Protestants in Paris to rally to his help. Lord Hatton and Lord Ormonde both hastily came forward and that very day my son Henry left Paris for Cologne. It was what he had wanted in the first place. He had gone to join his brother Charles.

I was very upset by what I called Henry's desertion. Queen Anne comforted me. She too had hoped that my son would cease to be a heretic. We were at Chaillot together where we often discussed the difficulties of life. I reminded her that she had little to complain of. She had two fine boys and Louis, now seventeen, seemed secure on the throne; he was growing more and more kingly every day.

She smiled with pleasure. She doted on her elder son and I could well understand it. He did not bring her the sorrow my children brought me.

'I worry a great deal,' I said. 'The months pass and the years . . . and my son is still without his throne and every day the wicked rebels of England would seem to grow stronger and because of their strength are accepted by others in a manner which is difficult to understand.'

I could not resist reminding her of my resentment that

members of my own family should be ready to make treaties with
the roundheaded traitors.

It was not Anne's fault, of course. She was not the true
governor of France – merely the Regent – and with Louis growing
up she would not be that much longer. She mentioned that
Cromwell now called himself the Lord Protector and that the
people appeared to be accepting him.

'I worry a great deal about my little Henriette. What will
become of her? Here she is Princess . . . daughter of the King of
England . . . living as she does!'

'We must give a ball for her.'

'Oh dear sister, you are so good, but we could not afford the
gown . . . and all the necessities. It would be a travesty of what a
ball for a Princess of England should be.'

Anne was thoughtful. Then she said: 'I will give some little
parties in my apartments. The King and his brother will be there
and a few well chosen younger people. Henriette shall come and
show us how well she dances.'

I was excited. We could fit her up in a dress which would be
suitable for such an occasion; she was only eleven years old as yet
and the small party would be ideal.

I was very anxious for her to become good friends with her
cousin. Louis was by no means unkind. He loved to dance and
Henriette was the best dancer at Court. I can say that quite
honestly, setting aside all maternal pride. She was delicate and
dainty and she had appeared to enchant people when she had
appeared in the *Nuptials of Peleus and Thetis*.

I was thinking: She is only eleven; Louis is seventeen. There is
time. Oh, if only Charles could regain his throne his sister would
be a fitting mate for the King of France.

How I looked forward to that occasion. Little did I realize how
mortified I was going to be; and my little Henriette too.

I went back to Henriette and told her that she was going to an
assembly in the Queen's apartments. 'It will be your party really,' I
said, 'for I suspect the Queen is giving it for you. She will insist that
the King is there. Have you practised your steps? You must not
disgrace us. You will be dancing with the King of France and that,
my darling, shall be as great an honour for him as it is for you.'

Henriette said: 'Mam, you say strange things at times. How
could that be?'

'Never forget you are the daughter of a King of England.'

'How wonderful it would be if Charles could win his throne and we could all go back to England. I can think of nothing to wish for which would please me more than to live with Charles for ever.'

Foolish child's talk! When he regained the throne she should still be here. Queen of France. I wanted nothing less for my favourite child. She was the only one who had not disappointed me – except Elizabeth, who had in a way disappointed me by dying, poor darling.

The great day came. How charming my little Henriette looked! Her dress might not have been splendid – La Grande Mademoiselle would have smiled at its simplicity had she been present and I was thankful that she was not. How I should laugh if my Henriette carried off the prize which she – ridiculous old spinster – was hoping to catch. Louis would never agree to marry a woman older than himself. It was becoming clear that Louis would have his way. 'He is young yet,' I had said to Anne. 'But you wait. That one has a will of his own and knows what is due to him.'

'He always did have,' said Anne proudly; and she recalled the incident when he had been taken to see the Carmelite nuns – which I had heard at least twenty times – when he had turned his back on them and showed great interest in the latch of the door. Anne loved to relate it because of his words. She had ordered him to stop playing with the latch and pay attention to the nuns. 'But it is a good latch,' he had said, 'and the King likes it.' 'I reproved him,' said Anne, 'for his ill manners towards ladies and holy nuns at that. "Come, say a word of greeting to them," I pleaded. Louis replied. "I will say nothing. I wish to play with this latch. But one day I shall speak so loudly that I shall make myself heard." ' Whether he actually said that or whether Anne embellished it to make it sound prophetic I was not sure. She was really besotted with her little King.

Well, he was not so little now and he was going to dance with Henriette. He must. Etiquette would demand that he ask first the lady of highest rank and as neither I nor his mother would dance, it would have to be Henriette.

I was seated beside Anne on a small dais. Henriette was just below us; the musicians were there but no one could dance until the King did and he had not yet made his entrance. It would be such a pleasure to sit here beside Anne while we watched our beloved children together. She would have her eyes on Louis all the time but I would point out to her the grace of Henriette and what a charming couple they made . . . so graceful . . . so *royal*.

Louis had arrived. He really did look quite magnificent. He was growing up. He was very sure of himself, very much the King. I glanced at Anne whose eyes were glowing with pride.

Everyone stood up as he entered except Anne and myself and he came to the dais and took first his mother's hand, which he kissed, and then mine.

Now that the King had arrived the musicians began to play. Louis looked round the company; he seemed just a little bored. Nobody of course could dance until he did and everyone was eager for him to select a partner – which must be Henriette – and open the dance.

Louis did not seem in any hurry. I was watching him closely and I saw his eyes alight on Henriette but instead of approaching her he selected some relation of Cardinal Mazarin – a good looking woman several years his senior.

The Queen was not very easily aroused to anger but she had always been adamant that etiquette should be observed. Not to do so was one of the few things which could really upset her.

She could not allow this to pass although it would have been easier for us all if she had. She rose rather unsteadily; like myself she had got cramped through sitting too long. She was beside the King just as he was offering his arm to the woman.

'Dearest,' she whispered but so that all those around could hear, 'you have forgotten that the Princess Henriette is here. Your first dance should be with her.'

'I shall dance with whom I wish,' retorted Louis.

I could bear no more. This was an insult to my daughter. It had to stop at once. I dashed out onto the floor and laid a hand on Anne's arm. I said quickly and so that all could hear: 'My daughter cannot dance tonight. She has hurt her foot.'

Anne, who rarely lost her temper, did so at that moment. She had, out of the kindness of her heart, arranged this gathering for Henriette. That there should have been a breach of etiquette on such an occasion was more than she could endure and that it should have been caused by her son, who was the very centre of her life – with his brother, of course – was enough to make her anger break through her usual lethargy.

I had never seen her so angry. She said: 'If the Princess is unable to dance tonight then the King cannot either.'

With that she called Henriette to her. My poor child, overcome with shame, must of course obey the summons. When she was close enough Queen Anne took her hand and rammed it into that of Louis.

'Dance!' she commanded.

Louis looked at the frightened little girl whose hand he held and I think he felt some contrition for he was not naturally unkind and he must suddenly have realized how he had slighted her in the presence of many people.

They danced – but there was no life in either of them. He gave my daughter a rather wintry smile and said: 'It is not your fault, Henriette. It is just that I am in no mood for children tonight.'

He was in a sombre frame of mind for the rest of the evening. What did that matter? It was spoilt in any case.

The incident had a deep effect on Henriette. More than ever she wanted to get away and join her brother Charles.

The months passed. There was no good news from Charles; he was living that unsatisfactory life of peregrinations to which his fate had driven him. Henry was with him and, said Charles, very happy to be there. He was going to make a fine soldier. I did not want to hear of Henry.

My children were a disappointment to me . . . except Henriette, and if I could get her married to Louis I would snap my fingers at everything else and say that all I had done was worth while.

Meanwhile we went on in this monotonous and most unsatis-factory manner.

Then my daughter Mary proposed to come to Paris.

I was not very pleased with Mary since she had defied me over naming her son. William! What a dreadful name! It could not compare with Charles. I knew that the House of Orange was spattered with Williams but how much more appropriate Charles would have been . . . in loving memory of her father and in hope for her brother. But Mary had to be obstinate, as her brothers were. She had to have her way and was more influenced by that overbearing mother-in-law of hers than by me. So naturally I was not feeling very pleased with my daughter.

She had written that she had not been well for some time and thought a trip to Paris would be beneficial to her. I wrote back and said that she would probably like to stay at Chaillot which was ideal for an invalid who needed to rest.

Mary very soon made it clear that she had not come to Paris to rest. She had brought with her a collection of clothes and jewels with which she hoped to impress the French Court. They must have cost a great deal, I commented; I did not add that it was money which might have gone to her brother's cause, but I implied it. Of course I had to admit that Mary had done a great deal to help Charles and she had always made her Court a haven for him when he needed it. I was, naturally, a little angry with her still about being so insistent in getting her own way over the name of her son.

I had to admit that she was very pretty; she had lovely brown hair with a tinge of red in it and eyes like topaz. Not only did she not wish to stay at Chaillot but expressed only the mildest interest in my beautiful retreat. Her gaiety and good looks made her very popular and the Queen immediately liked her and made sure she was invited to meet all the most interesting people at the Court.

I was pleased that she was popular and then I noticed that in her retinue was Edward Hyde's daughter and I thought it most inconsiderate of Mary to have brought the girl to Paris.

'I never liked Edward Hyde,' I said. 'I cannot understand why your brother thinks so highly of him.'

'Because he is clever, Mam,' retorted Mary. 'Charles needs men like Edward Hyde about him. All rulers should have such men to rely on.'

'*I* never liked him,' I said firmly. 'You know this and yet you bring his daughter in your train.'

'*I* quite like the girl.'

'But you know I would rather not see any of the Hyde family.'

'I do not feel so and being mistress in my own household I choose those I like.'

I was hurt. I could not understand why my children were so inconsiderate towards me.

I was quite amused, however, when the Queen made it known

that she thought it inappropriate for widows to dance, which meant that Mary had to sit beside the Queen and me to watch. She was not really very old and she did seem to forget that she was a widow. I wondered whether she would marry again and whether I should be looking round for a suitable husband for her. It would not surprise me if she told me that was no affair of mine.

One of the balls given for Mary was that of the Duc d'Anjou. The Duc was there looking what I can only describe as 'pretty'. He had such a flair for clothes and the colours he chose were quite exquisite. His jewellery was lovely too. The Queen confided in me that young Philippe was not in the least like his brother. Louis was all for manly sports but Philippe liked better to discuss clothes, to design them and choose materials; and he had said that he liked women's clothes better than men's and oddly enough sometimes dressed in them. He was a graceful dancer and when he partnered Henriette they looked beautiful dancing together. I think they were acknowledged to be the best dancers in the Court and this made quite a bond between them. But what pleased me most about the ball was that the King was there, and this time, without hesitation, he chose Henriette to open it with him. It showed my little girl was growing up and could no longer be regarded as a child.

I prayed fervently that Charles would regain his throne and that Louis and Henriette would marry. Anne had hinted to me that she was very fond of Henriette and that she would welcome her as a daughter-in-law if it were possible for the pair of them to marry, of course.

But Louis was the King of France and Henriette . . . ? Well she was the daughter of a King who had lost his throne with his head, and the sister of a King who had not yet regained that throne and showed little sign of doing so.

'Oh Lord,' I prayed. 'Give Charles his throne . . . soon, and Henriette Louis.'

All the festivities at that time were in honour of Mary. The King commanded that a ballet should be performed for her pleasure; and of course Henriette danced in it. The Queen gave a banquet for Mary, and the Grande Mademoiselle, not to be outdone although still in exile from the Court, invited her to the *Château* of Chilly where she put on a very grand entertainment. Mary and Mademoiselle got on remarkably well. I couldn't help feeling that

Mary was a little too talkative and that Mademoiselle led her on, and I was sure she was going to repeat everything Mary said so I hoped my daughter would not be too indiscreet. When I saw the lavish manner in which Mademoiselle entertained I thought again what a suitable wife she would make for Charles, and I deeply regretted that all that money which was being wasted on lavish clothes, jewels, food, wines and spectacle could not be used to raise an army for Charles.

I did get a chance to talk to her. I thought she was looking older and she had never been a beauty. No one would have thought of marrying her if it were not for her fortune; and after so many proposed marriages which had come to nothing she must be wondering whether she was going to get married at all.

I said: 'You must be wondering how Charles is faring.'

'Oh? Must I?'

She was insolent. Foolish woman! If she was not careful she would remain a spinster all her days.

'He is in love with you, you know,' I said. 'He does not think of any other woman.'

'I was under the impression that he thought a good deal about a number of them.'

'I am talking of marriage.'

'Oh, dear little aunt, I cannot believe it is I who am the cause of his single state rather than the fact that he is scarcely in a position to keep himself let alone a wife.'

'He has been so upset. When he was here he and I quarrelled often. It is because he is unhappy that he is so quarrelsome. If he had a wife, I am sure we should be on far better terms.'

'Dear Majesty,' she said lightly, 'if he cannot live happily with you, why should he do so with someone else?'

I could have slapped her simpering face. She was mocking me. She knew I only wanted her money for Charles. Indeed what else could I want from her?

She always contrived to spoil any occasion for me. Even the sight of my little Henriette stepping a measure with a handsome nobleman with such grace could not restore my good humour.

There was something else which disturbed me very deeply although I did not realize then how very significant it would prove to be. This was the growing attitude of my son James towards Anne Hyde. He was a few years older than she was and like his brother Charles had always had an eye for women. It was a trait in them which they did not get from their father or from me. But I often wonder whether it actually came through me as it would not surprise me in the least if Charles at any rate should become such another as my father had been as far as women were concerned.

I had seen James follow Anne Hyde surreptitiously. Once I went after them and my suspicions were confirmed. My son was embracing the young woman and she was making a great show of reluctance which was an absolute indication of her willingness.

At that time my irritation was simply because I disliked the Hydes. Then it occurred to me that although it was not disastrous for my sons to have passing love affairs with women like Lucy Walter, who could be cast aside when the matter had run itself out, it was not quite the same thing with the daughter of a man in Edward Hyde's position.

I decided to tackle James.

I said: 'It has come to my ears that you are indulging in an amour with Anne Hyde.'

'You mean it has come to your eyes, Mam,' retorted James. 'I was aware of you . . . spying on us.'

I was amazed at the insolence of my children. First Henry, then Mary, now James. At least Charles was always respectful although he ignored my advice – and Charles was the King and might have been forgiven a little assertiveness.

'I consider it my duty. . . .'

He dared to interrupt. 'Oh, Mam, a little amusement is not a matter of state.'

'I would rather you gave up this woman.'

'I would rather not,' he replied.

'James!'

'Yes, Mam.'

'You are my son.'

'Dear Mam, I know that well, but I am of age, you know. I am no longer a child and I cannot brook interference with my personal affairs.'

There were dangerous lights in his eyes. He had a temper to match mine and was the easiest of my children to quarrel with. Out of sympathy with Mary as I was, I did not want trouble with James.

With great restraint I sighed and said: 'I beg of you to take care. This is the daughter of Edward Hyde of whom your brother seems to think so highly. She is not a woman like that Lucy Walter who was at the centre of that disgraceful affair with your brother, which I am sure did him a great deal of harm and no doubt held him back from his throne.'

'That's ridiculous,' cried James. 'Charles had a very pleasant time with Lucy. She's a nice creature and you know how Charles dotes on young James . . . when he sees him.'

'I cannot bear to hear such talk. I wish you were like your father . . . both of you.'

James looked solemn then as mention of the late King could always make him. He was going to make some bitter retort, I think, but he did not do so. I felt more gentle towards him and said: 'Take care, James.'

He softened too. The moment when his temper was about to flare up had passed.

'Don't fret, Mam,' he said. 'I can take care of my own affairs. You should not concern yourself with them.'

It was tantamount to what Mary had told me. Keep out of my business. It is no affair of yours. Oddly enough both incidents revolved about Anne Hyde. It was foolish to allow such a silly simpering creature to make trouble for me. She was not very bright, I gathered, though I had to admit she had a certain feminine appeal.

It would pass, I promised myself; and I did not want to quarrel any more with members of my family.

Soon after that came news from Holland. Little William had developed measles and very reluctantly Mary tore herself away from the delights of Paris to go to him.

The time was passing and nothing seemed to change much except that I was growing poorer. I found it so hard to exist on my pension for I felt I owed it to Charles to live as royally as possible. I did not want anyone to lose sight of the fact that I was the mother of the King of England.

I was growing tired of ceremonies – not that so many came my way, but I disliked sitting with Queen Anne watching some ballet or dance. She was not the most exciting of companions, although

God forbid that I should criticize one who had shown me such kindness. I often wondered how I could go on without her help, and sometimes I thought longingly of the life of some noble lady who was not close to Court and did not have to worry constantly whether she was receiving the respect due to her, who did not have to provide certain clothes that she might not appear shabby, who did not have to keep a retinue of servants whose wages she could not afford.

Yes, it would indeed be pleasant to retire to the country, with Henry Jermyn, of course – that dear faithful man who was getting so fat now but still retained his healthy complexion and was quite handsome for his years. I should like to find little Geoffrey again. I often smiled to think how he had stepped out of the pie and come to me. What a happy and amusing introduction and what a sad parting it had been!

Yes, I should like to retire to the country, but I had a daughter for whom I must find a husband. Henriette was my main concern – the only one of my children to be a Catholic and to live close to me. I watched her all the time, worrying about her fragile looks – the child was so thin and looked so pale often – and marvelling at her grace when she danced, delighting when she received invitations to assemblies at which the King would be present. But when she went to these entertainments I was always anxious as to whether she would receive her due respect and whether it would be remembered that she was a princess, a king's daughter, next in precedence to the Queen and myself.

Nothing ever went smoothly and there were so many upsets. For one thing Louis was in love and because he was so inexperienced the whole Court knew it. Marie Mancini was one of the seven beautiful nieces whom Mazarin had brought to France from Italy and no sooner had they arrived than they had become prominent because of their outstanding good looks. Marie I thought the least beautiful; her sister Hortense was quite startlingly so. However it was Marie who caught Louis's attention and he was quite obsessed by her. Anne told me that he had come to her and told her that he wished to marry Marie.

'Marry her!' I cried indignantly. 'He must be mad.'

Anne was thoughtful and I was alarmed. 'He says he cannot live without her,' she said.

'He is but a child!'

Anne was staring ahead of her and I was suddenly filled with horror. What of all those stories I had heard about Anne and Mazarin? Some said she had actually married him. Could she really be considering a marriage between the King of France and the niece of the Cardinal?

She looked at me helplessly. 'He will clearly have to marry soon.'

'I have great hopes that Charles will recover his crown. I heard only yesterday that a wise man had prophesied that he would be back within the next few years.'

'I should like him to marry an Infanta of Spain from my own country,' said Anne frankly. 'But if that failed my next choice would be Henriette, whom you know I love as a daughter. He has a will of his own.' Her eyes shone with pride. She admired this quality in her son which I deplored in my children. 'I have spoken to him.'

'Of Henriette?'

She nodded.

'He loves her I believe,' I almost whispered.

'Yes he loves her . . . as a sister. He says he is sorry for her because she is so frail and poor and unwell . . . His heart is set on Marie Mancini.'

'That is quite impossible.'

She hesitated and then said: 'I have spoken to the Cardinal.'

I stared at her in horror. She had spoken to the Cardinal! She must be mad. Of course the Cardinal would do everything he could to bring about the marriage.

Her next words surprised me. 'The Cardinal says it is impossible.'

'His own niece!'

'Yes. He is such a wise man. He said it would go against royal tradition. The people would never agree to it and would probably rise against it. And they would blame him. He says unthinking people always blame their rulers for anything that goes wrong even when it is in no way connected with them. He said a marriage between Louis and Marie Mancini would be disastrous for the country . . . and for the Cardinal himself.'

'He is a very wise man.'

'The wisest,' said Anne fondly. 'But Louis is angry. Oh, sister, I shall have to find a bride for him soon.'

I thought: It must be Henriette. I have set my heart on Louis for Henriette. If I could see Henriette Queen of France I would go away, live quietly and leave the rest to fate.

There came another irritation and once more it concerned the Grande Mademoiselle. Wherever she was there was trouble. She was no longer banned from Court on account of activities in the Fronde and was now to be seen at functions as flamboyant as ever, though perhaps a little faded. Cardinal Mazarin had invited us to a supper party at which the King and the Duc d'Anjou would be present. I was always so delighted to take Henriette where the King was, and it was a pleasant evening apart from one incident. As we were leaving Mademoiselle walked out ahead of my daughter, which was tantamount to saying that she came before Henriette in precedence.

I had gone out just ahead of them and had expected Henriette to be immediately behind me and was very angry when I discovered what had happened and inwardly railed against Mademoiselle, wishing that she could be exiled forever.

That was not the end of the matter for what had happened came to the Cardinal's ears. He was a stickler for etiquette and was most annoyed, first because one of the laws of protocol had been ignored and secondly because Henriette and I had been at the supper party as his guests.

A few days later there was a party at his apartments to which the King, the Duc d'Anjou and Mademoiselle had been invited. Fortunately neither I nor Henriette were present but there were plenty of people to report to me what had been said.

The Cardinal asked Mademoiselle if it was true that she had taken precedence over the Princess Henriette while the King and the Duc d'Anjou were listening.

It was the Duc d'Anjou who answered. He said very loudly so that all could hear: 'And what if my cousin did? Why should people who rely on us for their food and lodging take precedence over us? If they do not like the treatment they get here, they should go somewhere else.'

I was terribly upset. So they regarded us as beggars! And this to come from the brother of the King – and Louis stood by and did nothing about it. It was more than I could endure.

The horrible realization came to me that they were getting tired of us.

I was so upset that I went to see the Cardinal and I told him that it was humiliating to accept a pension from the Queen. She was bountiful and had been a wonderful friend to me; I could never repay her for all she had done in my times of need; but I would like to be independent of her. I thought that as I was the Queen of England who had brought a dowry with her when I married the King, I should have some of that dowry back now. It was not the Queen of France who should be paying me a pension, but the English Parliament.

Mazarin shook his head. 'Your Majesty cannot really believe that the English Parliament would give you a pension!'

'I don't know. You have become friendly with this Oliver Cromwell. You say he is a man of integrity. Let us see something of that quality.'

'Such a request could only end in failure.'

'Will you make it?'

'If you insist.'

'I do,' I told him.

The result was more than failure. It was insulting. As I had never been crowned Queen of England the Parliament did not consider me as such.

When I heard those words I was so furious that I lost my temper with the Cardinal.

'Are they suggesting that I was the King's concubine? Is the King of France going to stand aside and hear that said of his aunt, the daughter of his grandfather. . . .'

Mazarin said quietly: 'They have merely said that as you were not crowned you lack the rights of a queen. I believe the reason that you were not crowned was your own objection to the ceremony.'

'I can see,' I said, 'that you are ready to accept the logic of your *dear* friend Oliver Cromwell.'

Anne asked me to see her. She was a good kind woman and I wished that she did not bore me so much for I should be truly grateful.

She said: 'I know how you long for a place of your own . . . somewhere not too large . . . somewhere where you could get away from Court and live quietly when you are in the mood to do so.'

'I have Chaillot.'

'I did not mean a convent. I meant a little home. I do understand for I often feel I should like to do the same myself. It is
impossible for me, of course, though perhaps later when Louis is
married and has growing children . . . who knows? But I have
been thinking of you, sister. Life is very hard for you.'

'You speak truth there. I am poor and dependent, and I and my
daughter are the targets for insults.'

'Oh, that affair of the Grande Mademoiselle. I do not take her
very seriously.'

'Her behaviour touches me little. It was the remarks of the Duc
d'Anjou. . . .'

'Philippe sometimes speaks without thinking. I have repri-
manded him strongly for his lack of courtesy. I think he was
contrite. Let us look round for a suitable place. Do you remember
the pleasure we had over Chaillot?'

'Oh, Anne, dear sister, you are so good and kind.'

'I understand your feelings so well,' she replied. 'I should like
to make life a little easier for you.'

'I could never afford to buy such a place if I found it.'

'Let us first look for the place and then consider that.'

The dear generous creature was comforting me again.

The outcome was that together we discovered the small *château*
in the village of Colombes. It was only seven miles from Paris and
yet in the heart of the country. The village was beautiful and
peaceful as only such villages can be, brooded over by the church
with its twelfth-century tower. The *château* was small, like a
country house rather than a castle and I knew that I could be
happy in it.

I was considerably cheered when Anne and I planned together
what furniture would be put in it and when the place was completed it was indeed a haven.

Perhaps that was the beginning of better days. It was not long
after – a beautiful September day in the year 1658 – when the
messenger came to Colombes where I was staying.

I knew he had some exciting news to tell me for he could
scarcely wait.

'A message for the Queen,' he cried. 'Oliver Cromwell is dead!'

So England had a new Lord Protector – Richard Cromwell, son
of Oliver.

The Court was buzzing with the news and messages were coming all the time from England. Richard was not the man his father had been; he lacked authority; he had no desire to govern; he was too soft; some said he was more like the martyred King than Oliver's son.

What now? everyone was asking.

After the first months the excitement died down and it seemed as though Charles was no nearer winning his rights from Richard than he had been from Oliver.

Still, the old ogre was dead and we continued to hear that the new Protector lacked those qualities which had brought victory to his father.

Anne was growing more and more eager to find a bride for Louis and my niece Marguerite, daughter of my sister Christine, was brought to Paris, on trial as it were. She was a very plain girl and older than Louis. He took an instant dislike to her and I was sorry for Marguerite but relieved all the same on account of Henriette.

It was quite clear that Louis had a mind of his own. He was both the delight and terror of his mother's life. But she was beside herself with joy when the Cardinal was able to tell her that his clever diplomacy had not only brought about peace with Spain but the promise of the Infanta Marie Theresa as bride for Louis.

It was what she had always wanted and she could not hide her joy, although she tried to from me, knowing my aspirations for Henriette.

But I was accustomed to disappointments and I could not help feeling a twinge of relief that at least my sister Christine's plain daughter had not been chosen. I now had to accept that Henriette would never be Queen of France.

The French Court had gone to the Spanish border to meet the Spanish Infanta, and Henriette and I remained in Paris. How glad I was that we did! I had taken Henriette to Colombes with me. She was rather sad. I do believe that she was a little in love with Louis and it must have been painful for her to have been rejected by him, even though she could console herself that the main reason was that she was a dependant on his Court and that had her brother regained his throne there might have been a match between them.

I was seated in my favourite room with some of my friends when a visitor was announced and a tall dark man came into the room.

'Charles!'

It was indeed. Changed after all the years. It must have been six since I had seen him and we had parted not such good friends on account of Henry. In spite of the change in him he had lost none of that charm which was going to smooth his path through life.

He said: 'A fleeting visit, Mam. I do not think it will be long now. I verily believe they are going to ask me to go back.'

Then he turned and seizing one of my most handsome ladies picked her up in his arms and kissed her fervently. We were all astonished – until he called her his dear sister Henriette. Then I realized that he had mistaken the lady for the Princess. Or had he? I wondered. Or just pretended to? It gave him an opportunity of kissing the pretty girl. I could not be sure. But no matter. He was here and it was wonderful to see him.

I sent at once for Henriette. She ran to him and they embraced. The affection between those two had not diminished with his absence.

My little Henriette was almost in tears to see the brother whom she adored. There was complete devotion between those two. I envied it in a way. I should have liked to be on such terms with Charles but I really could not completely forgive him for taking Henry's side and I knew he could not forgive me for my behaviour towards the boy.

But it was too great an occasion for resentments.

He was excited. He was receiving letters from General Monck. The people were tired of Puritan rule. They looked for the colour and gaiety of a Court. They yearned for the old days. In fact they wanted the King to come home.

I dismissed all my attendants and sent them to make as grand a meal as they could for this most honoured arrival; and when I was alone with Charles and Henriette, Charles talked of the state of affairs.

'I do not wish to say too much about this just yet,' he said, 'in case it fails as so many attempts have before. But this is different. This is not war. This is peace. It is not a challenge. It is an

invitation. I have a very good friend in General Monck. He was a supporter of Cromwell at one time, but I don't think he ever took to the way of life the Roundheads established. Oliver Cromwell did not trust him . . . and rightly so. Monck is a great character, a rough soldier perhaps, but with a love for royalty. He shall be rewarded when I am back. He married his washerwoman. . . .'
He gave me an odd look when he said that. 'Ah, that shocks you, Mam, but I believe the lady had many desirable attributes and one of these was that she was always an ardent royalist.'

'Do you mean he will help you regain your kingdom . . . this General?' I asked.

'He is *the* General, the Head of the Army. He does not like the Roundheads' rule since Oliver died. He endured it then he said because Oliver was a *good* ruler and a strong man. Now it is different. I will have to be asked to go back. I have no intention of making a false start. I promise myself that when I go home it will be to stay. I have no intention to go wandering again.'

We were too excited to eat. I was glad we were at Colombes so that we could be alone . . . just a family . . . to talk and talk . . . and wait.

And so, after all our abortive attempts, all the selling of precious possessions to raise money for arms, all the tragedies and defeats and disappointments, it had happened in a totally unexpected manner.

Charles was invited to go home and on that glorious May day of the year 1660 he landed at Dover where he was greeted by General Monck, and all the way to London the people assembled in their crowds to throw flowers at his feet, to cheer him, to welcome him home from his exile.

This was the happiest day I had known since our troubles began.

The Restoration was truly here and I knew that life would be different for us all from now on.

Henriette

Oh yes, life had changed. My dream had come true. My son was now the King of England. I knew it could not be all joy and happiness but the great tragedy was at an end. I had no doubt that Charles would be able to hold the throne. He was not like his father. He lacked the strong moral attitudes; he had shown more than once that he would never cling rigidly to controversial doctrines if by doing so he endangered himself and his throne. He had said he had no intention of wandering again and he meant it. The people adored him already as they never had his father. How strange life was! The good man – moral, religious, virtuous in every way – failed to win them, and yet my son with his ugly looks and excessive charm of manner, his easy-going acceptance of whatever life had to offer, won their hearts in a matter of days. They loved him for his sins – for his love affairs were notorious – as they had never loved his father for his virtues.

It was wonderful for me and for Henriette to hold up our heads again.

Henriette was longing to go to London but I held off for a while as a very interesting situation had arisen.

I had greatly enjoyed the entry into Paris of Louis and his bride Marie Theresa – a rather insipid girl who made me feel how much happier it would have been for everyone if Louis and Anne had not been in such a hurry and had waited until Charles's restoration which would have made my Henriette an acceptable bride.

However, in spite of that disappointment it was a great joy to be no longer a poor supplicant.

Henriette and I sat with the Queen on a balcony of the Hôtel de Beauvais, the canopy of crimson velvet over us – completely royal now. I was proud to be of a similar rank to Anne – mothers, both of us, of reigning sovereigns and nothing to choose between us.

What a magnificent procession it was – magistrates, musket-
eers, heralds and the grand equerry holding the royal sword in its
scabbard of blue velvet decorated with the golden fleurs-de-lis.
And then there was Louis – a King for any country to be proud of,
looking magnificently regal seated on his bay horse with a
brocaded canopy held over him.

The people cheered him wildly. I felt proud of my nephew and
I was thinking of course of that other King who had made such
another entry into his capital city a short time ago. Louis looked
like a god in silver lace covered with pearls, the elegant plumes in
his hat – which was pinned on by a large diamond brooch – falling
over his shoulders. Behind him rode Philippe and I could not look
at him without speculation. He was not the first prize, of course,
but he was a worthy second. He looked very handsome; he was
in fact better looking than his brother though he lacked Louis'
manliness. He was also in silver most beautifully embroidered
with jewels scintillating from his person. I looked sharply at
Henriette. She was gazing ahead at Louis. Perhaps a little wistfully. I was not sure.

The bride came next – not nearly beautiful and elegant enough
for Louis. And to think it might have been Henriette riding there,
Queen of France! If only they had had the good sense to wait. My
Henriette was not such an undesirable proposition now.

Marie Theresa's coach was covered in gold lace and she herself
was dressed in material which looked like gold. She looked quite
beautiful – and who would not, so attired and in such a setting? –
but a little coarse if one looked closely. And how elegant and
ethereal *my* little one would have looked. I should not have
dressed her in gold either. It was faintly vulgar and the bride
wore too many jewels of contrasting colours. I should have
dressed Henriette in silver and her only jewels would have been
diamonds.

But what was the use? The prize had gone to that little Spanish
Infanta. They would regret it, I knew.

Now I was laughing to myself for behind the bride's coach
came that of the Princesses of France and there sat the Grande
Mademoiselle. She glanced up as she passed so that we were able
to exchange glances. I smiled at her sardonically and managed to
infuse a certain condolence into the smile. She would have inter-
preted it and not been very pleased, I knew. I was implying: 'My

poor dear niece, so you have missed again. Dear, dear, are we ever going to find a husband for you?'

I guessed now that she would have her eyes on Philippe. Oh no. That must not be. The daughter of a King is of far greater standing than the daughter of the brother of a King – particularly one who had disgraced himself by becoming involved with the Fronde.

The King was on a level with the balcony now and he paused to salute us. I noticed that his eyes lingered on Henriette and hers on him. They smiled at each other almost tenderly.

I was filled with chagrin.

Too late, I thought angrily. This is another mocking trick which fate has played on me.

Queen Anne embraced me warmly. It was the day after Louis's entry with his bride. She was smiling as she did when she had something pleasant to convey.

She said: 'I have been made so happy. My son Philippe has been talking to me. He is in love and wishes to marry.'

My heart started to bounce about in a most uncomfortable way. It must be Henriette. If it were not she could not look so happy.

I tried to steady myself and she went on: 'He wishes to marry Henriette.'

I was wildly happy. If it could not be Louis – and that was now quite out of the question – then Philippe was the next best chance. My little Henriette would be the third lady in France and if Louis were to die without heirs – but that little Spaniard did look as though she might be fertile – my Henriette could still be Queen of France.

'I am so delighted,' Anne was saying, 'and he is so much in love.'

It was hard to imagine Philippe's being in love with anyone but himself, although he might spare some affection for that close friend of his, the Comte de Guiche, a young and extremely handsome nobleman, who had been married at a very early age to the heiress of the House of Sully though he had never shown much interest in his bride, except with regard to her fortune, and was delighted to be Philippe's close friend.

However he was the brother of the King – next in line to the throne at the moment, and Henriette had known him for most of her life. When she married she would not have to go away. I should not lose her. To say the least I was delighted with the prospect.

Anne knew I should be and rejoiced with me.

'Louis has given his consent to the match and the Cardinal is in favour of it.'

Of course he would be, the old fox, I thought. Close ties with Spain through Louis' marriage and with England through that of Henriette and Philippe.

It was what I wanted though, what I had angled for, and I had learned most bitterly through the latter part of my life that if you cannot get your heart's desire you must settle for the next best thing.

There was another reason for my pleasure. I knew the Grande Mademoiselle had wanted Philippe when Louis was out of her reach, so this was a blow for her. I really did believe she was never going to get a husband and I could not wait to see her face when she heard that Philippe and Henriette were betrothed.

Henriette was less enthusiastic about the proposed marriage. It was often difficult to know what my daughter was thinking. She looked rather sad and said: 'Does Philippe really want to marry . . . and to marry me?'

'Of course he wants to marry. It is his duty. Why, if his brother died tomorrow he could be King of France.'

'Dear Mam, you should not say such things.'

'So even you are telling me now what I should say and what I should not say. I begin to believe that I have brought a family of tutors into the world.'

She kissed me and said she knew how I had always loved and cared for my family and if I wished it and Philippe wished it she supposed she must marry him.

'My dear daughter,' I cried, 'you do not sound very appreciative of the second best match in France.'

'I think I would have chosen not to marry for a while. I have a great fancy to go to England and to be near Charles.'

'Charles is the King and it is right that you should love and admire him, but he is only your brother, remember. You have your own life to lead.'

'But we *are* going to England.'

'We are. As soon as I have made sure that the betrothal is firm, we shall visit your brother and then we shall come back for the wedding . . . your wedding, my dear child. I shall see my son on his throne and my best-loved child married. I really begin to see a great deal of brightness in the sky. It has been so dark . . . so very dark . . . for such a long time.'

Enjoyable weeks followed. I revelled in the preparations and tried not to think of the sea voyage which I always loathed. But it would be worthwhile this time. I had had the pleasure of a little conversation with Mademoiselle who was beside herself with jealousy of Henriette. She called on me and I was sure there was a purpose in this for in view of the betrothal I should have thought she would have wanted to keep out of the way.

'You have come to congratulate me,' I said slyly, knowing it was the last thing she would come to do.

'You must be very pleased that your plans have at last borne fruit,' she said.

'Plans!' I said opening my eyes very wide. 'I had no plans. I can tell you, niece, I was amazed when the Queen told me that Philippe had declared his love for Henriette and had stated that he would have no other for his wife.'

'It must have been a surprise,' she said. 'One would not have thought Philippe had time to consider such matters, he being so preoccupied with his dear friend de Guiche.'

'Oh, he has had his eyes on Henriette for a long time. The dear child is overjoyed. I wish I could let you know how delightful it is to be loved by such a man.'

There was a slightly strained look on her face. 'I hear you are planning to visit London.'

'That is our intention. Then we shall return and the wedding will take place.'

'How fares the King of England?'

'Well . . . well indeed.'

'I daresay he remembers his days here in Paris . . . and some of his old friends. It is a pity to let old friends disappear. I should like to see the King again.'

I smiled to myself. So that is it, is it? No Louis. No Philippe. Let's try Charles.

Oh no, my dear Mademoiselle. It is too late now. Then he was an exiled Prince. You declined him. Now he is the King of

England – and the most desirable bachelor in Europe. Poor Mademoiselle, you have failed again. Too late. You should have taken a chance.

She looked so forlorn and so clearly ageing that I felt almost sorry for her. But she was not for Charles now – in spite of all her money.

A visit to London in the present circumstances should have been pure delight; but life never worked out quite like that for me.

As we were on the point of departure news came fom England which completely stunned me. I read the despatch through and could not believe it. I read it again and again. There was no mistake. This terrible thing had happened.

Henriette came in and found me almost dazed by the shock.

She sat beside me and took my hand. I snatched it away. My fury was so great that it would be restrained no longer.

'I cannot believe it,' I cried. 'I simply cannot believe it.'

'Charles . . . ' she murmured turning pale.

'Charles!' I spat out. 'He has given his consent to this folly. Are they all mad?'

She begged me to tell her what had happened and I cried out: 'It is your brother James. He has married that scheming harlot, Anne Hyde. That rogue, her father, has planned this, you can be sure. Without my consent . . . without the King's consent . . . he married her in secret.'

'He must love her dearly,' said Henriette a little wistfully.

I could have struck her – yes, even my best-loved child.

'Love!' I cried. 'She has trapped him. I saw it from the first. Mary should never have taken her into her Court. She should never have brought her to Paris in the first place. This is disaster. My son James . . . married to that woman . . . and just in time it seems that her bastard may be born in wedlock.'

'James would want his own child to be born in wedlock, Mam.'

'She wanted it. A child. It has gone as far as that. If only *I* had been there. Charles should have stopped it.'

'But they did it in secret.'

'And your brother Charles is actually receiving the woman at his Court.'

'It is because she is James's wife, Mam.'

'James's harlot! Thank God we shall soon be in England. I may be able to put a stop to all this. We might get the marriage annulled. And Charles . . . allowing it all, shrugging his shoulders and telling them to go their merry ways. . . . He will lose his crown if he is not careful.'

Henriette was fierce as always when anything derogatory was said about Charles. 'I think his kindness and good humour will help him to keep it, Mam.'

I could have shaken her. Was she suggesting that her father lost his crown because he was not like her brother? I turned away from her and she said pleadingly: 'Mam, we must be kind to James's wife.'

I retorted stonily: 'James has no wife as far as I am concerned.'

She was silent for some time and then she said, perhaps thinking to turn me away from my rage, 'And there is Henry.'

I stared at her in anger, which she had succeeded in increasing.

'He will be there, Mam, and you remember you parted bad friends.'

'I remember what a disobedient boy he was. He defied me and I vowed I would not look on his face again.'

'He will be at Court. Charles loves him dearly and has told me that he has done good service for him. Mam, could you not forget all that? Could you not be friends? It would so please Charles, and Henry is your son.'

'I vowed to the saints that I would never see Henry until he became a Catholic. He never has done so and until he does I shall not see him for I would not break my vow.'

For once Henriette became quite fierce. 'You would spurn your own child, you would hurt your son, the King, for the sake of a vow.'

'A vow made to God, child.'

She turned away and did not speak. I could not bear that she, my beloved one, should be on bad terms with me and I said her name softly. She turned back to me and threw herself into my arms.

There were tears on her cheeks.

'There, my little one,' I said, 'we must not storm against each other. I must be able to rely on my little Henriette.'

'Mam, then you will see Henry?'

'No, child, I do not break my vows.'

So this much-looked-forward-to visit was to be marred by
James's wicked act and Henry's stubbornness. It was not the
Roundheads who were making me unhappy now; it was my own
family.

There was another blow waiting for me.

We had set out for Calais when we received despatches from
London. An epidemic of small pox had invaded the capital and
had claimed a number of victims. One of these was my son Henry.

I felt completely numb when I read that. We had been talking
of him so recently and I was preparing myself to refuse to
see him. Now I never could. Never again. I remembered when
he had been born, what pleasure his coming had given Charles
and me; and then our bitter quarrel and how he had defied me
and how I had turned him away . . . stripped him of his food and
lodging, even ordered that the sheets should be taken from his
bed to show him that there was no home for him with me.

Poor Henriette, she was stricken with grief. It was a long time
since she had seen Henry, but she had a strong family feeling and
she was particularly upset on my account because she felt that I
would reproach myself.

It was some time before she could bring herself to talk of it.
Then she said : 'Dear Mam, you must not blame yourself.'

'Blame myself?' I cried. 'Why should I?'

'Because he died while there was this quarrel between you . . .
because you parted in anger.'

'My dear child, everything I did was for his good. If he had
embraced our Faith we should have been as happy together as
you and I have been. I am not sorry that I kept to my vow.
Haven't the nuns taught you that vows are sacred when made to
God?'

'Perhaps God would have forgiven you for breaking this one if
you had had the chance.'

'I have nothing with which to reproach myself,' I said firmly.
'Everything I did was for his good.'

But when I was alone I wept for him, wept inconsolably, for I
could only remember my little baby whom I had once loved so
dearly, and thinking of him – brave boy that he was – I realized
that he believed he had been right too. It was religion which had
divided us, and religion had played a major part in all that had
happened to me.

The fact remained I had lost a son; I had lost my daughter Elizabeth; and both of them had died heretics.

I prayed for them that they might be forgiven.

'It was not their fault,' I said. 'They were brought up to be heretics.'

That was what upset me, I tried to tell myself. But it was not entirely true.

James came to Calais to meet us with a squadron of ships. James was now becoming renowned for his seamanship.

He embraced me warmly. He looked jaunty and handsome and said nothing about Anne Hyde. Nor did I. But I had made up my mind that as soon as I could I would have a private word with Charles. I would put a stop to that little adventure. My son was not going to marry a nobody; nor was he going to give her child his name if I could help it.

But at the moment my handsome son James had come to escort me across the Channel and I gave myself up to the pleasure of returning to England in the manner which I had always dreamed of doing.

The sea was unusually calm. How different from the face it usually showed me! So there was no sickness for which I was extremely grateful, but the crossing took two whole days because we were becalmed. However, in due course those white cliffs came into sight and I was filled with emotion thinking of the last time I had seen them and that brought back poignant memories of my beloved Charles.

Waiting for us, surrounded by a glittering assembly, was that other Charles. I was proud of him. He seemed to have grown taller but that was probably because I had not seen him for some time. He was very gracious and charming to me and his eyes shone with affection when they rested on Henriette.

Crowds had gathered on the seashore to see the meeting. I thought the cheers were not quite so spontaneous for me as they were for the King and James, but it was clear that Henriette delighted them and the people were pleased to see Charles's affection for her.

Inside the castle a banquet had been prepared for us and I sat on one side of Charles, Henriette on the other. Charles told us that Mary was on her way to England and it would make him very happy to have the entire family together.

Later we talked privately and I asked about Henry. Charles had been present at his death, which was rather foolish of him, I pointed out. Henry had died of small pox which was highly contagious. What if Charles had caught it and succumbed? Had he thought what would happen to England without a King?

'James would be waiting to step into my shoes, Mam.'

'The people would never accept him with that woman as his wife. How could you allow that, Charles?'

'Who am I to stand in the way of true love?' He could be very flippant but there were warning lights in his eyes. Charles had always been very fond of his sisters and brothers and hated family quarrels. But I was not going to be told what I must and must not do by my own son.

I repeated that he should not have risked his life by being with Henry but as he was there I should like to know if Henry had mentioned me on his death bed.

'Yes,' said Charles coolly, 'he did. He was grieved always because of the disagreement between you and how it had been when you were last together.'

I nodded. 'I thought he would be sorry in time.'

'I told him he should not grieve. I pointed out to him that if he had done what you wanted him to he would have broken his word to his father and gone against his own conscience. I assured him that in God's eyes he had done the right thing.'

'The right thing! He died a heretic. If he had listened to me. . . .'

'Somehow, Mam, I do not think the good Lord will be as hard on him as you have been.'

I protested but there was something about Charles which warned me that it would be unwise to continue. He could be very much the King at times.

He looked at me sadly for a moment and then he said: 'The years of exile have taught you nothing, Mam. Life is short. Let us enjoy it. Let there be no trouble in the heart of the family.'

Then he rose and left me. I could never really understand this son of mine. Of all my children he was the most difficult to know and had been ever since he was the serious little boy who had refused to give up the wooden toy he took to bed with him.

Henriette seemed happier than I had ever known her to be. She was so content to be at her brother's Court and when Charles suggested that she arrange one of the ballets which were so popular at the Court of Louis XIV, she threw herself whole-heartedly into making the arrangements.

The Duke of Buckingham, that dissolute son of a father whom I had always believed to be evil, fell headlong in love with her. My dear child was a little bewildered at first and then appeared to enjoy the attentions of the young man. It was only a light flirta-tion, Buckingham having a wife and she being betrothed, and in any case she was a princess and he was only a duke so I did not attempt to reprove her. When I thought of the way she had been treated at the Court of France at one time, I thought it would do her no harm to realize that she was growing into a very attractive young woman.

Mary arrived and it was good to see her and we were for once in complete agreement for she was incensed when she heard about James's marriage to Anne Hyde. I could not resist reminding her that she was the one who had allowed this folly to begin by making the upstart young woman a member of her household.

'How much better it would have been if you had taken my advice then,' I said.

She did not exactly agree, but she refused to receive Anne Hyde and the woman would have been very miserable indeed if Charles had not gone out of his way to be gracious to her.

The weeks began to fly past – very pleasant weeks. If only I could forget Henry's death and Charles's thinly veiled criticism of my treatment of him, and the fact that James had made this monstrous marriage, I could have been happy.

Anne Hyde's child was a boy but a weakling and it did not look as though the child's chances of survival would be great.

'James should have waited awhile,' I said. 'Then the child might not have been a reason for the marriage.'

I was delighted when Sir Charles Berkeley declared that he had been Anne's lover and that he knew of several other gentlemen who had shared her favours and that it was therefore by no means certain that the father of the child was James.

I wanted to confront James with that evidence, but he had already heard it and was so upset that he became quite ill and went down with a fever. We were all afraid that he might be another victim of small pox.

Anne Hyde was completely ostracized now. Her father was upset and even he railed against her, and she had no friends at Court at all. I wanted Charles to dismiss her father – who was now the Earl of Clarendon – but he would not do so. Clarendon was an excellent Chancellor, he said, and was not to be blamed for his daughter's affairs.

Christmas was almost upon us. Charles had insisted that we stay for the festivities and I was nothing loth. I was delighted to be on better terms with Mary and it was wonderful to see Henriette blossoming, leading the dancing and amusing herself with the Duke of Buckingham.

Then about five days before Christmas Mary became ill. She had been feeling unwell for some days and thought this was due to some minor cause. My distress was great when the doctors reported that she was suffering from small pox.

Charles said I was to leave Whitehall at once with Henriette. 'Take her to St James's,' he said, 'and stay there with her.'

'Henriette shall go to St James's,' I declared, 'but I shall stay and nurse Mary.'

'You must not go to the sick room,' Charles retorted firmly.

'My dear Charles,' I replied, 'King you may be, but you are my son and this is my daughter. If she is sick I must be with her.'

'Do you realize that you could catch the disease?'

'Of course I know what small pox is. I want to be with my daughter. She will need me.'

'Mam,' he said slowly, 'this is no time for deathbed conversions. Mary is ill. She is too sick to be troubled with your views on what will happen to her soul.'

'I want to nurse her.'

'How could you do that? Go back to Henriette. You would never forgive yourself if you caught the disease and passed it on to her.'

That really did frighten me. The thought of anything happening to my precious child made me waver. On the other hand

Mary was my daughter too. Henry had just died, a heretic. Mary might die one too, if nothing was done.

Charles said quietly: 'It would be dangerous. Besides, I forbid it.'

So I went to St James's and told Henriette that her sister was gravely ill, and we prayed for her recovery adding that if she were destined to die let her come to an understanding of the truth that she might not, like her brother Henry, die a heretic.

Alas our prayers were not answered and on Christmas Eve Mary passed away. She was only twenty-nine years old.

Charles was with her at the end. He was very shaken. He was very fond of his family, particularly his sisters.

I was in tears. 'It seems as though God has determined to punish me,' I cried. 'Is there a blight on my family? Elizabeth . . . then Henry . . . now Mary. Why? Why?'

'Who can say?' answered Charles. 'But there is something I wish to tell you. When she was dying Mary was very concerned about one matter.'

I turned to him, my eyes shining.

'No . . . no . . .' he went on a little impatiently, 'it is nothing to do with religion. It was Anne Hyde. Mary had a good deal on her conscience.'

'I know,' I said. 'If she had not taken that woman into her household. . . . I told her she was wrong at the time.'

'No, Mam,' said Charles. 'She did not mean that. She was upset because she had maligned Anne. She said she had helped to spread the gossip about her when in her heart she did not believe that it was true. She believed that James loved Anne and Anne truly loved James and that James had given her a promise of marriage before she became his mistress.'

'She was delirious.'

'She was quite clear in her head. She thought that there were people who had fabricated those stories about Anne because they knew it was an unpopular marriage. Mary blamed herself most bitterly. She wanted Anne to come to her that she might beg her forgiveness. I could not allow Anne, with a new baby, to come to the sick bed.'

'I should think not. . . .'

'The infectious nature of the disease prevented that,' he went on firmly. 'But I shall go to Anne and tell her that the Princess Mary craved her pardon and that I give it on her behalf.'

'I never heard such nonsense.'
He just smiled at me and said no more.

Our next concern was James. He was becoming very ill.

'That woman is a witch,' I said to Henriette. 'First she lured him into marriage and now because he disowns her she is willing him to die.'

Henriette did not answer. I could not understand Henriette. The quiet girl who had been so thin – Louis had referred to her as the Bones of the Holy Innocents – now in clothes which were worthy of her had blossomed into a beauty. Her fragility had become fashionable and ladies of the Court were trying to suppress those protuberances which at one time they had been at great pains to display. Henriette was at the centre of all the entertainments, with Buckingham in attendance. In fact there was some scandalous gossip about them. I had to make sure that nothing dangerous could come of that. Charles doted on her and was making as much of her as he did of his favourite mistress Barbara Castlemaine, and knowing his insatiable sexuality, some even dared hint at the most objectionable slander about his relationship with Henriette.

It was a situation to be watched closely and I told myself that as soon as we reached France Henriette must be married to Philippe, who was now the Duc d'Orléans on the death of my brother Gaston. His death did not affect me greatly because, although we had been close as children in the nursery, his involvement in the Fronde had turned me against him.

James's health began to give us cause for alarm. He was not, fortunately, suffering from the small pox, but I really believed he was so upset because he was regretting his marriage to that woman and was now realizing in what an unsavoury involvement he had become entangled.

The doctors thought his malady had been brought about through emotional stress and Sir Charles Berkeley created quite a furore when he burst into James's bedchamber, threw himself on his knees, and declared that the accusations he had made against Anne Hyde were false. She was a pure woman and had never had any lover other than James. Berkeley had prevailed upon other men to join with him in accusing her and they had done this because they thought the Duke of York would be happier if the marriage were dissolved and he could make another more suitable to his position.

The news spread round the Court. Anne Hyde was vindicated. James quickly recovered, which proved it was the slander about Anne Hyde which had so upset him that he became ill.

Charles was pleased about this and said that Anne must come back to Court and there must be a christening for her son.

He then came to tell me what had happened.

'So,' I said, 'you are bringing her to Court. Is that what you are telling me?'

'That is so,' he answered, 'and I am very happy at this outcome. Anne is a woman of great wit and excellent parts. She will take advice from her father and be a good influence on James – who is in need of it.'

'When you have finished singing her praises let me tell you that if this woman enters Whitehall by one door, I shall go out by another.'

Charles was angry. 'I have long known that you cannot exist in peace,' he said coldly. 'If it is forced on you, you will immediately set out raising storms.'

He left me then.

I sighed. What difficult children I had! They either died or defied me.

Charles was very cool and made no attempt to prevent the preparations I was making to return to France. Moreover he insisted on bringing Anne Hyde to Court, which meant of course that I must leave. Henriette was heartbroken. No one would have thought she was going back to a brilliant marriage. She said she would be loth to tear herself away from England and her brother and she went about with a woebegone face. But I considered I had been insulted. My son had given preference to a woman of no standing who had brought a child into the world which had come near to being a bastard – and in any case she was not of the rank to mate with royalty. And for this woman he was turning his own mother out of Court!

Henriette explained with exasperating patience that he was not turning me out. I was going of my own free will.

I said: 'He leaves me no alternative. He forgets that though he is a King I am a Queen . . . and his mother.'

362*Myself My Enemy*

'He does not forget, Mam. He is grieved that you are going like this.'

'A strange way of showing grief! All he has to do is not receive that woman and I will postpone my departure.'

'He can't do that. She is James's wife.'

'Wife! To how many men has she been what you call a wife?'

'But they have all confessed to lying about her. I think they are despicable . . . every one of them.'

I turned away. Even Henriette was against me.

A few days before I was to leave a messenger came from France. News of what had happened had reached the Court there, for scandalous news always travelled faster than any other. The letter was from Mazarin and was very discreetly worded, but I read the meaning between the lines and there could be no mistaking their intent. He clearly implied that if I quarrelled with my son I should not be very welcome in France. The fact was that Charles had given both me and Henriette handsome pensions and had promised a sizable dowry for Henriette, and Mazarin doubted Charles would pay this if there was a rift between us. And would Philippe want to marry Henriette without a dowry? It was the return of Charles to the throne which had made Henriette so desirable.

I was in a dilemma. What could I do? Hold up my pride and return to France . . . a beggar almost, for it might well be that our money from England would not be paid. No dowry for Henriette! Charles might be pleased for his favourite sister to stay in England and I knew *she* would like that very much. No, I could not exist again as I had all those years depending on the charity of others, and in my heart I felt I might be in danger of doing so if I did not remain on good terms with my son; and I certainly should not be if I left England as I was proposing to do.

The only alternative was to accept Anne Hyde. So I agreed to receive the woman.

I shall never forget the scene of my humiliation. Charles must have decided not to spare me. It could have been done more quietly but Charles pointed out that it must be *seen* to be done.

I was obliged to ask my son James, most formally, to bring his wife to my bedchamber that I might receive her. Naturally, because so many knew what had gone before, my bedchamber was crowded with busybodies who had come to witness the reconciliation.

I was furious and all the time had to keep reminding myself of the old days of humiliation and that on no account must they recur. It was blackmail. Still I had worked hard for my husband; I could do the same for my daughter.

When the woman came with James it was less difficult than I had anticipated, for she showed no triumph or aggression and was in fact most humble. I had sent Henriette away as I did not want her to see me act as I should have to. My excuse was that with the small pox epidemic raging I feared there might be danger for her among so many people.

Anne Hyde knelt to me most deferentially when James presented her and I bent over and kissed her. She was a pleasant-looking young woman with, I had to admit, an open honest face. If she had been of nobler birth I could easily have accepted her.

I did feel a twinge of gratitude to her for making my task slightly easier than it could have been. I led her into the anteroom and with her on one side and James on the other we made our way through the press of courtiers and sat down and talked a little.

I asked about the baby whom they were going to call Charles, and James asked if I would be a godmother. I said I would.

Then I had done all that was required of me, I thought. But it appeared not quite, for Charles wanted me to receive the Earl of Clarendon, which I did, although I had always disliked the man and more so since the trouble with his daughter had arisen.

He was very respectful to me and I told him that I was happy to be a mother to his daughter. Then I hinted that in return for my capitulation he should do all he could for me. He knew what I meant, for he was a most astute man and as Chancellor had a great influence in the country. What I was implying was that there should be no holding back of Henriette's dowry and our pensions.

I felt exhausted after the interview, but I was aware that Clarendon was very pleased at the outcome and I trusted him to do what he had promised for me.

The day after the public reconciliation we prepared to leave for

France and then I had my greatest fright, for I greatly feared that in spite of my efforts to protect Henriette she too might have caught the small pox which had carried off her brother and sister. No sooner had we left Portsmouth and were indeed still in sight of the harbour than Henriette became violently ill. I was terrified because this was not due to the sea. I consulted with the Captain and persuaded him to take the ship back into port. My daughter was in need of the best possible medical attention.

He did this and I was faintly relieved to be back on shore. I sent a message to the King. He was most distressed and declared that nothing must be left undone to save Henriette.

To our great joy we discovered that she was suffering from measles and not small pox as we had feared and after fourteen anxious days we were ready to sail for France once more.

This time we made a good journey and landed safely at Le Havre.

What a welcome was given us! Our journey to Paris was slow as I did not want to go through Rouen, where I heard that small pox was rife. I had preserved my darling so far and had no intention of letting her take more risks.

It was a great joy to see Queen Anne again and to receive her warm welcome. Philippe seemed very much in love with Henriette and very jealous of the Duke of Buckingham, who had insisted on accompanying us because he could not tear himself away from Henriette. However we managed to subdue Philippe's jealousy. Louis was very gracious to us and made it clear that he loved Henriette very much. There were rumours of his interest in various young women at Court, but I had been right in realizing that after spurning Henriette when they were children he had come to see that special beauty of hers which made her different from the other ladies at Court.

Mazarin died suddenly to the great sorrow of the Queen and Louis. I guessed that would mean a period of Court mourning which would postpone the wedding. However, the dispensation from the Pope – which had been required because of the close relationship of Philippe and Henriette – arrived on the day the Cardinal died and Louis declared that perhaps preparations for the wedding should go on, although quietly.

It was at the end of March when the wedding took place. The ceremony was performed in a private chapel of the Palais Royal and my own dear Henry Jermyn – I had prevailed on Charles to create him Earl of St Albans – stood as proxy for Charles.

My dear little Henriette, at seventeen years old, had become the Duchesse d'Orléans. I was very happy. Not the first prize . . . but the second . . . and I could always hope. . . .

My fortunes must be changing. Charles was on the throne of England and seemed firmly seated there; and my little girl, the best loved of them all, had come through her delicate childhood, her severe illnesses, and was the second lady in France.

Colombes

The years have now begun to slip by me quickly. I feel that I am no longer a participant but a looker-on, living on the fringe of affairs, which was strange at first as I had for so long been at the centre of them.

Henriette had no need of me now. She was the star of the Court. The King was in love with her and sometimes, I suspected, she with him. Philippe . . . well, we had always known that he would be an indifferent husband, being more attached to his handsome men friends than to any woman. Henriette shrugged that aside; she had become very worldly, quite unlike the quiet little girl who used to cause me so much anxiety.

She seemed indefatigable. She designed and wrote ballets for the King's entertainments; and she was always at the centre of these for she danced exquisitely. The new life she was leading had beautified her considerably. People said that her complexion was like a mingling of jasmine and roses and that she had power in her sapphire blue eyes to command the devotion of all men. Certainly Louis was her admirer, deferring to her decisions until his little Queen was so jealous that she complained to her mother-in-law. Anne had always hated controversy and she spoke to me about Henriette's friendship with the King. 'Henriette must not always be at the King's side,' insisted Anne. 'That is the Queen's place.'

I listened and commiserated and all the time was secretly pleased that my daughter was now the most attractive and desirable woman at Court. I told Anne that I would tell Henriette what she had said, but was it not the King who set the pace and should she not speak to him?

But I was very contented and there was nothing I liked to hear more than of Henriette's conquests.

At that time Louis dominated her life and I was sure she did his. I would grow furious contemplating what an ideal pair they would have made. They were always together and people were beginning to say: 'Where the King is, there is Madame.'

She was very happy at that time and her happiness was the greater because of the deprivations of her youth. Her beloved brother was safe on the throne; and the King of France was in love with her. She had the deep affection of the two most powerful men in Europe.

She had a great influence over the King. Through her the Court became more intellectual. She had always been interested in writers and musicians and she made Louis so too. She brought Lulli the musician to the Court. She patronized Molière. Madeleine de Scudery's works were being widely read. The Court was not only becoming more elegant but more cultured. And it was all due to Henriette.

Those were the triumphant days of Henriette's life and what would have been the outcome I cannot say if she had not become pregnant. I knew enough of her to believe that the child was Philippe's and not Louis's. Henriette was like me; she wanted the trimmings of courtship not the culmination. I had never liked *that* side of marriage, much as I had cared for Charles, and I could happily have dispensed with it altogether had it not been my duty to produce a family. Henriette was the same. When her child was born, it must be that of her husband.

But pregnancy was not easy for her. She became ill. I took her with me to the Palais Royal. Louis came to see her and to avoid gossip we arranged that one of Henriette's ladies in waiting should be seen with him so that it might seem he had come to visit her.

This was an insignificant girl who was a little lame and quiet and unassuming. Her name was Louise de la Vallière; and now we know what the outcome of that was!

In due course Henriette gave birth to a child – a daughter – and neither Philippe nor Henriette could disguise their disappointment that she was not a boy.

Henriette was recovering from her confinement but she was a little sad. Rumours about the King and La Vallière were numerous. Then there was news from England. Charles had married Catherine de Braganza and I knew it was time for me to pay a visit to England.

Henriette accompanied me as far as Beauvais. She was regaining her health rapidly and although she still seemed frail was as beautiful as ever. It was a great wrench for us to part and we both wept bitterly; I think she would have given a great deal to come with me and she sent many messages for me to give to Charles.

I had in my party a young man of about thirteen or fourteen. He was known as James Crofts because when his mother, the notorious Lucy Walter died, he had been put in the charge of Lord Crofts, who passed him off as a kinsman, although everyone knew he was the King's son.

James himself was well aware of it and if I knew anything he was going to make sure that nobody forgot it. He was extremely handsome and had a decided look of the Stuarts. If Charles had wanted to deny paternity – and he certainly did not – he would have scarcely been able to.

James Crofts was amusing, bright, and with a manner so audaciously regal and at the same time engaging that I could not help liking him.

I was looking forward to meeting my new daughter-in-law. Henry Jermyn had been to England recently and had brought back excellent reports of her, and since she was a Catholic that delighted me. I hoped she would have some influence on Charles.

The crossing was atrocious as it usually was for me. I hated crossing the sea and was going to England as a duty; I much preferred my native land and would never forgive the English for turning us out and the barbarous treatment of Charles. My son might forget it; I never could. He seemed to have cast off all resentments and was perfectly happy; and although he had been forced to travel widely on the Continent, England appeared to be his natural home.

It was a great relief to step onto dry land and we went by stages to Greenwich where the King and his wife were waiting to greet us.

It was a wonderful moment to stand face to face with him and to feel his kiss on my hand and cheek. He always startled me when I saw him after a lapse of time. It was his imposing height, I think, and that dark ugly face which always baffled me because it was so charming.

And there was his Queen! I embraced her warmly. Henry had not lied. She was delightful.

I said to her: 'I should not have come to England but for the pleasure of seeing you. I shall love you as my daughter and serve you as a Queen.'

The soft eyes filled with tears and she looked surprised and relieved and I wondered whether her life in England was all that a happy wife's should be.

She replied that in love and obedience none of my children – not even the King – should exceed her. Which I thought charming.

Charles smiled at her indulgently and I could see that she was in love with him as I supposed most women would be. I hoped that he would make her happy; but I had heard many rumours about the life he led and I knew that he had always been promiscuous. When he was wandering in Europe perhaps he could be forgiven, but it must be different now that he had a Queen and was restored to the throne.

He was absolutely delighted and amused by James Crofts and made much of him, which I thought he should not have done quite so openly before the Queen. I promised myself I would point this out to him when we were alone.

During his brief stay at Greenwich, Charles asked if I would like to have Somerset House as a residence while I was in England. 'I know you were always fond of the place,' he said; and I told him I should like that very much.

In due course Charles and the Queen returned to Hampton Court and it was arranged that I should follow later. I would need a little rest, Charles said, after the rigours of the journey, for he knew how I loathed those sea crossings.

I was not sorry to have a quiet time to myself.

James Crofts had gone off with the King's party and just a few of my intimates remained so I looked forward to a few peaceful days before we moved on. It was pleasant to sit quietly overlooking the river and talk in a desultory way to Henry, whose conversation I always found so amusing.

Henry was a man who always seemed to know what was going on. He could sniff out scandals and rumours and devote himself to the task of discovering the truth behind them; and it was only to be expected that he must know of the troubles between the King and his new Queen.

I said that I thought Charles was extremely lucky in his Queen and how delighted I was that they seemed so happy.

'Ah,' said Henry, 'I am not sure that the Queen is so happy.'

'What do you mean?' I demanded.

Henry's eyes were sparkling. He loved imparting gossip, although as this concerned my son he was quickly looking rather grave.

'The Queen is hurt and angry.'

'She did not appear to be so.'

'She would not wish you to know of her troubles as soon as you arrived.'

'What troubles are these?'

'The King's mistress. It is Barbara Castlemaine who is at the root of the trouble.'

'I have heard her name.'

'Dearest Majesty, who has not heard of her name? She has completely enslaved the King. She is a most handsome woman . . . the most beautiful in England, some say . . . and a virago into the bargain. It is she who is causing the trouble between the King and the Queen.'

'She was his mistress . . . was she not? . . . before the Queen arrived in England?'

'Before and after, dear lady. And now the King wants to make her one of the women of the bedchamber.'

'No! Surely not.'

'I will tell you what happened. When the list was presented to the Queen, Barbara Castlemaine's name was at the top of it. She struck it through. Later the King led in the Castlemaine and presented her to the Queen, who received her graciously and gave her her hand to be kissed. She was not familiar with English, and although she must have heard of the Castlemaine and her place in the King's affections, she did not recognize her name when it was written down and so behaved in a welcoming way. Then one of her women whispered to her who the lady was, and the Queen was so shocked and tried so hard to restrain her feelings that the blood gushed from her nose and she fell to the floor in a fit.'

'The poor child! Charles should have known better.'

'Charles was horrified at her behaviour. You see, Madam, he is completely under the spell of the Castlemaine. He said the Queen had behaved badly and incorrectly and should make amends to the lady.'

'Charles said that!'

'I agree that it was most unlike him but when the best of us are in the wrong we seek to make our actions right and perhaps act as we would not in other circumstances. Catherine however refused to receive the lady, and Charles insists that she should.'

'It is monstrous!' I cried.

'Clarendon tried to persuade the King that he was acting unkindly and the King doubtless knew it and it was against his nature to act so, but as I said he is the slave of my lady Castlemaine.'

I was very angry because I had taken a great liking to the Queen on sight. I thought she was a gentle woman who would be amenable and want to learn; moreover she was an ardent Catholic and I thought that she would be a good influence on Charles.

What a situation to find as soon as I arrived in England! I sat for a long time talking it over with Henry.

'Whenever I come to this country there is trouble,' I said. 'Oh, Henry, how I long to be back at Chaillot or Colombes.'

Then I thought of all that was happening in France and of my dear Henriette, whose life was presenting many problems, and suddenly I felt old and for the first time in my life indifferent to the actions of my family. They were men and women now – no longer children. I felt a great urge to cut myself off from trouble, to live in that little *château* of Colombes where I could surround myself with trusted friends. Most of them were as old as I – or almost. We understood each other. There we could live in peace.

My great desire now was to go back there. I did not want conflict with Charles for I had a feeling that he would always get the better of me. I did not want to quarrel with James and I knew we should if I attempted to tell him where he was wrong. And Henriette had shown me that even she would go her own way. They were the only ones left to me and I did not want to quarrel with any of them.

It seemed a wise decision. Charles and Catherine sorted out their differences about Lady Castlemaine. He had his way – I have come now to think he always did – and Catherine, while accepting Lady Castlemaine and his other mistresses, did not seem to love him any less.

Charles had arranged for me to stay at Greenwich until Somerset House could be ready. Like many beautiful places in England it had been ravaged by Oliver Cromwell and for a while I lived between Greenwich Palace and Denmark House. I was pleased when I could get into Somerset House which was not until late summer. I found that since I had decided to let them all go their own way and not worry too much about the mistakes they were making, they all seemed to like me so much better.

I was very fond of the Queen and she visited me often. She was a sad little creature and I am sure felt very much alone. She longed for a child but although she had miscarriages and so could not be barren, she did not seem to be able to produce a healthy one. It was a great disappointment to Charles but far more so to her. He knew he was not at fault because he had numerous bastards and he never refused to recognize any of them.

I longed to be in my native land. I hated the London winters which seemed so cold, but most of all I disliked the fogs. They affected my chest and I told myself that I must get back to France before long. I was expected to live in England mainly because Charles had given me a pension and Clarendon had wanted the money spent in England to give employment to English people. To have spent it in France would have been tantamount to the English crown's paying money to that country. So although there was no objection to my visiting France now and then, it was expected of me to make my home in England.

I was a little happier when I was installed in Somerset House. The Roundheads had actually occupied it and at first that made it distasteful to me. They had broken up the beautiful rooms but as was to be expected their most devastating work had been in my chapel; but a great deal of reconstruction had been done and I began to take an interest because I was introducing my own designs. I had the ceilings exquisitely painted and chandeliers of gilded brass installed. It was becoming magnificent and I was able to live there royally. I had crimson silk hung at the windows and beautiful screens made to keep out the draughts which blew in from the river. There was one room with a domed roof over-looking gardens which ran down to the river and from this there was a private staircase which led to a room where I could take hot and cold baths. Gardeners had set to work in the grounds, making paths down to the river so that I could walk without getting my feet muddy. I wanted to make it as different as it possibly could be from when those men had filled it with their ugly presence.

Then I had my household with my dear Henry Jermyn, Lord St Albans, as Chancellor, at the head of it; I had my Gentlemen of Music, Master of Games and Buckhounds and Bows. Whenever I went out it was in my Sedan chair or coach and I was accompanied by my halberdiers in black cassocks with embroidered gold badges; I had my twelve liveried bargemen to row me when I decided to travel by river. I lived royally. I thought I owed that to myself and to Charles. I wanted to wipe out forever the indignities I had suffered; and for so long I had lived parsimoniously saving everything I could to bring back the King to England.

Well, now it was done and it was my turn to enjoy luxury, to remind myself that I was no longer a poor relation. I was a royal Queen and now I would live like one.

I was very much in debt when Somerset House was finished and that disturbed me a little. Then I saw that it gave me an excuse to live quietly which I had discovered was what I wanted.

Many people came to see me and boats were constantly passing along the river. I gave concerts and in summer evenings the strains of sweet music would float along the river. There was always plenty to see from my windows because there was so much activity on the river. I was finding that I could be much happier if I did not allow myself to be tempted to tell people how they should act. I enjoyed my new role – observer rather than participator. Henry Jermyn agreed with me. When I looked back I realized that he had always been like that. Perhaps that was why he was a happy man. He had become fat and suffered from gout but he was the dearest companion and I enjoyed his company better than that of any other person.

I rarely made a decision now without first consulting him. I suppose that was why there were rumours about us. There were many who were absolutely sure that we were married. Some even credited me with having had a child by him. We laughed together at these rumours but we took no heed of them and continued to enjoy our pleasant relationship.

The Duchess of York had a daughter. She was called Mary and

it seemed as though she, unlike her brother who had lived only a few months, would survive. I did hope so. It is so tragic when children cannot seem to get a grip on life and I had to agree that Charles was right when he had said that Anne was a good woman. Unfortunately James had tired of her and he had his mistresses just like his brother. Their behaviour really did give the Court a reputation for immorality. But it was none of my business. I had learned to hold myself aloof from it now. I was still wondering how I could get back to Chaillot and Colombes. I longed to see Henriette and my good friend Queen Anne.

Because poor Queen Catherine did not seem to be able to get a child, Charles created James Crofts Duke of Monmouth. It was in a way an insult to Catherine, calling attention to the fact that the fault must be hers as he could get a handsome healthy boy like James Crofts from another woman.

There was a great deal of speculation about Charles's making Monmouth his heir. He would have had to legitimize him for that but I supposed he could easily do so.

Nothing came of that. Charles had a habit of shelving controversial matters and when I think how he came through I wonder whether that is not the wisest way.

Lady Castlemaine, I was glad to see, was losing her hold on him, which must have been good news for Catherine, but he was obsessed by a new beauty – Frances Stuart. It would always be like that with Charles and I wished Catherine could accept that fact. But it was difficult for her and I knew full well that had I been young again and in her place I should never have done so. I daresay I would have made his life a misery. He would never have had that calm resignation from a woman like me.

The winter which began in 1664 and went on into 1665 was a cold one. I became ill and had to take to my bed for a long time. My doctors told me that I should get out of England if possible and that was my excuse.

I begged Charles not to close my chapel if I left and he promised he would not do so and he was most eager for me to take the waters at the Bourbon springs which had been so beneficial to me before.

War with the Dutch had broken out and I was deeply concerned about that. Charles said that the French might decide to join with the Dutch and he believed that I might do good work for him in France, so I think he was rather glad that I was going. There was another matter. There had been some cases of plague in London and he feared if the summer was hot they might increase.

There were several good reasons why I should go besides my health.

I was due to leave at the end of June but before I left there came news of a great sea battle in which my son James had defeated the Dutch. James was the hero of the hour but I was afraid for him and begged Charles not to allow him to expose himself too rashly. There was something very rash about James which his impetuous marriage had proved.

As I sailed down the Thames I wondered if I should ever come back.

So there I was – after another dismal sea crossing – back in my native country. My spirits rose as soon as I set foot in it, but there was bad news awaiting me. Henriette was very ill. She had heard a false rumour that her brother James had been killed in battle and the shock had brought about the premature birth of the child she was carrying. She was delighted to see me and I do believe that my arrival helped to pull her through. She was far from happy and I began to wonder whether great titles were worth all one had to pay for them. I had found a crown and a happy marriage although it had ended in tragedy, but all through that marriage Charles and I had meant everything to each other.

I thought of Charles and his poor little Queen who had to accept his mistresses and could not get the child she longed for. I thought of James and Anne Hyde who had married so romantically and were now no longer in love; I thought most of all of Henriette who had married Philippe, Duc d'Orléans, brother of the King of France, and who was the most wretched of them all.

She confided to me that Philippe flew into jealous rages which were incomprehensible as he was not interested in her himself; but he simply could not bear her to enjoy the society of other men. Moreover he had brought his lover, the Chevalier of Lorraine, into the house and they conducted their amour openly for all to see and laugh at.

There was sad news from London. Two of my priests had died of the plague. The Court was no longer there and red crosses were put on the houses of the plague-stricken to warn people to keep away. Throughout the night the dismal knell of the death cart was heard in the deserted streets with the cry: 'Bring out your dead.'

I went to see my old friend Queen Anne. She was in a desperate state and suffering excruciating pain for she had a malignant growth in her breast which she knew would kill her.

Early the next year she died and I could not be sorry because, poor soul, she who had done so many kindnesses had suffered greatly. I could only be relieved that she had found peace at last.

To my dismay France declared war on England in support of the Dutch. Louis had no wish for it, I knew; and although the people of France hated the English and the people of England hated the French, both Charles and Louis were trying to come to some agreement. It was during this time that the Dutch fleet, smarting under the humiliation of the English victory at sea, sailed up the Medway and burned several men-of-war including the *Royal Charles*, which was lying at Chatham.

That was a year of disaster and the biggest of all was the great fire of London when two-thirds of the city were burned to the ground. Eighty-nine churches including St Paul's Cathedral were destroyed, with more than thirteen thousand dwelling houses. I was so pained when I heard that the Catholics had been accused of starting the fire and for the first time in years felt the old fighting spirit rising in me. I wanted to go to England to tell them how false that accusation was. I wanted to tell them how wicked and cruel they were to suggest it.

England was in a sorry state. The terrible plague had brought trade almost to a standstill; the war had crippled its finances even more. My pension was reduced and I was indignant and wrote to Charles to tell him so. I was trying so hard to live within my means and my greatest pleasure was to give to the poor and needy and at the same time bring those who had strayed from it back to the Catholic Faith.

I went to Colombes and lived as quietly as I could there. I had my friends about me – chief of all dear Henry without whom I should have been desolate indeed.

I had my music; my reading; my chapel. I prayed constantly and thought a good deal about the past.

I began to grow introspective, reliving those long-ago scenes and asking myself what might have happened if I had done, or not done, this and that. Such thoughts intruded and I found sleep difficult. My cough was worrying me and sometimes I felt very ill indeed.

Henriette came to see me and she expressed her horror at the sight of me. She said she was going to call in the doctors in whom she had great faith.

I said: 'There is nothing wrong with me. When I feel a little better I will go to Bourbon for the waters. Please do not make such a fuss, Henriette.'

'But, Mam,' she cried anxiously, 'I can see you are not well. You might as well admit it because it is obvious.'

'I do not want to be like those women who cry for a little pain in the head or a cut finger,' I retorted.

'Dear Mam, I am not going to ask your permission. I am going to call in the best doctors we have in France.'

I had to give way; and I certainly was feeling ill. 'If only I could sleep soundly,' I said. 'But I simply cannot. As soon as my head is down, I am going over the past and I am blaming myself so much, Henriette.'

'They will give you something to make you sleep.'

'And I shall not take it. Old Mayerne said I was never to take anything like that.'

'We will hear what the doctors have to say,' Henriette insisted firmly.

They were the leading doctors in France. M. Valot was one and he was the first physician to Louis. M. Espoit was first physician to Philippe and M. Juelin to Henriette. They came to Colombes to consult with M. d'Aquin, my own doctor.

I submitted to their examination and lay back listening while they talked to Henriette in a far corner where they had gone so that I should not hear too much of what they said.

I felt rather indifferent and impatient with them. I was old; I had had a long and arduous life; I must die soon and I was ready.

M. Valot was saying: 'By the grace of God the Queen has no fatal malady. Inconvenient . . . but not dangerous. She would be so much better if she slept and put whatever it is on her mind out of her thoughts. Now I am going to add three grains to the prescription you are giving her, M. d'Aquin. That will ensure sleep and when she is rested we shall find her disorder clearing.'

Grains! I thought. That means opium. I had never taken opium and I was not going to now.

They came to my bedside and I said: 'I am not taking your grains.'

'Your Majesty,' said M. Valot, 'they will do you no harm, only great good. They will bring you sleep.'

'Sir Theodore Mayerne said I was never to take any such things.'

'He was old and out of date, Your Majesty. Medicine has improved since then.'

They were all talking to me, including Henriette.

'Dear Mam, you will take it. You will feel so much better. . . .'

'I do not promise,' I said. 'I shall try to sleep without it.'

It has been a good day. I have worked a little, prayed a good deal and conversed with my friends.

At supper we were quite merry and Henry amused us all with some scandalous stories he had gleaned about people at Court.

I had had a good meal and could not help laughing at him. I am so tired. If I could only sleep, but however tired I am when I am in bed thoughts come between me and sleep.

I was prepared for bed as usual and the nearer the time came to say goodnight to my friends the more wide awake I became.

I am very thoughtful tonight. More than ever the past comes back – haunting me, robbing me of peace. I can see everything in especial clarity tonight – my coming to England, my quarrels with Charles. Oh what a foolish girl I was then! And then our great joy in each other . . . but the troubles came too quickly. I am very uneasy tonight. Something is telling me that everything might have been so different and I cannot stop myself wondering what would have happened to Charles if he had had a different Queen. How much had I contributed to that murder in Whitehall?

What has happened to me in the last years? I have become more myself than I ever was before. Had I in the past been living other people's lives? I had constantly told them what they should do. I had been estranged from my son Henry and he had died without a reconciliation. Mary and I had not been good friends. I had quarrelled with James and should have done so with Charles if he had been of a nature to quarrel.

I cannot endure this feeling of doubt which envelops me. I had always felt before that I knew, that I was right in everything I did.

Now I am haunted by fears. Perhaps I was not right. Perhaps I was tragically wrong.

These thoughts are tormenting me. They have completely chased away sleep. I am frightened. In the last years I have seen events more clearly than I did when they were happening and a fearful sense of guilt is settling on me. I had been so sure of my place in Heaven. I had loved my husband deeply; I had loved my children. But what had I done to them?

I must sleep. I will call in one of my attendants and tell her that I give in. I will take M. Valot's grains for I must sleep. I cannot endure this burden of guilt. I will take the grains . . . and sleep.

Now I will lay down my pen and call the attendant.

Epilogue

On that August night of the year 1669 Henriette Maria sent one of her ladies to M. d'Aquin to tell him that as she could not sleep she would take the medicine which the doctors had prescribed and it was brought to her in the white of an egg.

After she had drunk it she was soon fast asleep.

When her lady in waiting came to her bedside the next morning to ask how she had slept, there was no answer.

Henriette Maria was dead.

Bibliography

Aubrey, William Hickman Smith, *The National and Domestic History of England*

Birch, Thomas, *The Court and Times of Charles I*

Bone, Quentin, *Henrietta Maria*

Burnet, Gilbert (Bishop of Salisbury), *Bishop Burnet's History of his Own Time*

Cartwright, Julia, *Madame: Memoirs of Henrietta Duchess of Orleans*

Clarendon, Edward Earl of (edited by W. Dunn Macray), *The History of the Rebellion and Civil Wars in England*

Davies, Godfrey, *England under the Early Stuarts*

Diary of John Evelyn (edited by William Bray, Prefatory Notes by George W. E. Russell)

Firth, C. H., *Oliver Cromwell and the Rule of the Puritans in England*

Fraser, Antonia, *Cromwell, Our Chief of Men*

Gardiner, Samuel Rawson, *History of England from the Accession of James I to the Outbreak of the Civil War*

Green, Mary Anne Everett, *Letters of Royal and Illustrious Ladies*

Green, Mary Anne Everett, *Lives of the Princesses of England*

Guizot, M. (edited by Robert Black), *History of France*

Hexter, J. H., *King Pym*

Hume, David, *History of England*

Jackson, Lady Catherine Charlotte, *Old Paris: Its Court and Literary Salons*

Kenyon, J. P., *The Stuarts*

Letters of Charles I to Henrietta Maria (edited by John Bruce)

Macaulay, Lord, *History of England*

Mann, Heinrich, *The Last Days of Henri Quatre*

The Trial of Charles I Memoirs of Sir Thomas Herbert and John Rushworth (edited by Roger Lockyer, with Introduction by C. V. Wedgwood)

Patmore, Katherine Alexandra, *The Court of Louis XIII*

Pepys, Samuel, Diary and Correspondence of
Quennell, Marjorie and Peter, *A History of Everyday Things in England 1500–1799*
Roots, Ivan, *The Great Rebellion*
Sir Leslie Stevens and Sir Sydney Lee (editors), *The Dictionary of National Biography*
Timbs, John and Gunn, Alexander, *Abbeys, Castles and Ancient Halls of England and Wales*
Trevelyan, George Macaulay, *England under the Stuarts*
Wade, John, *British History*
Wedgwood, C.V., *The King's Peace*
Wedgwood, C.V., *The King's War*
Wingfield-Stratford, Esmé, *King Charles and the Conspirators*

JEAN PLAIDY HAS ALSO WRITTEN

The Norman Trilogy

THE BASTARD KING
THE LION OF JUSTICE
THE PASSIONATE ENEMIES

The Plantagenet Saga

PLANTAGENET PRELUDE
THE REVOLT OF THE EAGLETS
THE HEART OF THE LION
THE PRINCE OF DARKNESS
THE BATTLE OF THE QUEENS
THE QUEEN FROM PROVENCE
EDWARD LONGSHANKS
THE FOLLIES OF THE KING
THE VOW ON THE HERON
PASSAGE TO PONTEFRACT
THE STAR OF LANCASTER
EPITAPH FOR THREE WOMEN
RED ROSE OF ANJOU
THE SUN IN SPLENDOUR

The Tudor Novels

UNEASY LIES THE HEAD   Also available
KATHARINE, THE VIRGIN WIDOW   } in one volume:
THE SHADOW OF THE POMEGRANATE   } KATHARINE
THE KING'S SECRET MATTER   } OF ARAGON
MURDER MOST ROYAL
(Anne Boleyn and Catherine Howard)
ST THOMAS'S EVE (Sir Thomas More)
THE SIXTH WIFE (Katharine Parr)
THE THISTLE AND THE ROSE
(Margaret Tudor and James IV)
MARY, QUEEN OF FRANCE (Queen of Louis XII)
THE SPANISH BRIDEGROOM
(Philip II and his first three wives)
GAY LORD ROBERT (Elizabeth and Leicester)

The Mary Queen of Scots Series

ROYAL ROAD TO FOTHERINGAY
THE CAPTIVE QUEEN OF SCOTS

The Stuart Saga

THE MURDER IN THE TOWER
(Robert Carr and the Countess of Essex)
THE WANDERING PRINCE   } Also available in
A HEALTH UNTO HIS MAJESTY   } one volume:
HERE LIES OUR SOVEREIGN LORD   } CHARLES II
THE THREE CROWNS
(William of Orange)   } Also available in
THE HAUNTED SISTERS   } one volume:
(Mary and Anne)   } THE LAST OF THE
THE QUEEN'S FAVOURITES   } STUARTS
(Sarah Churchill and
Abigail Hill)